active√ MATHS 4

LEAVING CERTIFICATE MATHS HIGHER LEVEL   PAPER 2

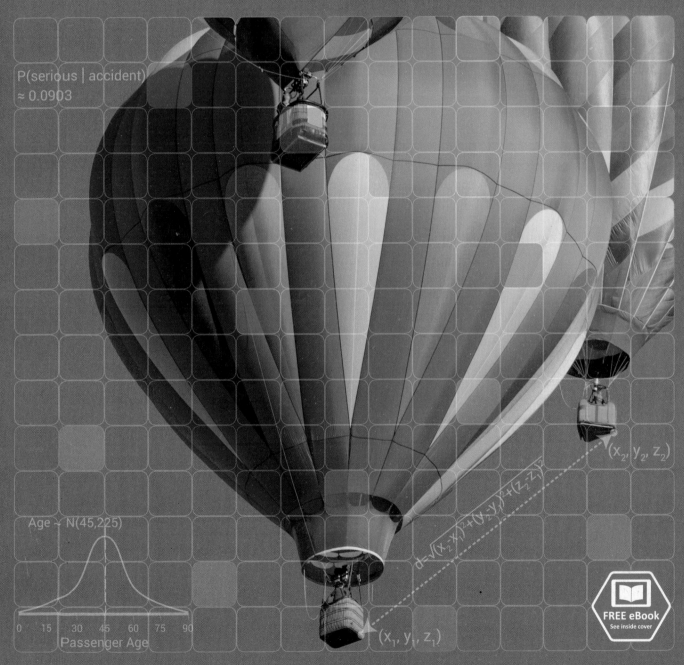

P(serious | accident)
≈ 0.0903

Age ~ N(45,225)

$d=\sqrt{(x_2-x_1)^2+(y_2-y_1)^2+(z_2-z_1)^2}$

(x_2, y_2, z_2)

(x_1, y_1, z_1)

0   15   30   45   60   75   90
Passenger Age

FREE eBook
See inside cover

Michael Keating, Derek Mulvany and James O'Loughlin

Special Advisors: Oliver Murphy, Colin Townsend and Jim McElroy

FOLENS

First published in 2016 by Folens Publishers

Hibernian Industrial Estate, Greenhills Road, Tallaght, Dublin 24

Illustrations: Oxford Designers and Illustrators

ISBN 978-1-78090-639-3

To the best of the publisher's knowledge, information in this book was correct at the time of going to press. No responsibility can be taken for any errors.

Acknowledgements

Answers were checked by Síobhán Allen, Tim Allen and Jonathan Webley.

The authors and publisher are grateful to the following for permission to reproduce photographs:
Alamy, iStock and Shutterstock.

The publisher has made every effort to contact all copyright holders but if any have been overlooked, we will be pleased to make any necessary arrangements.

Any links or references to external websites should not be construed as an endorsement by Folens of the content or views of these websites.

Contents

Introduction

Active Maths 4, 2nd edition, is a comprehensive revision of our two-book series to cover the complete Leaving Certificate Higher Level Maths course. This programme maintains all the benefits of the previous books, while introducing a range of new and improved features. As before:

- Book 1 corresponds to Paper 1 and therefore contains Strands 3 (Number), 4 (Algebra) and 5 (Functions).

- Book 2 corresponds to Paper 2 and therefore contains Strands 1 (Statistics and Probability) and 2 (Geometry and Trigonometry).

Active Maths 4, 2nd edition, allows teachers to meet the challenge of the Higher Level Maths syllabus, and encourages students to discover for themselves that maths can be enjoyable and relevant to everyday life while preparing for their exams.

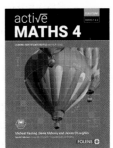

- Revised and current: Following a number of years of examination of Project Maths, additional worked examples, real-life examples, context questions and revised content reflect the reality of the curriculum.

- Exam-focused: End-of-chapter revision exercises, improved exam-focused questions and the inclusion of new past exam questions enable students to better self-assess and prepare for the Leaving Certificate.

- Digital resources: An improved bank of interactive digital resources, including chapter summaries, topic PowerPoints and constructions are available for use in the classroom, and for student revision.

- Worked solutions for students: To support independent learning in preparation for the exam.

- Differentiated learning: Comprehensive, carefully graded exercises facilitate progressive learning in mixed-ability classrooms.

- Improved layout: 'Handy Hints' boxes providing concept tips, and simplified, straightforward diagrams and graphs to help students learn effectively.

- Learning outcomes: A 'You Should Remember' section and a list of 'Key Words' are presented at the beginning of each chapter to inform students what they can expect to learn.

We believe we have improved the quality of these new books and hope that those who use them will achieve the best mark possible in the Leaving Cert Maths examinations.

Michael Keating, Jim McElroy, Derek Mulvany, Oliver Murphy, James O'Loughlin and Colin Townsend

March 2016

Key to icons used in this book

 **Learning outcomes**

 Formula

 **You should remember...**

 **Handy tips**

 **Key words**

 Digital resource available

01

Statistics I

In this chapter you will learn about:

- Populations and samples
- The importance of randomisation and the role of the control group in studies
- Selecting a sample (stratified, cluster and quota)
- The relationship between variables using scatterplots
- Correlation and line of best fit
- Calculating the correlation coefficient by calculator
- The existence of outliers

You should remember...

- How to write one number as a fraction and percentage of another number
- How to construct bar charts, pie charts, line plots and histograms
- How to construct stem-and-leaf plots and back-to-back stem-and-leaf plots

Key words

- Primary data
- Secondary data
- Categorical data
- Numerical data
- Population
- Sample
- Distributions
- Stem-and-leaf plot
- Histograms
- Correlation
- Scatterplot
- Outlier
- Line of best fit

In the modern world we are inundated with **statistics**. When we turn on our TVs, browse the Internet or open a newspaper, we meet with numbers, charts, tables, graphs and other statistical results.

Governments are one of the biggest employers of statisticians. Here in Ireland the Central Statistics Office (www.cso.ie) and the Economic and Social Research Institute (www.esri.ie) are just two bodies that provide the government and the public with valuable statistics.

The word statistics comes from the Latin word *status* (meaning 'state').

Statistics is concerned with proper scientific methods for collecting, analysing, presenting and interpreting **data**.

Any unordered list is called data. When this list is ordered in some way, it becomes information.

Statistics are now used in such diverse areas as agriculture, biology, chemistry, economics, engineering, education, medicine, physics and political science.

Statistics can be either **descriptive** or **inferential**.

- Statisticians are often faced with large amounts of data that must be summarised and presented to the public in a way that people can understand. Bar charts, pie charts and averages are just some of the methods statisticians use to summarise and present data. We call such statistics **descriptive statistics**.

- Before an election is held, statisticians try to predict the outcome of the election. They do this by asking a small number of people how they will vote in the upcoming election. They then try to predict the outcome from the responses of this group. When statisticians try to predict or forecast based on responses from a small group, they are then doing **inferential statistics**.

Statistical Investigations

Statistical investigations are an integral part of the work of many professionals. Economists, scientists and engineers use statistical investigations to solve numerous problems. Research students use statistical investigations to prove many of their theories. Newspapers often conduct statistical investigations to gauge the public mood on various issues. The modern world is, for the most part, dependent on the information provided by statistical investigations.

A large part of any statistical investigation is the production of data. At school we often produce data for projects and experiments. An agricultural science student measuring the heights of plants she has sown in her back garden or a geography student investigating family size in Cork city are both producing data. The characteristic being recorded about each individual is called a **variable**. In the case of the agricultural science student the variable is plant height, and for the geography student the variable is family size.

1.1 Types of Data

All data is either **categorical** data or **numerical** data.

Categorical Data

Questions that cannot be answered with numbers provide **categorical data**. The following are examples of such questions:

- What colour are your eyes?
- Did you book economy or first class flights?
- Do you live in an urban area or a rural area?

- What is your favourite soccer team?
- What colour is your phone?
- What grade did you receive in your last maths test?

There are two types of categorical data:

- **Ordinal** categorical data
- **Nominal** categorical data

Ordinal categorical data **can be ordered** in some way. Examples include exam grades (H1, H2, H3, H4, H5, H6, H7, H8), stress levels (low, medium, high) and blood pressure levels (low, normal, high).

Nominal categorical data **cannot be ordered**.

Examples include hair colour, phone colour and favourite band.

Numerical Data

Questions that can be answered with numbers provide **numerical** data.

- How many people in the EU are employed in the manufacturing industry?
- How many Irish people emigrated in 2014?
- How many houses were built in Ireland in 2011?
- What was the temperature in Dubai at midday on 5 June 1998?
- What is the average height of Leaving Certificate students in your school?
- How many rugby Grand Slams has Ireland won?

There are two types of numerical data:

- **Continuous** numerical data
- **Discrete** numerical data

The greatest annual total rainfall recorded in this country was at Ballaghbeema Gap, Co. Kerry. The year was 1960 and the amount of rainfall recorded for the year was 3964.9 mm. Of course, this measurement could have been 3964.89764 mm, but Met Éireann gives rainfall measurements corrected to one decimal place. Rainfall measurements are an example of **continuous numerical data**, as rainfall measurements for a particular region can be any one of an infinite number of values within a given range.

Numbers or measurements that can only have certain values, for example, shoe size and family size, are called **discrete numerical data**. Your shoe size must be a number such as 7, 7½, 8, 8½, 9, etc. It cannot be 8.1432. Discrete values move in steps.

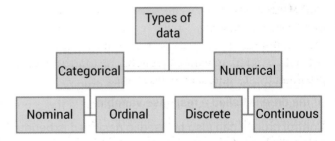

Worked Example 1.1

Which of the following are continuous numerical data and which are discrete numerical data?

 (i) The heights of basketball players

 (ii) The number of gold medals won by each country in the 2012 Olympic Games

 (iii) The sugar content (as a percentage of weight) in 30 brands of breakfast cereal

 (iv) The time taken by each student in your class to run 100 metres

 (v) The number of iPhones sold during August 2016

Solution

(i) The heights of basketball players are continuous numerical data, as these measurements can be any one of an infinite number of values within a given range.

(ii) The number of gold medals won by each country in the 2012 Olympic Games is discrete numerical data. A country may have won no gold medal or may have won some positive whole number of gold medals. The number of gold medals won increases in steps of 1.

(iii) Percentage sugar content is continuous numerical data. The percentage sugar content can take on any of the infinite number of values between 0 and 100.

(iv) Time is continuous numerical data.

(v) The number of iPhones sold during August 2016 is a discrete whole number. Therefore, this is discrete numerical data.

Primary Data

Primary data is collected by or for the person who is going to use it. Therefore, the person collecting the data will organise their own study to collect the data.

There are different types of studies that generate primary data. We will look at two types of studies.

Observational Studies

In an **observational study**, the researcher collects the information of interest but does not influence events. A study into the TV viewing habits of teenagers where data is collected by means of a questionnaire is an example of an observational study.

Observational studies also include **case-control** studies. For example, in a medical case-control study, two groups of people are compared. One group (the **cases**) has a disease or condition, while the other group (the **controls**) does not have the disease or condition. Researchers study the lifestyle histories of the people in each group to learn what causes the disease or condition.

> A very famous case-control study in 1950 established, for the first time, the link between lung cancer and smoking. The study was carried out by Austin Hill and Richard Doll.

Designed Experiments

In a designed experiment, we apply some treatment to a group of subjects and then observe the effects of the treatment on the subjects. Pharmaceutical companies carry out many designed experiments when they are testing new drugs. In this case the drug or drug dosage is called an **explanatory variable** and the effect of the drug is called a **response variable**.

Control groups can also be used in designed experiments. Suppose a pharmaceutical company advertises that a particular drug that the company has recently developed cures a sore throat. We would like to test this claim scientifically.

Firstly, we decide on the number of participants in the study. We then take measurements. Measurements have to be at the same time points and conditions for all participants.

Some of the participants are given the new drug, while the rest of the participants are given a placebo. The participants who are given the placebo belong to the control group.

> A placebo is a substance that has no therapeutic effect.

After an appropriate time has elapsed, measurements are once again taken. Only if there is a difference between the two groups may we relate this to an effect of the new drug. A treatment is considered effective if its results are significantly better than the results obtained from the placebo treatment.

Worked Example 1.2

Below are descriptions of two studies.

(a) A group of car passengers who suffer from motion sickness are given magnetic bracelets, which they agree to wear in an attempt to diminish the effects of the sickness. The passengers report back to the researcher on the effectiveness of the bracelet.

(b) An examination of over 40,000 medical records of Irish men showed that those who were overweight or who had high blood pressure had a higher risk of kidney cancer.

   (i) Which of the studies, (a) or (b), is an observational study, and which is an experiment?

   (ii) Is the observational study a case-control study? Explain.

   (iii) What is the explanatory variable and what is the response variable in the experiment?

Solution

   (i) The study showing the link between certain conditions and kidney cancer, (b), is the observational study. The researcher does not influence events. The study on motion sickness, (a), is an experiment. Here the researcher tries to diminish the effects of motion sickness by having the subjects wear magnetic bracelets, i.e. he/she applies a treatment to a group of subjects and observes the effects of this treatment on the subjects.

   (ii) Yes, the observational study is a case-control study. The researcher would have studied the records of people who had kidney cancer (the cases) and the records of people who did not have the disease (the controls).

   (iii) The explanatory variable is the magnetic bracelet. The response variable is the effectiveness of the treatment in combating motion sickness.

Secondary Data

Secondary data is not collected by the person who is going to use it.

Sources for secondary data include the Internet, newspapers, books, historical records and databases. Here are some specific sources of secondary data:

- *The Guinness Book of Records* (lists world records in both human achievement and extremes of the natural world)
- The Census of Population (a collection of information relating to persons and households in the country)
- The Central Statistics Office (an agency responsible for gathering information relating to economic and social activities in the country)
- CensusAtSchool (a website containing data on second-level students throughout the world)

Exercise 1.1

1. Explain the terms:

   (i) Descriptive statistics   (ii) Inferential statistics

2. What is categorical data?

3. Explain the difference between nominal categorical data and ordinal categorical data.

4. What is numerical data?

5. Explain the difference between continuous numerical data and discrete numerical data.

6. What is the difference between primary data and secondary data? (Give examples of each.)

7. What is the difference between an observational study and a designed experiment?

8. Explain the role played by a control group in a designed experiment.

9. A biology student has been studying the plants in her back garden. These tables give some of the measurements she has taken.

Heights of plants (cm)				
12.5	17.2	19.3	49.2	81.6
13.8	150.4	20.2	16.1	122.4

Colours of leaves				
Green	Yellow	Yellow	Green	Red
Green	Green	Green	Yellow	Green

(i) What variables did the student record?

(ii) State which variable is numerical and which variable is categorical.

(iii) Is the numerical variable discrete or continuous? Give a reason for your answer.

(iv) What are the units of measurements used for the numerical variable?

(v) Is the categorical variable nominal or ordinal? Explain.

10. Formulate two questions that can be answered with numerical data.

11. Formulate two questions that can be answered with categorical data.

12. A survey was carried out at a bank. Some numerical data was collected. State whether the following variables are continuous or discrete:

(i) The number of customers who entered the bank between 10.00 am and 11.00 am

(ii) The time taken to serve each customer

(iii) The total amount of money withdrawn on that day

(iv) The number of employees working on the day that the survey was carried out

13. Complete the table by naming the type of data formed by each of the measurements.

Measurement	Type of data
Number of births each month during 2014	Discrete numerical data
Concentration of volcanic ash particles in the atmosphere	
Weights of all beef slaughtered in Ireland during 2015	
Number of aeroplanes flying out of Shannon every day	
Number of pages in the books kept in the school library	
The grades of the students in your class in Junior Certificate maths	

14. (i) Give an example of an observational study that might be conducted in your school.

(ii) Give an example of a designed experiment that might be conducted in your school.

15. Explain the terms 'explanatory variable' and 'response variable'.

16. A sample of 500 households in Dublin was selected and several questions were asked of the householders. Which of the following is not correct?

(i) The total household income is ordinal categorical data.

(ii) The number of persons in the household is discrete data.

(iii) Socioeconomic status (coded as 1 = low income, 2 = middle income and 3 = high income) is nominal categorical data.

(iv) The primary language used at home is nominal categorical data.

Now correct the incorrect statements.

17. Alan would like to predict the winning time for the men's 100 m final in the next Olympic Games. He gathers data from past editions of *The Guinness Book of Records*. Explain why the data collected by Alan is secondary data.

1.2 Sample Surveys

Nowadays the news media rely on opinion polls to gauge public opinion on news issues. These polls are examples of **sample surveys**, which are designed to ask questions of a small group of people in the hope of learning something about the entire population.

Populations and Samples

Suppose that you wish to do a study on the TV viewing habits of students in your school, and now realise that it is impractical to interview everybody. You decide to interview 80 out of the 1,000 students in the school. In this case the group of all 1,000 students is called the **population**.

> The population is the entire group that is being studied.

The group of 80 students is called a **sample**.

> A census is a survey of the whole population.

> A sample is a group that is selected from the population in order to gather information.

It is very important that a sample is representative of the population if you wish to make predictions about the population from the sample. For example, the sample of 80 students mentioned above would not be representative of the whole school if they were all First Year students.

Sample surveys involve working with **statistics** and **parameters**. The average amount of time spent by the sample of 80 watching television is an example of a statistic. The average amount of time spent by the population of 1,000 watching television is an example of a parameter. When it is not possible to calculate a population parameter, we use the corresponding statistic from a sample of the population to estimate the parameter.

> A parameter is a numerical measurement describing some characteristic of a population. It is a fixed number, but in practice we do not know its value.

> A statistic is a numerical measurement describing some characteristic of a sample. The statistic can change from sample to sample.

Sampling Methods

We will now study sampling methods. On this course, you need to have a knowledge of simple random, stratified, cluster and quota sampling methods.

Simple Random Sample

> In a simple random sample, a sample of size n is selected in such a way that every possible sample of size n from the population has an equal chance of being selected.

If we wish to select a **simple random sample** of size 80 from a population of 1,000, then every possible combination of 80 must have an equal chance of being selected. A convenient way of achieving this is to assign a number to each member of the population, then draw 80 numbers out of a hat containing 1,000 numbers. Obviously, this method is not practical for larger populations, and we need to rely on a calculator, a computer or a table of random numbers to select the sample.

Stratified Random Sample

> To select a stratified random sample, first divide the population into at least two different subgroups so that the individuals or subjects within each subgroup share the same characteristics. Then a probability sample is drawn from each subgroup and combined to form the full sample. Probability sampling is when the researcher chooses subjects randomly to form a sample.

It is important to note that the subgroups must not overlap. The most common subgroups used in stratified random sampling are age, gender, socio-economic status, nationality and educational attainment.

Suppose that there are two candidates, one male and one female, running for president and that you would like to predict the winner of the upcoming election. You decide to select a random sample from the population. However, because the candidates are of opposite gender there is a good chance that a high proportion of the male voters will vote for the male candidate and a high proportion of the female voters will vote for the female candidate. In this case one should select a **stratified random sample**, i.e. randomly select the same number of males as females. This will eliminate the potential bias of having more of one gender than the other in the sample.

Cluster Sample

For **cluster sampling**, the population is divided into sections or clusters. Then some of those clusters are randomly selected and all members from those clusters are chosen.

Suppose we wanted to select a random sample of 300 maths teachers from the population of all maths teachers in the country. It is very difficult to get a list of all maths teachers from which to select our sample. However, getting a list of all second-level schools in the country is not difficult. Now randomly select, say, 40 schools (the number of maths teachers in a school will depend on the school size, but 40 schools should generate a sample size of at least 300). Every maths teacher in the chosen schools is selected.

Quota Sampling

Quota sampling is a non-probability sampling technique, where the sample has the same proportions of individuals as the entire population, with respect to known characteristics.

Quota sampling is widely used in opinion polls and market research. Here the person selecting the sample is given a quota to fill – a certain prescribed percentage of people who come from various subgroups, e.g. men over 50, women under 25. He/she then selects the sample in the most convenient way possible. Randomisation does not play any role in the selection process, and therefore this method of sampling is open to mistakes.

Ethical Issues

The collection and use of data often raises ethical issues. The most complex issues of data ethics arise when we collect data from people. **Informed consent** and **confidentiality** are the two most important issues to be considered.

- Subjects must be **informed** in advance about the nature of a study and any risk of harm it may bring.
- All individuals who are subjects in a study must give their **consent** before any data is collected.
  In the case of very young children, the usual procedure is to get parental consent for the study.
  Consent should be given in writing.

When data is collected it is important to protect the subjects' privacy, by keeping all data about individuals **confidential**. Any breach of confidentiality is a serious breach of data ethics.

Clinical trials are experiments that study the effectiveness of medical treatments on actual patients. A number of ethical issues arise when humans are the subjects of clinical trials.

- Experimental treatments may harm as well as heal.
- Most benefits of clinical trials go to future patients and not the subjects of the trials.
- In control trials, if a treatment is seen to be effective against a particular disease, then is it ethical to continue not giving the treatment to the control group? This is sometimes necessary in order to have a proper conclusion to the trial.

Worked Example 1.3

In each of the following, identify the type of sampling used:

(i) A marketing expert from RTÉ is conducting a survey in which 500 people will be selected from across the age groups 10–19, 20–29, 30–39 and so on. The people will be randomly selected from each age group. The number selected from each group will be in proportion to the number in that age group in the population.

(ii) A researcher is testing a new drug. She has already administered the drug to a large number of patients. She now wants to select a sample of 20 from this group. Fortunately, she has just addressed envelopes that she will use to send information to all the patients. She decides to put all the envelopes in a bag and randomly select 20.

Solution

(i) A stratified random sample is used.

(ii) A simple random sample is used.

Bias in Sampling

Samples that are not representative are called **biased** samples. If there is a tendency for a particular group in a population to be omitted from a sample, then the sample is biased. Online polls use **voluntary response samples**. A voluntary response sample consists of people who choose themselves by responding to a general appeal. Voluntary response samples are biased because people with strong opinions, especially negative opinions, are most likely to respond. Biased samples have a tendency to underestimate or overestimate the population parameter of interest.

When choosing a sample from a population, try to ensure:

- That the sample is large enough
- That the sample is a random selection from the population (this may not always be possible)
- That every subject has an equal chance of being selected
- As high a response rate as possible

If sample data is not collected in an appropriate way, then the data may be unreliable.

Choosing a Random Sample with a Calculator

Suppose we wish to select a random sample of size 20 from a population of 1,000. We will then have to generate 20 random numbers from all the numbers between 1 and 1,000. Here are the steps on the calculator:

> Individual calculators may vary.
> Look for the RANDOM or RND button.

Now, press [=] a further 19 times to generate all 20 random numbers. If a number is selected more than once, ignore it and select another.

STATISTICS I

Exercise 1.2

1. Assign a number to each member of your class. Using your calculator, randomly select five people. What type of sampling have you done?

2. An electronics company manufactures four different types of components. The number of each type manufactured per day is given in the table below. The company has a policy of randomly selecting 70 components each day for quality checks.

Component	A	B	C	D
Number	200	350	50	100

   (i) How many of each type of component should be selected?

   (ii) What type of sampling is being done here (assuming a simple random sample from each group)?

3. What type of sampling is being used in these cases?

   (i) On the day of a General Election, RTÉ organise an exit poll. They randomly select 100 polling stations and all voters are surveyed as they leave these stations.

   (ii) A researcher in the Department of Social Welfare has partitioned all Dublin adults into the following categories: unemployed, employed full-time and employed part-time. She is surveying 50 people from the first category, 200 people from the second category and 25 from the third category.

4. What type of sampling is being used in these cases?

   (i) In an MRBI poll of 1,000 adults, people were selected by using a computer to randomly generate telephone numbers that were then called.

   (ii) The school principal decides to interview all students in the school to get their opinion on some school matter.

5. Explain why a large sample may not necessarily be a good sample.

6. Explain what is meant by *stratified sampling* and *cluster sampling*. Your explanation should include:

   ● a clear indication of the difference between the two methods

   ● one reason why each method might be chosen instead of simple random sampling

7. Explain what is meant by quota sampling and give one reason why this method might be chosen instead of simple random sampling.

8. Explain the difference between a parameter and a statistic.

9. After the World Trade Center in New York was destroyed in 2001, an Internet poll asked the question, 'Should the World Trade Center be rebuilt?'

   Of the 1.3 million respondents, 769,000 said 'Yes', 287,000 said 'No' and 249,000 were undecided. Given that this sample is very large, should it be considered representative of the views of the population of the USA? Explain.

10. Suppose we want to estimate the number of students who watch *Modern Family* in a school with a population of 1,000 students. We randomly select 50 students. Our sample happens to contain 40 girls and 10 boys.

    (i) Is it possible that this sample could be biased? Explain.

    (ii) How could potential bias be eliminated in this particular case?

11. What ethical issues should be considered when data is either being collected or used?

1.3 Collecting Data

Steps in a Statistical Investigation

All statistical investigations begin with a question.
Here are the steps in a statistical investigation:

- Pose a question.
- Collect data.
- Present the data.
- Analyse the data.
- Interpret the data.

Statistical data can be collected in different ways.
The most common way of collecting data is by **survey**.

Data Handling Cycle

- Pose a question
- Collect data
- Present and analyse the data
- Interpret the results (in the light of the question)

Surveys

Most surveys use a questionnaire. The survey can be carried out by:

- Face-to-face interview
- Telephone interview
- Sending a questionnaire by post
- Making a questionnaire available online
- Observation

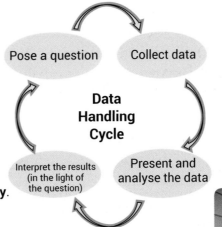

Here are the advantages and disadvantages of each type of survey.

Survey	Advantages	Disadvantages
Face-to-face interview	• Questions can be explained to the interviewee.	• Not random • Expensive to carry out • Respondents may not truthfully answer certain questions.
Telephone interview	• It is possible to select a sample from almost the entire adult population. • Questions can be explained to the interviewee.	• Expensive in comparison to postal and online surveys
Postal questionnaire	• Inexpensive	• People do not always reply to postal surveys and those who reply may not be representative of the whole population.
Online questionnaire	• Very low cost • Anonymity of respondents ensures more honest answers to sensitive questions.	• Not representative of the whole population. Only those who go online and do online surveys are represented.
Observation	• Low cost • Easy to administer	• Not suitable for many surveys • Questions cannot be explained.

Designing a Questionnaire

A **questionnaire** is an important method for collecting data.

Here are some important points to note when designing questionnaires.

Questionnaires should:

- Be useful and relevant to the survey you are undertaking
- Use clear and simple language
- Be as brief as possible

> A questionnaire is a set of questions designed to obtain data from a population.

STATISTICS I

- Begin with simple questions to encourage people to complete them
- Accommodate all possible answers
- Be clear where answers should be recorded
- Contain no leading questions, which give a clue as to how you would like the person to respond. For example, 'Manchester United are losing a lot of games this season. Do you think their manager should resign?'
- Contain no questions that ask for a response to more than one topic. An example of this type of question is, 'Do you think the government spends too much money on sport and should be voted out of office in the next election?'

Worked Example 1.4

Britney wants to gather information on people's interest in sport. Here is the questionnaire she designs.

1. What is your favourite sport?
   - (i) Tennis ☐
   - (ii) Rugby ☐
   - (iii) Athletics ☐

2. How far would you travel to see a competitive sports fixture?
   - (i) Less than 1 km ☐
   - (ii) 5–10 km ☐
   - (iii) Greater than 20 km ☐

3. Do you participate in sport or watch sport on TV?
   - (i) Yes ☐
   - (ii) No ☐

(a) What is wrong with these questions?

(b) Design better questions for Britney to use.

Solution

Question 1

(a) The question does not allow for all possible answers. While it may not be possible to include all types of sport, it is possible to cater for everybody if 'Other' and 'None' alternatives are used.

(b)
1. What is your favourite type of sport?
   - (i) Tennis ☐
   - (ii) Rugby ☐
   - (iii) Athletics ☐
   - (iv) Other ☐
   - (v) None ☐

Question 2

(a) There are gaps between 1 km and 5 km and also between 10 km and 20 km.

(b)
> **2.** How far would you travel to see a competitive sports fixture?
>
> (i) Less than 1 km ☐
>
> (ii) 1–10 km ☐
>
> (iii) Greater than 10 km but less than 20 km ☐
>
> (iv) 20 km or more ☐

Question 3

(a) This question needs to be split into two questions.

(b)
> **3.** Do you participate in sport?
>
> (i) Yes ☐
>
> (ii) No ☐
>
> **4.** Do you watch sport on TV?
>
> (i) Yes ☐
>
> (ii) No ☐

1.4 Tables

When data is collected, it is often convenient to display it in a frequency table. Frequency tables show you how frequently each piece of data occurs. It is good practice to include a tally row in your table. Tallies are marks to help you keep track of counts. The marks are bunched in groups of five.

Worked Example 1.5

The table below shows the number of draws each Premier League club had during the 2014–2015 season.

9	7	9	11	8
7	8	9	8	11
9	6	11	9	12
10	8	11	17	6

(i) Sort the data into a frequency table. Include a tally column in your table.

(ii) Sunderland had the greatest number of draws during the season, and finished 16th with 38 points. How many games did Sunderland win? (Win = 3 points, Draw = 1 point, Loss = 0 points.)

(iii) What percentage of clubs had fewer than nine draws?

Solution

(i)

Number of draws	6	7	8	9	10	11	12	13	14	15	16	17
Tally	II	II	IIII	JM1	I	IIII	I					I
Frequency	2	2	4	5	1	4	1	0	0	0	0	1

(ii) Greatest number of draws = 17

17 points accumulated from draws

38 − 17 = 21 points from wins

Number of games won = $\frac{21}{3}$ = 7

(iii) $\frac{8}{20} \times 100 = 40\%$

Exercise 1.3

1. Shauna rolls a die 50 times. Her scores are listed here.

   (i) Sort the data in a frequency table that includes a tally row.

   (ii) How many times did Shauna throw a 6?

   (iii) How many times did Shauna throw a 1?

   (iv) What percentage of the rolls were 4s?

5	3	3	3	5	1	2	5	1	5
1	3	3	6	4	6	1	2	1	1
1	6	5	6	3	4	2	2	5	2
4	6	5	1	2	6	1	1	6	2
2	6	2	5	2	3	4	4	6	6

2. Below is some data selected at random from the CensusAtSchool database.
   The data gives the different modes of transport a group of students uses to go to school.

   (i) Sort the data into a frequency table.

   (ii) What is the most popular mode of transport?

   (iii) What is the least popular mode of transport?

   (iv) Use an appropriate graph to represent the sample.

Walk	Bus	Walk	Walk	Walk
Bus	Walk	Car	Car	Bus
Walk	Bus	Car	Walk	Walk
Car	Rail	Bus	Walk	Rail

   (v) If it is intended to use a sample from CensusAtSchool to make predictions about the type
       of transport that students throughout the country use to go to school, then what questions
       need to be asked about such a sample?

3. A survey is made of the number of goals scored in a
   series of soccer matches. The findings are as follows:

   (i) Sort the data into a frequency table.

   (ii) How many soccer matches were played?

   (iii) How many scoreless draws were there?

   (iv) What is the maximum number of games that could have been drawn?

   (v) What is the minimum number of games that could have been drawn?

2	0	1	2	2	1	3
1	1	4	0	1	3	4
0	2	0	4	2	0	4
3	1	2	4	2	2	0
1	1	2	1	2	2	0

4. John takes three coins from his pocket and flips the three
   coins together. He repeats this experiment 25 times
   and records his results as follows:

   (i) Copy and complete the frequency table.

TTT	TTH	HTT	THT	HHH
HTH	THH	HHT	HHH	HTT
TTH	HHT	TTT	THH	HHH
THT	HTH	HTH	HTH	THH
THT	TTH	HHT	HTH	HTT

Result	3 Heads	2 Heads	1 Head	0 Heads
Tally				
Frequency				

   (ii) What percentage of the throws revealed one head only?

   (iii) Use an appropriate graph to display the data.

   (iv) Use the random coin generator on your calculator to simulate the experiment.

   To use the random coin generator on your calculator, press the following keys:

    Note that individual
   calculators may differ.

   1 = heads and 0 = tails.

   (v) Graph your results. Compare and contrast your graph with the graph of John's results.

5. The ages of all the teachers in a school are:

21, 21, 22, 23, 23, 25, 27, 28, 30, 31, 32, 34, 34, 35, 37, 38, 39, 40, 40, 41 42, 42, 43, 44,
44, 44, 45, 46, 46, 47, 49, 49, 50, 50, 50, 54, 55, 57, 57, 58, 59, 59, 60, 60, 63, 63, 64

(i) How many teachers were surveyed?

(ii) Copy and complete the frequency table below.

Age	20−29	30−39	40−49	50−59	60−69
Frequency					

(iii) You would like to know teachers' opinion on early retirement. Suggest a suitable way of selecting a sample of 12 teachers for interview on this issue.

6. Table 1 below gives details of the number of males (M) and females (F) aged 15 years and over at work, unemployed, or not in the labour force for each year in the period 2004 to 2013.

Table 1										
Labour Force Statistics 2004 to 2013 − Persons aged 15 years and over (000's)										
Year	At work			Unemployed			Not in labour force			Total
	M	F	Total	M	F	Total	M	F	Total	
2004	1045.9	738.9	1784.8	79.6	31.6	111.2	457.1	854.2	1311.3	3207.3
2005	1087.3	779.7	1867.0	81.3	33.5	114.8	459.5	846.6	1306.1	3287.9
2006	1139.8	815.1	1954.9	80.6	38.1	118.7	457.6	844.9	1302.5	3376.1
2007	1184.0	865.6	2049.6	84.3	39.2	123.5	472.4	852.7	1325.1	3498.2
2008	1170.9	889.5	2060.4	106.3	41.0	147.3	494.8	872.5	1367.3	3575.0
2009	1039.8	863.5	1903.3	234.0	82.4	316.4	505.6	874.9	1380.5	3600.2
2010	985.1	843.5	1828.6	257.6	98.2	355.8	529.2	884.6	1413.8	3598.2
2011	970.2	843.2	1813.4	260.7	103.4	364.1	540.1	881.5	1421.6	3599.1
2012	949.6	823.8	1773.4	265.2	108.4	373.2	546.5	896.9	1443.4	3590.0
2013	974.4	829.0	1803.4	227.7	102.3	330.0	557.8	895.0	1452.8	3586.2

Source: Central Statistics Office www.cso.ie

(a) Suggest two categories of people, aged 15 years and over, who might not be in the labour force.

(b) The following data was obtained from Table 1. The percentages of persons aged 15 years and over at work, unemployed or not in the labour force for the year 2006 are given below.

		At work	Unemployed	Not in the labour force
Persons aged 15 years and over	2006	57.9%	3.5%	38.6%
	2011			

(i) Complete the table for the year 2011. Give your answers correct to one decimal place.

(ii) A census in 2006 showed the there were 864,449 persons in the population aged under 15 years of age. The corresponding number in the 2011 census was 979,590. Assuming that none of these persons are in the labour force, complete the table below to give the percentages of the *total population* at work, unemployed, or not in the labour force for the year 2011.

		At work	Unemployed	Not in the labour force
Total population	2006	46.1%	2.8%	51.1%
	2011			

(iii) A commentator states that 'The changes reflected in the data from 2006 to 2011 make it more difficult to balance the Government's income and expenditure.' Do you agree with the statement? Give two reasons for your answer based on your calculations above.

STATISTICS I

7. What is wrong with the following question used in a questionnaire?

Most students in this school hate the uniform. Are you in favour of changing it?

Yes ☐   No ☐   Undecided ☐

8. Thomas is doing a survey on urban versus rural attitudes to drink-driving. He has included the following question in his questionnaire. What is wrong with it?

Where did you grow up?

Country ☐   Farm ☐   City ☐

9. Aisling has designed a questionnaire that includes the following question:

How old are you?

Young ☐   Middle-aged ☐   Old ☐

(i) What is wrong with the question?

(ii) Improve the question.

10. Máire is doing a survey on healthy eating habits. Design a questionnaire with three questions that would be relevant to the survey.

1.5 Graphing Data

In your Junior Certificate maths course, you learned how to graph data using bar charts, line plots, pie charts, stem-and-leaf plots and histograms.

Worked Example 1.6

The times in minutes between eruptions of the 'Old Faithful' geyser in Yellowstone National Park, USA, are displayed in the stem-and-leaf diagram below. This data was collected by a geologist in 1990.

Stem	Leaf
4	9, 9
5	1, 1, 5, 6, 7, 7, 8, 9
6	0, 0, 1, 5, 5, 8
7	3, 4, 5, 7, 7, 7, 8, 9, 9
8	0, 1, 2, 3, 3, 4, 4, 5, 6, 6, 7, 8, 9
9	0, 1 Key: 8|2 = 82 minutes

This key tells us that the stem denotes tens and the leaves denote units.

Using the stem-and-leaf diagram, answer the following questions:

(i) What was the shortest time interval recorded?

(ii) What was the longest time interval recorded?

(iii) How many eruptions did the geologist see while recording the data?

(iv) What percentage of time intervals recorded were greater than one hour?

Solution

(i) The shortest time interval was 49 minutes.

(ii) The longest time interval was 91 minutes.

(iii) 41 eruptions, as the number of eruptions will always be one greater than the number of time intervals.

(iv) $\frac{28}{40} \times 100 = 70\%$

Worked Example 1.7

Researchers for *Consumer Reports* analysed two types of hot dog: one with meat and one with poultry. The number of calories in each hot dog was recorded. The results are as follows:

Meat			
173	179	182	180
172	147	146	139
175	136	179	153
107	185	135	140
138	135	140	142

Poultry			
129	132	102	106
94	102	87	99
107	113	135	142
86	143	152	146
144	99	112	115

Source: *Consumer Reports*, June 1986, pp 336–367

(i) Represent the data on a back-to-back stem-and-leaf plot.

(ii) What feature of the plot tells you that, in general, meat hot dogs have a higher calorie count than poultry hot dogs?

Solution

(i)

Meat		Poultry
	8	6, 7
	9	4, 9, 9
7	10	2, 2, 6, 7
	11	2, 3, 5
	12	9
9, 8, 6, 5, 5	13	2, 5
7, 6, 2, 0, 0	14	2, 3, 4, 6
3	15	2
	16	
9, 9, 5, 3, 2	17	
5, 2, 0	18	

Key: 2|18| = 182 calories   Key: |15|2 = 152 calories

(ii) Much of the data on meat hot dogs is towards the bottom of the plot, whereas the data on poultry hot dogs is towards the top of the plot.

This would indicate that in general meat hot dogs have a higher calorie count than poultry hot dogs.

Worked Example 1.8

The time, in minutes, spent by a group of women in a boutique is shown in the table.

(i) Represent the data using a grouped frequency table.

(ii) Draw a histogram of the distribution.

(iii) How many of the group spent less than 30 minutes in the boutique?

1.4	38	31.2	15.3	35.6	20.6
37.8	18.6	28.8	39	39.5	23.4
21.6	36.3	49	41.3	12.7	25
48.4	42.6	43.7	48.9	49	26.2
40	21.5	24	19.2	45	29

STATISTICS 1

Solution

(i)

Time	0–10	10–20	20–30	30–40	40–50
Number	1	4	9	7	9

Note: 10–20 means 10 or more but less than 20, and so on.

(ii)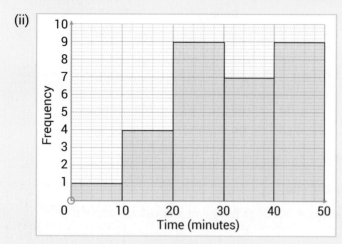

(iii) 1 + 4 + 9 = 14 women

Distribution of Data

Here are the times (in minutes) taken by a group of 14 students to complete a maths problem:

4.5	1.5	2	2.5	3	4	4.5
5	5.5	5.7	6	7	7.5	9.5

While it may not be obvious from the list, many of the times are between 4 and 6 minutes. Also, few people had very low times or very high times. A histogram shows this distribution very well.

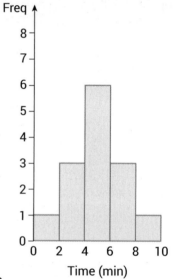

> We call a distribution a symmetric distribution if the values smaller and larger than its midpoint are mirror images of each other.

The histogram on the right is of a **symmetric distribution.** In the real world symmetric distributions are rare, but almost-symmetric distributions are common. Statisticians are happy to work with almost-symmetric distributions. When working with almost-symmetric distributions, the almost-symmetric distribution is replaced with an approximation that is symmetric.

Here are the times (in minutes) taken by a group of 21 students to complete the same maths problem:

1.5	2	2.4	3.8	4	4.2	4.5
5.7	5.8	6.1	6.3	6.4	7	7.2
8.2	8.3	8.5	8.8	9	9.2	9.5

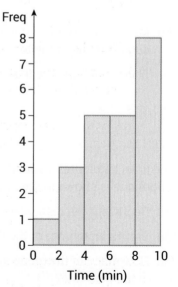

In this distribution many students would have taken a relatively long time to complete the problem. Here is the histogram for this distribution, which tails off towards the lower numbers on the left.

> We call this a negatively skewed distribution.
> It is also referred to as a skewed left distribution.

The following are the times of a group of 25 students who also completed the maths problem:

0.9	1.1	1.2	1.3	1.3	1.6	1.6	1.9	2	2
3.1	3.2	3.6	3.9	4.1	4.5	5.1	5.8	5.8	6
7.1	7.5	7.9	8	9					

In this distribution, many students solved the problem in a short time. Here is the histogram for this distribution, which tails off towards the higher numbers on the right.

We call this a positively skewed distribution.
It is also referred to as a skewed right distribution.

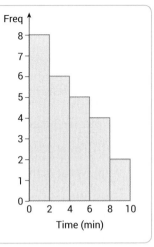

Exercise 1.4

1. Each year the Academy awards Oscars for Best Actor and Best Actress. The table below lists the ages of the Best Actor at the time of the awards ceremony. The ages are listed in order, beginning with Dustin Hoffmann's age in 1980 and ending with Eddie Redmayne's age in 2015.

42	37	76	39	53	45
36	62	43	51	32	42
54	52	37	38	32	45
60	46	40	36	47	29
43	37	38	45	50	48
60	50	39	55	44	33

(i) Display the data on an unordered stem-and-leaf plot.

(ii) Order the data in an ordered stem-and-leaf plot.

(iii) What was the age of the oldest actor to win an Oscar in the period 1980–2015?

(iv) What was the age of the youngest actor to win an Oscar in the period 1980–2015?

(v) Describe the shape of the stem-and-leaf plot.

(vi) What does the shape tell us about the age profile of the actors?

2. John measures the heights (in centimetres) of all the students in his class. Here are his results:

160	155	166	154	150
158	170	175	156	153
140	168	170	149	145
157	160	165	180	181
165	153	139	183	160

(i) Copy and complete the stem-and-leaf diagram.

Stem	Leaf
13	9
14	
15	
16	
17	
18	Key: 13|9 = 139

(ii) What variable is John measuring?

(iii) What type of data does this variable generate?

(iv) John's height is 166 cm. What proportion of the class is taller than him?

3. John randomly selects 20 students from his school. He asks the 20 students to take an Internet IQ test. Here are the results:

109, 100, 111, 127, 114, 103, 116, 120, 128, 132, 94, 88, 129, 108, 127, 110, 109, 104, 119, 133

(i) Show the results on a stem-and-leaf plot.

(ii) If 100 is the average IQ score for the whole population, then how many students scored higher than average?

(iii) How many students scored lower than 100?

(iv) What percentage of students had scores between 85 and 115?

STATISTICS I

4. The number of hours sleep taken by 50 people on a certain night was tabled as follows:

Time (hours)	0–3	3–6	6–9	9–12
Frequency	4	11	20	15

Note: 0–3 means 0 or more but less than 3, and so on.

(i) Draw a histogram that will represent the data.

(ii) What is the greatest possible number of people who had over 8 hours' sleep?

(iii) What is the least possible number who had over 8 hours' sleep?

5. The amount of rain, in millimetres, was recorded for 60 days. The results are shown in the frequency table.

Rain (mm)	0–4	4–8	8–12	12–16	16–20	20–24	24–28	28–32	32–36
No. of days	40	7	6	3	2	1	0	0	1

Note: 0–4 means 0 or more but less than 4, and so on.

(i) Represent the data on a histogram.

(ii) Describe the shape of the distribution.

6. Identify the following types of distribution (skewed left, symmetric, reasonably symmetric or skewed right).

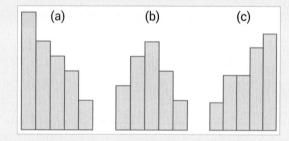

7. The time, in minutes, taken by each member of a group of students to solve a problem is represented in the histogram shown here.

Copy and complete the following table:

Time (min)	0–1	1–2	2–3	3–4	4–5
Frequency					

Note: 0–1 means 0 or more but less than 1, and so on.

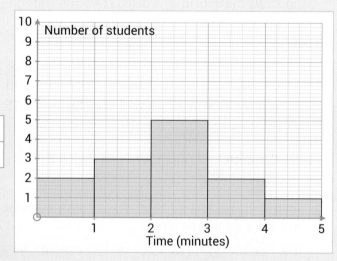

(i) How many students solved the problem in less than 3 minutes?

(ii) What percentage of students solved it in less than a minute (correct to two decimal places)?

(iii) Comment on the shape of the distribution.

8. The University of Arizona, as part of a study on refuse disposal, collected data from a number of households. The data in the table below gives the weight (in kilograms) of paper disposed from 78 of the households in one week.

2.41	1.09	2.75	3.03	6.85	3.10
7.57	3.44	6.18	4.50	1.27	5.18
7.55	4.34	3.17	5.78	2.92	7.30
8.22	4.00	6.51	4.46	2.66	2.90
8.42	3.96	6.04	7.44	5.03	5.92
6.96	3.16	1.48	2.87	5.64	5.16
6.83	4.17	4.27	4.29	5.59	5.70
8.13	3.50	2.8	3.62	4.38	3.67
6.08	4.99	5.95	1.48	0.75	4.54
6.38	4.07	4.29	2.67	3.75	5.65
7.05	4.80	2.66	3.99	5.01	5.58
1.36	5.60	5.7	4.50	1.57	4.53
5.09	4.20	3.7	5.60	7.8	7.50

(i) Complete the frequency distribution table.

Weight (kg)	0.5−1.5	1.5−2.5	2.5−3.5	3.5−4.5	4.5−5.5	5.5−6.5	6.5−7.5	7.5−8.5
Tally								
Frequency								

Note: 0.5−1.5 means 0.5 < Weight ≤ 1.5, and so on.

(ii) Display the distribution on a histogram.

(iii) Comment on the shape of the distribution.

9. The data below gives the weights (in kilograms) of a random sample of 30 newborn babies born in a maternity ward during 2009.

2.79	3.02	3.60	2.61	2.07
3.06	2.75	3.51	3.38	3.42
2.61	3.42	3.38	2.97	2.75
2.34	2.07	3.60	2.30	3.24
3.24	3.33	2.75	3.11	3.02
3.15	3.24	2.57	3.78	2.16

(i) Complete the frequency distribution table below.

Weight (kg)	2.0−2.5	2.5−3.0	3.0−3.5	3.5−4.0
Tally				
Frequency				

Note: 2.0−2.5 means 2.0 < Weight ≤ 2.5 and so on.

(ii) Display the distribution on a histogram.

(iii) Write the frequency of each class interval as a percentage of 30 (30 is the total sample size). These numbers are termed the **relative frequencies of the distribution**.
Give your answers correct to one decimal place.

(iv) Complete the following relative frequency distribution:

Weight (kg)	2.0–2.5	2.5–3.0	3.0–3.5	3.5–4.0
Relative frequency				

Note: 2.0–2.5 means 2.0 < Weight ≤ 2.5 and so on.

(v) Display the relative frequency distribution on a histogram. Use the following scaled axes as a guide.

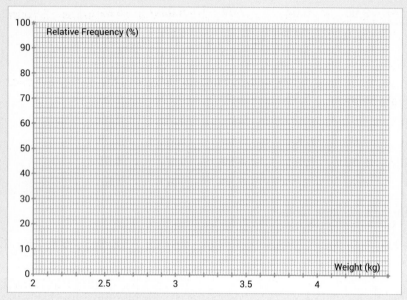

(vi) What advantage has the graph of the relative frequency distribution over the graph of the frequency distribution?

10. The table below gives the closing weekly share price for AIB shares from January 2015 to June 2015. All prices are in euro.

AIB share prices					
0.88	0.97	1.11	0.90	0.96	1.04
1.08	1.24	1.11	1.44	1.50	1.50
1.54	1.20	1.70	1.57	1.45	1.45
0.99	1.12	1.12	1.09	1.29	1.40
1.48	1.65				

(i) Copy and complete the stem-and-leaf diagram.

0.8	
0.9	
1.0	
1.1	1, 1, 2, 2
1.2	
1.3	
1.4	
1.5	
1.6	
1.7	Key: 0.8|8 = €0.88

(ii) Using your stem-and-leaf diagram, complete the frequency distribution.

Price (€)	0.8–0.9	0.9–1.0	1.0–1.1	1.1–1.2	1.2–1.3	1.3–1.4	1.4–1.5	1.5–1.6	1.6–1.7	1.7–1.8
Frequency										

Note: 0.8–0.9 means 0.8 or more but less than 0.9, and so on.

(iii) Display the distribution on a histogram.

(iv) 'For small data sets, stem-and-leaf plots give more information than histograms. Histograms are best used for large data sets.' Explain why this statement is true.

11. Mark conducted a survey about how accurately certain boys measured a piece of string. The piece of string was measured to the nearest millimetre. The results of the survey are given in the stem-and-leaf diagram below.

6	4, 5, 5, 7, 8
7	0, 0, 0, 0, 1, 1, 2, 3, 5

Key: 7|1 = 71 mm

Mark then drew a second stem-and-leaf diagram.

6	4
6	5, 5, 7, 8
7	0, 0, 0, 0, 1, 1, 2, 3
7	5

Key: 7|0 = 70 mm

(i) What are the advantages of using the second stem-and-leaf diagram rather than the first?

(ii) Write down the longest measurement recorded in the survey.

(iii) Mark measured the string as 63 mm. Add Mark's measurement to the second stem-and-leaf diagram.

12. The following back-to-back stem-and-leaf diagram compares the pulse rates of 25 people before and after a 5 km run.

Before run		After run
7, 5, 2	5	
9, 8, 6, 4, 2, 1, 1, 0	6	
8, 8, 8, 6, 5, 3, 3, 1	7	
3, 2, 1	8	0, 2, 5
8, 5	9	8, 6
9	10	0, 0, 1, 5, 6, 6, 8, 9
	11	1, 2, 2, 6, 9
	12	7, 8, 8
	13	0, 1, 7
	14	2

Key: 5|9| = 95 beats/min   Key: |11|1 = 111 beats/min

(i) How many people had pulse rates of more than 100 beats per minute after the run?

(ii) How many people had pulse rates of more than 100 beats per minute before the run?

(iii) What conclusions can you draw from the stem-and-leaf diagram?

13. The tables below show maximal breadth measurements (in millimetres) of adult male Egyptian skulls from two different time periods. The first table refers to skulls dated 4000 BCE (Before Common Era) and the second table to skulls dated 150 CE (Common Era). The data was collected as part of a study to show that skull sizes changed between 4000 BCE and 150 CE as a result of Egyptians interbreeding with immigrant populations.

4000 BCE					
131	125	131	119	136	138
139	125	131	134	129	134
126	132	141	131	135	132
139	132	126	135	134	130

150 CE					
137	136	128	130	138	126
136	126	132	139	143	141
135	137	142	139	138	137
133	145	138	131	143	134

(i) Draw a back-to-back stem-and-leaf diagram that will compare the maximal breadth measurements of the skulls from the two different periods.

(ii) Does your diagram indicate a difference? Explain.

14. The data below is from Charles Darwin's study of cross-fertilisation and self-fertilisation. Pairs of seedlings of the same age, one produced by cross-fertilisation and the other by self-fertilisation, are grown under nearly identical conditions. The data shows the final heights of each plant after a fixed period of time. All heights have been converted to centimetres.

Cross-fertilised plants				
59	55	46	58	30
30	48	55	53	58
53	54	51	54	55

Self-fertilised plants				
44	50	47	45	32
51	46	38	41	39
50	47	41	45	45

(i) Draw a back-to-back stem-and-leaf diagram that will compare the heights of cross-fertilised and self-fertilised plants.

(ii) The aim of Darwin's experiment was to demonstrate the greater vigour of the cross-fertilised plants. Based on your stem-and-leaf diagram, do you think the experiment demonstrates this?

(iii) How might Darwin have improved the experiment?

15. Here is some random data from the CensusAtSchool site. All lengths are measured in centimetres.

Gender	Height	Foot length	Gender	Height	Foot length
Male	167	25	Female	135	20
Female	151	22	Male	164	31
Female	171	31	Male	158	24
Male	151	24	Male	147	24
Female	158	24	Female	160	32
Male	158	24	Female	156	24
Male	170	24	Female	171	31
Female	149	21	Male	118	23
Male	154	24	Female	154	23
Female	150	22	Male	148	22

(i) Draw a back-to-back stem-and-leaf diagram that will compare the heights of males and females in the group.

(ii) Draw a back-to-back stem-and-leaf diagram that will compare the foot lengths of males and females in the group.

1.6 Scatter Graphs and Correlation

Scatter graphs are used to investigate relationships between two sets of numerical data.

On our course we will investigate the linear relationship, if any, between two sets of numerical data.

If the points on a scatter graph are vertically close to a straight line, then we say there is a strong **linear correlation** between the two sets of data.

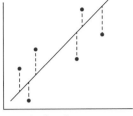

Correlation is not strong

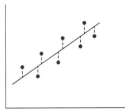

Correlation is strong

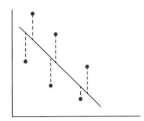

Correlation is not strong

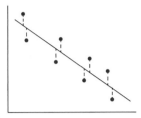

Correlation is strong

Suppose you measure the arm span and height of all students in your class. For each height measurement, there is a corresponding arm span measurement, so the data can be **paired**.

> Data that can be paired is known as paired data or bivariate data.

The following tables show the height and arm span measurements of a group of students.
All measurements are in centimetres.

Height (cm)	160	170	165	159	161	163	165	166
Arm span (cm)	159	168	162	161	162	164	164	164

Height (cm)	166	167	167	169	170	171	171	177
Arm span (cm)	165	166	167	171	169	169	170	175

Each height measurement and corresponding arm span measurement form a couple. Here are the couples for the data above:

(160, 159), (170, 168), (165, 162), (159, 161), (161, 162), (163, 164), (165, 164), (166, 164), (166, 165), (167, 166), (167, 167), (169, 171), (170, 169), (171, 169), (171, 170), (177, 175)

Always put the **explanatory variable**, if there is one, on the horizontal (x) axis. If there is no explanatory variable, then either variable can go on the horizontal axis.

> A response variable is the quantity that we ask a question about in our study.
> An explanatory variable is any factor that can influence the response variable.

Here is the scatter graph for the data:

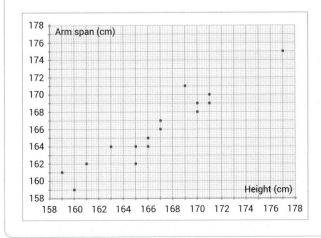

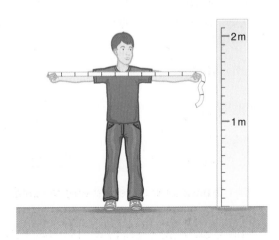

STATISTICS 1

You can see from the graph that the points lie reasonably close to a straight line. We can, in this case, conclude that there is a relationship between arm span and height. In general, the greater the height, the greater the arm span.

Are there any **outliers** in this data set? The answer is no. No point is such that it falls outside the overall pattern.

> An outlier is an individual value that falls outside the overall pattern.

- Correlation is positive when the two data sets increase together.
- Correlation is negative when one data set decreases as the other increases.

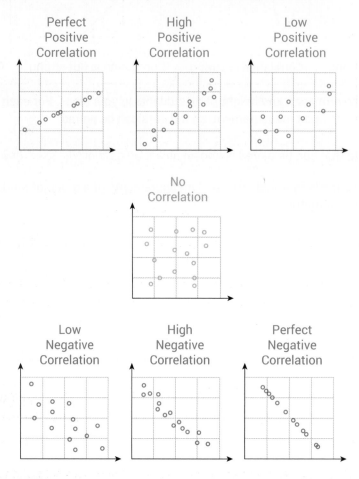

Worked Example 1.9

Listed below are the heights of mothers and the heights of their adult daughters. All measurements are in centimetres.

Mother's height	158	168	160	150	163	168	148	150
Daughter's height	147	162	164	153	164	169	153	158

(i) Draw a scatter diagram for the data.

(ii) Does there appear to be a linear correlation between mothers' heights and daughters' heights?

(iii) On the graph, circle the outlier of the data.

Solution

(i) The mother's height is the explanatory variable as we are trying to show that it influences the daughter's height (due to genetics).

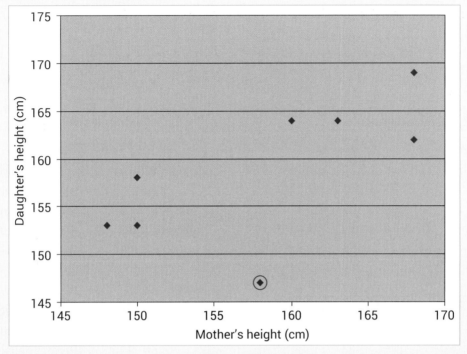

(ii) There appears to be a moderate positive linear correlation between mothers' heights and daughters' heights.

(iii) An outlier is a data point that falls outside the overall pattern. It is circled on the graph in part (i). We would expect the height of a daughter whose mother is 158 cm tall to be a lot taller than 147 cm, on average.

The Correlation Coefficient

The **correlation coefficient**, r, is a number in the following range: $-1 \leqslant r \leqslant 1$.

> The correlation coefficient is a measure of the strength of the linear relationship between two sets of data. It has a value between -1 and 1.

- If r is close to 1, then there is a **strong positive correlation** between two sets of data.
- If r is close to -1, we say there is a **strong negative correlation** between the two sets.
- If r is close to 0, then there is **no correlation** between the two sets.

Types of Correlation

It is important that you state both the **direction** (positive or negative) and the **strength** of a correlation when asked for the type of correlation.

(i) Strong positive correlation

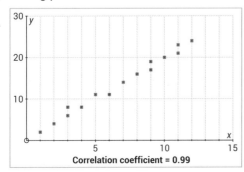

Correlation coefficient = 0.99

(ii) Strong negative correlation

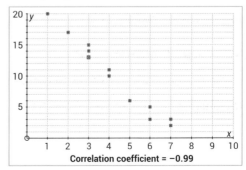

Correlation coefficient = −0.99

(iii) Weak positive correlation

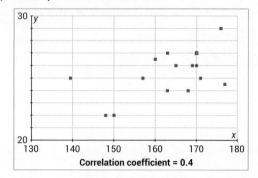

Correlation coefficient = 0.4

(iv) Weak negative correlation

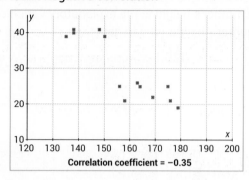

Correlation coefficient = −0.35

(v) No correlation

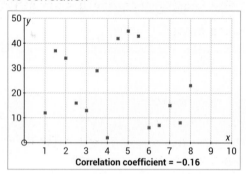

Correlation coefficient = −0.16

r-value	Correlation
$r = 1$	Perfect positive
$0.8 \leqslant r < 1$	Strong positive
$0.5 \leqslant r < 0.8$	Moderate positive
$0 < r < 0.5$	Weak positive
$r = 0$	Zero
$-0.5 < r < 0$	Weak negative
$-0.8 < r \leqslant -0.5$	Moderate negative
$-1 < r \leqslant -0.8$	Strong negative
$r = -1$	Perfect negative

Calculating the Correlation Coefficient

We are required to calculate the correlation coefficient using a calculator. Here is how we would calculate the correlation coefficient for the paired data given at the beginning of this section. The table of data is shown below.

Height (cm)	160	170	165	159	161	163	165	166
Arm span (cm)	159	168	162	161	162	164	164	164
Height (cm)	166	167	167	169	170	171	171	177
Arm span (cm)	165	166	167	171	169	169	170	175

Always clear the calculator's memory before each question, as most calculators store previously entered data.

Individual calculators may differ, and it is important that you know how to calculate r, the correlation coefficient, on your calculator.

Step 1 Put the calculator in STAT LINE mode.

Step 2 Enter the paired data. This is how to enter the two pairs (160, 159) and (170, 168):

Continue and enter all pairs of data.

Step 3 Calculate *r*, the correlation coefficient.

The value of *r* for this set of data to 2 decimal places is 0.95, which indicates a strong positive correlation.

This means that, in general, the taller you are, the wider will be your arm span.

Worked Example 1.10

At the end of a marathon, eight athletes are randomly selected. All of the athletes are asked to give their age (in years) and their time (in minutes) for the race. The results are given in the table below.

Age	33	33	31	26	26	25	30	29
Time	132.6	132.1	133.1	134.0	134.1	134.6	133	133.5

(i) Draw a scatter graph of the data.

(ii) Calculate the correlation coefficient, correct to two decimal places.

(iii) What is the type of correlation between the two sets of data?

(iv) Describe the correlation between age and time.

(v) Explain why the correlation described in part (iv) will probably not apply for athletes in the 55–64 age bracket.

Solution

(i)

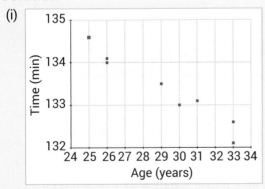

(ii) The correlation coefficient *r* = −0.97.

(iii) There is a strong negative linear correlation between the two sets of data.

(iv) As age increases, the times, in general, decrease.

(v) In the 55–64 age bracket, one would expect marathon times to increase as athletes get older. In the 25–34 age bracket, times improve as the athletes get older, as marathon athletes generally achieve their best times in their early thirties. Therefore, it is important that we are careful when making predictions that are outside the range of the sample data.

> When asked to describe a correlation, give the correlation coefficient (if possible) and also a non-technical explanation of the correlation. Always use the phrase 'in general' to take account of exceptions.

Correlation Versus Causality

In general, the amount of fuel burned by a car depends on the size of its engine, since bigger engines burn more fuel. We say there is a **causal relationship** between the size of the car's engine and the amount of fuel used.

If we find a statistical relationship between two variables, then we cannot always conclude that one of the variables is the cause of the other, i.e. **correlation does not always imply causality**.

During the 20 years between 1980 and 2000, there was a large increase in the sale of calculators and the sale of computers. As the sale of calculators increased, the sale of computers also increased, i.e. there was a strong positive correlation between the sale of calculators and the sale of computers. Did the increase in the sale of calculators cause an increase in the sale of computers? Of course, the answer is no. During this 20-year period, the cost of producing both of these technologies decreased dramatically, leading to an increase in sales. A third variable, the cost of production, was responsible for the increase in the other variables. We call this third variable a **lurking variable**.

Exercise 1.5

1. The heights (in centimetres) and ages (in years) of 10 girls are tabled as follows:

Age	8	9	9	10	11	12	12	13	14	15
Height	145	139	140	142	147	154	153	158	160	162

   (i) Using suitable scales, plot the scatter diagram for these results.

   (ii) Calculate the correlation coefficient.

   (iii) Describe the correlation between age and height.

2. The table shows the marks obtained by a group of students in a maths test, and the number of hours' sleep the students had on the night before the test.

Hours slept	9	8	6	8	5	8	9	5	7	8
Mark	85	89	70	87	71	84	90	63	80	70

   (i) Using suitable scales, plot the results on a scatter diagram.

   (ii) Calculate the correlation coefficient.

   (iii) Describe the type of correlation in the context of the question.

3. The table shows the age t (in years) and the number of hours h slept per day by 24 infants who were less than one year old.

Age, t	0.03	0.05	0.05	0.08	0.11	0.19	0.21	0.26	0.34	0.35	0.35	0.44
Sleep, h	15.0	15.8	16.4	16.2	14.8	14.7	14.5	15.4	15.2	15.3	14.4	13.9
Age, t	0.52	0.69	0.70	0.75	0.80	0.82	0.86	0.91	0.94	0.97	0.98	0.98
Sleep, h	14.4	13.2	14.1	14.2	13.4	13.2	13.9	13.1	13.7	12.7	13.7	13.6

   (i) Draw a scatter diagram for the data.

   (ii) Explain the correlation between age and number of hours slept.

4. During each heartbeat, blood pressure varies between a maximum (systolic) and a minimum (diastolic) pressure. The systolic and diastolic readings from 40 patients are displayed on the scatter graph.

(i) Describe the correlation between systolic and diastolic blood pressure.

(ii) Select the correct value of the correlation coefficient from this list: 0.2, 0.8, −0.5, 0.6, −0.1. Justify your selection.

(iii) What is the systolic reading and the diastolic reading of the outlier in this data?

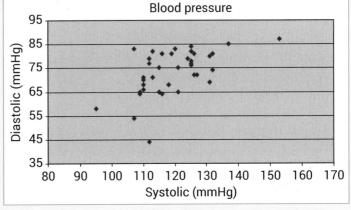

(iv) The blood pressure readings have been taken from 40 patients on a clinical trial. The trial is testing the effectiveness of a new treatment for severe migraine headaches. Outline three possible ethical issues that the trial would have to address.

5. For each of the following diagrams, describe the correlation.

(i)

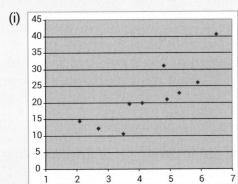

(iv)

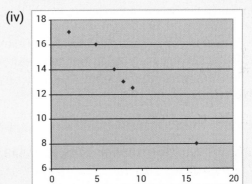

(ii)

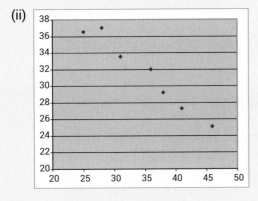

(v)

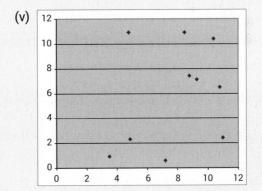

(iii)

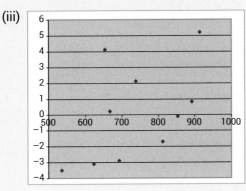

6. Haemoglobin is the component of red blood cells responsible for delivering oxygen from the lungs to the rest of the body. A red blood cell count is the number of red blood cells in a microlitre of blood. The scatter graph displays the haemoglobin and red blood cell count of 50 randomly selected adults.

(i) Describe the correlation between haemoglobin count and red blood cell count.

(ii) Select the correct value of the correlation coefficient from this list: −0.2, 0.8, 0.5, 0.1, −0.8. Justify your selection.

(iii) From the graph, estimate the red blood cell count of the four people with the lowest haemoglobin readings.

(iv) Using the graph, estimate the haemoglobin count of the person with a red blood cell count of 6.

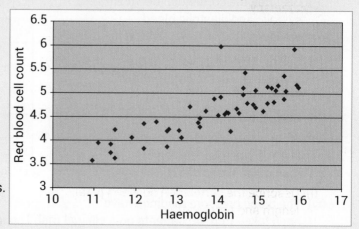

(v) It is known that a high iron diet increases haemoglobin levels. If the individual with the highest blood count was to change from his current diet to a high iron diet and the change of diet increased his haemoglobin levels, would this strengthen or weaken the correlation? Explain.

7. In 'The Effects of Temperature on Marathon Runners' Performance' by David Martin and John Buoncristiani (*Chance* magazine), high temperatures (in degrees Fahrenheit) and times (in minutes) were given for women who won the New York City marathon in recent years. The results are shown in the table below.

Temp (°F)	55	61	49	62	70	73	51	57
Time	145.28	148.72	148.30	148.10	147.62	146.40	144.67	147.53

(i) Represent the data on a scatter graph.

(ii) Calculate the correlation coefficient.

(iii) Does it appear that winning times are affected by temperature? Explain your answer.

(iv) How might this study be improved?

8. The scatter plot shows the fuel consumption (in litres/100 km) of seven petrol engines.

(i) What is the fuel consumption of the 1,400 cc engine?

(ii) What size engine has a fuel consumption rate of 4 litres/100 km?

(iii) Calculate and describe the correlation, with reference to the information given.

(iv) 'The data shows that bigger engines are more efficient.' Is this statement true or false? Justify your answer.

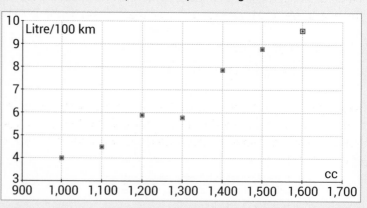

9. At a job interview, eight candidates were given tests on numeracy and IT skills. The tests are marked out of 10. The following table shows the results of the tests:

Numeracy	6	9	10	4	3	5	9	5
IT skills	7	8	9	2	1	5	6	4

(i) Draw a scatter diagram of the data. Let numeracy score be the explanatory variable.

(ii) Calculate the correlation coefficient.

(iii) Describe the correlation between numeracy and IT skills.

10. The petal width and petal length of a random sample of 150 irises are plotted on the scatter graph below. Three different classes of iris are included in the sample. All measurements are in centimetres.

(i) Describe the correlation between petal length and petal width.

(ii) Explain the gap in the plot.

(iii) Select the correct value of the correlation coefficient from this list:
−0.2, 0.96, 0.5, 0.1, −0.8.
Justify your selection.

(iv) Explain how you would have selected this sample.

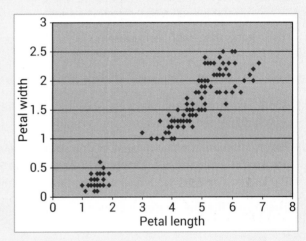

1.7 Linear Regression

The first step in determining the linear relationship between two variables is to draw a scatter graph. If the scatter graph suggests a linear relationship, then we calculate the correlation coefficient to determine the strength of the relationship. The next step is to find the equation of the straight line that best fits the data. The equation of this line will describe the relationship between the two variables. We call this line **the line of best fit** or the **regression line**.

On our course we draw the line of best fit by eye, and then find its equation.

When drawing the line of best fit, draw the line in such a way as to come vertically as close as possible to the points. We are trying to minimise the vertical distance between the points and the line of best fit.

Worked Example 1.11

A teacher decides to investigate the connection between progress at school and the number of hours of TV watched per week. He collects data from 10 randomly selected students. The data includes the number of hours of TV watched by each student per week and his/her mean mark across all subjects in a recent series of end-of-term tests.

TV hours	21	4	9	11	12	7	13	5	25	14
Mean mark	47	76	70	55	65	68	50	70	40	55

(i) Represent the data on a scatter graph.

(ii) Calculate, to two decimal places, the correlation coefficient, r.

(iii) What can you conclude from the scatter plot and the correlation coefficient?

(iv) Add the line of best fit to the scatter plot.

Solution

(i)

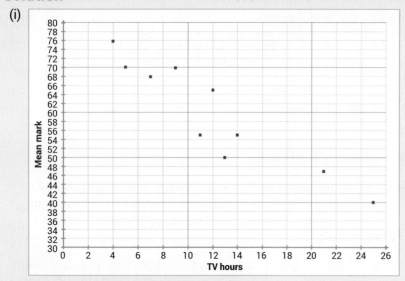

(ii) The correlation coefficient $r = -0.92$.

(iii) There is a strong negative correlation between the variables. In general, those who spend more time watching TV tend to have a lower average mark.

(iv) Before drawing the line of best fit, calculate $\bar{x}$, the mean of the first row of the table, and also $\bar{y}$, the mean of the second row of the table. In this case:

$\bar{x} = 12.1$ $\bar{y} = 59.6$

Then draw the line so that it comes as vertically close as possible to the points.

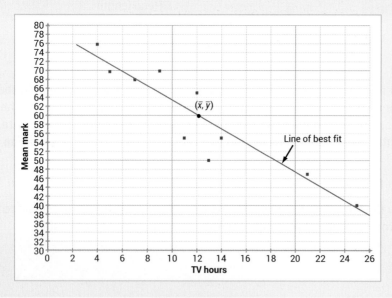

$(\bar{x}, \bar{y})$ is always a point on the line of best fit.

Finding $(\bar{x}, \bar{y})$ Using a Calculator

Step 1 Put the calculator in STAT LINE mode.

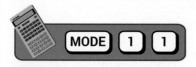

Step 2 Enter the paired data. This is how to enter the two pairs (21,47) and (4,76):

Step 3 Calculate $\bar{x}$.

$\bar{x} = 12.1$

Step 4 Calculate $\bar{y}$.

$\bar{y} = 59.6$

Worked Example 1.12

The manager of a company relies on travelling salespeople to sell the company's products. She wishes to investigate the relationship between sales and the amount of time spent with customers. She collects data from 10 salespeople. This data includes the sales for the month and the time (in hours) spent with customers. The results are given in the following table:

Time (hours)	3.1	4.5	3.8	5.2	6.0	4.1	5.5	5.2	5.0	7.0
Sales (€)	1,648	2,000	1,800	2,440	2,860	2,000	2,440	2,400	2,280	3,200

(i) Represent the data on a scatter graph.

(ii) Calculate the correlation coefficient.

(iii) What can you conclude from the scatter plot and the correlation coefficient?

(iv) Add the line of best fit to the scatter plot.

(v) By taking suitable readings from your plot, find the equation of the line of best fit.

(vi) Estimate the monthly sales for a salesperson who spends 5.8 hours with customers.

(vii) Explain how to interpret the slope of the line in this context.

Solution

(i)

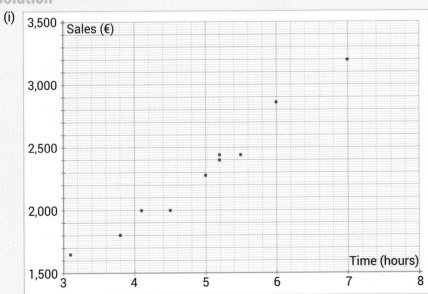

(ii) The correlation coefficient $r = 0.99$.

(iii) There is a strong positive correlation between the variables. In general, those who spend more time with their customers tend to have a higher monthly sales figure.

STATISTICS I

(iv)

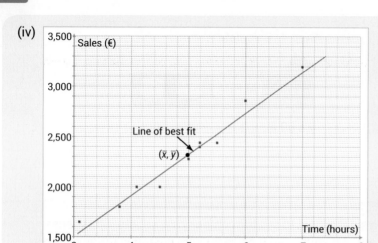

$\bar{x} = 4.94$

$\bar{y} = 2,306.8$

(v) From our graph, (4.2,2,000) and (6.6,3,000) are two points on the line of best fit.

The equation of the line of best fit should always be of the form: $y = mx + c$ or, more correctly, $y = a + bx$ (where b is the slope and a the vertical intercept).

Slope of the line of best fit:

$$m = \frac{y_2 - y_1}{x_2 - x_1}$$

$$m = \frac{3,000 - 2,000}{6.6 - 4.2}$$

$$m = \frac{1,000}{2.4} = \frac{1,250}{3}$$

Points chosen must be **on** the line of best fit.

You should take two points that are far apart on the line of best fit to reduce the error incurred from reading two points from a graph.

Equation of the line of best fit:

$$y - y_1 = m(x - x_1)$$

$$y - 2,000 = \frac{1,250}{3}(x - 4.2)$$

$$y - 2,000 = \frac{1,250}{3}x - 1,750$$

$$y = 250 + \frac{1,250}{3}x$$

- If slope = 0, then there is no correlation.
- Otherwise, where slope ≠ 0, the slope has no connection to the strength of the correlation.

(Always leave the equation in the form $y = a + bx$ as this explicitly states y, the response variable in terms of x, the explanatory variable.)

(vi)

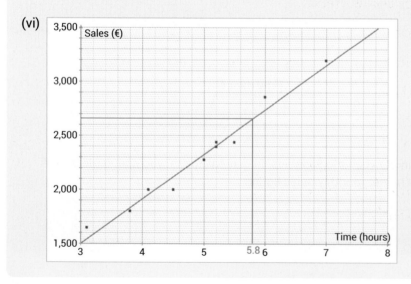

Method 1

Reading from the graph, we get an estimate of €2,660 monthly sales for a salesperson who spends 5.8 hours with the customer.

Method 2

We can also use the equation of the line of best fit to estimate the answer.

$$y = 250 + \frac{1,250}{3}x$$

$$\therefore y = 250 + \frac{1,250\,(5.8)}{3} = €2,666.67$$

(vii) The slope represents the expected increase in sales for each additional hour spent with customers. Therefore, each extra hour is expected to yield on average an increase of €416.67 in sales.

Exercise 1.6

1. Eleven students sat two construction studies tests. One test was a theory test and the other was a practical test. Here are the results:

Theory	6	10	8	12	21	5	7	18	13	11	16
Practical	7	9	10	15	22	9	8	17	16	9	19

   (i) Draw a scatter plot to represent the data. Let the theory score be the explanatory variable.

   (ii) Calculate the correlation coefficient.

   (iii) Add the line of best fit to your scatter plot.

2. The table below gives the age and the maximum distance at which a randomly selected sample of drivers could read a motorway sign.

Age (years)	19	21	40	29	45	80	75	62	64	55
Distance (m)	160	165	142	149	148	120	125	100	130	145

   (i) Draw a scatter plot to represent the data.   (iii) Add the line of best fit to your scatter plot.

   (ii) Calculate the correlation coefficient.   (iv) Describe the correlation between the two variables.

3. The following table shows the age (in years) and annual income of a sample of eight employees from a large company. The income is in thousands of euro.

Age	38	26	43	48	35	52	33	40
Income	36	29	53	55	34	62	38	46

   (i) Draw a scatter diagram of the data.

   (ii) Calculate the correlation coefficient.

   (iii) Add the line of best fit to your scatter plot.

   (iv) Describe the correlation between age and income.

   (v) Explain the correlation between age and income.

   (vi) Find the equation of the line of best fit.

4. Super Stores is a convenience shop that advertises sale items each month to boost sales. The shop manager believes that there is a linear relationship between the amount spent on advertising and sales figures. Here is the data for the past 10 months. All data is in thousands of euro.

Advertising	4.3	2.8	2.1	1.8	3.4	3.8	4.1	4.4	2.2	4.1
Sales	22	17	14	13	19	21	24	25	15	20

(i) Draw a scatter diagram of the data.

(ii) Calculate the correlation coefficient.

(iii) Comment on the correlation between advertising and sales.

(iv) Give one reason for the correlation you described in part (iii).

(v) Add the line of best fit to your scatter plot.

(vi) Find the equation of the line of best fit.

(vii) Use the equation of the line of best fit to predict the sales figure for a month in which €3,000 was spent on advertising.

5. The manager of Leinster Life Assurance has randomly selected 10 customers from the company's database. He wants to show the relationship between income and the amount of life cover a person buys. All data is in thousands of euro.

Income	35.4	40.5	42.3	50.8	40.4	48.6	61.5	56.5	48.6	39.8
Life cover	63	72	74	87	71	83	105	95	84	70

(i) Draw a scatter diagram of the data.

(ii) Calculate the correlation coefficient. Answer correct to four decimal places.

(iii) Add the line of best fit to your scatter plot.

(iv) Explain the correlation between amount of life cover and income for this sample.

(v) Find the equation of the line of best fit.

(vi) Do you think the manager should use this equation to predict the amount of life cover a future customer might take out? Explain your reasoning.

6. Peaches Beauty Salon is currently taking on beauticians at its new premises on Grafton Street. The owner of the salon wants to know what percentage of commission to pay the beauticians based on experience. A survey of 10 beauticians in Dublin was taken with the following results:

Commission (%)	41	21	25	34	45	26	36	36	42	31
Years of experience	11	2	4	9	13	5	8	9	11	6

(i) Draw a scatter diagram of the data.

(ii) Calculate the correlation coefficient.

(iii) Describe the correlation.

(iv) Add the line of best fit to your scatter plot.

(v) Find the equation of the line of best fit.

Peaches Beauty Salon has decided to adopt this equation as the model for determining the percentage of commission to pay to beauticians.

(vi) Allison has just applied to Peaches Beauty Salon for a position as a beautician. She has 10 years' experience. If Allison gets the job, what percentage of commission should she expect to receive?

Revision Exercises

1. Sonia O'Sullivan won gold for Ireland in the 5,000 m race at the World Championships in Gothenburg in 1995. She won the world title with a time of 14:46:47.

   For each of the following, identify the type of data:

   (i) The number of competitors in the race

   (ii) The time it took O'Sullivan to win the race

   (iii) The country she represented at the games

   (iv) The number on her singlet

   (v) The number of spectators in the stadium during the race

2. In a recent study on Internet shopping in Ireland, a random selection of 1,000 adults was surveyed, and 31% of them said they used the Internet for shopping at least a few times a year.

   (i) Identify the population of interest in this study.

   (ii) Identify the sample.

   (iii) Does the study involve descriptive or inferential statistics? Explain.

   (iv) What variable is being measured in the study?

   (v) Is the variable categorical or numerical?

3. A survey company hires 20 people to go out onto the streets, stop people and ask them questions. The company asks each surveyor to get 50 responses. The data is then used to make inferences about some characteristic of the population.

   (i) What type of sample is the company collecting?

   (ii) Do you think that the people who participate in these surveys are representative of the population? Explain.

   (iii) What type of people would not participate in a survey like this?

4. For each of the following, state which is the explanatory variable and which is the response variable:

   (i) The cost of a gold ring and its weight

   (ii) The mark a student receives in a mock exam and the mark the student receives in the final exam

   (iii) The distance an athlete runs in training and the time taken to do it

   (iv) The amount of electricity used to boil the water and the volume of water in an electric kettle

5. The school principal of a co-educational school has asked a student to conduct a survey in the school to decide whether a new uniform should be introduced. The uniform has a bright blue and pink striped design. The student decides to interview a sample of students. Explain how such a sample could be collected for each of the following different sampling strategies:

   (i) Cluster sampling

   (ii) Simple random sampling

   (iii) Stratified random sampling

   (iv) Quota sampling

6. The marks of 15 students in a test were as follows:

53	67	43	71	21
49	58	48	77	37
82	51	61	98	84

   (i) What variable is being measured?

   (ii) What type of data is being generated by the test?

   (iii) Use an appropriate graph to represent the data.

   (iv) Describe the distribution.

7. John wants to find out how fast students in his school can solve a maths problem. It is impractical to ask all students to solve the problem, so he decides to take a sample of students. He feels that students in exam years may be faster problem-solvers than students from non-exam classes.

He randomly selects two groups, one of size 12 and the other of size 20. The first group is selected from students who will be sitting the state exams in June. The second group is selected from non-exam years. He does this to reduce potential bias.

Each individual in both groups is given the same puzzle to complete. Here are the times (to the nearest minute) taken to complete the puzzle:

Group 1

12	12	20	11	17	32
15	21	40	9	20	17

Group 2

26	14	26	21	20	17	28	35	17	12
27	15	36	11	19	22	18	32	24	32

(i) Draw a back-to-back stem-and-leaf diagram for the data for each group.

(ii) What is this type of data called?

(iii) Describe the shape of each distribution.

(iv) What type of sample has John taken?

(v) If there are 600 students in the school, how many students are sitting exams in June?

(vi) Did the fastest and slowest times come from the same group?

8. A consultant orthopaedic surgeon is trying to establish whether a relationship exists between the age of patients who have had hip replacements and the number of days, following the operation, after which they were able to walk unaided.

He chooses a simple random sample of 10 patients and tabulates for each patient their age (in years) and the number of days after which they walked without assistance.

Age of patient	69	61	54	77	58	71	65	61	50	56
Number of days	50	45	40	50	42	47	48	38	32	33

(i) Show the data on a scatter plot.

(ii) Calculate the correlation coefficient.

(iii) Describe the correlation in the context of the question.

(iv) Show the line of best fit on your plot.

(v) Find the equation of the line of best fit.

(vi) Use your equation to predict the number of days after which a 63-year-old patient walks unaided.

(vii) Comment on a possible source of bias in the sample. What type of sample should the consultant have taken to eliminate this possible source of bias?

9. An expert from a local art gallery agreed to challenge a group of contestants to rank eight pieces of art correctly. Aoife agreed to take part and her rankings, along with those of the expert, were as follows:

Piece	A	B	C	D	E	F	G	H
Expert	3	1	6	8	7	2	4	5
Aoife	7	5	2	4	6	1	3	8

(i) Calculate the correlation coefficient for the two data sets.

(ii) Interpret the correlation in the context of the question.

(iii) A further five people entered the competition. The values of the correlation coefficients were 0.1, –0.4, 0.8, –0.5 and 0.9.

   (a) Which of these values show that there is almost no correlation between the rankings of the expert and the rankings of the contestant?

   (b) Which of these values shows the strongest correlation between the expert and the contestant?

10. Twenty students are asked how many minutes they spent watching television on a particular day. The following frequency distribution summarises their replies:

Time (min)	0–20	20–40	40–60	60–80	80–100
Frequency	2	6	5	3	4

Note: 0–20 means 0 or more but less than 20, and so on.

   (i) Draw a histogram to represent the data.

   (ii) Describe the shape of the distribution.

   (iii) What proportion of students spent 40 minutes or more watching television?

Exam Questions

1. A person's maximum heart rate is the highest rate at which their heart beats during certain extreme kinds of exercise. It is measured in beats per minute (bpm). It can be measured under controlled conditions. As part of a study in 2001, researchers measured the maximum heart rate of 514 adults and compared it to each person's age. The results were like those shown in the scatter plot.

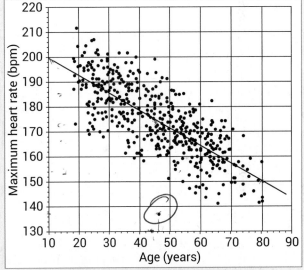

   (a) From the diagram, estimate the correlation coefficient.

   (b) Circle the **outlier** on the diagram and write down the person's age and maximum heart rate.

   (c) The line of best fit is shown on the diagram. Use the line of best fit to estimate the maximum heart rate of a 44-year-old person.

   (d) By taking suitable readings from the diagram, calculate the slope of the line of best fit.

   (e) Find the equation of the line of best fit and write it in the form: $MHR = a - b \times (age)$, where MHR is the maximum heart rate.

   (f) The researchers compared their new rule for estimating maximum heart rate to an older rule. The older rule is: $MHR = 220 - age$. The two rules can give different estimates of a person's maximum heart rate. Describe how the level of agreement between the two rules varies according to the age of the person. Illustrate your answer with two examples.

   (g) A particular exercise programme is based on the idea that a person will get most benefit by exercising at 75% of their estimated MHR. A 65-year-old man has been following this programme, using the old rule for estimating MHR. If he learns about the researchers' new rule for estimating MHR, how should he change what he is doing?

SEC Leaving Certificate Higher Level, Project Maths Paper 2, 2010

2. (a) Explain, with the aid of an example, what is meant by the statement:

'Correlation does not imply causality.'

(b) The data given in the table below and represented in the scatter diagram are pairs of observations of the variables x and y.

x	1	2	3	4	5	6
y	11	15	17	17	15	11

(i) Calculate the correlation coefficient.

(ii) What kind of relationship, if any, does the observed data suggest exists between x and y?

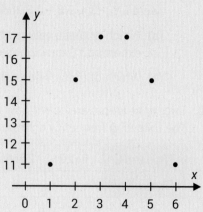

SEC Leaving Certificate Higher Level, Project Maths Paper 2, 2011

3. Table 1 below gives details of the number of males (M) and females (F) aged 15 years and over at work, unemployed, or not in the labour force for each year in the period 2004 to 2013.

		Table 1								
	Labour Force Statistics 2004 to 2013 – Persons aged 15 years and over (000's)									
Year	At work			Unemployed			Not in labour force			Total
	M	F	Total	M	F	Total	M	F	Total	
2004	1045.9	738.9	1784.8	79.6	31.6	111.2	457.1	854.2	1311.3	3207.3
2005	1087.3	779.7	1867.0	81.3	33.5	114.8	459.5	846.6	1306.1	3287.9
2006	1139.8	815.1	1954.9	80.6	38.1	118.7	457.6	844.9	1302.5	3376.1
2007	1184.0	865.6	2049.6	84.3	39.2	123.5	452.4	852.7	1325.1	3498.2
2008	1170.9	889.5	2060.4	106.3	41.0	147.3	494.8	872.5	1367.3	3575.0
2009	1039.8	863.5	1903.3	234.0	82.4	316.4	505.6	874.9	1380.5	3600.2
2010	985.1	843.5	1828.6	257.6	98.2	355.8	529.2	884.6	1413.8	3598.2
2011	970.2	843.2	1813.4	260.7	103.4	364.1	540.1	881.5	1421.6	3599.1
2012	949.6	823.8	1773.4	265.2	108.4	373.2	546.5	896.9	1443.4	3590.0
2013	974.4	829.0	1803.4	227.7	102.3	330.0	557.8	895.0	1452.8	3586.2

Source: Central Statistics Office www.cso.ie

Liam and Niamh are analysing the number of males and the number of females at work over the period 2004 to 2013.

Liam draws the following chart, using data from Table 1.

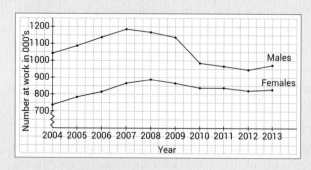

Niamh uses the same data and calculates the number of females at work as a percentage of the total number of persons at work and then draws the following chart.

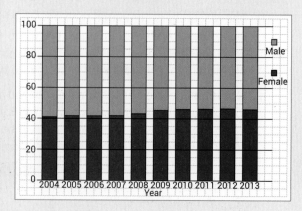

(i) Having examined both charts, a commentator states 'females were affected just as much as males by the downturn in employment'. Do you agree or disagree with this statement? Give a reason for your conclusion.

(ii) Which, if any, of the two charts did you find most useful in reaching your conclusion above? Give a reason for your answer.

(iii) Use the data in Table 1, for the years 2012 and 2013 only, to predict the percentage of persons, aged 15 years and over, who will be at work in 2014.

SEC Leaving Certificate Higher Level, Project Maths Paper 2, 2014

4. *Go Fast Airlines* provides internal flights in Ireland, short haul flights to Europe and long haul flights to America and Asia. On long haul flights the company sells economy class, business class and executive class tickets. All passengers have a baggage allowance of 20 kg and must pay a cost per kg for any weight over the 20 kg allowance.

Each month the company carries out a survey among 1,000 passengers. Some of the results of the survey for May are shown below.

Gender	Male: 479	Female: 521

Previously flown with *Go Fast Airlines*	Yes: 682	No: 318
Would fly again with *Go Fast Airlines*	Yes: 913	No: 87

Passenger Age	Mean age: 42 Median age: 31

Spend on in-flight facilities	Mean spend: €18.65 Median spend: €32.18

Was flight delayed?	Yes	No	Don't Know
	231	748	21

Passenger satisfaction with overall service	Satisfied	Not satisfied	Don't Know
	664	238	98

(a) *Go Fast Airlines* used a **stratified random sample** to conduct the survey.

   (i) Explain what is meant by a stratified random sample.

  (ii) Write down 4 different passenger groups that the company might have included in their sample.

(b) The responses of ten individual passengers to the questions on age and in-flight spend are given below.

Age (years)	46	29	37	18	25	75	52	35	40	31
In-flight spend (euro)	30	15	20	0	10	45	25	20	20	30

  (i) Draw a scatter plot of the data.

  (ii) Calculate the correlation coefficient between passenger age and in-flight spend.

  (iii) What can you conclude from the completed scatter plot and the correction coefficient?

  (iv) Sketch the line of best fit in the completed scatter plot.

 Solutions and chapter summary available online   *SEC Leaving Certificate Higher Level, Project Maths Paper 2, 2013*

STATISTICS I

02

Probability I

In this chapter you will learn:

- About the Fundamental Principle of Counting and how to apply it

- When and how to use the calculator buttons for ^nP_r and $n!$

- To understand the meaning of $\binom{n}{r}$ and apply it to solving problems

- To understand the difference between arranging objects and choosing objects

- To understand the idea of probability

- To apply laws of probability in real-life situations such as flipping coins, rolling dice, picking cards, birthdays falling on certain days, spinners and lotteries

- To understand the meaning of mutually exclusive events

- To understand conditional probability and apply it to solving problems

You should remember...

- Set notation
- Fractions, decimals and percentages

Key words

- Arrangement
- Factorial
- Choice
- Permutation
- Probability
- Mutually exclusive
- Trial
- Combination
- Outcome
- Sample space
- Event

2.1 The Fundamental Principle of Counting

Fundamental Principle of Counting

If one trial has *m* possible outcomes and a second trial has *n* possible outcomes, then the total number of possible outcomes is *m* × *n*.

Worked Example 2.1

In a restaurant there are three choices of main course (omelette, fish or burger) followed by two choices of dessert (ice-cream or apple pie). If you have a full meal in the restaurant, how many choices of meal will you have?

Solution

In accordance with the **Fundamental Principle of Counting**, there will be 3 × 2 = 6 choices. They are as follows:

1. Omelette followed by ice-cream
2. Omelette followed by apple pie
3. Fish followed by ice-cream
4. Fish followed by apple pie
5. Burger followed by ice-cream
6. Burger followed by apple pie

Worked Example 2.2

How many ways are there of arranging all the letters of the word MATH? (Math is the American word for maths.)

Solution

There are four choices for the first letter, three choices for the second letter, two choices for the third letter and one choice for the last letter. Hence, there are 4 × 3 × 2 × 1 = 24 ways. Here they are:

MATH	MTHA	AMTH	ATHM	THAM	TAHM	HATM	HTAM
MAHT	MHAT	AMHT	AHMT	THMA	TMHA	HAMT	HMAT
MTAH	MHTA	ATMH	AHTM	TAMH	TMAH	HTMA	HMTA

Factorials

There is a shorthand way of writing 4 × 3 × 2 × 1.

It is 4!, which we call 'four factorial'.

Similarly, 5! = 5 × 4 × 3 × 2 × 1 = 120.

$n! = n(n-1)(n-2) \ldots (3)(2)(1)$, which is called '*n* factorial'.

To get 5! on your calculator, press  .

The answer 120 should come up on the screen.

(On some calculators *n*! is written as *x*!)

Worked Example 2.3

Six horses enter a race. Punters are asked to guess which horse will come first, which second, which third, etc. all the way down to sixth place. How many different predictions can be made? Assume that dead heats are not possible.

Solution

When a punter is filling up the form, there will be six choices for first place, five choices for second place, four choices for third place, etc.

Hence, the number of different predictions is $6 \times 5 \times 4 \times 3 \times 2 \times 1 = 6! = 720$.

A Surprising Result

On your calculator press:

You might be surprised to find that the answer is 1.

That is $0! = 1$

Perhaps this argument may convince you:

5! = 120	Divide by 5	(120 ÷ 5 = 24)
4! = 24	Divide by 4	(24 ÷ 4 = 6)
3! = 6	Divide by 3	(6 ÷ 3 = 2)
2! = 2	Divide by 2	(2 ÷ 2 = 1)
1! = 1	Divide by 1	(1 ÷ 1 = 1)
0! = 1		

^nP_r : The Number of Ways of Arranging n Distinct Objects, r at a Time

Worked Example 2.4

In how many ways can the letters of the word COUNTER be arranged, taking them three at a time? No repetitions are allowed. (We can have RCE and EOU, for example – but not EEC or RRR.)

Solution

There are seven choices for the first letter, six choices for the next letter and five choices for the last letter.

This means than there are $7 \times 6 \times 5 = 210$ ways.

It is important to realise that

$$7 \times 6 \times 5 = \frac{7!}{4!}$$

and gives the number of permutations (or arrangements) of a population of seven distinct elements, taking them three at a time. It is called $^7P_3$.

In general, if you have a population of n distinct items, and you want to arrange r of them in order, then the number of possible arrangements (or permutations) is called ^nP_r and is defined as follows:

$$^nP_r = \frac{n!}{(n-r)!}$$

On all good calculators there is a button labelled $\boxed{nPr}$.

In Worked Example 2.4, the answer is $^7P_3$. We get this on a calculator by pressing:

The answer 210 comes up on the screen.

PROBABILITY I

Worked Example 2.5

How many numbers between 500 and 1,000 can be made from the digits 2, 4, 6 and 8:

(i) If no digit may be repeated (e.g. 824)

(ii) If digits may be repeated (e.g. 668)

Solution

We can deduce two things:

1. It will be a three-digit number.

2. The first digit will have to be either 6 or 8 (to make a number greater than 500).

(i) There are two choices for the first digit (6 and 8).

Having made this choice, there will be three choices left for the second digit.

Having made these choices, there will be two choices left for the third and last digit.

Hence, there are 2 × 3 × 2 = 12 numbers.

(ii) There are two choices for the first digit (6 and 8).

There are four choices for the next digit (as a digit can be repeated).

There are again four choices for the third digit.

Hence, there are 2 × 4 × 4 = 32 such numbers.

Worked Example 2.6

How many ways are there of arranging the letters of the word LEAVING:

(i) If there are no restrictions

(ii) If they must begin with N

(iii) If they must end with a vowel

(iv) If the three vowels must be together

(v) If L and N must be side by side

(vi) If L and N must be apart

Solution

(i) 7! = 5,040

(ii) 1 × 6 × 5 × 4 × 3 × 2 × 1 = 6! = 720 (since there is only **one** choice for the first letter)

(iii) There are three choices for the last letter, then the six remaining letters may be in any order. 6 × 5 × 4 × 3 × 2 × 1 × 3 = 6! × 3 = 2,160

Notice how **the place that has a restriction imposed on it is fixed up first**. Hence, we put one of the three vowels as the LAST letter and then fill the rest of the slots.

(iv) Treat the three vowels (glued together) as **one** letter. There are five letters to be arranged: L, V, N, G, AEI . There are 5! ways of arranging these.

But the vowels could be AEI, AIE, EAI, ... etc. There are 3! ways in which they can be arranged.

∴ The answer is 5! × 3! = 720

(v) Treat LN as one letter. There are six letters to be arranged: E, A, V, I, G, LN .

But LN can also be NL . (There are 2! ways of arranging LN .)

∴ The answer is 6! × 2! = 1,440

(vi) Use the 'subtraction method'. There are 5,040 arrangements altogether (see part (i)).

In 1,440 of these the L and N are together (see part (v)).

∴ There are 5,040 − 1,440 = 3,600 arrangements in which the L and N are apart.

The Subtraction Method

The number of ways that an event does NOT occur	=	Total number of ways	−	The number of ways that the event DOES occur

Worked Example 2.7

How many even numbers between 500 and 1000 can be made using only digits 3, 4, 5, 6, 7, 8 or 9 without repetitions?

Solution

If the first digit is even (6 or 8), then we have two choices for the last digit.

But if the first digit is odd (5, 7 or 9), we have three choices for the last digit (4, 6 and 8).

So we deal with these two cases separately.

Case 1 The first digit is even.

The number of arrangements = 2 × 5 × 2 = 20.

Case 2 The first digit is odd.

The number of arrangements = 3 × 5 × 3 = 45.

Hence, the total number of arrangements = 20 + 45 = 65.

Exercise 2.1

1. Evaluate the following:

   (i) 3!

   (ii) 2! + 4!

   (iii) 7! − 6!

   (iv) $\dfrac{8!}{7!}$

   (v) $\dfrac{9!}{6!}$

   (vi) 0! + 1! + 2! + 3!

   (vii) $\dfrac{11!}{10!}$

   (viii) $\dfrac{14!}{13!}$

   (ix) $\dfrac{20!}{19!}$

   (x) $\dfrac{21!}{19!}$

2. In a restaurant, there are three choices of starter, seven choices of main course and two choices of dessert. How many different full meals could be eaten at this restaurant?

3. A girl has five jumpers, two pairs of jeans and three pairs of socks. Ignoring the rest of her attire, in how many different possible ways could she dress?

4. A small town introduces 'registration numbers' for bicycles. Each registration number consists of a letter followed by a single digit (F3 and Y0 for example).

   What is the maximum number of bicycles that could have different registration numbers?

5. (a) Investigate if:

   (i) 3! + 2! = 5!   (iii) 0! + 1! = 2!

   (ii) 3! × 2! = 6!

   (b) How many ways are there of arranging all the letters of these words?

   (i) SUM

   (ii) MATHS

   (iii) TRIANGLE

6. How many ways are there of arranging the letters of THEORY if the letters are taken:

   (i) Three at a time

   (ii) Four at a time

   (iii) Six at a time

7. How many four-digit numbers can be made from the digits 1, 3, 4 and 5 (without repetition)?

   (i) How many of these are even?

   (ii) How many are odd?

   (iii) How many are over 4,000?

8. In how many different ways can the letters of the word RHOMBUS be arranged:

   (i) Taking the letters seven at a time

   (ii) Taking the letters five at a time

   (iii) Taking the letters two at a time

9. How many ways are there of arranging the letters of the word MATRIX:

   (i) If there are no restrictions

   (ii) If they must begin with T

   (iii) If they must begin with T and end with M

   (iv) If they must begin with a vowel

   (v) If they must **not** begin with a vowel

10. How many ways are there of arranging the letters of the word MONSTER:

   (i) If there are no restrictions

   (ii) If they must begin with a vowel

   (iii) If they must begin with a consonant

   (iv) If the vowels must be together

   (v) If the vowels must be apart

11. How many ways are there of arranging the letters of the word DUBLINER:

   (i) If there are no restrictions

   (ii) If they must begin with B and end in L

   (iii) If the three vowels must be together

   (iv) If E and R must be together

   (v) If E and R must be apart

12. How many ways are there of arranging the letters of the word TRIANGLES:

   (i) If there are no restrictions

   (ii) If the three vowels must be together

   (iii) If the six consonants must be together

   (iv) If the letter G must be immediately followed by the letter R

   (v) If they must begin and end with a consonant

13. (a) Evaluate:

   (i) $\dfrac{10!}{9!}$

   (iii) $\dfrac{23!}{22!}$

   (ii) $\dfrac{11!}{7!\,4!}$

   (iv) $\dfrac{13!}{11!}$

   (b) Simplify:

   (i) $\dfrac{n!}{(n-1)!}$

   (ii) $\dfrac{(n+1)!}{n!}$

   (iii) $n!\left[\dfrac{1}{(n-1)!} - \dfrac{1}{n!}\right]$

   (c) How many numbers between 3,000 and 10,000 can be made from the digits 1, 3, 5 and 7:

   (i) If digits may not be repeated

   (ii) If digits may be repeated

14. How many numbers between 500 and 1,000 do not contain the digits 0, 1 or 2?

15. How many natural numbers can be made using some or all of the digits 7, 8 and 9 – without repetitions?

16. How many natural numbers can be made using some or all of the digits 0, 1, 2 and 3, with no repetitions? (Note: Zero is not considered a natural number.)

17. A code for breaking into a computer system consists of two different letters followed by three different digits.

   (i) How many different codes are possible?

   (ii) A user has been given a code, but cannot remember it fully. All that she can remember is that the first letter is B and the first digit is 8. How many different possible codes fit this description?

18. How many five-digit numbers can be formed in which the first and the last digits are greater than 5, the three centre digits are identical, and the last digit is odd?

19. A raffle takes place in a school. Tickets are available in three colours: pink, yellow and green. Tickets are labelled with a letter followed by three digits. How many different tickets can be sold? (Note: Pink-N233 is not the same as Green-N233.)

PROBABILITY I

20. Forty horses are entered for the Grand National. Punters are asked to guess which will come first, which will come second and which will come third. In how many different ways can this be done? Assume no dead heats are possible.

21. How many four-digit numbers satisfy all these conditions at once:

- The number is a multiple of 10.
- The first three digits are all greater than 5.
- The first digit is even.

22. How many six-digit numbers fit this description: 'It is an odd number. It is a palindrome (i.e. it reads the same backwards as forwards). The two centre digits are odd and greater than 2'?

23. Two girls and three boys are to be lined up for a photograph. How many different arrangements are possible:

(i) If there are no restrictions

(ii) If they must be boy-girl-boy-girl-boy

24. Four girls and three boys are to be lined up side by side. No two persons of the same gender may be side by side. How many arrangements are possible?

25. Four girls and five boys are to be lined up. How many arrangements are possible:

(i) If there are no restrictions

(ii) If two particular girls must be together

(iii) If two particular boys must be kept apart

(iv) If no two people of the same gender may be together

26. (i) How many six-digit numbers can be made from the digits 1, 2, 3, 4, 5 and 7 without repetitions?

(ii) How many are even?

(iii) How many are even and over 300,000?

(Hint: In part (iii), deal with those which end in 2 and 4 separately.)

27. (i) How many five-digit odd numbers can be made from the digits 5, 6, 7, 8 and 9 without repetitions?

(ii) How many of these are under 80,000?

2.2 Choosing (Combinations)

There are seven members in our club: Ann, Bob, Carol, Dee, Eve, Fred and Gus. We have to choose three of them to represent the club at the National Congress in Athlone. How many different **choices** could we possibly make?

We'll refer to the members by their initial letter. So, we could choose ABC or CDG or ADG, etc.

We have already seen that there are $^7P_3 = \frac{7!}{4!}$ ways of **arranging** seven different letters in groups of three. But these would include ABC, ACB, BAC, BCA, CAB and CBA, all of which represent the **one team**: ABC.

Similarly, the six arrangements CDG, CGD, DCG, DGC, GCD, GDC all represent the **one team**: CDG.

In fact, there will be 3! (or six) arrangements for every one choice.

Hence, the number of choices will be $\frac{7!}{4!} \div 3! = \frac{7!}{4!3!} = 35$.

Using a similar argument we can show that the number of ways of **choosing** 5 people out of 12 is $\frac{12!}{5!7!}$.

Choices

In general, the number of teams of r, which can be chosen from a population of n (where $n \geq r$), is called $\binom{n}{r}$.

Europeans call this 'nCr'. Americans call it 'n choose r'.

There should be a button on your calculator labelled .

$$\binom{n}{r} = {}^nC_r = C(n, r) = \frac{n!}{r!(n-r)!}$$

This formula appears on page 20 of *Formulae and Tables*.

Worked Example 2.8

Evaluate $\binom{11}{3}$ and $\binom{11}{8}$.

Solution

$\binom{11}{3} = \dfrac{11!}{3!8!} = 165$

[1] [1] [nCr] [3] [=]

$\binom{11}{8} = \dfrac{11!}{8!3!} = 165$

[1] [1] [nCr] [8] [=]

The Twin Rule

It is no coincidence that the two solutions in Worked Example 2.8 are equal. It is an example of the Twin Rule. Read on …

The Twin Rule states that:

$$\binom{n}{r} = \binom{n}{n-r}$$

For example, $\binom{14}{12} = \binom{14}{2}$. Also $\binom{100}{11} = \binom{100}{89}$, etc.

The Twin Rule can be proved in the following way:

LHS $= \binom{n}{r} = \dfrac{n!}{r!(n-r)!}$

RHS $= \binom{n}{n-r} = \dfrac{n!}{(n-r)!(n-(n-r))!} = \dfrac{n!}{(n-r)!r!} = $ LHS

The Twin Rule: $\binom{n}{r} = \binom{n}{n-r}$

There is a quick way of calculating $\binom{n}{r}$.

Think of the countdown: $n, (n-1), (n-2), …, 4, 3, 2, 1$.

$$\binom{n}{r} = \frac{\text{First } r \text{ numbers in the countdown}}{\text{Last } r \text{ numbers in the countdown}}$$

For example, $\binom{10}{4} = \dfrac{10 \times 9 \times 8 \times 7}{4 \times 3 \times 2 \times 1} = 210$.

Of course, $\binom{10}{6}$ is also 210, under the Twin Rule.

$\binom{n}{n} = 1$ When you have to choose n people from a population of n there is only one combination possible.

Therefore, $\binom{n}{0} = \binom{n}{n} = 1$ under the Twin Rule.

Worked Example 2.9

There are 13 hockey players on a panel, including the captain. The manager has to choose a team of 11. How many different teams could she possibly pick:

  (i) If there are no further restrictions

  (ii) If the captain must be included in the 11

 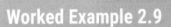

Solution

(i) The manager has to choose 11 players out of 13.

The number of choices $= \binom{13}{11} = \binom{13}{2} = \dfrac{13 \times 12}{2 \times 1} = 78$.

(ii) Since the captain must be included, the manager has to pick 10 players from the remaining 12 panel members.

The number of choices $= \binom{12}{10} = \binom{12}{2} = \dfrac{12 \times 11}{2 \times 1} = 66$.

Worked Example 2.10

A chess club has 11 members: six girls and five boys. A committee of five members is to be formed. How many choices are there:

(i) If there are no restrictions

(ii) If there must be more girls than boys on the committee

Solution

(i) $\binom{11}{5} = \dfrac{11 \times 10 \times 9 \times 8 \times 7}{5 \times 4 \times 3 \times 2 \times 1} = 462$

(ii) Here are the possibilities:

Three girls AND two boys OR four girls AND one boy OR five girls AND no boys.

$$\therefore \text{ choices} = \binom{6}{3} \times \binom{5}{2} + \binom{6}{4} \times \binom{5}{1} + \binom{6}{5} \times \binom{5}{0}$$

$$= (20 \times 10) + (15 \times 5) + (6 \times 1)$$

$$= 200 + 75 + 6$$

$$= 281$$

The above example illustrates how, in counting, the word AND gives rise to ×, but the word OR gives rise to +.

Worked Example 2.11

If $\binom{n}{2} = 21$, find the value of natural number n, where $n \geqslant 2$.

Solution

$\binom{n}{2} = 21$

$\Rightarrow \dfrac{n(n-1)}{(2)(1)} = 21 \quad \left[\binom{n}{2} \text{ is the first 2 in the countdown from } n, \text{ over the last 2 in the countdown.}\right]$

$n(n-1) = 42$

$n^2 - n - 42 = 0$

$(n-7)(n+6) = 0$

$\therefore n = 7 \quad \text{or} \quad n = -6$

But $n \geqslant 2$ so the only valid answer is $n = 7$.

Exercise 2.2

1. Evaluate the following:

$\binom{10}{2}$; $\binom{11}{3}$; $\binom{7}{4}$; $\binom{14}{1}$; $\binom{20}{2}$; $\binom{9}{3}$; $\binom{9}{6}$; $\binom{13}{11}$; $\binom{18}{4}$; $\binom{18}{14}$.

2. Verify that $\binom{13}{3} + \binom{13}{4} = \binom{14}{4}$.

3. Verify that $\binom{12}{7} - \binom{11}{7} = \binom{11}{6}$.

4. If $\binom{5}{0} + \binom{5}{1} + \binom{5}{2} + \binom{5}{3} + \binom{5}{4} + \binom{5}{5} = 2^k$, find k.

5. Investigate if $2\binom{13}{7} = \binom{14}{7}$.

6. Show that $\binom{11}{2} + \binom{11}{3} + \binom{12}{4} = \binom{13}{4}$.

7. A manager names a panel of 15 players for a hockey final. On the day of the final he must choose 11 of these.

   How many different teams could the manager possibly select?

8. A student has to choose three subjects from the following range: biology, music, art, chemistry, economics, history, Greek. How many different choices can the student make:

   (i) If there are no restrictions

   (ii) If Greek must be included as one of the three subjects

   (iii) If Greek must be excluded

9. A class consists of six girls and seven boys. A team of four tennis players must be chosen from this class.

   How many different teams could be picked:

   (i) If there are no restrictions

   (ii) If the team must have two girls and two boys

   (iii) If the team must be all female

10. Twelve points are drawn on a circle.

    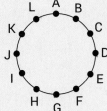

    (i) How many different chords could be drawn between these points?

    (ii) How many triangles may be drawn by connecting these points?

11. How many different teams of 13 players may be chosen from a panel of 15:

    (i) If any 13 players may be picked

    (ii) If the captain **must** be included

12. S = {a, b, c, d, e, f, g, h}

    (i) How many subsets of S, containing five elements, can be formed?

    (ii) How many of these contain h?

    (iii) How many do not contain h?

    (iv) How many contain h and g?

13. A committee of five persons is to be chosen from four women and seven men.

    If there must be more women than men on the committee, how many different committees could be formed?

14. Thirteen people are at a party. They all shake hands with one another once.

    How many handshakes take place?

15. (a) There are 20 teams in the English Premiership. Each team plays each other team at home and away. How many matches take place?

    (b) In the European Champions League (before the knock-out stages) there are eight groups of four. In each group of four, teams play each other at home and away. How many matches are there in this stage of the competition?

16. How many boards of five members can be chosen from a panel of four managers and five workers:

    (i) If there are no restrictions

    (ii) If there must be more workers than managers

    (iii) If there must be only one worker

PROBABILITY I

17. Three friends are filling out lottery cards. Each has to choose 6 numbers out of 45.

   (i) How many different ways are there for Sarah to fill out a single card if she is not fussy about what numbers she chooses?

   (ii) Sarah's friend Tanya is 19 and decides that she will definitely use 19 as one of her numbers. In how many different ways could Tanya fill out a single lottery card?

   (iii) Their friend Sam says that 19 is unlucky for him and that he would never use 19 as one of his numbers. In how many ways could Sam fill out a card without using the number 19?

   (iv) Tanya has decided to fill out a second lottery card on which 19 will be her third lowest number. How many ways are there for her to do this?

18. (i) Evaluate $\binom{10}{5}$.

   (ii) Show that there are 126 ways of dividing a group of 10 people into two groups of five.

   (iii) How many ways are there of dividing up eight players into two teams for a four-a-side match?

   (iv) How many ways are there of dividing 12 players into two teams for a six-a-side match?

19. Mr and Mrs Zimmerman want to give their baby a first name and a second name so that the baby's three initials are in alphabetical order.

   How many different initials could the baby end up with? (For example, B, G, Z is acceptable, but G, B, Z and B, B, Z are not acceptable.)

20. In how many ways can a committee of five be chosen from 11 people:

   (i) If one particular person must be included

   (ii) If one particular person must be excluded

   (iii) If two particular people will not work on the same committee (that is, if one is included, the other must be excluded)

21. In how many ways may a team of four oarsmen be chosen from a panel of 13 people if two individuals refuse to work on the **same** rowing team as each other?

22. (i) How many different poker hands can be dealt to a player? (A poker hand consists of five cards, dealt from a pack of 52.)

   (ii) How many hands include the Ace of Spades?

   (iii) How many poker hands do not include the Ace of Spades?

   (iv) How many hands include all four Aces?

   (v) How many hands contain exactly three Aces?

23. If $\binom{n}{2} = 210$, find the value of n, where $n \geqslant 2$.

24. If $\binom{n}{3} = 15n$, $n \geqslant 3$, find the value of n.
   Verify your answer.

25. Solve for $x \geqslant 3$:
   $$3\binom{x}{3} = 2\binom{x}{2} + 5\binom{x}{1}.$$
   Verify your answer.

2.3 Probability

In probability we encounter many common terms that have special meanings we must be aware of.

A trial is the act of doing an experiment in probability.

The flipping of a coin is an example of a **trial**.

An outcome is one of the possible results of the trial.

When flipping a coin, the **outcomes** are that you could flip a head or a tail.

The set or list of all possible outcomes in a trial is called the sample space.

For a coin, the **sample space** is {head, tail}.

An event is the occurrence of one or more specific outcomes.

The flipped coin landing on a head would be an **event**.

Any subset of the sample space (S) is an event (E). If a six-sided die is rolled, S = {1, 2, 3, 4, 5, 6}. Getting an even number is an event, E = {2, 4, 6}.

The probability of an event lies between 0 and 1. The nearer the probability of an event is to 1, the more likely it is to happen. The nearer the probability of an event is to 0, the more unlikely it is to happen.

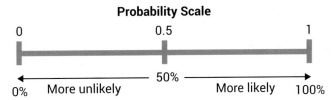

Probability Scale

We sometimes use percentages when giving the probability of an event. If an event is certain to happen (for example, that the day after next Saturday will be a Sunday), we say its probability is 100%. If an event has an evens chance of happening (for example, getting tails when you flip a fair coin), we say the probability is 50%. If an event is impossible (for example, that you will be dealt a hand with five Aces), we say the probability is 0%.

2.4 Relative Frequency (Experimental Probability)

Sometimes it can be very difficult to work out the probability of an event. For example, will a football team win their next match? In this case, we can use statistical evidence from observations or experiments to determine the experimental probability or **relative frequency** of an event.

> **Relative frequency** is a good estimate of the true probability of an event, provided that the number of trials is sufficiently large.

The relative frequency of an event is the number of times that an event happens in a trial out of the total number of trials.

$$\text{Relative frequency} = \frac{\text{frequency or number of times the event happens in a trial}}{\text{total number of trials}}$$

> It is important to note that increasing the number of times an experiment is repeated generally leads to better estimates of probability.

Worked Example 2.12

An experiment is conducted to show how the number of trials improves the accuracy of the relative frequency. Michelle flips a fair coin and records her results every 10 flips:

After 10 flips	Total	Relative frequency
Head	6	0.6
Tail	4	0.4

After 40 flips	Total	Relative frequency
Head	18	0.45
Tail	22	0.55

After 20 flips	Total	Relative frequency
Head	13	0.65
Tail	7	0.35

After 50 flips	Total	Relative frequency
Head	24	0.48
Tail	26	0.52

After 30 flips	Total	Relative frequency
Head	13	0.43
Tail	17	0.57

Note: Results for relative frequency are rounded to two decimal places where necessary.

(i) Plot the relative frequency of tails on a trend graph.

(ii) Is a relative frequency of 0.35 more likely after 20 flips or after 50 flips?

Solution

(i)

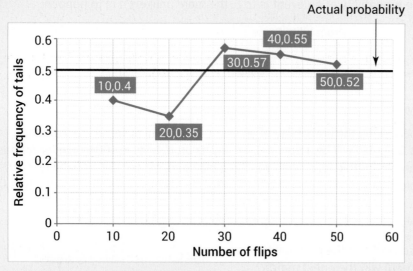

Actual probability

(ii) Notice that the more the experiment is repeated, the closer the relative frequency is to the actual probability (in this Worked Example: $\frac{1}{2}$ or 0.5). Therefore, a relative frequency of 0.35 is more likely after 20 flips than after 50, because after 50 flips, you would expect the relative frequency to be quite close to 0.5.

Exercise 2.3

1.

0   0.5   1

A   B   C   D   E

Five events (A, B, C, D and E) are shown on a probability scale. Copy and complete the following table:

Probability	Event
Fifty–fifty	C
Certain	
Very unlikely	
Impossible	
Very likely	

2. A gardener plants 50 parsley seeds in 50 pots. Three months later, he finds that he has 40 parsley plants: the rest were unsuccessful.

(i) What is the relative frequency of success?

(ii) If he plants 60 seeds next year, how many would he expect to grow successfully?

3.

0%   50%   100%

P   Q   R   S   T

Five events (P, Q, R, S and T) are shown on a probability scale. Copy and complete the following table, by filling in the appropriate letter in the right-hand column (P, Q, R, S or T):

Event	Letter
Getting tails on a single flip of a fair coin	
Getting a 4 on a single roll of a fair six-sided die	
Getting a 7 on a single roll of a fair six-sided die	
A person being born on a day that ends with the letter 'y'	
A person not being born on a Sunday	

4. Last year there were 167 school days and Conor was late for school 22 times.

   (i) Give the relative frequency of 'late days' for the school year as a percentage (to the nearest per cent).

   (ii) The Deputy Principal demands an improvement. The following September, Conor is late for three of the 20 school days. Has Conor's punctuality improved or not? Refer to 'relative frequency' in your answer.

5. Beth flips a coin over and over. Here are the results:

Number of flips	After 20	After 40	After 60	After 80	After 100
Number of heads	14	24	31	39	51
Number of tails	6	16	29	41	49
Relative frequency of tails	0.3				

   (i) Copy the table and fill in the last row.

   (ii) Plot these results for the relative frequency of tails on a trend graph.

   (iii) Beth says, 'It is not surprising to get a relative value of 0.3 after 20 flips. It would be very surprising to get a relative frequency of 0.3 after 100 flips.' Is Beth correct? Explain your answer.

6. In the soccer World Cup finals between 1986 and 2002, there were 211 penalties taken. Of these, 161 were successful.

   (i) What is the relative frequency of successful penalties in these finals to the nearest per cent?

   (ii) If, during the next World Cup finals, 46 penalties are awarded, how many would you expect to be successful, assuming the same relative frequency is maintained? Give your answer to the nearest whole number.

   (iii) Three pundits on different television channels make the following statements:

   Pundit A: 'When a penalty kick is taken during the World Cup finals, there is one chance in four of the kick being saved or missed.'

   Pundit B: 'Nerves play a big part in World Cup finals. Penalty kicks are more likely to be missed than scored.'

   Pundit C: 'If a player takes a penalty in the World Cup finals, there is more than a 50–50 chance that he will score.'

Which of the three statements (A, B, or C) is the most accurate?	
Which of the three statements is the least accurate?	

7. The Las Vegas Tourist Board boasts, 'Las Vegas has 210 days of sunshine in a year. Come to Las Vegas and enjoy the sun's rays!'

   Mr and Mrs Abercrombie took a three-week holiday in Las Vegas. They wrote to the Tourist Board complaining, 'We had nine dull days in three weeks. We were very disappointed. We felt let down and misled.'

   (i) Give the relative frequency of sunny days in Las Vegas to the nearest half per cent.

   (ii) Is the complaint by Mr and Mrs Abercrombie reasonable? Justify your answer with reference to relative frequency.

PROBABILITY I

8. Eoin rolls a die over and over. He keeps a tally of his results. Here they are:

	After 10 rolls	After 20 rolls	After 30 rolls	After 40 rolls	After 50 rolls
No. of sixes	1	3	6	7	8

(i) Copy this table and write down the relative frequencies of 'getting sixes' (as a decimal) in the appropriate box; the first one has been done for you.

	After 10 rolls	After 20 rolls	After 30 rolls	After 40 rolls	After 50 rolls
Relative frequency of sixes	0.1				

(ii) Using this table of results, draw a trend graph of the relative frequency of sixes as the number of rolls increases.

(iii) After 10 rolls, Eoin felt that the die was biased against sixes. Given all of the above data, do you think he was right? Explain your answer.

9. In the Women's Rugby World Cup (WRWC) in 2006, there were 179 conversion attempts, 94 of which were successful. In the same tournament, there were 57 penalty kicks.

(i) What was the relative frequency (as a percentage to one decimal place) of successful conversions?

(ii) Assuming the same relative frequency, how many penalty kicks would you expect to be successful?

(iii) In fact, 31 of the penalty kicks were successful. Does this statistic satisfy you or disappoint you? Why?

(iv) A male commentator said, 'In the WRWC, place kicking was atrocious. The players missed more kicks than they scored.' Is his statement true?

10. Three students each have four unbiased coins, which they flip repeatedly. They keep a tally to record if all four coins show the same outcome or not (that is, whether or not they get HHHH or TTTT). Here are the results:

Name	Number of trials	All four coins show the same outcome	All four coins do NOT show the same outcome
Alan	40	7	33
Beth	30	3	27
Cathal	90	11	79
Total	**160**	**21**	**139**

(i) Which student's data is likely to give the **best estimate** of the probability of getting all four coins to show the same outcome? Give a reason for your answer.

(ii) The actual probability that all four coins will show the same outcome is $\frac{1}{8}$. How many times would you theoretically expect this to happen in 160 trials?

(iii) Give a reason why the total result of the students is different from what was theoretically expected.

11. One very interesting and surprising mathematical law is Benford's Law. It states that if you have a large set of numerical data (e.g. the ages of humans in days, the weights of horses in kilograms, etc.) and you write down the **first digit** in each case, then the most frequent is 1, the next frequent is 2, all the way down to the least frequent, which is 9. You'd expect each digit to be equally frequent – but that is not the case! Here is a table that shows the relative frequency for the first digit of data, according to Benford's Law.

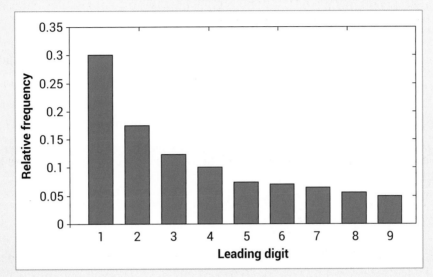

A research student looked up a social networking site and logged 1,500 numbers that appeared (e.g. 'I have five dogs', 'I hate my three sisters', 'Today is my 17th birthday'). She noted the first digit of each. Here are the results:

First digit on data	Frequency	Relative frequency (out of 1,500) as a decimal
1	444	0.296
2	255	
3	165	
4	141	
5	117	
6	108	
7	98	
8	85	
9	87	

(i)   Copy and complete the table.

(ii) Does this data support Benford's Law?

(iii) Can you give any reason why Benford's Law works? Why are all first digits not equally likely?

(iv) Ryan says, 'Under Benford's Law, numbers whose first digit is 1 occur about three times as often as numbers whose first digit is 4.' Is this true or false?

2.5 Probability When All Outcomes are Equally Likely

When an experiment takes place and all outcomes are equally likely, the probability of a certain event, E, taking place is written as P(E), and is defined by:

$$P(E) = \frac{\text{number of elements in the event}}{\text{number of all possible outcomes}} = \frac{\#E}{\#S}$$

S is the sample space, the set of all possible outcomes.

Worked Example 2.13

(i) A fair six-sided die is rolled. What is the probability of getting a number greater than 4?

(ii) If this die is rolled 60 times, how many times would you expect to get a number greater than 4?

Solution

(i) There are six possible outcomes. S = {1, 2, 3, 4, 5, 6}

The desired event, E, has two elements: {5, 6}.

$$\therefore P(E) = \frac{\#E}{\#S} = \frac{2}{6} = \frac{1}{3}$$

(ii) You would expect to get a number higher than 4 one-third of the time. Hence, the expected frequency of getting 'more than 4' is:

$$\frac{1}{3} \times 60 = 20 \text{ occasions}$$

Worked Example 2.14

A card is drawn from a standard pack at random. What is the probability that the card drawn is:

(i) A Jack   (iv) A Jack or a Spade

(ii) A Spade   (v) A Spade or a red card

(iii) A red card

Solution

(i) There are 52 cards altogether in a pack. There are four Jacks.

$$\therefore P(\text{Jack}) = \frac{4}{52} = \frac{1}{13}$$

(ii) There are 13 Spades in a pack of 52.

$$\therefore P(\text{Spade}) = \frac{13}{52} = \frac{1}{4}$$

(iii) There are 26 red cards in the pack.

$$\therefore P(\text{red card}) = \frac{26}{52} = \frac{1}{2}$$

(iv) There are 13 Spades and three **other** Jacks (we must be careful not to count the Jack of Spades twice). Hence, this event has 16 elements.

$$\therefore P(\text{Spade or Jack}) = \frac{16}{52} = \frac{4}{13}$$

(v) There are 13 Spades and 26 red cards, making 39 altogether.

$$\therefore P(\text{Spade or red card}) = \frac{39}{52} = \frac{3}{4}$$

2.6 Probability Theory

Mutually Exclusive Events and Non-Mutually Exclusive Events

Two events E and F are said to be mutually exclusive if E ∩ F = ∅.

For example, when a card is picked from a pack, if E = getting a Diamond and F = getting a black card, then E and F are **mutually exclusive** since E ∩ F = ∅.

If E and F are mutually exclusive, then

$P(E \cup F) = P(E) + P(F)$.

If E = getting a Diamond, then $P(E) = \dfrac{13}{52} = \dfrac{1}{4}$.

If F = getting a black card, then $P(F) = \dfrac{26}{52} = \dfrac{1}{2}$.

$P(E \cup F) = P(\text{getting a Diamond or a black card}) = \dfrac{1}{4} + \dfrac{1}{2} = \dfrac{3}{4}$.

However, very often events are **not mutually exclusive**. For example, if J = getting a Jack and S = getting a Spade, then J ∩ S ≠ ∅, since the Jack of Spades is in both sets.

$P(J) = \dfrac{4}{52} = \dfrac{1}{13} \qquad P(S) = \dfrac{13}{52} = \dfrac{1}{4}$

In this case,

$P(J \cup S) \neq P(J) + P(S)$, because that would be counting the Jack of Spades twice.

In general: 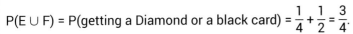 $P(E \cup F) = P(E \text{ or } F) = P(E) + P(F) - P(E \cap F)$

Let's check this out in the above case:

$P(J) = \dfrac{4}{52} = \dfrac{1}{13} \qquad\qquad P(S) = \dfrac{13}{52} = \dfrac{1}{4}$

J ∩ S = {Jack of Spades}

$\therefore P(J \cap S) = \dfrac{1}{52}$

$\therefore P(J \cup S) = P(\text{Jack or Spade}) = P(J) + P(S) - P(J \cap S) = \dfrac{1}{13} + \dfrac{1}{4} - \dfrac{1}{52} = \dfrac{4}{13}$

This result agrees with our result in Worked Example 2.14.

Conclusion:

1. $P(E \cup F) = P(E) + P(F) - P(E \cap F)$

2. If E and F are mutually exclusive, then $P(E \cap F) = 0$, and so:

   $P(E \cup F) = P(E) + P(F)$

Worked Example 2.15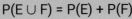

X, Y and Z are three events. X and Y are mutually exclusive. P(X) = 0.7, P(Y) = 0.1 and P(Z) = 0.6.

(i) Find P(X ∪ Y).

(ii) Explain why it is not possible for X and Z to be mutually exclusive.

Solution

(i) Because X and Y are mutually exclusive,

$P(X \cup Y) = P(X) + P(Y) = 0.7 + 0.1 = 0.8$.

(ii) Let us suppose that X and Z are mutually exclusive. Then

$P(X \cup Z) = P(X) + P(Z) = 0.7 + 0.6 = 1.3 > 1$.

This is impossible as no probability can be greater than 1.

Hence, X and Z cannot be mutually exclusive.

[Note this kind of argument is known as *reductio ad absurdum* ('leading to absurdity').]

Worked Example 2.16

Given the Venn diagram below, write down:

(i) P(E)

(ii) P(F)

(iii) P(E ∩ F)

(iv) P(E ∪ F)

(v) Verify that:

$P(E \cup F) = P(E) + P(F) - P(E \cap F)$

E   F   S

0.1   0.2   0.3

0.4

Note that the sum of all probabilities in S is 0.1 + 0.2 + 0.3 + 0.4 = 1, which is essential in all Venn diagrams of probabilities.

Solution

(i) P(E) = 0.1 + 0.2 = 0.3

(ii) P(F) = 0.2 + 0.3 = 0.5

(iii) P(E ∩ F) = 0.2

(iv) P(E ∪ F) = 0.1 + 0.2 + 0.3 = 0.6

(v) To verify that $P(E \cup F) = P(E) + P(F) - P(E \cap F)$:

LHS = 0.6

RHS = 0.3 + 0.5 − 0.2 = 0.6 = LHS   **QED**

Worked Example 2.17

(i) Two fair six-sided dice are rolled. What is the probability that there will be a total of 8 on the two dice?

(ii) If, in a game, a pair of dice is rolled 1,000 times, how many times (to the nearest integer) would you expect to get a total of 8?

Solution

In accordance with the Fundamental Principle of Counting, there are 6 × 6 = 36 possible outcomes.

This sample space can be represented by a two-way table in which the number on the left represents the outcome from the first die and the number on top represents the outcome from the second die.

For example, the asterisk represents when you get 2 on the first die and 6 on the second die.

(i) There are five different ways of getting a total of 8, as shown by the five orange cells in the table. Hence:

$P \text{ (Total is 8)} = \dfrac{\#E}{\#S} = \dfrac{5}{36}$

(ii) If you rolled a pair of dice 1,000 times, then the number of times you would expect to get a total of 8 is:

$\dfrac{5}{36} \times 1{,}000 = \dfrac{5{,}000}{36} = 139$ (to the nearest integer)

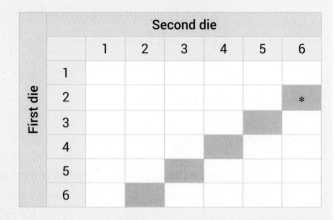

		Second die				
	1	2	3	4	5	6
1						
2						*
3						
4						
5						
6						

First die

PROBABILITY I

Exercise 2.4

1. An unbiased coin is flipped once. What is the probability of getting 'heads'?

2. An unbiased six-sided die is rolled. What is the probability that the number that appears will be:

   (i) An odd number

   (ii) A factor of 6

   (iii) A factor of 4

3. A letter is chosen at random from the word PARALLEL. What is the probability that the letter chosen will be:

   (i) A vowel (ii) An L (iii) Not an L

4. In a class there are 14 boys and 16 girls. Three of the boys and two of the girls wear glasses. A student is chosen at random from this class.

   Find the probability that this student will be:

   (i) A girl (iii) A person who wears glasses

   (ii) A boy (iv) A boy who wears glasses

If a person is chosen at random from this same class every day for 180 days, on how many days would you expect to find that a girl who wears glasses would be chosen?

5. A card is chosen from a standard pack. Find the probability that the card is:

   (i) A Diamond (iv) A Diamond or a black card

   (ii) A black card (v) A Diamond or a King

   (iii) A King (vi) A black card or a King

6. X, Y and Z are three events. X and Y are mutually exclusive. Y and Z are mutually exclusive. $P(X) = \frac{3}{5}$, $P(Y) = \frac{1}{10}$ and $P(Y \cup Z) = \frac{17}{20}$.

   (i) Find $P(X \cup Y)$.

   (ii) Find $P(Z)$.

   (iii) Find $P(X) + P(Z)$.

   (iv) Johanna says, 'It is impossible for X and Z to be mutually exclusive.' Is she right? Give a reason to back up your answer.

7. State, giving a reason, if the events E and F are mutually exclusive in each case:

	Experiment	E and F	Mutually exclusive?	Reason
(i)	A six-sided die is rolled.	E = Getting an odd number. F = Getting a 6.	✓	6 is even
(ii)	A card is drawn from a standard pack.	E = Getting a black card. F = Getting a King.	✗	K can be any
(iii)	A person is asked which day of the week they were born on.	E = It is a weekday. F = It begins with the letter S.	✓	has weekend
(iv)	A female student sits the Leaving Certificate exam.	E = She will get over 90% in maths. F = She will get over 90% in Irish.	✗	
(v)	An Irish cyclist takes part in the Tour de France.	E = He fails to finish. F = He wins the Tour de France.	✓	
(vi)	A couple have two children.	E = The first-born is a daughter. F = The second-born is a son.	✗	
(vii)	A coin is flipped 10 times.	E = The first nine flips all show heads. F = The 10th flip shows heads.	✗	
(viii)	A male student sits the Leaving Certificate exam.	E = He will get over 90% in maths. F = He fails maths.	✗	
(ix)	You follow an Irish soccer team.	E = They win the FAI cup next season. F = They win the League of Ireland Championship next season.	✗	
(x)	A woman gives birth to twins.	E = They are identical twins. F = One is a boy and one is a girl.	✗	

PROBABILITY I

8.

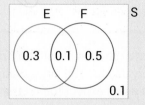

Given the Venn diagram above, write down:

P(E), P(F), P(E ∩ F), P(E ∪ F)

Verify that:

P(E ∪ F) = P(E) + P(F) − P(E ∩ F)

9. The Venn diagram below shows the **number of elements** in each subset, e.g. #(A ∩ B) = 3.

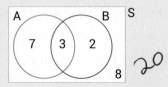

(a) An element is chosen at random from the set S, as shown. Write down the probability that the element will be in the set:

(i) A

(ii) B

(iii) A ∩ B

(iv) A ∪ B

(v) A \ B

(vi) (A \ B) ∪ (B \ A)

(vii) A′

(viii) (A ∪ B)′

(b) Verify the following:

(i) P(A \ B) = P(A) − P(A ∩ B)

(ii) P(A ∪ B) = P(A) + P(B) − P(A ∩ B)

10. There are 24 people in a class. Eighteen play basketball, 11 play chess and three play neither.

Copy and fill out the Venn diagram below. (B = the set of basketball players; C = the set of chess players.)

The class

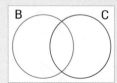

A person is chosen from the class at random. If P(X) is taken to mean the probability that the person is from set X, write down:

(i) P(B)

(ii) P(C)

(iii) P(B ∩ C)

(iv) P(B ∪ C)

(v) P(B′)

Investigate if the following are true or false:

(vi) P(B ∪ C) = P(B) + P(C)

(vii) P(B ∪ C) = P(B) + P(C) − P(B ∩ C)

(viii) P(B \ C) = P(B) − P(C)

(ix) P(B \ C) = P(B) − P(B ∩ C)

(x) P(B′) = 1 − P(B)

11. (i) In how many ways can the letters of the word DONEGAL be arranged?

(ii) In how many of these arrangements are the three vowels together?

(iii) The letters of the word DONEGAL are arranged at random on a Scrabble tile-holder. What is the probability that the three vowels will be together, as shown?

12. P(B) = 0.8

P(A ∩ B) = 0.3

P(A′) = 0.6

(a) Find (i) P(A) and (ii) P(A ∪ B).

(b) Verify that:

P(A ∪ B) = P(A) + P(B) − P(A ∩ B)

13. A pair of fair six-sided dice is rolled. Find the probability that the total on the pair of dice is:

(i) Equal to 4

(ii) 4 or less

(iii) Greater than 9

(iv) An even number

(v) Less than 6 or equal to a prime number

(vi) Exactly twice as great as other possible totals

(vii) 10 or less

14. Three fair coins are flipped. Copy and complete the sample space, S:

S = {(H, H, H), (H, H, T), (H, T, H), …}

Hence find:

(i) The numbers of elements in S

(ii) The probability of getting three tails

(iii) The probability of getting at least one head

(iv) The probability of getting two or more heads

15. A fair six-sided die is rolled and an unbiased coin is flipped.

Represent the sample space in a two-way table.

Find the probability of getting:

(i) A five followed by a head

(ii) A prime number followed by a tail (Note: 1 is **not** a prime number.)

(iii) An even number with a head or an odd number with a tail

16. There are 20 tickets in a bag numbered 1–20. The numbers 1–10 are red, 11–16 are blue and 17–20 are green. A ticket is drawn at random from the bag.

(a) Find the probability of getting:

(i) A green ticket

(ii) A ticket that is not blue

(iii) A ticket that is red or even-numbered

(iv) A ticket that is green or odd-numbered

(v) A ticket that is red and even-numbered

(b) Is it true to say that 'getting a multiple of 7' and 'getting a green ticket' are mutually exclusive events?

17. A bag contains 11 yellow marbles, 13 green marbles and n blue marbles. When a marble is drawn at random, the probability of getting a blue marble is $\frac{1}{4}$. Find the value of n.

18. The data shows the number of boys and girls aged either 17 or 18 on a school trip, in which only these 50 students took part.

	Boys	Girls
Aged 17	18	12
Aged 18	15	5

A student is chosen at random from the party. Find the probability that the student:

(i) Is a boy

(ii) Is aged 18

(iii) Is a girl of 18 years

(iv) Is a girl aged 17 or a boy aged 18

19. A fair six-sided die is rolled three times.

(i) What is the number of elements in the sample space?

(ii) What is the probability that three 6s appear?

(iii) What is the probability that the first roll yields a 6 and that the sum on all three rolls is 14?

(iv) What is the probability that the first roll is an even number and that the sum on all three rolls is 14?

20. There were 31 days in January and 28 in February in 1997. A person was born in 1997.

Write down, correct to two significant figures, the probability that the person was born:

(i) In January

(ii) In February

(iii) In January or February

21.

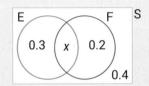

(i) Given the probability Venn diagram above, find the value of x.

(ii) Are E and F mutually exclusive?

(iii) Write down:

P(E), P(F), P(E ∩ F), P(E ∪ F)

(iv) Verify that:

P(E ∪ F) = P(E) + P(F) − P(E ∩ F)

22.

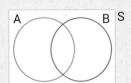

P(A ∪ B) = 0.8   P(A ∩ B) = 0.2

P(A) = 0.35

(i) Find P(B).

(ii) Find P(B′).

(iii) Verify that P(A ∪ B) = P(A) + P(B) − P(A ∩ B).

PROBABILITY I

23.

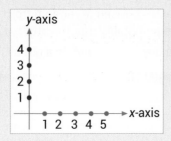

A point is chosen randomly from one of the green points (1,0) (2,0) (3,0) (4,0) (5,0) on the x-axis. Another point is chosen randomly from the blue points (0,1) (0,2) (0,3) (0,4) on the y-axis.

A line segment is drawn linking the two points. Use this two-way table to represent the sample space. Fill in the lengths in the table.

	(0,1)	(0,2)	(0,3)	(0,4)
(1,0)	$\sqrt{2}$			$\sqrt{17}$
(2,0)				
(3,0)				
(4,0)	$\sqrt{17}$			
(5,0)				

Find the probability (as a percentage) that the line segment will:

(i) Be 5 units long

(ii) Be greater than 5 units long

(iii) Have a slope of −1

24.

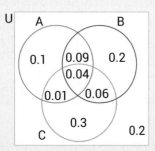

Given the Venn diagram above, which shows the probabilities of various sets, write down:

(i) $P(A \cap B)$ (iii) $P(C \setminus A)$

(ii) $P(A \cup C)$ (iv) $P(C \setminus (A \cup B))$

Verify that:

$P(B \cup C) = P(B) + P(C) - P(B \cap C)$

25.

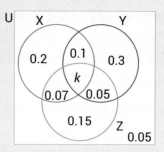

(a) Use the probability Venn diagram to find the value of:

  (i) k (iv) $P(Y \setminus (X \cup Z))$

  (ii) $P(X \cup Z)$ (v) $P(Z')$

  (iii) $P(X \cap Z)$

(b) Verify that:

  (i) $P(Y \cup Z) = P(Y) + P(Z) - P(Y \cap Z)$

  (ii) $P(Y') = 1 - P(Y)$

26. A number is chosen randomly from the set A = {1, 2, 3, 4, 5}.

Another number is chosen randomly from the set B = {6, 7, 8, 9, 10}.

(a) Use a two-way table to represent the sample space.

(b) E = {The sum of the numbers is less than 9}

   F = {The product of the numbers is greater than 20}

  (i) Find P(E) and P(F).

  (ii) Are E and F mutually exclusive?

     Explain your answer.

  (iii) Find $P(E \cup F)$.

  (iv) Kate and Kevin play a game. They use two spinners to choose a number from A and a number from B. Kate wins if the product of the two numbers is less than 23, Kevin if the product is greater than 23. Is this fair?

27. Two fair six-sided dice are rolled.

(i) Copy and complete the following table for the probabilities of different possible sums:

Sum on two dice	2	3	4	5	6	7	8	9	10	11	12
Probability					$\frac{5}{36}$						$\frac{1}{36}$

(ii) Copy and complete the bar chart below, showing the probabilities, using one 'brick' for every $\frac{1}{36}$.

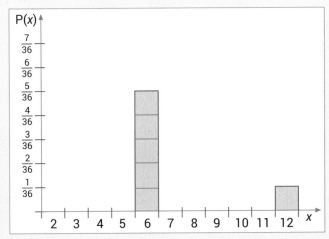

(iii) Kilian and Shane play a game. They roll a pair of fair dice. If the total on the dice is 5, 6, 7 or 8 Kilian wins. If the total is anything else, Shane wins. Is this fair?

(iv) They now change the game so that it is fair. Kilian now wins if the total on the dice is one of four consecutive numbers, otherwise Shane wins. Write down two possible lists of these four consecutive numbers.

(v) A spinner is designed so that the probability of each outcome is the same as the total when two fair dice are rolled. Write down the angle for each outcome (one has already been filled in for you).

Sum on two dice	2	3	4	5	6	7	8	9	10	11	12
Angle on spinner						60°					

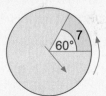

2.7 Conditional Probability

In a class there are 15 male students, five of whom wear glasses, and 10 female students, three of whom wear glasses. We will let M = {Male students}, F = {Female students} and G = {Students who wear glasses}.

A student is picked at random from this class. What is the probability that the student is female, given that the student wears glasses?

Mathematically, we write this probability as:

P(F|G) [Spoken: 'The probability of F, given G']

To find P(F|G), we examine the set of those who wear glasses (G). This set has eight members.

Of this set, the number of females is three. Hence, $P(F|G) = \frac{3}{8}$.

Note that three is the number of elements in (F ∩ G), and eight is the number of elements in G. Hence, it should be clear that:

$$P(F|G) = \frac{\#(F \cap G)}{\#(G)} = \frac{P(F \cap G)}{P(G)}$$

In general, P(A|B), the probability of A given B, is determined by:

$$P(A|B) = \frac{\#(A \cap B)}{\#B} = \frac{P(A \cap B)}{P(B)}$$

Worked Example 2.18

A couple have three children. Find the probability that all three are girls, given that at least one is a girl.

Solution

Taking the three children in order of age, there are eight elements in the outcome space:

S = {BBB, BBG, BGB, GBB, BGG, GBG, GGB, GGG}

Let A = {All three are girls} = {GGG}.

Let B = {At least one is a girl} = {BBG, BGB, GBB, BGG, GBG, GGB, GGG}.

∴ A ∩ B = {GGG}

$$P(A|B) = \frac{\#(A \cap B)}{\#B} = \frac{1}{7}$$

Worked Example 2.19

Given the Venn diagram, find P(X|Y) and P(Y|X).

Solution

$$P(X|Y) = \frac{P(X \cap Y)}{P(Y)} = \frac{0.2}{(0.2 + 0.1)} = \frac{0.2}{0.3} = \frac{2}{3}$$

$$P(Y|X) = \frac{P(X \cap Y)}{P(X)} = \frac{0.2}{(0.3 + 0.2)} = \frac{0.2}{0.5} = \frac{2}{5}$$

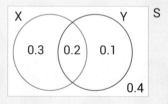

From this, it is clear that P(X|Y) and P(Y|X) are not necessarily equal.

Worked Example 2.20

X and Y are two events such that P(X) = 0.4, P(Y) = 0.3 and P(X ∪ Y) = 0.5.

(i) Find P(X ∩ Y).

(ii) Find P(X|Y).

Solution

(i) P(X ∪ Y) = P(X) + P(Y) − P(X ∩ Y)

$\Rightarrow$ 0.5 = 0.4 + 0.3 − P(X ∩ Y)

∴ P(X ∩ Y) = 0.2

(ii) Here is a Venn diagram of the sample space.

$$P(X|Y) = \frac{P(X \cap Y)}{P(Y)} = \frac{0.2}{0.3} = \frac{2}{3}$$

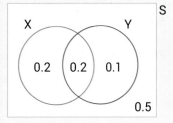

Worked Example 2.21

In a certain country there are only two parties: the Red Party and the Blue Party. In elections, 60% of the country votes Red, and 40% votes Blue. Of the Red supporters, 70% favour disarmament. Of Blue supporters, 10% favour disarmament.

A voter is chosen at random and announces that she favours disarmament. What is the probability that she supports the Blue Party?

Solution

Let R = {Red Party supporters}. ∴ P(R) = 0.6

Let B = {Blue Party supporters}. ∴ P(B) = 0.4

Let D = {Disarmament supporters}.

P(D) = 70% of 60% + 10% of 40% = (0.7)(0.6) + (0.1)(0.4) = 0.46

P(B ∩ D) = 10% of 40% = (0.1)(0.4) = 0.04

We are required to find $P(B|D) = \frac{P(B \cap D)}{P(D)} = \frac{0.04}{0.46} = \frac{2}{23}$.

Exercise 2.5

1.

The probabilities of two events, E and F, are given in the Venn diagram above.

Find:

(i) P(E|F)   (ii) P(F|E)

2. Two fair six-sided dice are rolled.

A = The total is over 8.

B = At least one die shows a 6.

(a) List the elements of A, B and A ∩ B.

(b) Find:

(i) P(B|A)

(ii) P(A|B)

3. In a class of 25 students, 14 play gaelic football and 10 play hurling, while 7 play neither gaelic nor hurling.

(i) How many play both gaelic and hurling?

(ii) What is the probability that a student plays gaelic, given that the student plays hurling?

4. A family has three children. Complete the outcome space {GGG, GGB, …}, where GGB means the first two are girls and the third is a boy.

Find the probability that all three children are girls, given that the family has at least two girls.

5. $P(A) = \frac{1}{2}$ $P(B) = \frac{1}{3}$ $P(A \cap B) = \frac{1}{4}$

Find:

(i) $P(A|B)$ (iv) $P(A|B')$

(ii) $P(B|A)$ (v) $P(A \cup B)$

(iii) $P(A'|B)$ (vi) $P(A|(A \cup B))$

6. In a school there are 150 girls and 100 boys. One hundred and twenty of the girls and 50 of the boys play hockey.

A student is picked at random. Find the probability that this student:

(i) Is a girl, given that the student plays hockey

(ii) Plays hockey, given that the student is a girl

7. In a certain county 70% of the population live in a townland and 30% live in a rural area. Fifty per cent of townlanders listen to the local radio station, whereas only 20% of rural dwellers listen to the local radio station. A person from the county is picked at random. Find the probability that this person is a townlander, given that the person listens to the local radio station.

8. If $A \subset B$, prove that $P(B|A) = 1$.

9. E and F are two events such that $P(E) = \frac{2}{5}$, $P(F) = \frac{1}{2}$, and $P(E|F) = \frac{1}{9}$.

Find:

(i) $P(E \cap F)$

(ii) $P(F|E)$

(iii) $P(E \cup F)$

10. You meet a man who tells you that he has two children. Later you meet his wife, who tells you that one of the children is a girl. What is the probability that the other child is:

(i) A boy   (ii) A girl

11. A pair of fair six-sided dice is rolled.

E = {The sum on the two dice is 7}

F = {3 appears on at least one die}

Find $P(F|E)$ and $P(E|F)$.

12. A bag contains 11 snooker balls numbered 1 to 11. A ball is drawn at random from the bag and the number is noted.

A = {The number is even}

B = {The number is greater than 6}

Find $P(A|B)$ and $P(B|A)$.

13. In a certain school 27% of students got an A in Junior Certificate maths, 15% got an A in science and 9% got an A in both. A student is selected at random. Find the probability that:

(i) This student got an A in maths, given that she got an A in science.

(ii) This student got an A in science, given that she got an A in maths.

(iii) This student got an A in maths or science.

(iv) This student got an A in neither maths nor science.

14. A and B are two events such that $P(A) = \frac{3}{10}$, $P(B) = \frac{1}{2}$ and $P(A \cup B) = \frac{3}{5}$.

Find $P(A|B)$ and $P(B|A)$.

15. $P(A) = 0.5$ $P(A \cup B) = 0.6$ $P(A|B) = 0.75$

Find $P(B)$.

(Hint: Let $P(B) = x$ and let $P(A \cap B) = y$. You should be able to set up a pair of 'simultaneous equations'.)

16.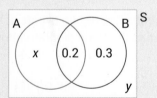

(i) Given that $P(B|A) = \frac{1}{2}$, find the values of x and y.

(ii) Find also $P(A|B)$.

17.

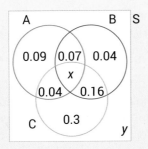

    (i) Given that P(A) = 0.3, find the values of *x* and *y*.

    (ii) Find P(B|C) and P(C|B).

    (iii) Find P(B|(A ∪ C)).

    (iv) Find P((A ∩ C)|(A ∪ B ∪ C)).

    (v) Find P((A \ B)|(A ∪ B)).

18. The Venn diagram below shows the probability of events A, B and C.

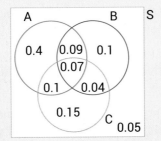

Find:

    (i) P(A)

    (ii) P(A ∩ B)

    (iii) P(A|B)

    (iv) P(B|A)

    (v) P(A|(B ∪ C))

    (vi) P(C|(A ∩ B))

19. Enzyme immunoassay (EIA) tests are needed to screen specimens for the presence of HIV, the virus that causes AIDS. 0.3% of the population has HIV.

If the person has HIV, the EIA test will give a positive result 99.85% of the time.

However, if the person does not have HIV, the EIA test gives a positive (i.e. a false-positive) result 0.6% of the time.

Sarah goes for an EIA test and tests positive. Find (to the nearest per cent) the probability that she actually has HIV.

20. A and B are two events such that P(A) = 0.3, P(A ∩ B) = 0.25 and P(A' ∩ B) = 0.4.

    (i) Complete the Venn diagram:

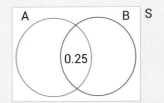

    (ii) Find the probability that neither A nor B happens.

    (iii) Find the conditional probability P(B|A).

21. A team wins 60% of home matches and 20% of away matches. Half of their matches are at home and half are away. They won their last match. Find the probability that:

    (i) It was at home. (ii) It was away.

Revision Exercises

1. (a) (i) How many arrangements are there of the letters of the word MUNSTER?

      (ii) How many of these begin and end with a vowel?

   (b) Two fair six-sided dice are rolled. Use a two-way table to find the probability of getting:

      (i) 6 on each of the two dice

      (ii) 6 on at least one of the dice

      (iii) A total of 6 on the two dice

      (iv) A total of 11, given that the total is odd

2. (i) How many ways are there of arranging the letters of the word NICHOLAS, taking them three at a time?

    (ii) In how many different ways can you choose three letters from the word NICHOLAS?

    (iii) If you choose three letters from the word NICHOLAS, what is the probability of getting three vowels?

    (iv) If you choose three letters from the word NICHOLAS, what is the probability of getting at least one consonant?

3.

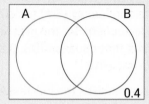

P(A) = 0.5, P(B) = 0.3 and P[(A ∪ B)′] = 0.4, as shown.

Find: (i) P(A ∩ B)

(ii) P(A|B)

(iii) P(B|A)

4. Two spinners are shown below.

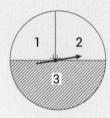 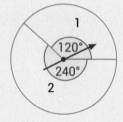

(i) If these two spinners are spun, which are you more likely to get: a **sum** of 3 from the two outcomes, or a **product** of 3 from the two outcomes? Justify your answers.

(ii) Calculate the probabilities of all the different possible **sums** when the two spinners are spun.

(iii) A single spinner is designed whose outcomes have the same probabilities as the four possible sums on the two spinners above. The angle at the sector representing the sum 2 is 30°. What are the angles for the sectors representing the sums 3, 4 and 5?

5. (a) How many numbers between 5,000 and 10,000 can be made from the digits 1, 3, 5, 7 and 9 if no digit may be repeated?

(b) (i) How many ways are there of arranging the letters of the word IRELAND?

(ii) How many of these arrangements begin with L and end with a vowel?

(iii) How many of these arrangements have the three vowels side by side?

(iv) The letters of the word IRELAND are arranged at random. What is the probability that the three vowels will be together?

6. A subcommittee of three people is to be chosen from a committee of 10.

(i) How many subcommittees are possible?

(ii) How many subcommittees are possible if two particular people on the committee refuse to work together on the subcommittee?

(iii) If the subcommittee is chosen at random, what is the probability that the two people who refuse to work together will both end up on the subcommittee?

7. Last year the local soccer team (The Hamiltonian Academicals) played 21 home games and 20 away games. They won 14 of their home games and only four of their away games.

(i) Find (as a fraction in its lowest terms) the relative frequency of their winning a home game last year.

(ii) Find (as a fraction in its lowest terms) the relative frequency of their winning an away game.

(iii) Taking these values as determining the probabilities, find the probability that their final match was a home game, given that they won.

8. X, Y and Z are three mutually exclusive events. P(X) = 0.4, P(Y) = 0.3 and P(X ∪ Z) = 0.6. Find:

(i) P(X ∪ Y)

(ii) P(Z)

(iii) The probability that none of X, Y or Z happens

9. S = {a, b, c, d, e, f, g}

(i) How many different subsets with four elements can be chosen from S?

(ii) How many of these contain f?

(iii) How many do not contain f?

(iv) A subset of four elements is chosen at random from S. What is the probability that it will include f?

10. The police in a certain town reported that during one year there were 25 muggings in the town in 365 days. The mayor of the town makes a speech saying that things will improve.

    (i) In the 31 days of January of the next year, there are two muggings. Have things improved or disimproved, and by how much? Make reference to relative frequency (using percentages).

    (ii) Over the first six months of the next year, there was a 20% reduction in muggings. Estimate how many muggings took place during those six months.

11. (a) A traffic light goes green for 50 seconds, then orange for 5 seconds and then red for 25 seconds. If a car arrives at random, find the probability that:

    (i) It will get a green light.

    (ii) It will not get a green light.

    (b) If $\binom{n}{2}$ = 91, find the value of

    $n \in N, n \geqslant 2$.

12. A coin is flipped twice and then a four-sided die (with numbers 1, 2, 3 and 4) is rolled. The coin and the die are both fair.

    (i) Copy and complete the sample space: {HH1, HH2, ...}.

    (ii) What is the probability of getting TT3?

    (iii) What is the probability of getting two heads followed by an even number?

    (iv) What is the probability of getting one head, one tail and an odd number?

13. (i) Three letters are chosen at random from the letters of the word FACETIOUS. How many different choices are possible?

    (ii) How many of these choices consist of two vowels and a consonant?

    (iii) If three letters are chosen at random from the word FACETIOUS, what is the probability of getting an A, E and I (in any order)?

    (iv) Sue says, 'If I choose three letters from the word FACETIOUS at random, the chances of getting the letters of my name (S, U, E) is a little under 1%.'

    Is this statement true or false? Justify your answer.

14. An online club is formed and is called the Alphabetical Order Club. In order to be a member, your first name, middle name and surname must have initials which are in alphabetical order. The same initial cannot be repeated, e.g. they do not allow BBK, HPP or RRR. Only one person with particular initials is allowed into the club. So, if Alan Craig Peterson (ACP) is a member, they will not allow Alice Carol Partridge to join.

    (i) State which of the following names are acceptable: Fred Harry Murphy, Yvonne Victoria Sullivan, Leah Nadia Nagle, Oisín Oscar Walsh.

    (ii) What is the maximum number of members that the club could have?

15. A and B are two events such that P(A) = 0.4, P(B) = 0.6 and P(B|A) = 0.25.

    (i) Find P(A ∩ B).

    (ii) Are A and B mutually exclusive?

    (iii) Find P(A|B), the probability of A given B.

    (iv) Find P(A ∪ B).

16. (a) (i) How many ways are there of choosing five numbers from the first 12 natural numbers?

    (ii) Five numbers are chosen at random from the first 12 natural numbers. Find the probability that 7 will be the median of the five chosen numbers.

    (b) X, Y and Z are three events such that P(X) = 0.6 and P(Y) = 0.3. X and Y are mutually exclusive.

    (i) Find P(X ∪ Y).

    (ii) If Y and Z are mutually exclusive, what is the greatest possible value for P(Z)?

17. (a) State whether or not the events A and B are mutually exclusive in each case:

What happens	Events A and B	Are A and B mutually exclusive (Yes or No)?
A card is drawn at random from a full pack	A = it is a King B = it is a Heart	
A child will be born next year	A = it will be born on a Sunday B = it will not be born on a weekday	
Two numbers are chosen from the first 100 natural numbers	A = their product is odd B = at most one of the numbers is odd	

(b) In a large sample of married couples in an Irish city in 2005 it was found that 83% of fathers worked outside the home and 47% of mothers worked outside the home. In 40% of cases, both the husband and the wife worked outside the home. Assume that this sample is a fair representation of the male–female married couples throughout the city.

   (i) Find the probability that at least one spouse works outside the home.

   (ii) Find the probability that neither spouse works outside the home.

   (iii) Given that exactly **one** spouse in a family works outside the home, find the probability that it is the wife who works outside the home.

Exam Questions

1. A property is said to be in 'negative equity' if the person owes more on the mortgage than the property is worth. A report about mortgaged properties in Ireland in December 2010 has the following information:

   - Of the 475,136 properties examined, 145,414 of them were in negative equity.
   - Of the ones in negative equity, 11,644 were in arrears.
   - There were 317,355 properties that were neither in arrears nor in negative equity.

   (i) What is the probability that a property selected at random (from all those examined) will be in negative equity? Give your answer correct to two decimal places.

   (ii) What is the probability that a property selected at random from all those in negative equity will also be in arrears? Give your answer correct to two decimal places.

   (iii) Find the probability that a property selected at random from all those in arrears will also be in negative equity? Give your answer correct to two decimal places.

   SEC Leaving Certificate Higher Level, Project Maths Paper 2, 2012

2. There are 16 girls and 8 boys in a class. Half of these 24 students study French. The probability that a randomly selected girl studies French is 1.5 times the probability that a randomly selected boy studies French. How many of the boys in the class study French?

   SEC Leaving Certificate Higher Level, Project Maths Paper 2, 2011

Solutions and chapter summary available online

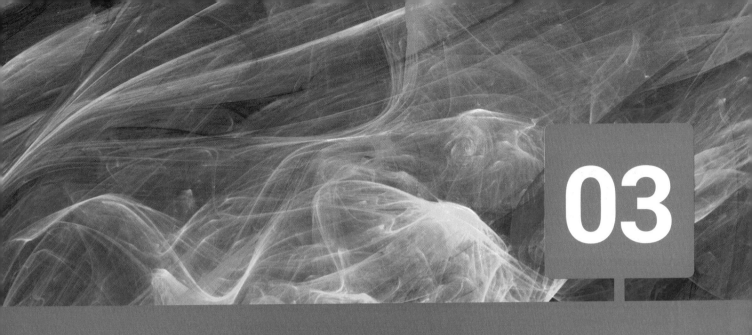

Probability II

 In this chapter you will learn about:

- The laws of probability

- Independent events

- Expected Value and its implications for fair, good and bad bets

- The Binomial Distribution and Bernoulli trials

- Discrete and continuous random variables

- The Normal Distribution and its applications

 You should remember...

- $P(A \cup B) = P(A) + P(B) - P(A \cap B)$

- $P(A \mid B) = \dfrac{P(A \cap B)}{P(B)} = \dfrac{\#(A \cap B)}{\#B}$

 Key words

- Independent events

- Expected value

- Binomial distribution

- Bernoulli trial

- Normal distribution

- Discrete/continuous

3.1 Events that Happen One after Another

The Multiplication Law

If two events happen one after the other then the probability that A happens followed by B is given by
$P(A \cap B) = P(A) . P(B|A)$

This means that the probability that A and then B happen is the product of the probability that A happens and the probability that B happens (given that A happened first). The fact that we **multiply** the probabilities is really an extension of the Fundamental Principle of Counting.

For example, if you draw a card from a full pack and then draw another card from the pack (without replacement), what is the probability that you get a King followed by a Queen?

$$P(\text{King then Queen}) = P(\text{King}) . P(\text{Queen} \mid \text{First card was a King}) = \frac{4}{52} . \frac{4}{51} = \frac{4}{663}$$

In other words, we assume that the sequence of events **does** happen, and calculate the probabilities accordingly.

Worked Example 3.1

Two cards are drawn from a standard pack, without replacement.
Find the probability that:

(i) They are both Hearts   (ii) At least one is not a Heart

Solution

(i) There are 13 Hearts in a pack of 52. Therefore, the probability that the first card is a Heart is:

$$\frac{13}{52} = \frac{1}{4}$$

When the second card is drawn, there will be 51 cards left in the pack, and only 12 of these will be Hearts. Hence, the probability that the second card is a Heart is:

$$\frac{12}{51} = \frac{4}{17}$$

Under the **Multiplication Law**, the probability that **both** are Hearts is:

$$\frac{1}{4} \times \frac{4}{17} = \frac{1}{17}$$

(ii) If at least one is not a Heart, then they cannot both be Hearts. Hence, the probability that at least one is not a Heart is:

$$1 - P(\text{both Hearts}) = 1 - \frac{1}{17} = \frac{16}{17}$$

Worked Example 3.2

Three cards are chosen at random from a standard pack. Find the probability that:

(i) All three are Kings

(iii) At least one is a King

(ii) None of the three cards is a King

(iv) Exactly two are Spades

Solution 1

The step-by-step method

(i) P(all three are Kings) = P(1st is a King **and** 2nd is a King **and** 3rd is a King)

$$= \frac{4}{52} \times \frac{3}{51} \times \frac{2}{50} = \frac{1}{5{,}525}$$

Here we assume that the sequence of events **does** happen and calculate the probabilities accordingly.

(ii) P(none is a King) = P(1st is not a King **and** 2nd is not a King **and** 3rd is not a King)

$$= \frac{48}{52} \times \frac{47}{51} \times \frac{46}{50} = \frac{4{,}324}{5{,}525}$$

(iii) P(at least one is a King) = 1 − P(none is a King) = $1 - \frac{4{,}324}{5{,}525} = \frac{1{,}201}{5{,}525}$

(iv) Let S = getting a Spade and N = not getting a Spade

P(exactly 2 Spades) = P(S **and** S **and** N **or** S **and** N **and** S **or** N **and** S **and** S)

$$= \left(\frac{13}{52} \times \frac{12}{51} \times \frac{39}{50}\right) + \left(\frac{13}{52} \times \frac{39}{51} \times \frac{12}{50}\right) + \left(\frac{39}{52} \times \frac{13}{51} \times \frac{12}{50}\right)$$

$$= \frac{117}{850}$$

Solution 2

The choosing method

'And' gives rise to ×

'Or' gives rise to +

(i) P(all three are Kings)

$$= \frac{\text{\# ways of choosing 3 Kings out of 4}}{\text{\# ways of choosing 3 cards from 52}} = \frac{\binom{4}{3}}{\binom{52}{3}} = \frac{4}{22{,}100} = \frac{1}{5{,}525}$$

(ii) P(none is a King)

$$= \frac{\text{\# ways of choosing 3 non-Kings from 48}}{\text{\# ways of choosing 3 cards from 52}} = \frac{\binom{48}{3}}{\binom{52}{3}} = \frac{17{,}296}{22{,}100} = \frac{4{,}324}{5{,}525}$$

(iii) P(at least one is a King) = 1 − P(none is a King) = $1 - \frac{4{,}324}{5{,}525} = \frac{1{,}201}{5{,}525}$

(iv) P(exactly two are Spades)

$$= \frac{\text{\# ways of choosing 2 Spades (from 13) \textbf{and} 1 non-Spade (from 39)}}{\text{\# ways of choosing 3 cards from 52}}$$

$$= \frac{\binom{13}{2} \times \binom{39}{1}}{\binom{52}{3}} = \frac{3{,}042}{22{,}100} = \frac{117}{850}$$

3.2 Independent Events

Two events are said to be independent if the occurrence of one in no way affects the likelihood of occurrence of the other. In this chapter, we will look more formally at this definition.

For example, suppose a coin is flipped and then a die is rolled.
Let E = {Getting a tail on the coin} and F = {Getting a 6 on the die}. Clearly, if you get a tail on the coin, this will have no bearing whatsoever on whether you will get a 6 on the die. These events are **independent**.

However, suppose you roll a fair die twice. E = {Getting a 6 on the first roll}. F = {Getting a total of 10 or more on the two rolls}. Clearly, if you get a 6 on the first die, you are more likely to get a high total. These events are **not** independent.

Mathematically, two events A and B are independent if P(B) = P(B | A). That is to say, the probability that B will happen is the same whether A happens or not.

Alternatively, you could say that A and B are independent if P(A) = P(A | B).

Let us develop this formula further. A and B are independent $\Rightarrow$ P(A) = P(A | B)

$$\therefore P(A) = \frac{P(A \cap B)}{P(B)}$$

$$\therefore P(A \cap B) = P(A)P(B)$$

Hence, we have three possible ways of establishing independence.

A and B are independent if:

P(A) = P(A | B) or P(B) = P(B | A) or P(A ∩ B) = P(A)P(B)

Three Laws of Probability

Law 1

$0 \leqslant P(E) \leqslant 1$, where P(E) is the probability of any event E.

Law 2

If p is the probability of an event E happening, then the probability that E will not happen is $1 - p$.

Law 3

If p is the probability of an event E happening, and if q is the probability of an independent event F happening, then the probability that, in two successive experiments, E happens and then F happens is pq.

If you roll a fair die and then flip a coin, the probability of getting a five and then a tail is $\frac{1}{6} \times \frac{1}{2} = \frac{1}{12}$ in accordance with Law 3 above, since these events are independent.

Worked Example 3.3

Four people are asked 'On what day of the week were you born?' Find, correct to two decimal places, the probability that at least two were born on the same day of the week.

Solution

First, we will find the probability that they were all born on different days of the week.

- The first person can have any day at all: $P = \frac{7}{7}$.

- The second person's birthday must be on one of the six other days of the week: $P = \frac{6}{7}$.

- That leaves five days for the third person: $P = \frac{5}{7}$.

- And, finally, four days for the last person: $P = \frac{4}{7}$.

Again, we assume that the sequence of events **does** happen and calculate the probabilities accordingly.

$$\therefore P(\text{all different}) = \frac{7}{7} \times \frac{6}{7} \times \frac{5}{7} \times \frac{4}{7} = \frac{120}{343} = 0.35 \text{ (to 2 d.p.)}$$

$\therefore$ P(at least two are the same)

= 1 − P(all different)

= 1 − 0.35

= 0.65

Worked Example 3.4

Given the Venn diagram of the sample space, prove that A and B are independent.

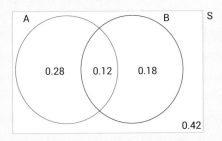

Solution
P(A) = 0.28 + 0.12 = 0.4

P(B) = 0.18 + 0.12 = 0.3

∴ P(A) . P(B) = 0.4 × 0.3 = 0.12 = P(A ∩ B)

Therefore, A and B are independent, since
P(A ∩ B) = P(A) . P(B)

3.3 Tree Diagrams

Tree diagrams are useful when dealing with successive events.

Worked Example 3.5

A bag contains seven green marbles and three red ones. Two marbles are drawn at random but not replaced. Use a tree diagram to find the probability that they will have different colours.

Solution
There are two ways that this can happen: The first is green **and** the second is red **or** the first is red **and** the second is green. We show these on a tree diagram.

1st Draw	2nd Draw	Outcome	Probability
$\frac{7}{10}$ G	$\frac{6}{9}$ G	G, G	$\frac{7}{10} \times \frac{6}{9} = \frac{7}{15}$
	$\frac{3}{9}$ R	G, R	$\frac{7}{10} \times \frac{3}{9} = \frac{7}{30}$
$\frac{3}{10}$ R	$\frac{7}{9}$ G	R, G	$\frac{3}{10} \times \frac{7}{9} = \frac{7}{30}$
	$\frac{2}{9}$ R	R, R	$\frac{3}{10} \times \frac{2}{9} = \frac{1}{15}$

Check: Total = 1

We are looking for the probability that the two marbles drawn will have different colours.

The desirable outcomes are:

Green, Red **or** Red, Green

∴ P(different colours) = $\frac{7}{30} + \frac{7}{30} = \frac{14}{30} = \frac{7}{15}$

Worked Example 3.6

The table shows the ages and gender of 28 students on a school tour.

	Boys	Girls
Aged 17	4	6
Aged 18	8	10

Two students are chosen from this group at random.
Find the probability that:

(i) One is a girl and one is a boy.

(ii) Both have the same age and gender.

Solution

(i)

1st Student	2nd Student	Outcome	Probability
$\frac{12}{28}$ Boy	$\frac{11}{27}$ Boy	B, B	$\frac{12}{28} \times \frac{11}{27} = \frac{11}{63}$
	$\frac{16}{27}$ Girl	B, G	$\frac{12}{28} \times \frac{16}{27} = \frac{16}{63}$
$\frac{16}{28}$ Girl	$\frac{12}{27}$ Boy	G, B	$\frac{16}{28} \times \frac{12}{27} = \frac{16}{63}$
	$\frac{15}{27}$ Girl	G, G	$\frac{16}{28} \times \frac{15}{27} = \frac{20}{63}$

Check: Total = 1

P(one girl and one boy) = P(G, B) + P(B, G)

$$= \frac{16}{63} + \frac{16}{63}$$

$$= \frac{32}{63}$$

(ii) For this probability tree, we show only the branches that we are interested in.

There are four branches on the 'probability tree' of the desired result.

1st Student	2nd Student	Outcome	Probability
$\frac{4}{28}$ B(17)	$\frac{3}{27}$ B(17)	B(17), B(17)	$\frac{4}{28} \times \frac{3}{27} = \frac{1}{63}$
$\frac{8}{28}$ B(18)	$\frac{7}{27}$ B(18)	B(18), B(18)	$\frac{8}{28} \times \frac{7}{27} = \frac{2}{27}$
$\frac{6}{28}$ G(17)	$\frac{5}{27}$ G(17)	G(17), G(17)	$\frac{6}{28} \times \frac{5}{27} = \frac{5}{126}$
$\frac{10}{28}$ G(18)	$\frac{9}{27}$ G(18)	G(18), G(18)	$\frac{10}{28} \times \frac{9}{27} = \frac{5}{42}$

∴ P(both have the same age and gender)

$$= \frac{1}{63} + \frac{2}{27} + \frac{5}{126} + \frac{5}{42}$$

$$= \frac{47}{189}$$

Worked Example 3.7

Let a fair six-sided die be rolled twice.

Let E = {6 turns up on the first roll}.

Let F = {6 turns up on the second roll}.

Let G = {The total on the two rolls is 8 or more}.

Our intuition would tell us that E and F are independent, whereas E and G are NOT independent. (Surely, a total of 8 or more is made more likely by the fact that the first roll produced a 6?)

Prove mathematically that:

(i) E and F are independent.

(ii) E and G are not independent.

Solution

S = outcome space = {(1,1), (1,2), (1,3), ..., (6,5), (6,6)}   #S = 36

E = {(6,1), (6,2), (6,3), (6,4), (6,5), (6,6)}   #E = 6

F = {(1,6), (2,6), (3,6), (4,6), (5,6), (6,6)}   #F = 6

G = {(2,6), (3,5), (3,6), (4,4), (4,5), (4,6), (5,3), (5,4), (5,5), (5,6), (6,2), (6,3), (6,4), (6,5), (6,6)}   #G = 15

E ∩ F = {(6,6)}   #(E ∩ F) = 1

E ∩ G = {(6,2), (6,3), (6,4), (6,5), (6,6)}   #(E ∩ G) = 5

> 'Sample space' can be called 'outcome space'.

(i) $P(E) = \frac{6}{36} = \frac{1}{6}$
$P(F) = \frac{6}{36} = \frac{1}{6}$ $\Big\}$ $\therefore P(E) \cdot P(F) = \frac{1}{6} \cdot \frac{1}{6} = \frac{1}{36}$

$P(E \cap F) = \frac{1}{36}$

Since $P(E \cap F) = P(E) \cdot P(F)$, E and F are independent.

(ii) $P(E) = \frac{1}{6}$
$P(G) = \frac{15}{36} = \frac{5}{12}$ $\Big\}$ $\therefore P(E) \cdot P(G) = \frac{1}{6} \cdot \frac{5}{12} = \frac{5}{72}$

$P(E \cap G) = \frac{5}{36}$

$P(E) \cdot P(G) \neq P(E \cap G)$

$\therefore$ E and G are NOT independent.

Worked Example 3.8

A and B are independent events such that:

$P(A) = 0.3$ and $P(A \cup B) = 0.5$

Find $P(B)$.

Solution

Let $P(B) = x$.

$P(A \cup B) = P(A) + P(B) - P(A \cap B)$

$\Rightarrow P(A \cup B) = P(A) + P(B) - P(A) \cdot P(B)$ (since A, B are independent)

$\Rightarrow 0.5 = 0.3 + x - 0.3x$

$\Rightarrow 5 = 3 + 10x - 3x$ (multiplying by 10)

$\Rightarrow 2 = 7x$

$\Rightarrow x = \frac{2}{7}$

Answer: $P(B) = \frac{2}{7}$

Exercise 3.1

1. A fair coin is flipped twice. Find:

   (i) The probability of getting two heads

   (ii) The probability of getting at least one tail

2. A fair six-sided die is rolled three times. Find the probability of getting:

   (i) Three 6s

   (ii) A 6 followed by an even number followed by an odd number

3. A fair coin is flipped four times. Find the probability of getting:

   (i) Four heads   (ii) At least one tail

4. A couple have five children. What is the probability that:

   (i) They are all girls.   (ii) At least one is a boy.

5. A classroom contains 14 girls and 16 boys. A student is picked at random and leaves the room. Another student is then picked at random. Find the probability that:

   (i) Both are boys.   (iii) At least one is a boy.

   (ii) Both are girls.

6. A card is drawn from a standard pack but not replaced. Then another card is drawn from the remainder of the pack. Find the probability that:

   (i) The first card is a Jack and the second is a Queen.

   (ii) Both of the cards are Jacks.

   (iii) Neither of the cards is a Jack.

   (iv) At least one of the cards is a Jack.

7. (a) Three cards are drawn from a standard pack without replacement. Find the probability that:

      (i) All three are Queens.

      (ii) At least one is not a Queen.

   (b) A card is drawn from a full pack, noted and replaced. This is done three times. Find the probability that:

      (i) All three are Queens.

      (ii) At least one is not a Queen.

8. (a) Last season, a centre-forward took 20 penalties and scored 12. Find the probability that she scores a penalty, using the relative frequency.

   (b) If, in a match, the centre-forward takes two penalty kicks, find the probability that:

      (i) She scores both.

      (ii) She scores neither.

      (iii) She scores at least once.

      (iv) She scores one but not the other.

9. (a) Last year, a certain student was late for school 21 times out of 168 days.

      Find the probability that this student will be on time for school on a specific day, using the relative frequency.

   (b) Find, correct to three significant figures, the probability that this student will be on time:

      (i) For two successive days

      (ii) For three successive days

      (iii) For five successive days

10. Jim, Ken and Leah are given a maths problem to solve. Their probabilities of success are shown in this table:

Person	Jim	Ken	Leah
Probability of success	$\frac{1}{2}$	$\frac{1}{4}$	$\frac{1}{3}$

   Find the probability that:

   (i) All three are successful.

   (ii) All three fail.

   (iii) At least one is successful.

11.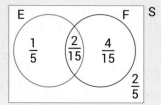

   Prove that E and F are independent events, given the Venn diagram above.

12. A and B are independent events, such that $P(A) = \frac{1}{2}$ and $P(B) = \frac{3}{4}$.

   Find:

   (i) $P(A \cap B)$ (ii) $P(A \cup B)$

13. E and F are subsets of an outcome space, S, in which all single elements are equally likely.

   $\#(E \setminus F) = 1$ $\#(F \setminus E) = 9$

   $\#(E \cap F) = 7$ $\#S = 20$

   Investigate if E and F are independent.

14. E and F are independent events, such that $P(E) = 0.2$ and $P(F) = 0.5$. Evaluate $P(E \cup F)$.

15. Three people are picked at random. What is the probability that:

   (i) All three have birthdays in different months.

   (ii) At least two have their birthdays in the same month.

   (Note: Take all months to be equally likely.)

16. (i) A poker hand of five cards is dealt randomly from a pack of 52. Find, correct to four decimal places, the probability of being dealt a flush of Spades (where all five cards are Spades).

   (ii) Find the probability of being dealt a flush in **any** suit.

17. Five people are chosen at random. Find the probability that two or more were born:

   (i) On the same day of the week

   (ii) In the same month (taking all months to be equally likely)

18. A bag contains five black marbles and two white ones. Two marbles are taken out, without replacement. Use a tree diagram to find the probability that one is white and the other is black.

19. Two cards are taken from a standard pack, without replacement. Use a tree diagram to find the probability that one will be a Club and the other a Spade.

20. When a certain player takes a penalty, the probability that he will score is $\frac{5}{6}$ each time. In a match, he takes two penalties. Use a tree diagram to find the probability that he will score exactly once.

21. A student sits a multiple choice test. In each question, four possible answers are offered, but only one is correct. The student guesses the answers to two of the questions.

   What is the probability that she gets exactly one of these right?

22. Three-quarters of all light bulbs in a country are made by Glare and one-quarter are made by Brighteyes. Five per cent of all Glare lightbulbs last for a year (or more). Ten per cent of all Brighteyes lightbulbs last for a year (or more).

Draw a tree diagram of the probabilities. If you buy a lightbulb at random in this country, what is the probability that it will last for at least a year?

23. If a day is fine, the probability that Mary will be late for school is 0.4. If the day is wet, the probability goes up to 0.5. In Ireland, 20% of all school days are wet.

Find, using a tree diagram, the probability that on a random school day in Ireland, Mary will be late for school.

24. A bag contains five red sweets and four green ones. Pete takes three sweets out in succession and eats them.

What is the probability that:

(i) All three are red?

(ii) One is red and two are green?

25. A bag contains five green, three blue and four red marbles. Two marbles are withdrawn, without replacement.

Find the probability that:

(i) Both are green.

(ii) Both are green or both are blue.

(iii) Both are the same colour.

(iv) They are different colours.

(v) One is red and one is not red.

26. A card is drawn from a pack at random.
E is the event that the chosen card is a Spade.
F is the event that the chosen card is a 'picture card' (i.e. a Jack, Queen or King).
Prove that E and F are independent.

27. A green six-sided die and a red six-sided die are rolled. E is the event that the score on the green die is 1. F is the event that the total on the two dice is 7.

Investigate if E and F are independent.

28. E and F are two independent events of an outcome space, S, as shown in the Venn diagram. Assume that all single elements are equally likely.

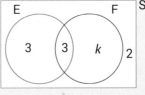

(i) Find the value of k.

(ii) Find P(E′), P(F′) and P(E′ ∩ F′).

(iii) Investigate if E′ and F′ are also independent.

29. A fair six-sided die is rolled twice.

E = {2 appears on the first roll}

F = {The total on the two rolls is an even number}

G = {The total on the two dice is less than 5}

Investigate if:

(i) E and F are independent.

(ii) E and G are independent.

30. E and F are independent events, such that P(E) = $\frac{2}{5}$ and P(E ∪ F) = $\frac{3}{5}$.

Find P(F).

31. E and F are independent events, whose cardinal numbers are given in the Venn diagram. Find the value of x.

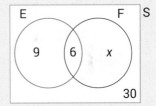

You may assume that all single elements are equally likely.

32. There are 20 raffle tickets in a hat, numbered 1 to 20. Four of the tickets (numbers 5, 10, 15, 20) are green. The rest are pink.

A ticket is picked at random from the hat and then replaced in the hat.

Once more, a ticket is picked from the hat.

E is the event that the first ticket is pink.

F is the event that the total on the two numbers is 35 or more.

(i) Without listing them, state the number of elements in the outcome space S for picking two tickets.

(ii) Find P(E), P(F) and P(E ∩ F).

(iii) Are E and F independent events? Justify your answer.

3.4 Mixing it Around

There is often more than one way of reaching a solution to a problem. In the following exercise, try to select an appropriate method of reaching the right answer. You might use tree diagrams, Venn diagrams, multiplications and additions of probabilities or $\binom{n}{r}$s, etc.

Exercise 3.2

1. (a) A bag contains eight black, three white and five red beads. Three beads are picked at random, without replacement. Find the probability that:

    (i) All three have the same colour.

    (ii) One is white and the others are not white.

    (iii) All three are of different colours.

    (iv) At least two are the same colour.

   (b) Answer the same four questions from part (a), but this time the bead is replaced each time.

2. Nine tickets, numbered 11, 12, 13, 14, 15, 16, 17, 18 and 19, are placed in a hat. One ticket is taken out but not replaced. Another ticket is taken out. Find the probability that:

    (i) Both are prime numbers.

    (ii) Both are even or both are odd.

    (iii) One is prime but the other is not.

3. Twenty tickets are numbered 1–20. Numbers 1–10 are red, 11–16 are yellow and 17–20 are green. A ticket is picked at random and replaced. A second ticket is then picked at random. Find the probability that:

    (i) Both are red.

    (ii) Both are yellow and even-numbered.

    (iii) Both are yellow or even-numbered.

    (iv) The sum of the numbers on the two tickets is 36.

4. (i) A tennis player gets 50% of his first serves 'in' and 80% of his second serves 'in'. Find the probability that this player will get a 'double fault' (where both first and second serves go out).

   (ii) Another player gets 70% of both her first and her second serves 'in'. What is the probability that this player will get a 'double fault'?

5. Three girls and one boy meet and discuss their birthdays. They discover that three of them have their birthdays in the same week (i.e. a seven-day week). Find the probability that:

    (i) The three whose birthdays lie in that week are all girls.

    (ii) All four were born on different days of the week.

6. Seven people are picked at random. Ignoring leap years, find the probability (correct to two significant figures) that their birthdays in a certain year:

    (i) Fall on different days of the week

    (ii) Fall in different months (taking all months as equally likely)

    (iii) Fall on different dates of the year

7. Four people are asked (independently) to think of one letter in the word TRIANGLES. Find the probability that:

    (i) They all think of the letter T.

    (ii) They all think of vowels.

    (iii) They all think of different letters.

8. Three people are asked to choose at random one of the whole numbers between 1 and 10 (inclusive). Find the probability that:

    (i) They all choose the same number.

    (ii) They all choose different numbers.

    (iii) At least two choose the same number.

9. A wheel of fortune is divided into eight sections, each of which is equally likely to end up the 'winning' sector (where the arrow points). Sections 1, 2 and 3 are grey. Sections 4, 5, 6 and 7 are black. Section 8 is white.

   The wheel is turned twice. Find the probability that:

    (i) Black wins twice.

    (ii) The same colour wins twice.

    (iii) The total of the two winning numbers is 13.

10. Two people are asked (independently of one another) to choose two letters (each) from the letters of the word FRACTION.
Find the probability that:

   (i) They both choose two consonants.

   (ii) One chooses two consonants and the other chooses two vowels.

   (iii) They have no letters in common.

   (iv) They both choose the same pair of letters.

11. There are 11 white socks and n black socks in a drawer. A person draws out two socks, at random. The probability that both are black is $\frac{1}{12}$. Find n.

12. There are four black balls, 10 white balls and n red balls in a bag. Two balls are drawn without replacement. The probability that one is red and one is not red is found to be $\frac{7}{15}$. Find two possible values for n.

13.

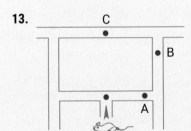

A rat is placed in a maze as shown. When it goes for a walk, it turns left at a 'T-junction' twice as often as it turns right.
What is the probability that:

   (i) It passes A after one turn?

   (ii) It passes B after two turns?

   (iii) It passes C after three turns?

14. (i) Four people are asked their birthday (e.g. 10th Nov., 25th Jan. etc.) Show that the probability that two or more of them have the same birthday is (correct to four decimal places) 0.0164. (Ignore 29th Feb.)

   (ii) The Famous Birthday Problem: There are 23 people in a room. Show that the probability that two or more have the same birthday is greater than 0.5.

15. A fair cubic die is relabelled so that it has three 1s, two 2s and one 6. The die is rolled.

   T = {The number showing is 2}

   E = {The number showing is even}

   O = {The number showing is 1}

(a) Find:

   (i) P(T)

   (ii) P(E)

   (iii) P(O)

   (iv) P(T')

   (v) P(E')

   (vi) P(T ∩ E)

   (vii) P(E' ∩ T)

   (viii) P(O' ∩ T')

(b) Are these pairs of sets mutually exclusive?

   (i) T and E

   (ii) T and O

   (iii) E and O

   (iv) T' and O'

(c) Find the conditional probability P(T|E).

16.

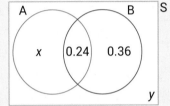

   (i) Given that A and B (as shown in the Venn diagram above) are independent events, find the values of x and y.

   (ii) Prove that A' and B' are independent.

   (iii) Find P(B | A).

17. Eva has a bag into which she places copper coins and silver coins. She places six copper coins and x silver coins in the bag. She then draws a coin at random from the bag.

(a) Find the value of x:

   (i) If P(the coin is copper) = 0.5

   (ii) If P(the coin is silver) = 0.25

   (iii) If P(the coin is copper) = 0.2

(b) Why is it impossible for P(the coin is silver) = 0.2?

18. In a certain city, 60% of the cars are from country A, 30% from country B and 10% from country C. Thirty per cent of cars from country A, 25% of cars from country B and 20% of cars from country C last for 10 years or more.

Find the probability that:

   (i) A car, bought at random in this city, will last for 10 years or more.

   (ii) A car will last for 10 years or more, given that it is not from country A.

   (iii) A car is from country C, given that it is 10 years old.

19. Three fair six-sided dice are rolled. Find the probability that the total on all three dice is 5 or less.

20. A soccer team has five penalty takers (A, B, C, D and E) for a penalty shoot-out. Each of the five has to take one penalty. The probabilities for each player's success are given in the following table:

Player	A	B	C	D	E
Probability of scoring	0.9	0.8	0.75	0.5	0.4

Find the probability that:

(i) All five score their penalties.

(ii) At least one misses.

(iii) They all score, except for E.

(iv) They all score, except for B.

(v) Exactly four of the five score.

21. A university student walks, cycles or drives to college with probabilities 0.1, 0.3 and 0.6, respectively. If she walks, she has a probability of 0.35 of being late. If she cycles, the probability of being late is 0.1. If she drives, the probability of being late is 0.55.

Find, correct to three decimal places, the probability that:

(i) She will be late on a particular day

(ii) She walked, given that she was late

(iii) She walked, given that she was **not** late

22. During the season, a hurling team (called the Random Variables) played 32 matches. Twenty of these matches were in fine weather and they won 16 of them. The other 12 were in rainy weather and they won only four of these.

Give your answers to the following questions as fractions in their lowest terms:

(i) What is the relative frequency of the Random Variables winning in fine weather?

(ii) What is the relative frequency of the Random Variables winning in rainy weather?

(iii) The Random Variables are playing in the Cup Final next Sunday. The weather forecasters say that the probability of fine weather is $\frac{3}{4}$ and the probability of rainy weather is $\frac{1}{4}$. Using the relative frequencies as probabilities, find the probability that they will win.

23. A teacher has one euro coin and three 50c coins in his back pocket. He has two euro coins and one 50c coin in his left pocket. He has three euro coins only in his right pocket.

He rolls a fair die. If it comes up as 1, 2 or 3, he will give a coin randomly from his back pocket as a prize to the best pupil. If a 4 or 5 comes up, he will give a coin from his left pocket. If a 6 comes up, he will give a coin from his right pocket.

What is the probability that the coin given will be a euro?

24. Suzie enters a penalty-taking competition in which she has to take three penalties in a row. It has been found that the probability that Suzie will score on the first penalty is 0.6. For subsequent penalties, this probability increases to 0.7 if she has been successful on the previous penalty and decreases to 0.5 if she has been unsuccessful on the previous penalty.

We will let S represent a successful penalty attempt and U an unsuccessful attempt.

(i) Find P(SSS), the probability that Suzie will be successful with all three penalties.

(ii) Find P(UUU), the probability that Suzie will be unsuccessful with all three penalties.

(iii) Find P(SSU), the probability that she will be unsuccessful only with the last penalty attempt.

(iv) Find the probability that she will score exactly twice.

(v) Find the probability that she will score just once.

25. Ben shoots four arrows at a target. The probability that he hits the target in general is 0.3. This increases to 0.4 if he has hit the target on the previous shot. It decreases to 0.25 if he has missed with the previous shot. We will call H a hit and M a miss. Answer these correct to 3 significant figures:

(i) Find P(HHHH), the probability that Ben will hit the target with all four arrows.

(ii) Find P(MMMM), the probability that he will miss each time.

(iii) Find P(MHMM), the probability that he will be successful only with the second arrow.

(iv) Find the probability that he will hit the target with just one arrow.

3.5 Expected Value

Here is a spinner. You bet €5, then spin the wheel and you win whatever amount the arrow is pointing to. Is this a good or a bad bet? We can decide mathematically by calculating the **expected value** (or mean). The expected value $E(x)$ is defined as $E(x) = \sum x . P(x)$ (where $\sum$ means 'the sum of'). In this case, the probability of getting €2 is $\frac{1}{2}$, of getting €4 is $\frac{1}{4}$ and of getting €6 is $\frac{1}{4}$.

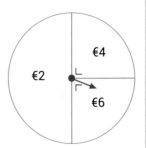

The expected return = $E(x) = \sum x . P(x)$

$$\therefore E(x) = 2\left(\frac{1}{2}\right) + 4\left(\frac{1}{4}\right) + 6\left(\frac{1}{4}\right)$$

$$= 1 + 1 + 1.5$$

$$= 3.5$$

$$\therefore E(x) = €3.50 \text{ (in money)}$$

But you paid out €5, so the expected value of the transaction is:

$$€(3.50 - 5) = -€1.50$$

This means that you expect to lose €1.50. It is therefore a bad bet.

When we say, 'you expect to lose €1.50', we mean that if you played this spinning game over and over, the mean outcome would be a loss of €1.50 per game. For this reason, it is a bad bet.

$E(x) = \sum x . P(x)$

Expected value — Sum — Outcome — Probability of outcome

Fair, Good and Bad Bets
If the expected return from a bet is zero [$E(x) = 0$], then the bet is said to be a **fair bet**.
If the expected return is greater than zero [$E(x) > 0$], then the bet is a **good bet**.
If the expected return is less than zero [$E(x) < 0$], then the bet is a **bad bet**.

Worked Example 3.9

At a Garden Fete, there is a stall where you pay €10 for a 'Pick the Envelope' competition. You then pick one of 10 blank envelopes and you can keep whatever is inside the envelope. Two of the envelopes are empty, five of them contain €5, one contains €10, one contains €20 and one contains €50. Alexa has €10 but she is wondering if this competition is a good bet. Calculate whether or not it is a good bet.

Solution
The expected prize (in euro) $= \sum x . P(x) = 0\left(\frac{2}{10}\right) + 5\left(\frac{5}{10}\right) + 10\left(\frac{1}{10}\right) + 20\left(\frac{1}{10}\right) + 50\left(\frac{1}{10}\right) = €10.50$

But you paid €10, so the expected return = €(10.50 − 10) = €0.50.

Since $E(x) > 0$, this is a **good bet** − Alexa would expect to win 50c with each play.

Note: It is worth noting that the **expected value** does not necessarily have to be an actual possible outcome. In this Worked Example, the expected value is €0.50 even though this is not one of the five possible outcomes (€0, €5, €10, €20 and €50). This is true of any mean: for example, the average family might have 2.4 children, even though it is not possible to give birth to 2.4 children.

Worked Example 3.10

A GAA club holds a weekly lottery. If you buy a ticket for €1, you choose three numbers from {1, 2, 3, ..., 20}. Every Saturday the winning three numbers are drawn out of a drum. If you have the correct three numbers, you win €500. If you have a 'Match Two' (with any two of the winning three numbers), you win €5. Is buying a ticket for €1 a fair bet, a good bet or a bad bet?

Solution

There are $\binom{20}{3} = 1{,}140$ different combinations when you fill out a ticket. Only one is correct. Hence, the chances of winning are $\frac{1}{1{,}140}$.

The number of ways of getting a 'Match Two' are $\binom{3}{2}\binom{17}{1} = 3 \times 17 = 51$ (since you'd have to choose two of the three winning numbers and one of the 17 non-winning numbers to get a 'Match Two').

Hence, the probability of winning a 'Match Two' is $= \frac{51}{1{,}140} = \frac{17}{380}$.

The expected win $= \sum x \cdot P(x) = 500\left(\frac{1}{1{,}140}\right) + 5\left(\frac{17}{380}\right) = 0.6622 = €0.66$ (to the nearest cent)

But you paid €1 for the bet, so the expected return is given by $E(x) = €(0.66 - 1) = -€0.34$.
Since $E(x) < 0$, this is a **bad bet** – you would expect to lose 34c with each play.

Exercise 3.3

PROBABILITY II

1. When a fair six-sided die is rolled, show that the expected value is 3.5.

2.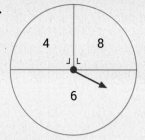

   Find the expected value when this spinner is spun.

3.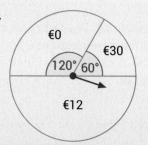

   You bet €10, then spin the spinner and you win the amount pointed at. Is this a good or bad bet? Justify your answer with reference to the expected value.

4. A card is chosen at random from this poker hand and the number on the card is noted.

   (i) Copy and complete this probability distribution table:

Number on card	10	5
Probability		

   (ii) Find the expected value of the number on the card.

   (iii) Is the expected value one of the possible outcomes?

5. A friend of yours offers you a bet: you have to bet €1. Then you pick a card from a pack.

   • If you choose the Ace of Spades, you win €20.

   • If you pick any Diamond card, you win €2.

   Is this a good bet? Justify your answer with reference to the expected value.

6. A pair of fair six-sided dice is rolled and the total on the two dice is noted.

   (i) Copy and complete the following probability distribution table:

Total (x)	2	3	4	5	6	7	8	9	10	11	12
P(x)	$\frac{1}{36}$				$\frac{5}{36}$						$\frac{1}{36}$

   (ii) Calculate the expected value.

   (iii) Is the expected value a possible outcome?

7.

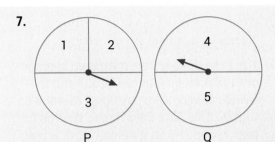

P   Q

Two spinners P and Q are spun and the sum total is noted.

(i) Copy and complete this probability distribution table:

Total (x)	5	6	7	8
P(x)	$\frac{1}{8}$			

(ii) Calculate the expected value of the sum.

(iii) Daria and Daniel play a **fair** game in which Daniel spins the two spinners. If the sum on the spinners is 5 or 6, Daniel gives Daria €1. If the sum is 7 or 8, Daria gives Daniel n cent. Find the value of n.

8.

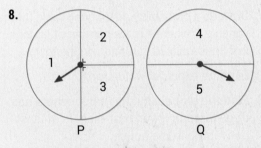

P   Q

Spinners P and Q are spun and the product of the two numbers is noted. Calculate the expected value of the product.

9. In a game, a contestant is given the chance to choose one of eight plain white envelopes, but must pay €10 for this game. The contestant keeps the contents of the envelope.

Four envelopes are empty, one contains a €5 note, one a €10 note, one a €20 note, and finally, one a €50 note.

Is this a good game for the contestant to play? Explain your answer with reference to the expected value.

10.

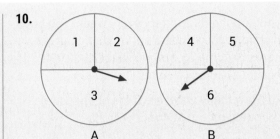

A   B

Spinners A and B are spun and the sum of the outcomes is noted.

(i) Calculate the expected value.

(ii) Design a single spinner with the same probabilities as the sum of A and B, showing the degrees in each sector.

11. A school holds a weekly lottery to raise funds. If you buy a ticket for €1, you choose four numbers from {1, 2, 3, 4, 5, 6, 7, 8, 9, 10, 11, 12}. Every Friday the principal draws the winning four numbers from a hat. If you have the correct four numbers, you win the jackpot of €100. If you have a 'Match Three' (with any three of the winning four numbers), you win €10. Is buying a ticket for €1 a fair bet, a good bet or a bad bet?

12. A girl is in a show on television. She has answered a question correctly and so she has won €1,000. Now she is offered three choices:

Choice 1 She can take the money and go.

Choice 2 She can pick a card at random from a standard pack of cards and, if she picks an Ace, she wins €10,000. (In this case, she does not get the €1,000 as well.) If she does not get an Ace, she goes home with nothing.

Choice 3 She can roll a pair of fair six-sided dice and if she throws a double 6, she wins €100,000. (In this case also, she does not get the €1,000 as well.) If she does not throw a double 6, she goes home empty-handed.

(i) Copy and complete the following table to the nearest euro:

Choice	Expected value
Choice 1	€1,000
Choice 2	
Choice 3	

(ii) What should the girl do? Justify your answer.

13. A country holds a lottery every week. You have to choose six numbers out of 45. If your six numbers come up, you will win €3,000,000. It costs €1 to buy a ticket.

   (i) How many ways are there of choosing six numbers out of 45?

   (ii) What is the probability of winning? Give your answer in scientific notation correct to three significant figures.

   (iii) Is it good value to buy a ticket for this lottery? Justify your answer with reference to expected value.

14. The table below gives motor insurance information for fully licensed, 17–20-year-old drivers in Ireland in 2007. All drivers who had their own insurance policy are included.

	Number of drivers	Number of claims	Average cost per claim
Male	9,634	977	€6,108
Female	6,743	581	€6,051

Source: Adapted from: Financial Regulator.
Private Motor Insurance Statistics 2007

Questions (a) to (e) refer to drivers in the table above only.

(a) What is the probability that a randomly selected male driver made a claim during the year?

   Give your answer correct to three decimal places.

(b) What is the probability that a randomly selected female driver made a claim during the year?

   Give your answer correct to three decimal places.

(c) What is the expected value of the cost of claims on a male driver's policy?

(d) What is the expected value of the cost of claims on a female driver's policy?

(e) The male drivers were paying an average of €1,688 for insurance in 2007 and the female drivers were paying an average of €1,024. Calculate the average surplus for each group and comment on your answer.

   (Note: The surplus is the amount paid for the policy minus the expected cost of claims.)

(f) A 40-year-old female driver with a full licence has a probability of 0.07 of making a claim during the year. The average cost of such claims is €3,900. How much should a company charge such drivers for insurance in order to show a surplus of €175 per policy?

15. The number of laptops per household in a survey of 100 houses in a town gave the following frequency distribution:

Number of laptops	0	1	2	3
Frequency	10	75	10	5

   (i) Draw up a probability distribution table for the variable X, where X is the number of laptops in a house picked at random in the town.

   (ii) Find the expected value for X.

   (iii) Find the probability that a household has three laptops, given that there is at least one laptop in the house.

16. The random variable X has the following probability distribution:

x	1	2	3	4	5
$P(X = x)$	0.1	a	b	0.2	0.1

   (i) Given that the expected value $E(X) = 2.9$, find the value of a and the value of b.

   (ii) Find $P(X = 5 \mid X > 3)$.

3.6 The Binomial Distribution: Bernoulli Trials

There are 300 girls and 100 boys in a school. Each weekday, the headmistress chooses one student at random to read the announcements at Assembly. Over a certain five-day week, find the probability that the headmistress chooses a girl exactly three times and a boy exactly twice.

It is easy to be misled here. One might imagine that she must choose a girl for the first three days and a boy for the next two days. Hence, the probability would be:

$$\frac{3}{4} \times \frac{3}{4} \times \frac{3}{4} \times \frac{1}{4} \times \frac{1}{4} = \frac{27}{1,024}$$

But this answer is too restrictive, since it is allowable to have the sequence

Girl-Girl-Boy-Girl-Boy, with a probability of $\frac{3}{4} \times \frac{3}{4} \times \frac{1}{4} \times \frac{3}{4} \times \frac{1}{4} = \frac{27}{1,024}$

or Girl-Boy-Girl-Boy-Girl, again with a probability of $\frac{27}{1,024}$

or, indeed, ANY acceptable order, each of which yields a probability of $\frac{27}{1,024}$.

So, the correct answer will be $k\left(\frac{27}{1,024}\right)$, where k is the number of different ways in which the three girls and two boys can be ordered.

So, what is k?

k, in this case, is 10 because there are 10 ways of ordering three girls and two boys:

GGGBB, GGBGB, GBGGB, BGGGB, GGBBG,

GBGBG, BGGBG, GBBGG, BGBGG, BBGGG

The **reason** why there are 10 is that we are **choosing** three days out of five for the girls.

There are $\binom{5}{3}$ = 10 ways of doing this.

Here the correct answer is:

$$\binom{5}{3}\left(\frac{3}{4}\right)^3\left(\frac{1}{4}\right)^2 = 10\left(\frac{27}{1,024}\right) = \frac{135}{512}$$

In general, let us conduct the **same** experiment n times – each with two possible outcomes, which we will call 'success' and 'failure'. Let the probability of success in each trial be p and the probability of failure be q (where $q = 1 - p$). The probability of getting exactly r successes (where $r \leqslant n$) will be:

$\binom{n}{r}p^r q^{n-r}$ — This formula appears on page 33 of *Formulae and Tables*.

The formula is a term in the binomial expansion of $(p + q)^n$. Hence the name **binomial distribution**.

It is important for you to recognise when to use the binomial distribution formula. Remember to use the formula when the following four criteria are satisfied:

- There is a finite number of trials (n).
- There are only two outcomes – success and failure.
- Trials are independent of each other.
- The probability of success (p) is the same for each trial.

A **Bernoulli trial** is a trial whose outcome is random and is one of just two possibilities, which are called 'success' and 'failure'. Each trial is often referred to as a Bernoulli trial, after the Swiss mathematician Jakob Bernoulli (1655–1705).

PROBABILITY II

Worked Example 3.11

A couple have six children. Find the probability that they have four girls and two boys.

Solution

We will let 'success' be 'having a girl' and 'failure' be 'having a boy' (although each is, of course, as much a success as the other).

$\therefore p = \frac{1}{2}$ and $q = \frac{1}{2}$

We require four successes out of six. $\therefore n = 6, r = 4$

Probability $= \binom{6}{4}\left(\frac{1}{2}\right)^4\left(\frac{1}{2}\right)^2 = (15)\left(\frac{1}{16}\right)\left(\frac{1}{4}\right) = \frac{15}{64}$

Worked Example 3.12

One person in 10 is left-footed. Eleven football players are picked at random. Find as a percentage the probability that less than two will be left-footed (to the nearest per cent).

Solution

'Success' = Being left-footed $\therefore p = 0.1$

'Failure' = Being right-footed $\therefore q = 0.9$

P(Less than two are left-footed) = P(None is left-footed) + P(One is left-footed)

$$= \binom{11}{0}(0.1)^0(0.9)^{11} + \binom{11}{1}(0.1)^1(0.9)^{10}$$

$$= (1)(1)(0.3138106) + (11)(0.1)(0.3486784)$$

$$= 0.3138106 + 0.3835462$$

$$= 0.697 \text{ (correct to three decimal places)}$$

$$= 70\% \text{ (to the nearest per cent)}$$

Exercise 3.4

1. In each case, put a tick (✓) in the box if the problem is solved using the binomial distribution formula. If not, put a cross (✗) in the box.

   (There is no need to solve these problems.)

	Problem	Binomial distribution formula?
1	The probability of getting exactly two tails when a fair coin is flipped five times.	✓
2	A coin is flipped until four heads turn up.	✗
3	In 100 football games, the probability of getting 50 wins, 30 losses and 20 draws.	✗
4	In a family of seven children, the probability of having four girls and three boys.	✓
5	A bag contains 10 white and five green balls. Three balls are taken out in turn. The probability that only one is green if: (i) The ball is replaced each time. (ii) The ball is **not** replaced each time.	(i) ✓ (ii) ✗
6	The probability of finding exactly two left-handed tennis players in a class of 20 students.	✓
7	The probability of being dealt exactly two Aces when you are dealt a poker hand of five cards.	✗
8	When 50 people take a certain medicine, the probability that two suffer side-effects.	✓

2. A couple has five children. Find the probability that they have two girls and three boys.

3. A fair six-sided die is rolled four times. Find the probability that a 6 comes up exactly one time.

4. A fair coin is flipped eight times. Find, as a fraction, the probability that heads comes up:

   (i) Exactly four times   (ii) Exactly seven times   (iii) Seven times or more

5. In the first 56 days of school, Samantha was late 14 times. Take the relative frequency as the probability that she will be late.

   In five consecutive days, find the probability that she will be late (correct to 4 decimal places):

   (i) Never   (iii) More than once

   (ii) Once only

6. In a family of six children, what is the probability of having three girls and three boys?

   Of 400 such families, how many would you expect to have three girls and three boys?

7. One-eighth of the Irish population is left-handed. Three Irish people are chosen at random. Find the probability that one (and one only) is a left-hander, correct to 3 decimal places.

8. In Ireland, 40% of the cars are Japanese. Ten cars pass a point in Ireland randomly. What is the probability that exactly four are Japanese (correct to 2 decimal places)?

9. A survey shows that 60% of the population of Dublin is female. Four Dubliners are picked at random. Find the probability that at least two are female.

10. Show that in five throws of an unbiased six-sided die, the probability of throwing one 6 is the same as the probability of throwing no 6.

11. In a certain country, 30% of the population is suffering from AIDS. If a sample of 10 people from this country is chosen at random, find the probability that exactly 30% of the people chosen will be found to be suffering from AIDS.

12. A student is doing a multiple choice test. Only one answer (of the four possible answers) in each question is correct. The student answers five questions using guesswork alone. What is the probability (to 2 significant figures) of getting three or more correct?

13. If you drop a drawing pin on a wooden floor, it will face point up 80% of the time. A person drops five drawing pins. Find the probability that:

    (i) Exactly two will face point up.

    (ii) Two or fewer will face point up.

14. Whenever Jimmy fires an arrow he has $\frac{1}{4}$ chance of hitting a target. He fires 10 arrows. Find the probability (to the nearest percentage) that:

    (i) He hits the target the first three times but misses the rest.

    (ii) He hits the target exactly three times.

    (iii) He hits the target at least once.

15. When Susan rings her mother, the chance that her mother will answer the phone is $\frac{3}{5}$.

    Susan rings her mother every day for a week. Find (correct to 2 significant figures) the probability that her mother answers:

    (i) Exactly four times

    (ii) Six or more times

    (iii) On Monday and Tuesday only

16. An insurance firm calculates that a client has a $\frac{1}{20}$ chance of having one or more accidents during a given year. If this client is insured for 10 consecutive years, find the probability that:

    (i) He will have no accidents.

    (ii) He will have an accident in more than one year.

17. Leah is the team's penalty taker. Last season, she took 20 penalties and scored 16 times. Use the relative frequency as the probability of scoring.

    During the next season she takes eight penalties. Find the probability (correct to 2 decimal places) that:

    (i) She scores the first six penalties but misses the last two.

    (ii) She scores exactly six penalties.

    (iii) She scores six or more.

18. A fair coin is flipped n times. Show that the probability of getting one head or less is $\frac{n+1}{2^n}$.

19. When a certain drug is used, there is a 5% chance that side-effects will be suffered. Twenty people are given the drug. Find, to the nearest per cent, the probability that:

    (i) None will suffer side-effects.

    (ii) More than one will suffer side-effects.

    (iii) The company that produces the drug claims, 'When 20 people are tested at random, there is a less than 8% chance that three or more will suffer side-effects.' Is this claim true?

3.7 The Binomial Distribution Extended

Worked Example 3.13

A fair six-sided die is thrown repeatedly until a 6 appears for the third time. Find the probability that this will take exactly 15 throws. Give your answer to the nearest per cent.

Solution

There is only one way this can happen: if there are exactly two 6s in the first 14 throws **and** the 15th throw is a 6.

The probability that this will happen is:

$$\binom{14}{2}\left(\frac{1}{6}\right)^2\left(\frac{5}{6}\right)^{12} \times \frac{1}{6}$$

$$= \binom{14}{2}\left(\frac{1}{6}\right)^3\left(\frac{5}{6}\right)^{12}$$

= 0.04725

= 5% (to the nearest per cent)

Worked Example 3.14

A coin is flipped repeatedly until 10 heads appear. Find the probability that this will take exactly 17 flips. Give your answer correct to three decimal places.

Solution

There is only one way this can happen: if there are nine heads in the first 16 flips **and** the 17th flip gives a head.

$$P = \binom{16}{9}\left(\frac{1}{2}\right)^9\left(\frac{1}{2}\right)^7 \times \frac{1}{2}$$

$$= \binom{16}{9}\left(\frac{1}{2}\right)^{17}$$

= 0.087 (correct to three decimal places)

Exercise 3.5

1. A fair coin is flipped repeatedly until exactly four heads appear. Find the probability that this will take exactly six flips.

2. A fair six-sided die is rolled repeatedly until two 6s appear.
   Find the probability that this will take exactly 10 rolls, correct to 2 significant figures.

3. A couple decide to keep having children until they have exactly two boys. Find the probability that this will happen:
   (i) At the birth of their second child
   (ii) At the birth of their fifth child

4. When a thumb tack is thrown on the floor, the probability that it lands pin up is $\frac{1}{5}$. The thumb-tack is thrown repeatedly onto the floor until it lands pin up for the third time. Find the probability that this will take exactly 10 throws.

5. A card is drawn randomly from a standard pack, noted and replaced. This procedure is repeated over and over again until two spades appear.
   Find the probability that this will happen when the eighth card is drawn.

6. People are stopped at random on a street and asked what day of the week they were born on. This process is repeated until two people who were born on Sunday are stopped.
   Find the probability that this will take exactly 12 people. (You may assume they all know the day of their birth).

7. A golfer has a 30% chance of landing the ball on the green each time he tees off from a par-three hole. He decides to keep hitting balls until he gets three balls on the green.
   Find the probability that this will happen after only six balls.

8. A woman phones householders randomly. She finds that only 20% of householders reply to her questions. She decides to keep ringing until she gets four householders who reply to her questions.

   Find the probability that this will take 10 calls.

9. In the USA, 10% of the population is left-handed. A researcher stops people randomly in a street in the USA until she comes across two left-handed people.

   Find the probability (correct to two significant figures) that she will stop exactly 15 people.

10. A missile has a 25% chance of hitting a target. How many missiles must be fired to ensure that there is a greater than 90% chance that the target will be hit at least once?

11. How many times must a fair six-sided die be rolled so that the chances of getting at least one 6 is greater than 90%?

12. How many times must a fair coin be flipped in order to ensure that there is at least a 99% chance of getting at least one tail?

3.8 The Normal Distribution

When you roll a pair of dice and evaluate the total of the numbers that turn up, the possible outcomes are the following:

$$\{2, 3, 4, 5, 6, 7, 8, 9, 10, 11, 12\}$$

There is a *countable* number of *individual* elements in this outcome space. We call such a set a **discrete** set. It is important to note that only whole number outcomes are possible; hence, outcomes of $7\frac{1}{2}$ or 5.34 are both impossible. Now every time we roll this pair of dice, we cannot be sure which outcome is going to turn up. The result varies randomly, from roll to roll. However, we *can* say that some outcomes are more likely than others. Indeed, we can graph the probabilities of each outcome (see right).

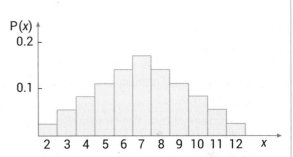

The sum total when any pair of dice is rolled is called a **discrete random variable** (**discrete**, because the possible outcomes are individual and countable; **random**, because the results are unpredictable; **variable**, because the results vary from roll to roll).

The mean of this data is 7 and the standard deviation from the mean is 2.415. Standard deviation is a measure of **spread**, which will be explained further in Chapter 4.

Another example of a discrete random variable would be the results of picking houses randomly in Ireland and asking how many occupants are in each house. The results of this might have a mean of 2.3 with a standard deviation of 0.6.

Now let us look at a random variable that is *not* discrete. We will pick people at random and ask, 'What is your weight in kilograms?' The set of possible outcomes, in this case, is an infinite continuous set, since all positive real numbers are now possible. (Your weight could be 60.00387543... kg, etc.)

We call such variables **continuous random variables**. We graph the probabilities of such variables with a continuous, smooth curve (see right).

In the first case, the mean is 70 kg, with a standard deviation of 15 kg.

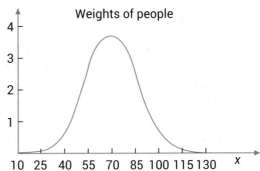

Weights of people

Another continuous random variable is the height of Irish soldiers (in centimetres). The mean is 170 cm, with a standard deviation of 3 cm. Below is the graph of the probability density function in this case.

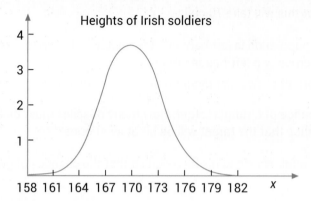

These two curves are remarkably similar. Many other curves that occur in real life have exactly this shape. Any random variable whose probability density function has this shape is said to have a **normal distribution**. The curve is often described as bell-shaped.

In the above cases, the probability that a result will be within one standard deviation of the mean will be the same. That is to say, the probability that a person's weight will be between 55 kg and 85 kg will be the same as the probability that an Irish soldier's height will be between 167 cm and 173 cm.

If a random variable has a normal distribution with mean μ and standard deviation σ, we say it has distribution $N(\mu, \sigma^2)$, for short. For example, the height of Irish soldiers has distribution $N(170, 9)$.

3.9 The Normal Distribution Table

If a random variable has a normal distribution, we can use the table on pages 36–37 of *Formulae and Tables* to calculate probabilities.

> The next page shows the Normal Distribution Table as it appears in *Formulae and Tables*.

The normal distribution table opposite is based on the standard normal variable, z, with a mean 0 and a standard deviation 1. That is, it has distribution $N(0, 1)$.

If we are asked: 'Find $P(z \leqslant 1.3)$', we are really being asked: 'Find the probability that the result will be less than (or equal to) 1.3 standard deviations above the mean.' We look up the value of 1.3 and find that $P(z \leqslant 1.3) = 0.9032$.

This means that 90.32% of the population of any normally distributed random variable will give readings that are less than (or equal to) 1.3 standard deviations above the mean.

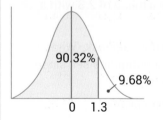

> The total area under the curve is 1.
> The total percentage is 100%.

> $P(z < k)$ and $P(z \leqslant k)$ give the same result, because the probability that z is exactly equal to k is infinitely small. So, $P(z < 1.3) = P(z \leqslant 1.3) = 0.9032$.

NORMAL DISTRIBUTION TABLE

z	0.00	0.01	0.02	0.03	0.04	0.05	0.06	0.07	0.08	0.09
0.0	0.5000	.5040	.5080	.5120	.5160	.5199	.5239	.5279	.5319	.5359
0.1	0.5398	.5438	.5478	.5517	.5557	.5596	.5636	.5675	.5714	.5753
0.2	0.5793	.5832	.5871	.5910	.5948	.5987	.6026	.6064	.6103	.6141
0.3	0.6179	.6217	.6255	.6293	.6331	.6368	.6406	.6443	.6480	.6517
0.4	0.6554	.6591	.6628	.6664	.6700	.6736	.6772	.6808	.6844	.6879
0.5	0.6915	.6950	.6985	.7019	.7054	.7088	.7123	.7157	.1790	.7224
0.6	0.7257	.7291	.7324	.7357	.7389	.7422	.7454	.7486	.7517	.7549
0.7	0.7580	.7611	.7642	.7673	.7704	.7734	.7764	.7794	.7823	.7852
0.8	0.7881	.7910	.7939	.7967	.7995	.8023	.8051	.8078	.8106	.8133
0.9	0.8159	.8186	.8212	.8238	.8264	.8289	.8315	.8340	.8365	.8389
1.0	0.8413	.8438	.8461	.8485	.8508	.8531	.8554	.8577	.8599	.8621
1.1	0.8643	.8665	.8686	.8708	.8729	.8749	.8770	.8790	.8810	.8830
1.2	0.8849	.8869	.8888	.8907	.8925	.8944	.8962	.8980	.8997	.9015
1.3	0.9032	.9049	.9066	.9082	.9099	.9115	.9131	.9147	.9162	.9177
1.4	0.9192	.9207	.9222	.9236	.9251	.9265	.9279	.9292	.9306	.9319
1.5	0.9332	.9345	.9357	.9370	.9382	.9394	.9406	.9418	.9429	.9441
1.6	0.9452	.9463	.9474	.9484	.9495	.9505	.9515	.9525	.9535	.9545
1.7	0.9554	.9564	.9573	.9582	.9591	.9599	.9608	.9616	.9625	.9633
1.8	0.9641	.9649	.9656	.9664	.9671	.9678	.9686	.9693	.9699	.9706
1.9	0.9713	.9719	.9726	.9732	.9738	.9744	.9750	.9756	.9761	.9767
2.0	0.9772	.9778	.9783	.9788	.9793	.9798	.9803	.9808	.9812	.9817
2.1	0.9821	.9826	.9830	.9834	.9838	.9842	.9846	.9850	.9854	.9857
2.2	0.9861	.9864	.9868	.9871	.9875	.9878	.9881	.9884	.9887	.9890
2.3	0.9893	.9896	.9898	.9901	.9904	.9906	.9909	.9911	.9913	.9916
2.4	0.9918	.9920	.9922	.9925	.9927	.9929	.9931	.9932	.9934	.9936
2.5	0.9938	.9940	.9941	.9943	.9945	.9946	.9948	.9949	.9951	.9952
2.6	0.9953	.9955	.9956	.9957	.9959	.9960	.9961	.9962	.9963	.9964
2.7	0.9965	.9966	.9967	.9968	.9969	.9970	.9971	.9972	.9973	.9974
2.8	0.9974	.9975	.9976	.9977	.9977	.9978	.9979	.9979	.9980	.9981
2.9	0.9981	.9982	.9982	.9983	.9984	.9984	.9985	.9985	.9986	.9986
3.0	0.9987	.9987	.9987	.9988	.9988	.9989	.9989	.9989	.9990	.9990

Worked Example 3.15

Assuming that z is normally distributed with mean 0 and standard deviation 1, find:

(i) P($z < 1.22$)

(ii) P($z \geqslant 2.37$)

(iii) P($z \geqslant -0.56$)

(iv) P($z < -0.82$)

Solution

(i) P($z < 1.22$) = 0.8888 (reading from pages 36–37 of *Formulae and Tables*)

(ii)

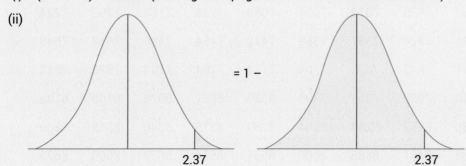

The area under the entire curve is 1.

Hence, P($z \geqslant 2.37$) = 1 − P($z < 2.37$) = 1 − 0.9911 = 0.0089.

(iii)

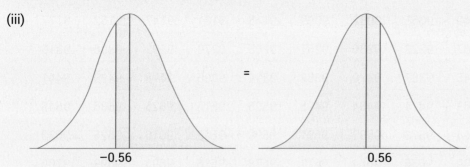

The normal curve is symmetrical. Hence, P($z \geqslant -0.56$) = P($z \leqslant 0.56$) = 0.7123.

(iv)

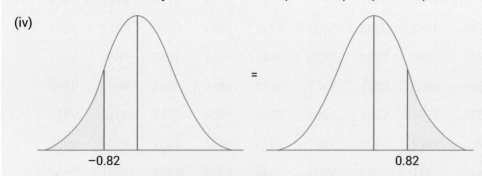

By symmetry, P($z < -0.82$) = P($z > 0.82$) = 1 − P($z \leqslant 0.82$) = 1 − 0.7939 = 0.2061.

> In general, P($z < -k$) = P($z > k$) and P($z \geqslant -k$) = P($z \leqslant k$).

Assuming that z is normally distributed with mean 0 and standard deviation 1, find:

(i) $P(1 < z < 2)$

(ii) $P(-1.4 \leqslant z \leqslant -1.145)$

(iii) $P(-1.2 < z < 1.75)$

Solution

(i)

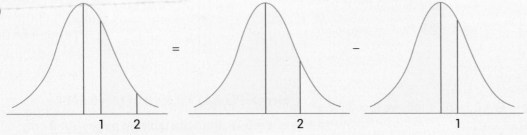

$P(1 < z < 2) = P(z < 2) - P(z \leqslant 1) = 0.9772 - 0.8413 = 0.1359$

(ii) When z lies between two negative numbers, we use symmetry.

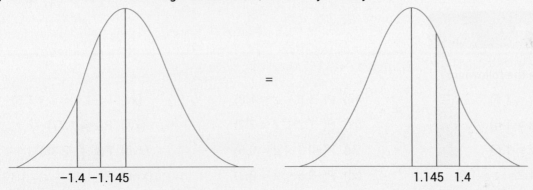

By symmetry:

$P(-1.4 \leqslant z \leqslant -1.145) = P(1.145 \leqslant z \leqslant 1.4) = P(z \leqslant 1.4) - P(z < 1.145) = 0.9192 - 0.8739 = 0.0453$

The reading for 1.145 is half-way between the reading for 1.14 (= 0.8729) and the reading for 1.15 (= 0.8749).

(iii)

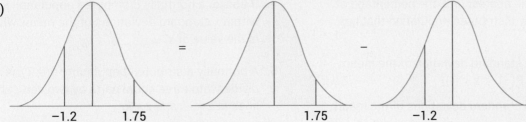

$P(-1.2 < z < 1.75) = P(z < 1.75) - P(z \leqslant -1.2)$

$\qquad = P(z < 1.75) - P(z \geqslant 1.2)$

$\qquad = P(z < 1.75) - [1 - (P(z < 1.2)]$

$\qquad = P(z < 1.75) - 1 + P(z < 1.2)$

$\qquad = 0.9599 - 1 + 0.8849$

$\qquad = 0.8448$

Worked Example 3.17

z has the standard normal distribution $N(0, 1)$.

If $P(-k < z < k) = 0.1428$, find the value of k.

Solution

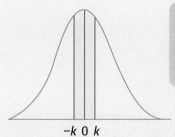

Start by drawing a normal curve and shading in the area required.

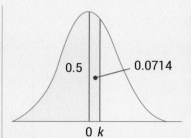

0.5   0.0714

Since the area under the whole curve is 1, the area under half the curve must be 0.5.

Since $P(-k < z < k) = 0.1428$, it follows (because of symmetry) that:

$$P(0 < z < k) = \frac{1}{2}(0.1428) = 0.0714$$

Hence, $P(z < k) = 0.5 + 0.0714 = 0.5714$.

$\therefore z = 0.18$, from the table on pages 36–37 of *Formulae and Tables*.

Exercise 3.6

1. Evaluate the following:

   (i) $P(z \leqslant 1.6)$
   (ii) $P(z > 1.6)$
   (iii) $P(z \geqslant 1.6)$
   (iv) $P(1.2 \leqslant z \leqslant 1.8)$
   (v) $P(1 < z < 2)$
   (vi) $P(1.1 < z < 2.2)$
   (vii) $P(z < -1.2)$

   (viii) $P(-1.5 \leqslant z \leqslant 1.8)$
   (ix) $P(-1.2 < z < 2.2)$
   (x) $P(-0.3 < z < 0.5)$
   (xi) $P(-0.5 < z < 0.3)$
   (xii) $P(-2.5 < z < 2.5)$
   (xiii) $P(-3 < z < -2)$
   (xiv) $P(-1.2 < z < -1.1)$

   (xv) $P(-1.5 < z < 1.5)$
   (xvi) $P(z \leqslant 1.77)$
   (xvii) $P(z < -2.35)$
   (xviii) $P(-1.12 \leqslant z \leqslant 1.12)$
   (xix) $P(-1.96 < z < 1.96)$
   (xx) $P(-1.645 < z < 1.645)$

2. Find, to the nearest unit, the percentage of a normally distributed population that lies within:

   (i)   One standard deviation of the mean (i.e. $P(-1 < z < 1)$)

   (ii) Two standard deviations of the mean

   (iii) Three standard deviations of the mean

3. Find the values of k in each case, where z has distribution $N(0, 1)$:

   (i) $P(z < k) = 0.9671$

   (ii) $P(z > k) = 0.1788$

   (iii) $P(z < k) = 0.2643$

   (iv) $P(-k < z < k) = 0.5098$

   (v) $P(-k < z < k) = 0.34$

4. If 95% of a normally distributed population lies within x standard deviations of the mean, what is the value of x?

5. A normally distributed population, $N(0, 1)$, is divided into three equal parts by two vertical lines at $z = -k$ and $z = k$.

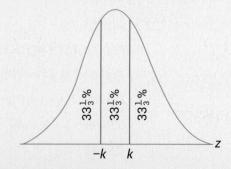

Find the value of k as accurately as the tables allow.

6. Find the value of k if $P(1.1 < z < k) = 0.125$.

7. Find the value of t if $P(-0.51 \leqslant z \leqslant t) = 0.32$.

8. A normally distributed population, $N(0, 1)$, is divided into four quartiles (each containing 25% of the population) by three vertical lines. Find the equations of the lines.

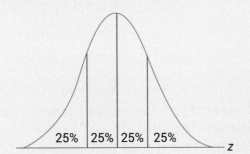

9. A normally distributed population, $N(0, 1)$, is divided into three sections by the lines $z = k$ and $z = t$. The sections contain 20%, 50% and 30% of the population, respectively.

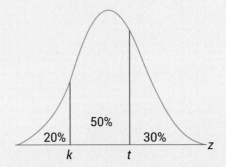

Find the values of k and t, correct to two decimal places.

10. Ninety-nine per cent of a normally distributed population lies within k standard deviations of the mean. Find the value of k correct to two decimal places.

3.10 Solving Problems Involving the Normal Distribution

In this section we will look at real-life situations in which we can find the probabilities of normally distributed variables. If x is normally distributed with mean μ and standard deviation σ, then the formula for converting x to z (which is normally distributed with mean 0 and standard deviation 1) is as given here.

This formula appears on page 34 of *Formulae and Tables*.

$$z = \frac{x - \mu}{\sigma}$$

Worked Example 3.18

The mean total score in Irish Basketball Superleague games is 137 with a standard deviation of 10. If you go to a match, what is the probability that there will be 150 or more points scored by the two teams?

Solution

Let x be the number of points scored. The question asks: 'What is $P(x \geqslant 150)$?'

To solve such problems, use the following steps:

Step 1	Convert the x-values to z-values, using the formula $z = \frac{x - \mu}{\sigma}$.
Step 2	Draw a rough sketch of a normal curve and shade in the desired region.
Step 3	Look up the normal distribution table to find the required probability.

Step 1 In this case, $\mu = 137$ and $\sigma = 10$.

$$P(x \geqslant 150) = P\left(z \geqslant \frac{x - \mu}{\sigma}\right) = P\left(z \geqslant \frac{150 - 137}{10}\right) = P(z \geqslant 1.3)$$

This means that the number 150 is 1.3 standard deviations above the mean.

Step 2 Draw a rough sketch of the normal curve and shade in the desired region.

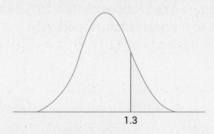

1.3

Step 3 Look up the normal distribution table to find the required probability (as before).

$$P(z \geqslant 1.3) = 1 - P(z < 1.3)$$
$$= 1 - 0.9032$$
$$= 0.0968$$

Worked Example 3.19

The heights of women in Ireland are normally distributed with mean 163 cm and standard deviation 5 cm. A film producer is seeking an Irish actress whose height is between 170 cm and 175 cm. The director says to the producer, 'You are being too fussy. The chance of finding an actress with the right height is less than 5%.' Is this statement correct? Justify your answer.

Solution

Step 1 Let x be the height. In this case, $\mu = 163$ and $\sigma = 5$.

We are asked to find $P(170 \leqslant x \leqslant 175)$. Convert the x-values to z-values using the formula $z = \dfrac{x - \mu}{\sigma}$.

$$P(170 \leqslant x \leqslant 175) = P\left(\frac{170 - 163}{5} \leqslant z \leqslant \frac{175 - 163}{5}\right) = P(1.4 \leqslant z \leqslant 2.4)$$

Step 2 Draw a rough sketch of the normal curve and shade in the desired region.

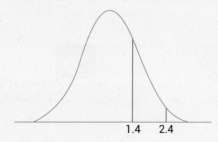

1.4   2.4

Step 3 Look up the normal distribution table to find the required probability.

$$P(1.4 \leqslant z \leqslant 2.4) = P(z \leqslant 2.4) - P(z < 1.4)$$
$$= 0.9918 - 0.9192$$
$$= 0.0726$$
$$= 7.26\%$$
$$> 5\%$$

Therefore, it is not true to say that the chance of finding such an actress is less than 5%.

Exercise 3.7

1. The mean cricket score in a 50-over match is 200, with a standard deviation of 50. Assuming that such scores are normally distributed, what percentage of these scores are greater than 300?

2. (a) X is a random variable that is normally distributed with mean 68 and standard deviation 10. Find:

   (i) $P(X < 80)$ (iii) $P(60 \leqslant X \leqslant 80)$

   (ii) $P(X > 90)$

   (b) If Leaving Certificate Higher Level maths marks are normally distributed with mean 68 and standard deviation 10, what percentage of students will get a mark of 85 or more?

3. The heights of men in Ireland are normally distributed with a mean of 168 cm and a standard deviation of 6 cm. Find the probability that an Irishman selected at random will be greater than 180 cm in height.

4. The weights of people in Ireland are normally distributed with a mean of 68 kg and a standard deviation of 10 kg. If an Irish person, chosen at random, has a weight of x kg, find the probability that:

   (i) $x < 61$ (iii) $60 < x < 61$

   (ii) $63 < x < 73$

PROBABILITY II

5. The life expectancy of a newborn baby in Japan is normally distributed with mean 81 years and standard deviation 8 years. Is the following statement true or false?

   'Less than 1% of Japanese newborn babies will live to be 100.'

6. The number of hours of sleep got by pupils in a school has a distribution $N(9,1)$, i.e. normally distributed with mean 9 and standard deviation 1.

   (i) A pupil is chosen at random in this school. Find the probability that this pupil got more than 10.5 hours of sleep.

   (ii) If there are 350 students in this school, how many would you expect to get between 9.4 and 10.7 hours of sleep?

7. The number of runs scored by the Irish cricket team in Twenty-20 matches is normally distributed with a mean of 157 and a standard deviation of 16. In a match against Bangladesh, the opponents score 168. The Irish team must score 169 or more to win the game.

   (i) What is the probability that Ireland will win?

   (ii) An online bookie is offering odds of 2−1 for an Irish victory at this point. (This means that if you bet €100, you win €200 if Ireland wins.) Is this a good bet? Justify your answer with reference to the expected value.

8. The wages of workers in the motor industry in Ireland are normally distributed with a mean of €38,430 and a standard deviation of €6,400. What percentage of workers in the motor industry in Ireland earn over €50,000? Give your answer to the nearest per cent.

9. The annual number of hours of sunshine in Ireland is normally distributed with a mean of 1,550 hours and a standard deviation of 150 hours. What is the probability that next year there will be:

   (i) Less than 1,300 hours of sunshine in Ireland

   (ii) More than 1,800 hours of sunshine in Ireland

   (iii) Between 1,300 and 1,800 hours of sunshine in Ireland

10. The height of American adult males is normally distributed with mean 177 cm and standard deviation 7.5 cm. What percentage of American adult males are 6 feet or more in height? Give your answer to the nearest per cent. (The following information is given: 1 inch = 2.54 cm; 1 foot = 12 inches.)

11. Every day the maximum air temperature at Athlone is measured. The mean maximum air temperature for Athlone is 9.6 °C with a standard deviation of 8 °C. Assuming that the maximum temperatures are normally distributed:

    (i) Find the probability that the temperature will reach 25 °C or higher on a random day.

    (ii) On how many days of next year would you expect the temperature to reach 25 °C or higher at Athlone? Give your answer to the nearest whole number.

    (iii) A weatherman says that he would expect the temperature at Athlone to break over 30 °C on two days in the year. Is this a reasonably accurate statement?

12. The life span of a light bulb is normally distributed with a mean of 1,020 hours. Find the standard deviation if 12% of the light bulbs have a life span of 1,067 hours or more.

13. The time (in minutes) taken by a group of students to complete a maths test is normally distributed with a mean of 60 and a standard deviation of σ. If 34% of these students took between 51.2 and 68.8 minutes, find the value of σ.

14. The heights of male Gardaí have a normal distribution with a mean of 173 cm and a standard deviation of 2 cm. If the tallest 2.5% of male Gardaí have heights greater than x cm, find the value of x.

15. The table shows the mean scores (and standard deviations from the mean) in Gaelic football, soccer and cricket.

Sport	Gaelic football	Soccer	Cricket
Mean score per team	18 points	2.8 goals	140 runs
Standard deviation	6 points	0.9 goals	47 runs

The captains of the Gaelic football team, the soccer team and the cricket team at Pythagoras College are arguing as to which team is the most prolific at scoring. Seán, the captain of the Gaelic football team, announces that his team scored an average of 25 points. Nigel, the captain of the soccer team, maintains that his team's average score of 3.8 goals per match is better. James, the cricket XI captain, disagrees: his team's average for the season was 191, well above the average for cricket in general.

By calculating the *z*-scores for each team, state which captain is correct in claiming that their team is the most prolific at scoring.

Revision Exercises

PROBABILITY II

1. (a) A fair six-sided die is rolled five times. Find (correct to 3 decimal places) the probability of getting:

   (i) No 6

   (ii) Exactly one 6

   (iii) More than one 6

   (b) A fair six-sided die is rolled over and over until two 6s appear. Find the probability that this will happen on the sixth roll, correct to 3 decimal places.

   (c) E and F are independent events, such that $P(E) = \frac{1}{5}$ and $P(F) = \frac{5}{8}$.

   Find:

   (i) $P(E \cap F)$ (ii) $P(E \cup F)$

2. (a) A random variable *X* follows a normal distribution with mean 20 and standard deviation 5. Find $P(14 \leqslant X \leqslant 26)$.

   (b) There are 25 students in Mr Bounderby's class: 15 girls and 10 boys. Mr Bounderby selects a student at random each day to ring the bell at the end of break. If he does this every day for 10 days, what is the probability that he will select a girl exactly 7 times? Give your answer correct to three decimal places.

3. (a) Explain each of the following terms:

   (i) Sample space

   (ii) Mutually exclusive events

   (iii) Independent events

(b) In a class of 30 students, 20 study Physics, 6 study Biology and 4 study both Physics and Biology.

   (i) Represent the information on the Venn diagram.

   A student is selected at random from this class. The events E and F are:

   E: The student studies Physics.

   F: The student studies Biology.

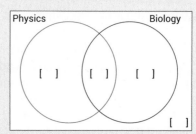

   (ii) By calculating probabilities, investigate if the events E and F are independent.

4. A certain basketball player scores 60% of the free-throw shots she attempts. During a particular game, she gets six free-throws.

   (a) What assumption(s) must be made in order to regard this as a sequence of Bernoulli trials?

   (b) Based on such assumption(s), find, correct to three decimal places, the probability that:

   (i) She scores on exactly four of the six shots.

   (ii) She scores for the second time on the fifth shot.

(vi) The manufacturer of this gaming machine alters the jackpot prize so that the game is perfectly fair (so that the expected value is 'breaking even'). What is the new jackpot prize?

(vii) Sam says, 'Every time you play that slot machine, you are twice as likely to lose as to get any money back.' Is this statement accurate? Explain your answer.

(viii) If you play this game 10 times, what is the probability (to the nearest half per cent) of winning the jackpot exactly once?

10. James says, 'There are six people in the next office. I reckon there is a 50-50 chance that two or more were born in the same month.'

Karen says, 'You are wrong. I will offer you a bet. If the six were all born in different months, you win and I will give you €2. If two or more are born in the same month, I win – but you will have to give me only €1, since I feel confident of winning.'

'You're on,' replies James, 'since that is a good bet for me.'

'No, it's a good bet for me,' says Karen.

(i) Find the probability that all six people are born in different months (assuming that all months are equally likely).

(ii) Find the probability that two or more were born in the same month.

(iii) Who has the better bet, James or Karen? Justify your answer with reference to the expected value.

(iv) There are k people in a room. The probability that they are all born in different months is zero. What is the lowest possible value of k?

11. Paula and Rose enter the school sports competition. They both take part in the 100 m and then the 200 m race. The probabilities that they will win are given in the following table:

	Probability that Paula wins	Probability that Rose wins	Probability that neither wins
100 m	$\frac{1}{2}$	$\frac{3}{8}$	$\frac{1}{8}$
200 m	$\frac{1}{4}$	$\frac{1}{8}$	x

(a) Find the value of x.

(b) Complete this tree diagram.

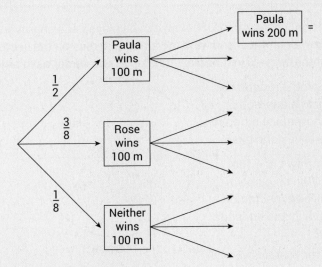

(c) (i) Find the probability that Rose wins both races.

(ii) Find the probability that Paula and Rose win one race each.

12. A €2 coin has diameter 26 mm. It is dropped at random onto lined paper. The lines are 40 mm apart. The task is to calculate the probability that the coin will **not** land on a line. The key is to work out where the **centre** of the €2 coin must land.

(i) Let's say the coin lands between the two lines drawn here. Shade in the area where the **centre** of the coin must land in order that the coin will not land on a line.

(ii) Show that the probability that the coin will not land on a line is 0.35.

(iii) If six €2 coins land on the lined paper at random, find the probability that exactly four of them land on a line, correct to 3 decimal places.

(iv) A €2 coin lands on **squared** paper, the lines of which are 40 mm apart. Show that the probability that the coin will not land on a line is 0.1225.

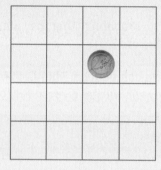

(v) At a funfair, there is a game in which you roll your own €2 coin onto squared paper of sides 40 mm. If your coin lands on a line, you lose it. If it doesn't land on a line, you win €10. Is this a good bet? Justify your answer with reference to expected value.

Exam Questions

1. Two different games of chance, shown below, can be played at a charity fundraiser. In each game, the player spins an arrow on a wheel and wins the amount shown on the sector that the arrow stops in. Each game is fair in that the arrow is just as likely to stop in one sector as in any other sector on that wheel.

(a) John played Game A four times and tells us that he has won a total of €8. In how many different ways could he have done this?

(b) To spin either arrow once, the player pays €3. Which game of chance would you expect to be more successful in raising funds for the charity?

Give a reason for your answer.

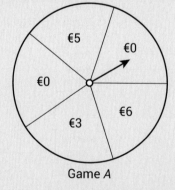

Game A

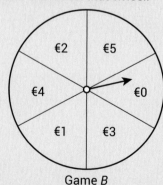

Game B

(c) Mary plays Game B six times. Find the probability that the arrow stops in the €4 sector exactly twice.

SEC Leaving Certificate Higher Level, Paper 2, 2014

2. An experiment consists of throwing two fair, standard, six-sided dice and noting the sum of the two numbers thrown. If the sum is 9 or greater it is recorded as a 'win' (W). If the sum is 8 or less it is recorded as a 'loss' (L).

(a) Complete the table below to show all possible outcomes of the experiment.

		Die 2					
		1	**2**	**3**	**4**	**5**	**6**
Die 1	**1**		L				
	2						
	3						
	4						
	5						W
	6						

(b) (i) Find the probability of a win on one throw of the two dice.

　(ii) Find the probability that each of three successive throws of the two dice results in a loss. Give your answer correct to four decimal places.

(c) The experiment is repeated until a total of three wins occur. Find the probability that the third win occurs on the tenth throw of the two dice. Give your answer correct to four decimal places.

SEC Leaving Certificate Higher Level, Paper 2, 2015

3. Two events A and B are such that P(A) = 0.2, P(A∩B) = 0.15 and P(A'∩B) = 0.6.

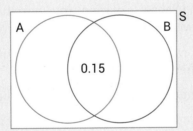

(a) Complete the Venn diagram.

(b) Find the probability that neither A nor B happens.

(c) Find the conditional probability P(A|B).

(d) State whether A and B are independent and justify your answer.

SEC Leaving Certificate Higher Level, Project Maths Paper 2, 2010

4. In basketball, players often have to take free throws. When Michael takes his first free throw in any game, the probability that he is successful is 0.7.

For all subsequent free throws in the game, the probability that he is successful is:

- 0.8 if he has been successful on the previous throw
- 0.6 if he has been unsuccessful on the previous throw

(a) Find the probability that Michael is successful (S) with all three of his first three free throws in a game.

P(S, S, S) =

(b) Find the probability that Michael is unsuccessful (U) with his first two free throws and successful with the third.

P(U, U, S) =

(c) List all the ways that Michael could be successful with his third free throw in a game and hence find the probability that Michael is successful with his third free throw.

(d) (i) Let p_n be the probability that Michael is successful with his nth free throw in the game (and hence $(1 - p_n)$ is the probability that Michael is unsuccessful with his nth free throw). Show that $p_{n+1} = 0.6 + 0.2p_n$.

(ii) Assume that p is Michael's success rate in the long run; that is, for large values of n, we have $p_{n+1} \approx p_n \approx p$.

Using the result from part (d) (i) above, or otherwise, show that $p = 0.75$.

(e) For all positive integers n, let $a_n = p - p_n$, where $p = 0.75$ as above.

(i) Use the ratio $\dfrac{a_{n+1}}{a_n}$ to show that a_n is a geometric sequence with common ratio $\dfrac{1}{5}$.

(ii) Find the smallest value of n for which $p - p_n < 0.00001$.

(f) You arrive at a game in which Michael is playing. You know that he has already taken many free throws, but you do not know what pattern of success he has had.

(i) Based on this knowledge, what is your estimate of the probability that Michael will be successful with his next free throw in the game?

(ii) Why would it **not** be appropriate to consider Michael's subsequent free throws as a sequence of Bernoulli trials?

SEC Leaving Certificate Higher Level, Paper 2, 2015

Solutions and chapter summary available online

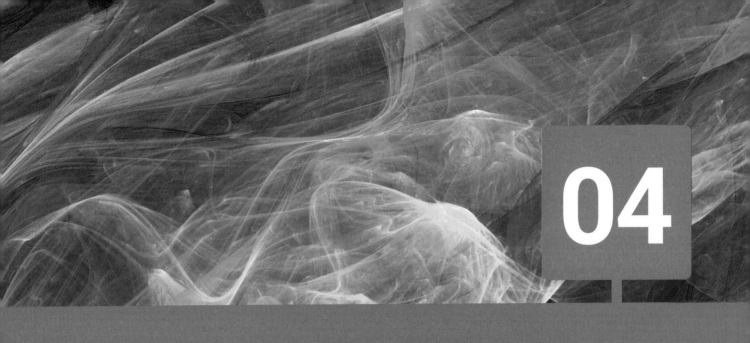

04

Statistics II

In this chapter you will learn to:

- Calculate and use interquartile range and standard deviation as measures of spread
- Analyse plots of data to explain differences in measures of centre and spread
- Recognise the existence and effect of outliers
- Use percentiles to assign relative standing
- Make decisions based on the empirical rule

You should remember...

- How to construct a bar chart, line plot, pie chart, histogram and stem-and-leaf plot
- Measures of centre (mean, mode, median)
- Measures of spread (range, quartiles and inter-quartile range)

Key words

- Mean, median and mode
- Range
- Quartiles and interquartile range
- Standard deviation
- Outliers
- Percentiles
- z-scores
- The normal distribution and the empirical rule

When describing and comparing data sets, **measure of centre**, **measure of spread**, **shape of distribution** and **outliers** are the key characteristics we look for.

A measure of centre, sometimes called an average, is a number that is typical of most numbers in the data set.

A measure of spread, sometimes called a measure of variation (dispersion), measures how spread out the data points are from the centre of the data set.

The shape of a distribution could be (among other things) symmetric, skewed left or skewed right.

Outliers are extreme values that are not typical of the other values within a set.

4.1 Measures of Centre

Measures of centre are sometimes called **measures of location, measures of central tendency** or **averages**. Statisticians use different measures of centre, depending on the type and distribution of the data being analysed. We will look at three measures of centre: the **mean**, the **mode** and the **median**.

The Mean

The mean of a set of values is the sum of all the values divided by the number of values.

The mean uses all values in the data set.

For example, the mean of the set {2, 2, 3, 5, 9, 9} is:

$$\text{Mean} = \frac{2+2+3+5+9+9}{6} = \frac{30}{6} = 5$$

The mean can be used with numerical data.

The Mode

The mode of a data set is the value that has the greatest frequency (occurs the most often).

For example, the mode of the set {2, 2, 2, 3, 3, 3, 3, 5, 5} is 3.

The mode can be used with numerical data, but can also be used with categorical data. For example, the mode of the set {red, red, green} is red.

Sometimes a data set has more than one mode (for example, {1, 1, 2, 2, 3}) or no mode (for example, {2, 3, 5, 6, 11}).

The Median

The median of a set of values is the middle value when the values are arranged in order.

The median is the value that divides an ordered data set into two equal parts.

The first step in finding the median is to arrange the data in order of increasing magnitude. This is called ranking the data. Suppose we want to find the median of the following set:

{4, 7, 11, 9, 12, 10, 8, 11, 14, 2, 6}

Ranking the set gives:

{2, 4, 6, 7, 8, ⑨, 10, 11, 11, 12, 14}

The number in the middle of the ranked set is called the median, which in this case equals 9. There are five values greater than 9 and five values less than 9; therefore 9 has divided the data set into two equal parts.

What happens if the set contains an even number of values?

For example, the set {2, 1, 4, 3} contains an even number of values.

First, ranking the set gives {1, 2, 3, 4}. As there are two middle values, the median is the mean of these two numbers. In this case, we sum the two middle numbers, 2 and 3, and divide our result by 2:

$$\text{Median} = \frac{2+3}{2} = \frac{5}{2} = 2.5$$

Worked Example 4.1

Below are the winning times for the Men's 100 m Final at nine consecutive summer Olympic games.

Year	Venue	Winner	Time (seconds)
1980	Moscow	Allan Wells (GBR)	10.25
1984	Los Angeles	Carl Lewis (USA)	9.99
1988	Seoul	Carl Lewis (USA)	9.92
1992	Barcelona	Linford Christie (GBR)	9.96
1996	Atlanta	Donovan Bailey (CAN)	9.84
2000	Sydney	Maurice Green (USA)	9.87
2004	Athens	Justin Gatlin (USA)	9.85
2008	Beijing	Usain Bolt (JAM)	9.69
2012	London	Usain Bolt (JAM)	9.63

Find, for this data set:

(i) The median

(ii) The mean

Furthermore:

(iii) Explain why the mode is not a useful measure of centre for this data set.

(iv) Is there an outlier value in this data set? If 'yes', what is this outlier value?

Solution

(i) Rank the data set.

9.63, 9.69, 9.84, 9.85, 9.87, 9.92, 9.96, 9.99, 10.25

There is an odd number of data points, so the median is the middle value.

∴ Median = 9.87 seconds

(ii) $\text{Mean} = \dfrac{9.63 + 9.69 + 9.84 + 9.85 + 9.87 + 9.92 + 9.96 + 9.99 + 10.25}{9}$

$= \dfrac{89}{9}$

$= 9.\dot{8}$ seconds (9.89 seconds to two decimal places)

(iii) There is no mode as each data point has the same frequency.

(iv) The value furthest away from the median or the mean is 10.25.

The distance from 10.25 to its nearest data point is 0.26 seconds.

No other data point is so far removed from the rest of the data set.

So 10.25 seconds can be considered an outlier value.

[Note: The USA-led boycott of the 1980 Moscow Games resulted in many of the world's top sprinters not competing. Wells' winning time was the slowest winning time since the 1950s.]

Worked Example 4.2

The stem-and-leaf diagram below displays the predicted high-water tides at the North Wall, Dublin, for 14 consecutive days in April 2015.

Find the median predicted high-water mark at the North Wall during this period.

Stem	Leaf
32	7, 7
33	6, 9
34	9
35	7
36	1
37	0, 3, 7
38	1, 5
39	6
40	1 Key : 33|6 = 3.36 m

Solution

To find the median, cross out the smallest number and the largest number (3.27 and 4.01), then the second largest and the second smallest, and so on until you are left with the two middle numbers. The mean of these two numbers is the median.

32	7̶, 7̶
33	6̶, 9̶
34	9̶
35	7̶
36	①
37	⓪, 3̶, 7̶
38	1̶, 5̶
39	6̶
40	1̶ Key : 33|6 = 3.36 m

$$\text{Median} = \frac{3.61 + 3.70}{2}$$

$$= 3.655 \text{ m}$$

Grouped Frequency Distribution

When working with data in a grouped frequency distribution, we do not know the exact values falling within a particular interval. To make calculations possible, we give all values in a particular interval a value equal to the mid-interval value.

Worked Example 4.3

A group of 82 randomly selected adults have their resting pulse rates measured. The table summarises the results of the survey. All measurements are in beats per minute.

Pulse rate	60–70	70–80	80–90	90–100	100–110	110–120
Frequency	5	8	22	29	13	5

Note: 60–70 means that 60 is included but not 70, and so on.

(i) Estimate the mean of the distribution. Answer correct to the nearest whole number.

(ii) What percentage of the sample had a pulse rate greater than or equal to 90 bpm?

(iii) Describe the shape of the distribution.

Solution

(i) We can see from the table that five people had a pulse rate between 60 and 70 beats per minute. However, the table does not tell us the exact pulse rates of each person. In order to estimate the mean resting pulse rate, each person has to be assigned a resting pulse rate. We choose the mid-interval rates as the rate for each interval.

To calculate the mid-interval value (M.I.V.) for an interval, calculate the mean of the two boundary values. For the 60–70 interval, the M.I.V. is $\frac{60 + 70}{2} = 65$.

The grouped frequency table is rewritten as:

M.I.V.	65	75	85	95	105	115
Frequency	5	8	22	29	13	5

$$\text{Mean} = \frac{(65)(5) + (75)(8) + (85)(22) + (95)(29) + (105)(13) + (115)(5)}{5 + 8 + 22 + 29 + 13 + 5}$$

$$= \frac{7,490}{82}$$

≈ 91 beats per minute

This answer is correct to the nearest beat per minute.

(ii) $29 + 13 + 5 = 47$

$\therefore$ Percentage $= \dfrac{47}{82} \times 100$

$= 57.32\%$ (correct to two decimal places)

(iii) There are six intervals of equal width.

The first three intervals contain $5 + 8 + 22 = 35$ data points.

The second three intervals contain $82 - 35 = 47$ data points.

The distribution is (slightly) skewed left.

Exercise 4.1

1. Find the mean and the median of these sets of numbers:

    (i) {67.2, 82.5, 66.7, 93.0, 82.6, 75.4, 73.6, 81.4, 99.4, 67.7}

    (ii) {41.6, 42.8, 39.0, 40.2, 36.2, 43.2, 38.7, 41.0, 43.8, 37.3}

    (iii) {6.0, 6.7, 5.7, 6.2, 5.5, 6.0, 5.7, 6.8, 7.8, 6.6}

    (iv) {23.6, 26.3, 26.3, 32.6, 29.2, 26.4, 27.9, 33.0, 38.6}

    (v) {98, 99, 97, 95, 98, 98, 98}

2. The stem-and-leaf plot below records the weights (in grams) of a sample of plums.

    (i) How many plums were in the sample?

    (ii) Calculate the mean plum weight.

    (iii) Calculate the median plum weight.

    (iv) What do you notice about your answers to (ii) and (iii)?

    (v) Describe the shape of the distribution.

    (vi) Does the distribution have a unique mode?

```
2 | 6
3 | 1, 3, 4
3 | 6, 6, 8, 8, 9
4 | 2, 2, 2, 3, 4, 4, 4, 4
4 | 5, 5, 5, 6, 6, 7, 7, 7, 7, 9
5 | 0, 1, 2, 2
5 | 6, 7, 8
6 | 1                    Key: 4|5 = 45 g
```

3. The table below shows average monthly sea temperatures, in degrees Celsius, at Malin Head, Co. Donegal, for the year 2009. Average monthly readings for the period 1961–1990 are also given.

Year/month	2009	1961–1990
January	7.3	7.3
February	6.9	6.7
March	7.6	7
April	8.8	8.1
May	10.4	9.9
June	12.4	12
July	14.3	13.8
August	15.3	14.6
September	14.4	14
October	13.6	12.4
November	11.1	10.2
December	8.8	8.5

(i) Using the monthly averages, estimate the mean annual sea temperature at Malin Head for 2009. (Give your answer correct to two decimal places.)

(ii) Using the monthly averages, estimate the mean annual sea temperature at Malin Head for the period 1961 to 1990. Comment on the difference between the 2009 figure and the 1961–1990 figure. (Give your answer correct to two decimal places.)

(iii) Is the comparison made in part (ii) a fair comparison? Explain.

Source: www.met.ie/marine/marine_climatology.asp

4. The table below shows the mean 10 cm soil temperature at Met Éireann's Dublin Airport weather station for each month in 2014. Mean monthly readings for the period 1981–2010 are also shown. All temperatures are in degrees Celsius.

Year	Jan	Feb	Mar	Apr	May	Jun	Jul	Aug	Sep	Oct	Nov	Dec
2014	4.4	4.8	6.7	10.7	13.1	17.6	18.8	15.3	15.2	11.2	7.9	4.8
1981–2010	4.1	4.1	5.5	7.9	11.5	14.6	16.2	15.4	13.0	9.7	6.6	4.8

(i) Using the monthly averages, estimate the mean annual 10 cm soil temperature at Dublin Airport for 2014. Answer correct to two decimal places.

(ii) Met Éireann calculated the actual mean annual 10 cm soil temperature at Dublin Airport for 2014 to be 10.9 °C. Calculate the percentage error in your answer to part (i).

Answer correct to two significant figures.

(iii) Using the monthly averages for 1981–2010, estimate the mean annual 10 cm soil temperature at Dublin Airport for this period.

Answer correct to two decimal places.

(iv) Make a comparison of your answers to parts (i) and (iii). What conclusions, if any, can you draw?

5. The table below gives the number of vehicles registered in Ireland for the first time. The table covers the period 2000–2009.

Number of vehicles registered for the first time, by year					
Year	2000	2001	2002	2003	2004
Number of new cars	225,269	160,908	150,485	142,992	149,635
Year	2005	2006	2007	2008	2009
Number of new cars	166,270	173,273	180,754	146,470	54,432

Source: www.cso.ie

(i) In what year was the highest number of vehicles registered?

(ii) In what year was the lowest number of vehicles registered?

(iii) What was the mean number of vehicles registered for the first time during these 10 years?

(iv) What was the median number of vehicles registered for the first time during these 10 years?

(v) There was a notable decline in first-time registered vehicles towards the end of this ten-year period. Give one possible reason for this decline.

6. The following frequency distribution shows the time (in minutes) taken by a group of people to complete a five-mile run.

Time (min)	30–35	35–40	40–45	45–50	50–55
Frequency	10	6	22	29	7

Note: 30–35 means 30 is included but 35 is not, etc.

(i) Using mid-interval values, calculate the mean finishing time.

(ii) What is the maximum number of people who could have completed the run in less than 37 minutes?

7. The frequency distribution shows the ages of people living in a street.

Age (years)	0–20	20–30	30–50	50–80
Frequency	24	16	41	15

Note: 0–20 means 0 is included but 20 is not, etc.

(i) How many people are living on the street?

(ii) Estimate the mean age.

(iii) What percentage of the people are less than 20 years old?

8. The number of hours per day that the secretary of a construction firm spends on the phone is recorded. The following data shows the number of hours per day over a 30-day period.

4.21	1.12	0.33	1.1	3.3	3.2	5.2	1.5	3.1	0.5
1.22	2.51	0.8	0.7	1.8	5.9	1.2	2.5	5.2	1.6
4	1.4	0.9	2.8	5	0.2	1.9	2.3	1.79	4

(i) Is this data discrete or continuous? Explain.

(ii) Complete the frequency table below.

Hours	0–1	1–2	2–3	3–4	4–5	5–6
Tally						
No. of days						

Note: 0–1 means 0 is included but 1 is not, etc.

(iii) Draw a histogram of the distribution.

(iv) Describe the shape of the distribution.

(v) Rank the raw data and calculate the median time.

(vi) Using mid-interval values, estimate the mean of the distribution.

(vii) Now using the raw data, calculate the mean.

(viii) What is the percentage error in the estimated mean?

9. The heights of a random sample of 1,000 women are given in the frequency distribution below.

Height (cm)	140–145	145–150	150–155	155–160	160–165	165–170	170–175	175–180
Frequency	9	65	177	325	253	133	31	7

Note: 140–145 means that 140 is included but 145 is not, etc.

(i) Estimate the mean height.

(ii) Construct a histogram to represent the data.

(iii) Describe the shape of the distribution.

10. The following are the daily maximum temperatures in Dubai for the month of June (in degrees Celsius).

29.2	29.4	34.1	36.3	36.5	32.1	32.0	35.7	35.6	34.9
36.2	32.3	32.6	36.5	33.8	32.1	32.2	38.8	36.5	35.7
31.1	33.9	34.7	34.3	37.3	40.9	33.8	32.2	40.9	34.2

(i) Is this data discrete or continuous? Explain.

(ii) Complete the frequency table below.

Temperature	29–31	31–33	33–35	35–37	37–39	39–41
Tally						
No. of days						

Note: 29–31 means that 29 is included but 31 is not, etc.

(iii) Draw a histogram of the distribution.

(iv) Describe the distribution.

(v) Rank the raw data and find the median.

(vi) Using mid-interval values, estimate the mean of the distribution.

(vii) Now using the raw data, calculate the mean.

(viii) What is the percentage error in the estimated mean?

4.2 Deciding Which Average to Use

The mean, median and mode of a set of data are all averages, but each one has a different meaning. The average, or measure of central tendency, that we choose depends on the characteristics of the data set we are studying.

Worked Example 4.4

Eight Premier League professional soccer players are selected at random. They are asked the following question: 'What is the most money any club has paid in transfer fees for you?' This is the data generated by the question. All amounts are in pounds sterling.

£3 million   £80 million   £5.8 million   £18.25 million

£3.5 million £3.7 million £8 million   £7 million

(i) Find the mean transfer fee for the sample (correct to two decimal places).

(ii) Find the median transfer fee.

(iii) Which of the above averages is the more typical of transfer fees?

Solution

(i) Mean $= \dfrac{3 + 80 + 5.8 + 18.25 + 3.5 + 3.7 + 8 + 7}{8}$

$= \dfrac{129.25}{8} \approx$ £16.16 million

(ii) Rank the data: {3, 3.5, 3.7, 5.8, 7, 8, 18.25, 80}

Median $= \dfrac{5.8 + 7}{2} =$ £6.4 million

(iii) The median is the more typical. Four players' fees are less than the median and four are above. On the other hand, six players' fees are less than the mean and only two are above. The high outlier value of £80 million has dragged the mean above the median.

The following table will help you decide when to use the mean, the median or the mode.

Average	When to use	Advantages/Disadvantages
Mode	• If data is **categorical**, then the mode is the only sensible measure of centre to use. Therefore, for data on hair colour, eye colour, gender, etc., use only the mode. • The mode can also be used with **numerical** data.	*Advantages* • It can be used with any type of data. • It is easy to find. • It is not affected by extreme values. *Disadvantages* • There is not always a mode, or there are several modes. • For sets of numerical data, the mode can be very different to the mean or median.
Median	• Used **only** with **numerical** data. • If there are **outliers** in the data set, or if the distribution is **skewed**, then use the median.	*Advantages* • It is easy to calculate. • It is not affected by outliers or skews.
Mean	• Used **only** with **numerical** data. • If there are **no outliers** and the distribution is **not skewed**, then use the mean.	*Advantage* • It uses all the data. *Disadvantage* • It is affected by outliers and skews.

Exercise 4.2

1. Decide which average you would use for each of the following. Give a reason for your answer.

   (i) The average height of students in your class

   (ii) The average eye colour of all teachers in the school

   (iii) The average mark in a maths exam

STATISTICS II

(iv) The average colour of all cars in the school car park

(v) The average wage of 100 workers in a company, given that 90 of the workers earn between €30,000 and €40,000 per annum, five workers earn between €60,000 and €80,000, and the remaining five workers earn over €600,000 per annum

2. Write down the type of average in each case:

(i) This average uses all values of the data.

(ii) This average is used with categorical data.

(iii) This average is useful with data that contains extreme values or for data that is skewed.

3. Find the mean and the median of the following set of numbers:

{1, 2, 12, 12, 18, 19, 20, 24, 188}

Which average would you use to describe these numbers? Give a reason for your answer.

4. Below is some data selected at random from the CensusAtSchool database. The data gives the different modes of transport the group uses to go to school.

Walk	Bus	Walk	Walk	Walk
Bus	Walk	Car	Car	Bus
Walk	Bus	Car	Walk	Walk
Car	Rail	Bus	Walk	Rail

(i) What type of data is contained in this sample?

(ii) What average are you using when you refer to the most popular mode of transport used by these students?

5. Rex has just been given the result of his last maths test. He does not know the results his classmates received, but would like to know how his result compares with those of his friends. The teacher has given the class the modal mark, the mean mark and the median mark for the test.

(i) Which average tells Rex whether he is in the top half or the bottom half of the class?

(ii) Is the modal mark useful to Rex? Explain.

(iii) Which average tells Rex how well he has done in comparison to everyone else?

6. The chart below shows the distribution of disposable household income for Ireland in 2011.

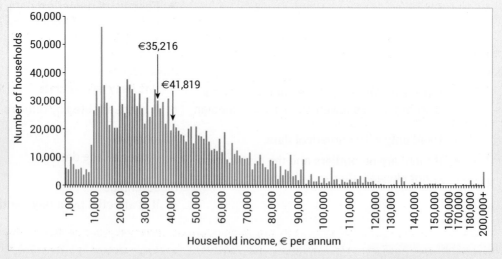

Source: Nevin Economic Research Institute

(i) Describe the shape of the distribution.

(ii) Two averages have been highlighted (€35,216 and €41,819).

Which figure refers to the mean value and which figure refers to the median value?

(iii) Give an example of a data set that would have a strong negative skew.

7. Here are some statistics on the heights of a group of famous Irish people. The group is:

Brian O'Driscoll   Cillian Murphy

Sonia O'Sullivan   Colin Farrell

Henry Shefflin   Liam Neeson

Rory McIlroy   Derval O'Rourke

Using only the information given below, find the height of each person in the group.

(a) Mode = 178 cm

(b) Mean = 178.375 cm

(c) Range = 25 cm (The range is the difference between the tallest and the shortest person.)

(d) Henry Shefflin is 14 cm taller than Rory McIlroy.

(e) Sonia O'Sullivan is 5 cm shorter than the modal height.

(f) Liam Neeson is the tallest person in the group. He has a height of 193 cm.

(g) Cillian Murphy is 1 cm taller than Rory McIlroy.

(h) Derval O'Rourke is the shortest person in the group.

(i) Brian O'Driscoll and Colin Farrell have the same height.

4.3 Measures of Variation

Variation 1: Range and Interquartile Range

Measures of centre supply us with one number to describe a set of data. However, such numbers give no indication of data variation or data spread (dispersion).

Consider the sets A = {8, 8, 9, 11, 14} and B = {1, 3, 8, 17, 21}.

- The mean of set A = $\dfrac{8 + 8 + 9 + 11 + 14}{5} = \dfrac{50}{5} = 10$.

- The mean of set B = $\dfrac{1 + 3 + 8 + 17 + 21}{5} = \dfrac{50}{5} = 10$.

Both sets have the same mean, but the members of set A are more tightly bunched around the mean than the members of set B. To measure the spread of values, we could use the **range**.

> The range of a set of data is the difference between the maximum value and the minimum value in the data set.
>
> Range = Maximum value − Minimum value

Range$_A$ = 14 − 8 = 6   Range$_B$ = 21 − 1 = 20

This indicates that the elements of set B have a greater spread of values.

Quartiles and the Interquartile Range

Quartiles divide a data set into four parts. There are three quartiles: the lower quartile, the median and the upper quartile. The **interquartile range** is the difference between the first, or lower, quartile (Q_1) and the third, or upper, quartile (Q_3). The interquartile range (or IQR) is more reliable than the range as a measure of spread, as it is not affected by extreme values (outliers). The IQR tells us how spread out the middle 50% of the data are.

> Q_1, the lower quartile of a ranked set of data, is a value such that one-quarter of the values are less than or equal to it. Q_2, the second quartile, is the median of the data.
>
> Q_3, the upper quartile of a ranked set of data, is a value such that three-quarters of the values are less than or equal to it.

Different acceptable methods exist for finding the interquartile range (IQR). Depending on the method used, answers may vary slightly. Two different methods for finding the interquartile range of the data set $\{7, 5, 1, 27, 2, 6, 19, 9, 12, 18, 15\}$ are outlined below.

Interquartile range = $Q_3 - Q_1$

Method 1

Step 1

Rank the data.

$\{1, 2, 5, 6, 7, 9, 12, 15, 18, 19, 27\}$

Step 2

Find the median of the data set.

$\{\cancel{1}, \cancel{2}, \cancel{5}, \cancel{6}, \cancel{7}, ⑨\ \cancel{12}, \cancel{15}, \cancel{18}, \cancel{19}, \cancel{27}\}$

Median = 9

Step 3

Find the median of the set $\{\cancel{1}, \cancel{2}, 5, \cancel{6}, \cancel{7}\}$.
[Set of numbers below the median in the original data set]

$Q_1 = 5$ (Lower quartile)

Find the median of the set $\{\cancel{12}, \cancel{15}, 18, \cancel{19}, \cancel{27}\}$.
[Set of numbers above the median in the original data set]

$Q_3 = 18$ (Upper quartile)

Step 4

Subtract Q_1 from Q_3 to find the interquartile range.

IQR = 18 – 5

= 13

Method 2

Step 1

Rank the data.

$\{1, 2, 5, 6, 7, 9, 12, 15, 18, 19, 27\}$

Step 2

Count the number of data points in the set. There are 11 data points in the set.

Step 3

Find $\frac{1}{4}$ of 11, which is 2.75. As this is not a whole number, round up to the nearest whole number (always round up), which is 3. The third value in the data set is Q_1, the lower quartile.

$Q_1 = 5$

Step 4

Find $\frac{3}{4}$ of 11, which is 8.25. Round up to the nearest whole number, which is 9. The ninth value in the data set is Q_3, the upper quartile.

$Q_3 = 18$

Step 5

Subtract Q_1 from Q_3 to find the interquartile range.

IQR = 18 – 5

= 13

Worked Example 4.5

As part of a laboratory experiment, 18 rats are weighed. Their weights (in grams) are given in the table below.

148	163	190	176	186	176
188	164	176	167	181	149
165	158	176	200	170	195

(i) Display the data on a stem-and-leaf plot.

(ii) Find Q_1, the lower quartile.

(iii) Find Q_2, the median.

(iv) Find Q_3, the upper quartile.

(v) Calculate the interquartile range.

Solution

(i)

14	8, 9
15	8
16	3, 4, 5, 7
17	0, 6, 6, 6, 6
18	1, 6, 8
19	0, 5
20	0

Key: 17|0 = 170 g

(ii) **Step 1**

Count the number of leaves in the stem-and-leaf plot. There are 18 leaves in total.

Step 2

Find $\frac{1}{4}$ of 18, which is 4.5. As this is not a whole number, we round up to the nearest whole number (always round up), which is 5. The fifth value in the plot is Q_1, the lower quartile.

$Q_1 = 164$ g

(iii) Find $\frac{1}{2}$ of 18 which is 9, a whole number. In this case the median lies between the 9th and 10th values.

$$Q_2 = \frac{176 + 176}{2}$$

$$= 176 \text{ g}$$

(iv) Find $\frac{3}{4}$ of 18 which is 13.5. Round up to 14, the next whole number. The 14th value in the plot is Q_3, the upper quartile.

$Q_3 = 186$ g

(v) The interquartile range is

$Q_3 - Q_1 = 186 - 164 = 22$ g.

Alternative Solution (parts (ii) – (iv))

(ii) **Step 1**

Find the median of the data set.

14	8, 9
15	8
16	3, 4, 5, 7
17	0, 6, 6, 6, 6
18	1, 6, 8
19	0, 5
20	0

Median $= \dfrac{176 + 176}{2}$

$= 176$

Key: 17|0 = 170 g

Step 2

Find the median of the set of numbers below the median of the original data set.

{148, 149, 158, 163, (164) 165, 167, 170, 176}

$Q_1 = 164$ g

(iii) Median = 176 g (from part ii)

(iv) Find the median of the set of numbers above the median of the original data set.

{176, 176, 176, 181, (186) 188, 190, 195, 200}

$Q_3 = 186$ g

Exercise 4.3

1. Find the lower quartile (Q_1), the upper quartile (Q_3) and the interquartile range (IQR) for the following sets:

   (i) {2, 5, 7, 3, 3, 2, 8}

   (ii) {5, 8, 6, 4, 5, 3, 4, 12}

   (iii) {8, 7, 6, 5, 4, 3, 2, 1}

   (iv) {8, 7, 8, 7, 6, 5, 6, 5, 4, 3, 4, 3}

   (v) {−3, −2, −1, 0, 1, 2, 3}

   (vi) {1, 2, −3, 8, 7, −5, −2}

2. Consider the following set:

   A = {139, 131, 136, 141, 121, 126, 121, 131, 131, 145, 143, 141, 130, 150}

   (i) Display the data on a stem-and-leaf diagram.

   (ii) Find the lower quartile and the upper quartile for the set.

   (iii) What percentage of values lies between the lower quartile and the upper quartile?

   (iv) Find the interquartile range.

3. The stem-and-leaf plot gives the ages of 31 people attending a meeting about a government proposal not to grant medical cards to all people over the age of 70.

5	1, 4, 4, 4
5	5, 9, 9, 9, 9
6	3, 3, 3, 4, 5
6	6, 6, 7, 7, 8, 8, 9
7	1, 1, 2, 3, 3, 3, 3, 3, 4
7	5 Key: 6|6 = 66 years

(i) Find Q_1, the lower quartile.

(ii) Find Q_3, the upper quartile.

(iii) Calculate the interquartile range.

(iv) Describe the shape of the distribution.

(v) Explain the shape of the distribution in the context of this question.

4. The following data indicates the electricity consumption (in kilowatt-hours) for 20 typical two-bedroom apartments in Dublin.

9	11	16	10	11	9	8	13	11	9
13	11	7	9	7	12	14	13	11	7

(i) Draw a stem-and-leaf diagram to illustrate the data.

(ii) Describe the shape of the distribution.

(iii) Find the range.

(iv) Find the median.

(v) Find the interquartile range.

5. The data below gives the diameter (in inches) at 54 inches above the ground for a sample of 30 black cherry trees in the Allegheny National Forest, Pennsylvania.

(i) Use a suitable diagram to represent this data.

(ii) Describe the shape of the distribution.

(iii) Find the range.

(iv) Find the median.

(v) Find the interquartile range.

8.3	10.8	11.4	12.9	14.2	17.5
8.6	11.0	11.4	13.3	14.5	17.9
8.8	11.1	11.7	13.7	16.0	18.0
10.5	11.2	12.0	13.8	16.3	18.0
10.7	11.3	12.9	14.0	17.3	20.6

6. The percentage of silica was calculated in each of 22 meteorites. The data is displayed below.

20.77 22.56 22.71 22.99 26.39 27.08 27.32 27.33 27.57 27.81 28.69
29.36 30.25 31.89 32.88 33.23 33.28 33.40 33.52 33.83 33.95 34.82

(a) Provide the following summary statistics:

(i) The mean

(ii) The median

(iii) The minimum value

(iv) The maximum value

(v) The range

(vi) The interquartile range

(b) (i) What is the difference between the mean and the median for the data set given above?

(ii) What does this difference tell us about the shape of the distribution?

7. The data gives sets of salinity values (parts per thousand) for three separate water masses in the Bimini Lagoon, the Bahamas.

Area 1	Area 2	Area 3
37.54	40.17	39.04
37.01	40.80	39.21
36.71	39.76	39.05
37.03	39.70	38.24
37.32	40.79	38.53
37.01	40.44	38.71
37.03	39.79	38.89
37.70	39.38	38.66
37.36		38.51
36.75		40.08
37.45		
38.85		

Copy and complete the following table:

	Area 1	Area 2	Area 3
Mean			
Minimum			
Q_1			
Median			
Q_3			
Maximum			
IQR			
Range			

Variation II: Standard Deviation

Standard deviation measures the average deviation or spread from the mean of all values in a set. It is a reliable measure of spread, as it takes account of all values in the set, unlike the range or interquartile range. However, if there are extreme values in the data set, it is best to use the interquartile range as a measure of spread.

Standard deviation

$$\sigma = \sqrt{\frac{\Sigma(x - \mu)^2}{n}}$$

σ is the standard deviation.

Σ means 'sum of'.

x is the variable.

μ is the mean (for a population).

n is the number of variables.

Σ This symbol means 'sum of'.

$$\sum_{r=1}^{3} r = 1 + 2 + 3 = 6$$

$$\sum_{r=1}^{4} (r - 1)^2 = (1 - 1)^2 + (2 - 1)^2 + (3 - 1)^2 + (4 - 1)^2 = 14$$

Worked Example 4.6

Set A = {8, 8, 9, 11, 14} and set B = {1, 5, 9, 14, 21}.

(i) Show that A and B have the same mean.

(ii) Find the range of A and the range of B.

(iii) Comment on the range as a measure of spread in the context of this question.

(iv) Why is the standard deviation a better measure of spread than the range?

(v) Calculate the standard deviation from the mean of both sets.

Solution

(i) The mean of set A, $\mu_A = \dfrac{8 + 8 + 9 + 11 + 14}{5} = \dfrac{50}{5} = 10$.

The mean of set B, $\mu_B = \dfrac{1 + 5 + 9 + 14 + 21}{5} = \dfrac{50}{5} = 10$.

(ii) $\text{Range}_A = 14 - 8 = 6$ $\text{Range}_B = 21 - 1 = 20$

(iii) The range indicates that set B has a greater spread than set A. However, as a measure of spread, it is limited to just two values in the set, the maximum value and the minimum value. If an outlier or extreme value exists in the data, then this will distort the true measure of spread.

(iv) The standard deviation uses all values in the set to calculate the spread and is therefore a much better measure. The standard deviation is a measure of the average spread of the data from the mean.

(v) We can calculate the standard deviation using the formula $\sigma = \sqrt{\dfrac{\Sigma(x - \mu)^2}{n}}$.

The work can be summarised in the following tables:

Set A			
x	μ	d	d^2
8	10	−2	4
8	10	−2	4
9	10	−1	1
11	10	1	1
14	10	4	16
			26

Set B			
x	μ	d	d^2
1	10	−9	81
5	10	−5	25
9	10	−1	1
14	10	4	16
21	10	11	121
			244

Note: $d = x - \mu$

$\sigma_A = \sqrt{\dfrac{26}{5}}$ $\sigma_B = \sqrt{\dfrac{244}{5}}$

$\sigma_A = \sqrt{5.2}$ $\sigma_B = \sqrt{48.8}$

$\sigma_A \approx 2.28$ $\sigma_B \approx 6.99$

The statistics functions on your calculator can also be used to find standard deviation. Here are the keystrokes for finding σ_A in the example above.

Individual calculators may differ and it is important that you know how to calculate the standard deviation on your own calculator.

STATISTICS II

Exercise 4.4

1. Examine the data sets A and B. Without doing any calculations, decide which set has the larger standard deviation. Then check by calculating the standard deviation.

   (i)   A = {11, 13, 15, 17, 19}   B = {10, 12, 14, 16, 18}

   (ii) A = {11, 15, 16, 17, 21}   B = {16, 20, 21, 22, 26}

   (iii) A = {500, 600, 700, 800}   B = {50, 60, 70, 80}

   (iv) A = {2, 5, 8, 9}   B = {22, 25, 28, 29}

   (v)   A = {9, 13, 14, 15, 19}   B = {14, 18, 19, 20, 24}

   (vi) A = {x, x + 1, x + 2, x + 3}   B = {x + 10, x + 11, x + 12, x + 13}

   (vii) A = {x + 2, x + 5, x + 8, x + 9}   B = {x + 22, x + 25, x + 28, x + 29}

2. Statisticians sometimes estimate the population standard deviation using $\sigma = \dfrac{\text{Range}}{4}$.

   Using the rough estimate $\sigma = \dfrac{\text{Range}}{4}$ rather than the formula $\sigma = \sqrt{\dfrac{\Sigma(x - \mu)^2}{n}}$, calculate the percentage error on set A = {98.6, 98.6, 98.0, 99.0, 98.4, 98.4, 98.4}.

3. The table below shows the prices on 1 August 2010 of a sample of Sunday newspapers.

Newspaper	Price (€)	Newspaper	Price (€)	Newspaper	Price (€)
Sunday Independent	2.50	Independent on Sunday	1.80	Observer	2.30
Sunday World	2.30	Sunday People	1.30	Sunday Express	1.40
Sunday Tribune	2.50	Sunday Mirror	1.30	Sunday Telegraph	2.90
Sunday Business Post	2.50	Irish Mail on Sunday	1.50	Sunday Times	2.50
Star on Sunday	2.10	News of the World	1.40	Sunday Racing Post	2.50

   (a) Provide the following summary statistics for the prices of the Sunday newspapers shown in the table:

      (i)   Count (i.e. the number of newspapers in the sample)

      (ii) Minimum price

      (iii) Maximum price

      (iv) Mean price

      (v)   Standard deviation from the mean

   (b) For most data sets, it is unusual to have a data value more than two standard deviations away from the mean. Comment in the context of this question.

4. The gross national product (GNP) is the value of all income accruing to domestic residents of a country in a year. The table gives Ireland's GNP (in €m) for the period 2011–2014.

Year	2011	2012	2013	2014
GNP	141,813	143,331	152,042	162,877

Source: www.cso.ie

(i) Calculate the mean and the standard deviation for the data.

(ii) Why would an economist be interested in the standard deviation from the mean?

(iii) In what year was the maximum value of GNP?

(iv) In what year was the minimum value of GNP?

(v) In your opinion, how did the economy perform over this period? Explain your answer.

5. A group of medical students measure the blood pressure of the same person. The systolic readings (in mmHg) are given below.

$$139 \quad 131 \quad 136 \quad 141 \quad 121 \quad 126 \quad 121$$
$$131 \quad 131 \quad 145 \quad 143 \quad 141 \quad 130 \quad 160$$

(i) Give two possible reasons why there is variation in the readings.

(ii) Plot the data on a stem-and-leaf diagram.

(iii) Circle the outlier in the data. Give a possible reason for the outlier in this data.

(iv) Describe the shape of the distribution.

(v) Calculate the mean and the standard deviation of the distribution.

(vi) If a group of qualified doctors had taken the readings, would you expect the standard deviation to be greater or less? Explain your answer.

6. Twenty students are asked how many minutes they spent watching television on a particular day. The following frequency distribution summarises their replies.

Time (min)	0–40	40–60	60–80	80–100	100–120
Frequency	2	6	5	3	4

Note: 0–40 means 0 is included but 40 is not, etc.

(i) Estimate the mean time spent watching television by the group.

(ii) Estimate to the nearest minute the standard deviation from the mean.

7. The frequency distribution shows the ages of 100 people.

Age	0–10	10–20	20–30	30–50	50–80
Frequency	10	19	25	30	16

Note: 0–10 means 0 is included but 10 is not, etc.

(i) Estimate the mean age.

(ii) Estimate to the nearest integer the standard deviation from the mean.

8. A garage owner recorded the amount of money spent by customers on petrol over a day. The frequency distribution shows the results.

Amount (€)	0–10	10–20	20–30	30–50	50–100
Frequency	50	150	400	300	100

Note: 0–10 means 0 is included but 10 is not, etc.

(i) Estimate the mean amount spent.

(ii) Estimate to the nearest euro the standard deviation from the mean.

9. The heights (in centimetres) of 140 plants are measured and recorded in the table below.

Height	55–60	60–65	65–70	70–75	75–80	80–85	85–90
Frequency	1	11	37	54	28	8	1

Note: 55–60 means 55 is included and 60 is not, etc.

(i) Using mid-interval values, estimate the mean height of the plants.

(ii) Estimate the standard deviation from the mean.

10. Weights (in grams) of samples of the contents in cans of regular Coke and Diet Coke are given below.

Regular Coke				
370	371	369	371	363
362	369	367	367	365

Diet Coke				
352	352	349	354	353
352	350	354	357	351

(i) Complete the grouped frequencies for the data.

Regular Coke			
Weight (g)	360–365	365–370	370–375
Frequency			

Note: 360–365 means 360 is included but 365 is not, etc.

Diet Coke			
Weight (g)	345–350	350–355	355–360
Frequency			

Note: 345–350 means 345 is included but 350 is not, etc.

(ii) Display the grouped frequency distributions on two histograms.

(iii) Using only evidence from your histograms, state which set has the greater standard deviation.

(iv) Confirm your answer to part (iii) by calculating the standard deviation for both distributions.

4.4 Measures of Relative Standing

In this section we will introduce measures that can be used to compare values within a data set or to compare values from different data sets. These measures are known as **measures of relative standing**. You have already met with some measures of relative standing (e.g. the lower quartile, the median and the upper quartile). The other measures of relative standing you will study are percentiles and z-scores.

Percentiles

Generally speaking, when we take tests we are more interested in how we compare to everybody else (our relative standing) than in our actual score on the test. The most common way to report relative standing is by using **percentiles**.

> The values that divide a data set into 100 equal parts are called **percentiles**.

There are 99 percentiles in a data set. Usually, percentiles are denoted by $P_1, P_2, P_3, \ldots, P_{99}$.

A percentile is not a score. Suppose your score on a particular test is reported to be the 75th percentile. This does not mean you have scored 75% in the test. It means that 75% of the students' scores were lower than yours.

- The median is the 50th percentile.
- The lower quartile is the 25th percentile.
- The upper quartile is the 75th percentile.

Calculating P_k – the kth percentile

Step 1 Rank the data.

Step 2 Find the number c, which is $k\%$ of the total number of numbers in the set.

$$c = \frac{k}{100} \times n$$

where n = number of numbers in the set and k = the required percentile.

Step 3 (a) If c **is** a whole number, find the mean of the values in the c and $(c + 1)$ positions in the ordered set. This mean value will be the required percentile.

Step 3 (b) If c is **not** a whole number, round up to the next whole number. Locate this position in the ordered set. The value in this location is the required percentile.

Note: This is an extension of a method for calculating quartiles described earlier in the text.

- If c is a whole number:

$$P_k = \frac{c\text{th value} + (c + 1)\text{th value}}{2}$$

- If c is not a whole number, then round up to d, the smallest whole number greater than c.

$$P_k = d\text{th value}$$

where P_k is the kth percentile.

Worked Example 4.7

Find (i) P_{30} and (ii) P_{80} for the following data set:

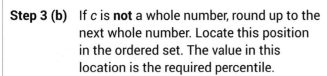
{98, 92, 95, 87, 96, 90, 65, 92, 95, 93, 98, 94, 98, 95, 96}

Solution

(i) To find P_{30}:

Step 1 Rank the data.

65, 87, 90, 92, 92, 93, 94, 95, 95, 95, 96, 96, 98, 98, 98 (There are 15 data entries.)

Step 2 Find c, 30% of 15.

$$c = \frac{30}{100} \times 15 = 4.5$$

Step 3 4.5 is not a whole number, so we round up to 5.

$$P_{30} = 5\text{th value} = 92$$

(ii) To find P_{80}: (**Step 1**, ranking the data, has been done in part (i))

Step 2 Find c, 80% of 15.

$$c = \frac{80}{100} \times 15 = 12$$

Step 3 12 is a whole number so:

$$P_{80} = \frac{12\text{th value} + 13\text{th value}}{2}$$

$$P_{80} = \frac{96 + 98}{2} = 97$$

Worked Example 4.8

The stem-and-leaf plot shown gives the marks of 30 students in a maths test.

(i) Calculate P_{90}, the 90th percentile.

(ii) If a student was told their score was in the 90th percentile, what would this mean?

(iii) John has scored 85 in the test. What is John's relative standing in the group for this test?

4	3, 5
5	2, 6, 8, 8, 9
6	1, 1, 3, 3, 3, 4, 7, 8
7	2, 2, 2, 3, 5, 7, 8, 9
8	3, 5, 7, 8, 9
9	7, 8 Key: 5|6 = 56 marks

Solution

(i) Calculate P_{90}.

$$c = \frac{90}{100} \times 30 = 27$$

c is a whole number, so:

$$P_{90} = \frac{27\text{th value} + 28\text{th value}}{2}$$

$$= \frac{88 + 89}{2}$$

$$= 88.5 \text{ marks}$$

(ii) It would mean their mark is in the top 10% of the group.

(iii) 24 students scored lower than John.

$$\frac{24}{30} \times 100 = 80\%$$

So 80% of the class scored lower than John.

z-Scores

We can use **z-scores** to compare values within a set and to compare values from different sets.

A *z-score* is the number of standard deviations a given value *x* is above or below the mean of a given data set.

z-scores are measures of position in that they tell us how many standard deviations a value is above or below the mean value.

If a value is equal to the mean value then its z-score is 0. If a value is one standard deviation above the mean, its z-score is 1. A z-score of −2 indicates that the value is two standard deviations below the mean.

For most distributions, a value that is more than two standard deviations from the mean would be considered unusual.

Unusual values for z-score: $z < -2$ or $z > 2$

The formula below can be used to calculate a z-score.

$$z = \frac{x - \mu}{\sigma}$$

x is a population value.

μ is the population mean.

σ is the population standard deviation.

This is on page 34 of *Formulae and Tables*.

Worked Example 4.9

Dublin's maximum daily temperatures in February average 6.5 °C with a standard deviation of 0.75 °C, while in July the mean maximum daily temperature is 18 °C with a standard deviation of 1.5 °C. In which month is it more unusual to have a maximum daily temperature of 10 °C?

Solution

February: $\quad z = \dfrac{10 - 6.5}{0.75}$

$$z = 4\tfrac{2}{3}$$

July: $\quad z = \dfrac{10 - 18}{1.5}$

$$z = -5\tfrac{1}{3}$$

It is more unusual to have a maximum daily temperature of 10 °C in July because $5\tfrac{1}{3} > 4\tfrac{2}{3}$.

Note that both z-scores are unusual values, as they lie outside the interval, $-2 \leqslant z \leqslant 2$.

Exercise 4.5

1. Consider the following data:

80	77	81	85	73
72	80	83	54	73
54	75	55	68	60
59	61	54	62	53
56	53	81	56	53
51	74	78	80	52

(i) Display the data on an ordered stem-and-leaf diagram.

Calculate:

(ii) P_{90}

(iii) P_{10}

(iv) Q_1

(v) Q_3

(vi) P_{98}

(vii) P_{40}

(viii) The value of 75 is in which percentile?

2. The table below gives the marks of a class on an end-of-term maths test.

100	94	89	77	67
56	99	95	87	76
65	48	97	47	43
98	90	86	74	61
95	89	83	71	58
18	87	88	42	56

(i) Display the data on an ordered stem-and-leaf diagram.

(ii) Calculate the 40th percentile.

(iii) Calculate the 70th percentile.

(iv) Interpret the meaning of the numbers calculated, in the context of this question.

(v) How would you evaluate the performance of the student who scored 61 on the test?

3. A group of Fifth Year students recorded their pulse rates (in beats per minute) when they were in a relaxed state. The results of the survey are shown in the table.

84	68	63	80	68	63	80	69	63	68	62	53
55	63	69	57	63	70	58	64	71	58	63	55
63	70	59	65	73	75	65	59	62	67	69	83

(i) Display the data on an ordered stem-and-leaf diagram.

(ii) Describe the shape of the distribution.

(iii) Calculate the 85th percentile.

(iv) Calculate the 15th percentile.

(v) Interpret the meaning of the numbers calculated, in the context of the question.

(vi) Calculate the difference between the 90th percentile and the 10th percentile.

(vii) How would you evaluate the pulse rate of a student whose pulse rate is 70 bpm?

4. Kevin is studying the cost of history books in his local bookshop. He presents the results of his survey on a stem-and-leaf diagram.

(i) Describe the shape of the distribution.

(ii) Find the median of the data.

(iii) Find the interquartile range of the data.

(iv) Find the difference between the 15th percentile and the 85th percentile of the data.

(v) Interpret your answer to part (iv) above.

0	6, 9
1	0, 0, 0, 2, 2, 8, 9, 9, 9, 9
2	0, 0, 0, 2, 2, 2, 3, 5, 7, 9, 9, 9, 9, 9
3	0, 0, 7, 7, 8, 9, 9, 9, 9
4	0, 0, 0, 5, 9, 9, 9
5	5, 8, 9
6	5, 9

Key : 2|7 = €27

5. The women's shot putt event at the 2009 World Athletics Championships was won by Valerie Vili of New Zealand. The table below gives the qualifying performances of the 28 competitors in the event. All distances are in metres.

19.70	19.36	19.12	19.08	18.92	18.69	18.62
18.53	18.44	18.25	18.14	18.10	17.99	17.95
17.92	17.89	17.86	17.71	17.61	17.30	17.25
17.19	16.92	16.80	16.60	16.09	16.01	14.98

(i) Copy and complete the frequency distribution table.

Distance (m)	14.25–15.00	15.00–15.75	15.75–16.50	16.50–17.25	17.25–18.00	18.00–18.75	18.75–19.50	19.50–20.25
Frequency								

Note: 14.25–15.00 includes 14.25 but not 15.00 and so on.

(ii) Draw a histogram of the distribution.

(iii) Describe the shape of the distribution.

(iv) Calculate the 90th percentile.

(v) Austra Skujyte of Lithuania was the only competitor to have a 'personal best' in the qualifying rounds. She putted a distance of 17.86 m. How would you evaluate Austra's performance in relation to the other competitors?

6. A sample consists of heights of Irish wolfhounds, measured in centimetres. If the height of one particular wolfhound is converted to a z-score, what units are used for the z-score?

7. For a large data set, Q_3 (the upper quartile) is 155. What does it mean when we say that 155 is the upper quartile?

8. John Keats (1795–1821), the English Romantic poet, had a height of 153 cm. During his life, the mean height for men was 176 cm, with a standard deviation of 7 cm.

    (i) What was the difference between Keats' height and the mean?

    (ii) How many standard deviations was his height from the mean?

    (iii) Convert Keats' height to a *z*-score.

    (iv) Was Keats' height usual or unusual? Explain.

9. IQ scores have a mean of 100 and a standard deviation of 16. Albert Einstein had an IQ of 160.

    (i) What was the difference between Einstein's IQ and the mean?

    (ii) How many standard deviations was his IQ from the mean?

    (iii) Convert Einstein's IQ to a *z*-score.

    (iv) Was Einstein's IQ usual or unusual? Explain.

10. Human body temperatures have a mean of 36.8 °C and a standard deviation from the mean of 0.2 °C. Convert the following temperatures to *z*-scores:

    (i) 36.6 °C   (ii) 37 °C   (iii) 36.3 °C   (iv) 38 °C

11. Which is relatively better, a score of 84 on an English test or a score of 48 on a maths test? Scores on the English test have a mean of 90 and a standard deviation of 10. Scores on the maths test have a mean of 55 and a standard deviation of 5.

4.5 The Normal Distribution and the Empirical Rule

In nature, there are many continuous distributions that are symmetric. For example, if one were to measure the heights of all adult males in Ireland, one would find a high proportion of the adult male population with heights close to the mean height of the population. As measurements increase or decrease away from the mean, the proportion of the population with these heights begins to decrease. This results in a symmetric distribution.

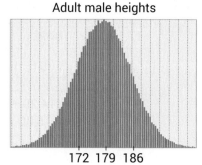

Adult male heights

172 179 186

If we could record the height of every adult male in Ireland and we allowed the class intervals (base widths of the rectangles) in the histogram above to become sufficiently narrow, the histogram would morph into a perfectly symmetrical bell shaped smooth curve shown here. This curve is an example of the **normal distribution curve**.

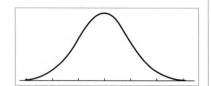

The famous French mathematician Abraham de Moivre (1667–1754) discovered a mathematical formula for constructing the normal curve.

In any normal distribution:

   (i) Approximately 68% of the population lies within one standard deviation of the mean, i.e. 68% lies in the range $[\mu - \sigma, \mu + \sigma]$.

   (ii) Approximately 95% of the population lies in the range $[\mu - 2\sigma, \mu + 2\sigma]$.

   (iii) Approximately 99.7% of the population lies in the range $[\mu - 3\sigma, \mu + 3\sigma]$.

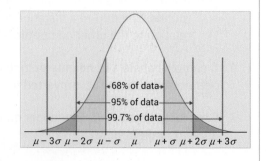

68% of data
95% of data
99.7% of data

$\mu - 3\sigma \quad \mu - 2\sigma \quad \mu - \sigma \quad \mu \quad \mu + \sigma \quad \mu + 2\sigma \quad \mu + 3\sigma$

Collectively, these characteristics are known as the **empirical rule**.

Worked Example 4.10

The frequency table below shows the number of hits a website received each day during a particular week.

Day	Mon	Tue	Wed	Thu	Fri
Number of hits	50	80	120	40	20

(i) Calculate μ, the mean number of hits per day during that week.

(ii) Calculate σ, the standard deviation from the mean.

(iii) Now find the range $[\mu - \sigma, \mu + \sigma]$.

Solution

(i) $\mu = \dfrac{50 + 80 + 120 + 40 + 20}{5} = 62$ hits per weekday

(ii) $\sigma = 34.87$ (calculator)

(iii) $[62 - 34.87, 62 + 34.87] = [27.13, 96.87]$

Worked Example 4.11

The distribution of heights of a large group of students is normal, with a mean of 158 cm and a standard deviation from the mean of 10 cm. The empirical rule says that approximately 68% of a normally distributed population lies within one standard deviation of the mean.

(i) Using the empirical rule, find the range of heights within which 68% of this population lies.

(ii) If a student is chosen at random from the population, find the probability that the student has a height between 138 cm and 178 cm.

Solution

(i) Range $= [\mu - \sigma, \mu + \sigma]$

$\qquad = [158 - 10, 158 + 10] = [148 \text{ cm}, 168 \text{ cm}]$

(ii) $[158 - 2(10), 158 + 2(10)] = [138 \text{ cm}, 178 \text{ cm}]$

This interval contains heights within two standard deviations of the mean.

We know that 95% of the population has heights within this interval. The answer is 95% or 0.95.

Worked Example 4.12

Washers are produced so that their inside diameter is normally distributed with a mean of 1.25 cm. If 95% of the diameters are between 1.2375 cm and 1.2625 cm, then what is the approximate standard deviation from the mean?

Solution

The empirical rule tells us that approximately 95% of the diameters will be in the range $[1.25 - 2\sigma, 1.25 + 2\sigma]$.

$\therefore 1.25 - 2\sigma = 1.2375$

$\qquad -2\sigma = 1.2375 - 1.25$

$\qquad -2\sigma = -0.0125$

$\qquad \sigma = 0.00625 \text{ cm}$

This method can be used since 1.25 lies halfway between 1.2375 and 1.2625.

Exercise 4.6

1. In a normal distribution:

   (i) Approximately what proportion of observations lie within one standard deviation of the mean?

   (ii) Approximately what proportion of observations lie within two standard deviations of the mean?

   (iii) Approximately what proportion of observations lie within three standard deviations of the mean?

2. The principal of Fermat High School records the number of pupils absent each day during a week in December. The results are displayed in the table below.

Day	Monday	Tuesday	Wednesday	Thursday	Friday
Number	12	19	17	25	20

   (i) Calculate μ, the mean number of students absent per day during that week.

   (ii) Calculate σ, the standard deviation from the mean.

   (iii) Now find the range $[\mu - \sigma, \mu + \sigma]$.

3. In each of the following, the mean (μ) and standard deviation (σ) of the normal distributions are given. For each distribution, find the range within which 68% of the distribution lies.

   (i) $\mu = 200$, $\sigma = 25$ (ii) $\mu = 100$, $\sigma = 20$ (iii) $\mu = 20$, $\sigma = 2$ (iv) $\mu = 25$, $\sigma = 2.5$

4. In each of the following, the mean (μ) and standard deviation (σ) of the normal distributions are given. For each distribution, find the range within which 95% of the distribution lies.

   (i) $\mu = 280$, $\sigma = 35$ (ii) $\mu = 120$, $\sigma = 30$ (iii) $\mu = 25$, $\sigma = 2$ (iv) $\mu = 35$, $\sigma = 5.5$

5. In each of the following, the mean (μ) and standard deviation (σ) of the normal distributions are given. For each distribution, find the range within which 99.7% of the distribution lies.

   (i) $\mu = 150$, $\sigma = 25$ (ii) $\mu = 300$, $\sigma = 15$ (iii) $\mu = 20$, $\sigma = 2$ (iv) $\mu = 100$, $\sigma = 5$

6. IQ scores are normally distributed with a mean of 100 and a standard deviation of 15. Isaac de Moivre has taken an IQ test and scored 130. His friend Eoin has remarked that Isaac's score is in the top 5% of all IQ scores. Isaac disagrees and says that he is actually in the top 2.5%. Whose remark is more accurate? Explain your reasoning.

7. Men's heights are normally distributed with a mean of 172.5 cm and a standard deviation from the mean of 7 cm. Séamus the statistician has designed a house with doorways high enough to allow all men, except the tallest 2.5%, to pass through without bending. What doorway height has Séamus used?

8. Human body temperatures are normally distributed with a mean of 36.8 °C and a standard deviation from the mean of 0.25 °C. Rita has a body temperature of 37.5 °C. Should Rita be concerned? Explain your reasoning.

9. Birth weights in Ireland are normally distributed with a mean of 3.42 kg and a standard deviation of 0.5 kg. What percentage of babies born will weigh between 2.92 kg and 3.92 kg? Explain your answer.

Revision Exercises

1. Find the mean and median of these sets of numbers:

   (i) {57.2, 72.5, 56.7, 83.0, 72.6, 65.4, 63.6, 71.4, 89.4, 77.7}

   (ii) {51.6, 52.8, 49.0, 50.2, 56.2, 53.2, 58.7, 51, 53.8}

   (iii) {16.0, 16.7, 15.7, 16.2, 15.5, 16.0, 15.7, 16.8, 17.8, 16.6}

2. Find the mean and median of the following set of numbers:

   {10, 20, 130, 130, 180, 190, 200, 240, 18, 800}

   Which average would you use to describe these numbers?

   Give a reason for your answer.

3. Find the mean and median of the following set of numbers:

   {35, 40, 45, 50, 55, 60, 65}

   Which average would you use to describe these numbers?

   Give a reason for your answer.

4. Find the lower quartile, Q_1, the upper quartile Q_3 and the interquartile range (IQR) for the following sets:

   (i) {5, 8, 10, 6, 6, 5, 11}   (iii) {5, 4, 3, 2, 1, 0, 2, 1}

   (ii) {50, 80, 60, 40, 50, 30, 40, 120}   (iv) {10, 20, −30, 80, 70, −50, −20}

5. Data representing the survival time of patients suffering from chronic granulocytic leukaemia, measured in days from the time of diagnosis, is given below.

7	47	58	74	177	232	273	285	317
429	440	445	455	468	495	497	532	571
579	581	650	702	715	779	881	900	930
968	1077	1109	1,314	1,334	1,367	1,534	1,712	1,784
1,877	1,886	2,045	2,056	2,260	2,429	2,509		

The histogram below shows the distribution.

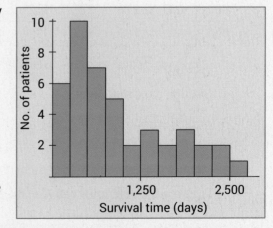

   (i) Using the information above, construct a frequency distribution.

   (ii) Calculate the mean survival time for the sample.

   (iii) Describe the shape of the distribution.

   (iv) Explain the shape of the distribution in the context of the question.

   (v) Do you think the mean calculated in part (ii) is a good measure of centre? Explain.

   (vi) Do you think that a doctor should give a patient the median or mean as the average survival time for patients with granulocytic leukaemia? Explain.

   (vii) This data was collected in 1969. If a similar sample were taken today, do you think the distribution would be different? If so, which summary statistics (minimum, maximum, mean, standard deviation, median, IQR) would be different?

6. Calculate the standard deviation of each of the following data sets:

   (i) {6, 8, 10, 12, 14} (ii) {13, 14, 15, 16, 17} (iii) {5, 10, 15, 20, 25} (iv) {100, 200, 300, 400, 500}

STATISTICS II

7. The following are the prices in euro of 30 different wooden toys in a rural craft shop:

8.20	4.50	11.36	5.45	5.12	4.99	8.75	5.39	15.40	15.60
6.00	9.12	8.69	7.90	4.90	13.80	6.15	1.99	5.85	5.74
10.30	6.00	9.80	6.60	5.35	1.70	7.00	10.00	6.85	16.20

(i) Using suitable intervals, construct a frequency distribution (have six intervals).

(ii) Display the distribution on a histogram.

(iii) Comment on the shape of the distribution.

(iv) Calculate an appropriate measure of centre.

(v) Calculate an appropriate measure of spread.

(vi) The proprietor of the craft shop decides to add €2 to the price of all toys in the shop. How will this affect the summary statistics (minimum, maximum, mean, standard deviation, median, IQR)?

8. Consider the following data:

70	67	71	75	63
62	70	73	44	63
44	65	45	58	50
49	51	44	52	43
46	43	71	46	43
41	64	68	70	42

(i) Display the data on an ordered stem-and-leaf diagram.

(ii) Calculate P_{90} and P_{10}.

(iii) Calculate Q_1 and Q_3.

9. The following are cholesterol readings (mg/dl) for a randomly selected group of 36 adults:

522	127	740	49	230	316	590	466	121	578	78	265
250	265	273	272	972	75	138	139	638	613	762	303
690	31	189	957	339	416	120	702	1252	288	176	277

(i) Display the distribution on an appropriate graph.

(ii) Describe the distribution.

(iii) Calculate the 85th percentile.

(iv) Calculate the 15th percentile.

(v) Interpret the meaning of the numbers calculated, in the context of the question.

(vi) Calculate the difference between the 90th percentile and the 10th percentile.

10. Chinese woman Yao Defin claims to be the world's tallest woman with a height of 233 cm. Women have heights with a mean of 159 cm and a standard deviation from the mean of 6.25 cm.

(i) What is the difference between Yao Defin's height and the mean?

(ii) How many standard deviations is the difference from the mean?

(iii) Convert Defin's height to a z-score.

(iv) In statistical terms, is Defin's height usual or unusual? Explain.

11. In each of the following, the mean μ and standard deviation σ of the normal distribution is given. For each distribution, find the range within which 68%, 95% and 99.7% of the distribution lie.

    (i) μ = 200, σ = 25   (iii) μ = 20, σ = 2

    (ii) μ = 100, σ = 20   (iv) μ = 25, σ = 2.5

Exam Questions

1. Some students are using a database of earthquakes to investigate the times between the occurrences of serious earthquakes around the world. They extract information about all of the earthquakes in the 20th century that caused at least 1,000 deaths. There are 115 of these.

The students wonder whether there are patterns in the timing of these earthquakes, so they look at the number of days between each successive pair of these earthquakes.

They make the following table, showing the number of earthquakes for which the time interval from the previous earthquake is as shown:

Time in days from previous earthquake	0–100	100–200	200–300	300–400	400–500	500–600	600–700	700–800	800–1,000	1,000–1,300
Number of earthquakes	31	24	12	14	8	7	5	6	5	3

Source: National geophysical data center, significant earthquake database: www.ngdc.noaa.gov

    (i) Create a suitable graphical representation of the distribution.

    (ii) Describe the distribution. Your description should refer to the shape of the distribution and should include an estimate of the median.

SEC Leaving Certificate Higher Level, Paper 2, 2011

2. To buy a home, people usually take out loans called *mortgages*. If one of the repayments is not made on time, the mortgage is said to be *in arrears*. One way of considering how much difficulty the borrowers in a country are having with their mortgages is to look at the percentage of all mortgages that are in arrears for 90 days or more. For the rest of this question, the term *in arrears* means in arrears for 90 days or more.

The two charts below are from a report about mortgages in Ireland. The charts are intended to illustrate the connection, if any, between the percentage of mortgages that are in arrears and the interest rates being charged for mortgages. Each dot on the charts represents a group of people paying a particular interest rate to a particular lender. The arrears rate is the percentage in arrears.

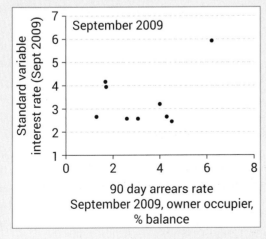
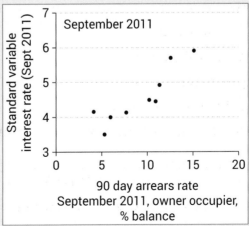

Source: Goggin et al. *Variable Mortgage Rate Pricing in Ireland*, Central Bank of Ireland, 2012

STATISTICS II

(a) Paying close attention to the scales on the charts, what can you say about the change from September 2009 to September 2011 with regard to:

   (i) the arrears rate?

   (ii) the rates of interest being paid?

   (iii) the relationship between the arrears rate and the interest rate?

(b) What additional information would you need before you could estimate the median interest rate being paid by mortgage holders in September 2011?

(c) Regarding the relationship between the arrears rate and the interest rate for September 2011, the authors of the report state: 'The direction of causality ... is important' and they go on to discuss this.

   Explain what is meant by 'direction of causality' in this context.

SEC Leaving Certificate Higher Level, Project Maths Paper 2, 2012

3. The shapes of the histograms of four different sets of data are shown below.

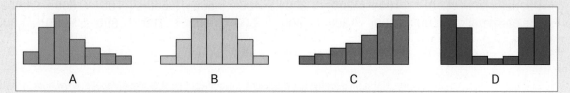

	A	B	C	D
The data are skewed to the left.				
The data are skewed to the right.				
The mean is equal to the median.				
The mean is greater than the median.				
There is a single mode.				

(a) Complete the table below, indicating whether the statement is correct (✓) or incorrect (✗) with respect to each data set.

(b) Assume that the four histograms are drawn on the same scale. State which of them has the largest standard deviation, and justify your answer.

SEC Leaving Certificate Higher Level, Project Maths Sample Paper 2, 2010

 Solutions and chapter summary available online

05

Statistics III

In this chapter you will learn to:

- Recognise sampling variability and use appropriate tools to describe variability drawing inferences about the population from the sample

- Use the concept of margin of error and understand that an increased confidence level implies wider intervals

- Construct 95% confidence intervals for the population mean from a large sample and for the population proportion, in both cases using z-tables

- Conduct an hypothesis test for a population proportion using confidence intervals

- Perform univariate large sample hypothesis tests of the population mean (two tailed z-test only)

- Use and interpret p-values

You should remember...

- How to construct a stem-and-leaf plot

- How to construct a histogram

- The normal distribution

- How to use the z-tables

- How to calculate the mean of a sample

- How to calculate the standard deviation of a sample

5

Key words

- Margin of error
- Population proportion
- Sample proportion
- Population mean
- Sample mean
- Confidence interval
- Hypothesis test
- H$_0$: the null hypothesis
- H$_1$: the alternative hypothesis
- p-values

Before an election is held, statisticians are often employed to predict the outcome of the election. They do this by asking a small number of people how they will vote in the upcoming election. They then try to predict the outcome from the responses of this group.

When statisticians make predictions based on responses from a small group, they are then doing **inferential statistics**.

Inferential statistics makes inferences about populations using data drawn from the population.

5.1 Sampling

Sample data must be collected in an appropriate way, such as through the process of random selection.

A **census** is the collection of data from every member of the population.

A **sample** is a subset of members selected from the population.

A **parameter** is a numerical measurement describing some characteristic of a population.

A **statistic** is a numerical measurement describing some characteristic of a sample.

In a particular school, 85% of the students play sport. The figure of 85% is a **parameter**, as it is based on the entire population of the school.

Based on a sample of 400 First Year college students, it is found that 45% of them achieved more than 400 points in their Leaving Certificate. The figure of 45% is a **statistic** because it is based on a sample, not on the entire population of all First Year college students.

When we select a sample from a population and the sample is representative of the population, then we can make inferences about the population from the sample.

Sampling Variability

You learned how to select random samples from a population in Chapter 1 in 1.2 Sample Surveys. The value of the mean, median or mode of the random sample depends on the particular values in the sample, and it generally varies from sample to sample. This variation is called **sampling variability**.

The Sampling Distribution of a Statistic

The **sampling distribution** of a statistic is the distribution of all values of that statistic when all possible samples of the same size are taken from the same population.

OR

The **sampling distribution** of a sample statistic calculated from a sample of n measurements is the probability distribution of the statistic.

STATISTICS III

Worked Example 5.1

A census was carried out and the following measurements were recorded for the population:

$$1, 1, 2, 2, 2, 3, 3$$

(i) Show the distribution in a frequency table.

(ii) Is the mean of the data a parameter or a statistic? Explain.

(iii) What is the mean of the data?

(iv) How many different possible samples of size 6 can be taken from the population?

(v) List all the possible samples of size 6.

(vi) Find the mean of each sample listed in part (v).

(vii) Is the mean of each sample an example of a parameter or a statistic? Explain.

(viii) Show the sampling distribution of the sample mean in a frequency table and display the distribution using a histogram.

(ix) Find the mean of the sampling distribution. What do you notice?

Solution

(i)

Measurement	1	2	3
Frequency	2	3	2

(ii) The mean of the data is a parameter, as it is a measurement describing a characteristic of the population.

(iii) $\mu = \dfrac{1(2) + 2(3) + 3(2)}{2 + 3 + 2}$

$= \dfrac{14}{7}$

$\therefore \mu = 2$

μ = population mean
σ = population standard deviation

(iv) $\dbinom{7}{6} = 7$

(v) 1, 1, 2, 2, 2, 3   1, 1, 2, 2, 2, 3

1, 1, 2, 2, 3, 3   1, 1, 2, 2, 3, 3

1, 1, 2, 2, 3, 3   1, 2, 2, 2, 3, 3

1, 2, 2, 2, 3, 3

(vi)

Sample number	Sample	Mean
1	1, 1, 2, 2, 2, 3	$1\frac{5}{6}$
2	1, 1, 2, 2, 2, 3	$1\frac{5}{6}$
3	1, 1, 2, 2, 3, 3	2
4	1, 1, 2, 2, 3, 3	2
5	1, 1, 2, 2, 3, 3	2
6	1, 2, 2, 2, 3, 3	$2\frac{1}{6}$
7	1, 2, 2, 2, 3, 3	$2\frac{1}{6}$

$\bar{x}$ = sample mean

(vii) The mean of each sample is an example of a statistic, as it is a measurement describing a characteristic of a sample.

(viii)

Sample mean	$1\frac{5}{6}$	2	$2\frac{1}{6}$
Frequency	2	3	2

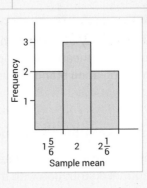

(ix) Mean of sampling distribution:

$= \dfrac{1\frac{5}{6}(2) + 2(3) + 2\frac{1}{6}(2)}{2 + 3 + 2}$

$= \dfrac{14}{7}$

$= 2$

The mean of the sampling distribution is equal to the mean of the population.

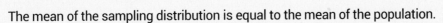

STATISTICS III

The Sampling Distribution of the Mean

If we are interested in the heights of all 16-year-old boys in Ireland, the information we require will generally be a measure of centre, such as the mean height of the population, and a measure of spread, such as the standard deviation of the population. In such a large population it is impossible to obtain everybody's height, so we need to rely on a sample. If we take lots of random samples of a given size from the population, find the mean of each sample and then plot the distribution of these sample means, we will find that the distribution is symmetric.

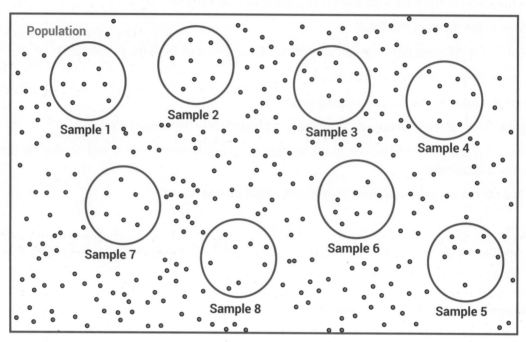

In fact, the distribution of any sample mean becomes normal as the sample size grows, regardless of the shape of the population distribution.

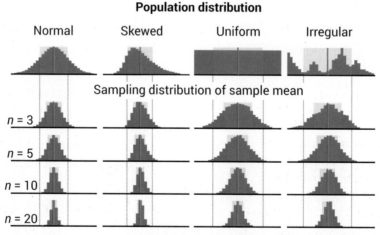

This surprising fact was proved in 1810 by the French mathematician Pierre-Simon Laplace. The mean of the sampling distribution is equal to the mean of the population, and the standard deviation of the sampling distribution is $\frac{\sigma}{\sqrt{n}}$, where σ is the population standard deviation and n is the sample size.

The Central Limit Theorem

When selecting a simple random sample of size n from a population with mean μ and standard deviation σ, then:

(a) If n is large enough, typically $n \geqslant 30$, the sample means for a given sample size n have a distribution that can be approximated by a normal distribution with mean μ and standard deviation $\frac{\sigma}{\sqrt{n}}$. (This guideline is commonly used regardless of the distribution of the underlying population; in other words, the population measurements may or may not be normal.)

(b) Even if $n < 30$ but the underlying population is normal, then the sample means for a given sample size n have a normal distribution with mean μ and standard deviation $\frac{\sigma}{\sqrt{n}}$.

The standard deviation of the sampling distribution of the sample means is often referred to as the **standard error of the mean**.

In the case of (a) and/or (b), the corresponding z-score for the sample mean is:

$$z = \frac{\bar{x} - \mu}{\left(\frac{\sigma}{\sqrt{n}}\right)}$$

This is on page 35 of *Formulae and Tables*.

Central Limit Theorem Summary

Mean: $\mu_{\bar{x}} = \mu$

Standard deviation: $\sigma_{\bar{x}} = \frac{\sigma}{\sqrt{n}}$

(Standard error)

$\mu_{\bar{x}}$ means 'the mean of the sampling distribution of the sample mean'.

$\sigma_{\bar{x}}$ means 'the standard deviation of the sampling distribution of the sample mean'. This is often referred to as 'the standard error'.

Worked Example 5.2

A car battery manufacturer claims that the distribution of the lengths of life of its premium battery has a mean of 54 months and a standard deviation of 6 months. A consumer magazine tests a random sample of 50 batteries to investigate the company's claim.

 (i) Describe the sampling distribution of the mean lifetime of a sample of 50 batteries, assuming the company's claim is true.

 (ii) What theorem have you used in answering part (i)?

 (iii) Sketch the sampling distribution described in part (i).

 (iv) Assuming that the company's claim is true, what is the probability that the magazine's sample has a mean life of 52 months or less?

 (v) If the magazine's sample had a mean life of 52 months and you were the journalist at the magazine reporting on the company's claim, what would you conclude regarding the claim?

Solution

 (i) Approximately normal with mean = 54 months and standard deviation of $\frac{6}{\sqrt{50}} \approx 0.85$ months.

 (ii) The Central Limit Theorem, which states that if $n > 30$, then the sampling distribution of the sample mean (sample size n) will be approximately normal with mean μ (population mean) and standard deviation of $\frac{\sigma}{\sqrt{n}}$ (where σ is the population standard deviation).

 (iii)

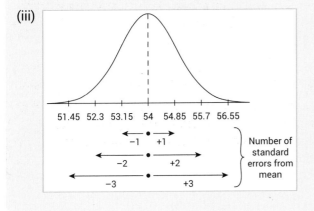

 (iv) $z = \dfrac{\bar{x} - \mu}{\left(\frac{\sigma}{\sqrt{n}}\right)}$

 Revise using the normal tables covered in Chapter 4 Section 4.5 The Normal Distribution.

$= \dfrac{52 - 54}{\left(\frac{6}{\sqrt{50}}\right)}$

$\therefore z \approx -2.36$

$P(z \leqslant -2.36) = 1 - P(z < 2.36)$

$= 1 - 0.9909$

$= 0.0091$

$= 0.91\%$

 (v) I would conclude that the investigation provides evidence that the company's claim is **not** true. If the company's claim were true, there would be a less than 1% chance of a random sample of size 50 having a sample mean of 52 or less.

OR

As $|z| > 2$, we dismiss the company's claims. A z-score of −2.36 seems to suggest that the true mean is lower than what the company is claiming.

5

Worked Example 5.3

In a computer simulation, random samples of size 400 are selected from a population. The mean measurement of each sample is recorded. Five thousand such sample means are recorded.

Describe the expected distribution of the sample means.

Solution
The expected distribution will approximate the sampling distribution of the sample mean. This is because of the very large number (5,000) of sample means recorded.

The Central Limit Theorem tells us that the sample means will have an approximately normal distribution. The mean of the distribution will approximate the mean of the population.

The standard deviation of the distribution will approximate $\frac{\sigma}{\sqrt{400}} = \frac{\sigma}{20}$, where σ is the standard deviation of the population.

Worked Example 5.4

A simple random sample of 400 is selected from a population having a mean height of $\mu = 1.77$ m and a standard deviation of $\sigma = 0.0775$ m.

Find the probability that the sample mean $\bar{x}$ lies in the range 1.76 m $\leq \bar{x} \leq 1.78$ m.

Solution
Since $n > 30$, the sampling distribution of the sample mean is approximately normal, with a mean $\mu_{\bar{x}} = \mu = 1.77$ and a standard deviation of $\sigma_{\bar{x}} = \frac{\sigma}{\sqrt{n}} = \frac{0.0775}{20} = 0.003875$.

We will now convert 1.76 and 1.78 to standard z-scores using the formula $z = \frac{\bar{x} - \mu}{\left(\frac{\sigma}{\sqrt{n}}\right)}$.

$$z_1 = \frac{1.76 - 1.77}{0.003875} \approx -2.58$$

$$z_2 = \frac{1.78 - 1.77}{0.003875} \approx 2.58$$

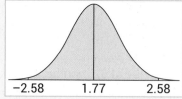

Therefore, the probability that the sample mean $\bar{x}$ lies in the range 1.76 m $\leq \bar{x} \leq 1.78$ m is given by:

$$P(-2.58 \leq z \leq 2.58) = 2[P(z < 2.58) - 0.5]$$
$$= 2[0.9951 - 0.5]$$
$$= 0.9902$$

There is a probability of approximately 99.02% that the sample mean lies in the range 1.76 m $\leq \bar{x} \leq 1.78$ m.

Worked Example 5.5

A population is normally distributed with a mean of 11 and a standard deviation of 3. Find the sample size n such that $P(\bar{x} > 11.5) = 0.05$, where $\bar{x}$ is the sample mean.

Solution
$P(z > z_1) = 0.05$

$P(z \leq z_1) = 0.95$

$\therefore z_1 = 1.645$

$$1.645 = \frac{11.5 - 11}{\frac{3}{\sqrt{n}}}$$

$$\frac{0.5\sqrt{n}}{3} = 1.645$$

$$\sqrt{n} = 9.87$$

$$n = 97.4169$$

Sample size = 97

Worked Example 5.6

The price/earnings ratio of a stock is an important consideration for financial analysts who put together financial portfolios. Suppose a population of all price/earnings ratios has a mean of 10.5 and a standard deviation of 4.5.

What is the probability that a randomly selected sample of 40 stocks will have an average price to earnings ratio less than 9?

Solution

The mean of the sampling distribution is 10.5 and the standard deviation is $\frac{4.5}{\sqrt{40}}$.

Convert to standard normal form:

$$z = \frac{9 - 10.5}{\left(\frac{4.5}{\sqrt{40}}\right)}$$

$$z = \frac{-2\sqrt{10}}{3}$$

$z = -2.11$ (to 2 decimal places)

$$P(z < -2.11) = 1 - P(z < 2.11)$$
$$= 1 - 0.9826$$
$$= 0.0174$$
$$= 1.74\%$$

Exercise 5.1

1. Numerical data for a large population is stored on a database. The data has a mean of μ and a standard deviation of σ. A computer simulation randomly selects samples of size 400 from the database and calculates the mean of each sample. This is done repeatedly until 1,200 such means are recorded.

   (i) Describe the expected distribution of the sample means.

   (ii) Write in terms of μ and σ the mean and standard deviation of the sampling distribution of the sample means.

2. A simple random sample of size 49 is chosen from a population that is known to be normal. The mean of the population is 9 with a standard deviation of 2.

   Find the probability that the sample mean is greater than 10.

3. Women's heights in Ireland are normally distributed with a mean given by $\mu = 164.4$ cm and a standard deviation given by $\sigma = 6.25$ cm.

   Source: Jaume Garcia and Climent Quintana-Domeque, 'The evolution of adult height in Europe', *Economics and Human Biology* 5(2) (2007), pp 340–349

   (i) If a woman is selected at random, find the probability that her height is less than 167 cm.

   (ii) A simple random sample of 25 women is selected. Find the probability that the mean height of the sample is less than 167 cm.

   (iii) Explain why you were able to use the Central Limit Theorem in part (ii), even though the sample size does not exceed 30.

4. Men's heights in Ireland are normally distributed with a mean given by $\mu = 177.5$ cm and a standard deviation given by $\sigma = 6.3$ cm.

   Source: Garcia and Quintana-Domeque, 'The evolution of adult height in Europe'

   (i) If a man is selected at random, find the probability that his height is between 173 cm and 182 cm.

   (ii) A simple random sample of 25 men is conducted. Find the probability that they have a mean height of between 173 cm and 182 cm.

5. A ski lift has a maximum capacity of 12 people or 912 kg. The capacity will be exceeded if 12 people have weights with a mean greater than $\frac{912 \text{ kg}}{12} = 76$ kg. As men tend to weigh more than women, a 'worst case' scenario involves 12 passengers who are all men. Men's weights are normally distributed with a mean of 78.1 kg and a standard deviation of 13.2 kg.

   (i) Find the probability that if an individual man is selected at random, his weight will be greater than 76 kg.

(ii) Find the probability that 12 randomly selected men will have a mean weight greater than 76 kg.

(iii) Does the ski lift appear to have the correct weight limit?

6. The manager of a hotel finds that guests spend a mean of 12.5 minutes each day in the shower. Assume shower times are normally distributed with a standard deviation of 2.8 minutes.

(i) Find the percentage of guests who shower for more than 13 minutes.

(ii) The hotel has installed a hot water system that can provide enough hot water, provided that the mean shower time for 100 guests is less than 13 minutes.

Find the probability that there will not be enough hot water on a morning that the hotel has 100 guests.

7. A normal distribution has a mean of 80 and a standard deviation of 8. A sample of size n is selected at random and the mean of the sample is $\bar{x}$.

Find n if $P(\bar{x} > 82) = 0.1977$.

8. A sample is chosen at random from a population that is strongly skewed to the left.

(i) Describe the shape of the sampling distribution of the sample mean if the sample size is large.

(ii) Describe the mean and standard deviation of the sampling distribution of the sample mean in terms of the underlying population.

9. Records indicate that the value of homes in a large town is positively skewed with a mean of €150,000 and standard deviation of €65,000. To check the accuracy of the records, officials plan to conduct a survey of 100 randomly selected homes.

Sketch the sampling distribution of the mean home value of a random sample of 100 homes. Clearly indicate on your diagram the location of the mean of this sampling distribution and the location of the points three standard errors above and below this mean.

10. Perfluoro-octanoic acid (PFOA) is a chemical used in Teflon-coated cookware. The US Environmental Protection Agency (EPA) is investigating if PFOA causes cancer. It is known that the blood concentration of PFOA in the general population has a mean of 6 ppb (parts per billion) and a standard deviation of 10 ppb. Tests for PFOA exposure were conducted on a sample of 326 people who live near DuPont's Teflon-making plant in West Virginia.

(i) What is the probability that the average blood concentration of PFOA in the sample is greater than 7.5 ppb?

(ii) What assumption did you make in answering part (i)?

(iii) If the actual study resulted in a sample mean of 7 ppb, what inference would you make about the true mean PFOA concentration for the population that lives near the DuPont Teflon facility?

11. On 1 May 1994, the triple World Champion, Ayrton Senna, was killed at the San Marino F1 Grand Prix at Imola, Italy, following a mechanical failure in his car. Later research revealed that the time x (in hours) to the first mechanical failure in an F1 Grand Prix is distributed with mean of 0.1 and standard deviation of 0.1.

A random sample of 40 F1 Grand Prix is selected by a computer.

(i) Describe the sampling distribution of the sample mean.

(ii) Sketch this distribution.

(iii) Find the probability that the sample mean time for the first mechanical failure exceeds 0.13 hours.

(iv) A computer generates 1,500 random samples each of 40 F1 Grand Prix. How many of these 1,500 random samples would you expect to have a sample mean exceeding 0.13 hours?

(v) Describe the expected distribution of the 1,500 sample means referred to in part (iv).

5.2 Confidence Interval for a Mean

Population measurements are often described by parameters, such as the mean and standard deviation. For example, the mean birthweight of infants born in maternity hospitals in Ireland during 2012 was 3,464 grams (ESRI - Perinatal Statistics Report, 2012). This measurement is a population parameter, as it is computed from data on the entire population.

Because populations are often very large or otherwise hard to investigate, we often have no way of knowing the exact values of the parameters. **Point estimators** are then used to estimate population parameters. A random sample is chosen from the population. Statistics are calculated and point estimates such as the sample mean and sample standard deviation are used to estimate the corresponding population parameters (population mean and population standard deviation).

> A point estimate is a single value used to estimate a population parameter.

Although a point estimate is the best single value for estimating a population parameter, it doesn't give us any indication of how good the estimate is. A **confidence interval** gives us information that enables us to better understand the accuracy of the estimate. For example, a confidence interval with a 95% confidence level gives us the success rate of the procedure used to construct the confidence interval. With a 95% confidence level, the population parameter is expected to lie within such an interval 95% of the time. In other words, if such an interval is constructed 100 times, the population parameter is expected to lie within the interval 95 times.

> A confidence interval is a range of values so defined that there is a specified probability (e.g. 95%) that the value of a parameter lies within it.

The **margin of error** E for the population mean at the 95% confidence level is given by

$$E = 1.96\frac{\sigma}{\sqrt{n}}$$

where σ is the population standard deviation and n is the sample size.

We rarely know the population standard deviation, so we use the standard deviation of the sample as an approximation. If $\bar{x}$ is the mean of a random sample of size n taken from a population with known standard deviation σ, then a 95% confidence interval for the population mean is given by the formula shown here, where μ is the population mean.

$$\bar{x} - 1.96\frac{\sigma}{\sqrt{n}} \leqslant \mu \leqslant \bar{x} + 1.96\frac{\sigma}{\sqrt{n}}$$

or

$$\left[\bar{x} - 1.96\frac{\sigma}{\sqrt{n}}, \bar{x} + 1.96\frac{\sigma}{\sqrt{n}}\right]$$

Worked Example 5.7

A random sample of 400 apples was taken from a large consignment with unknown mean μ and standard deviation 15 g. The mean weight of the random sample was 85.6 g.

Construct a 95% confidence interval for the mean weight of the apples in the consignment.

Solution

The 95% confidence interval for μ is:

$$\bar{x} - 1.96\frac{\sigma}{\sqrt{n}} \leqslant \mu \leqslant \bar{x} + 1.96\frac{\sigma}{\sqrt{n}}$$

$$85.6 - 1.96\frac{15}{\sqrt{400}} \leqslant \mu \leqslant 85.6 + 1.96\frac{15}{\sqrt{400}}$$

$$84.13 \leqslant \mu \leqslant 87.07 \text{ (weights in grams)}$$

Confidence intervals with confidence levels other than 95% are also possible. 90% and 99% confidence levels are also used by statisticians. A greater confidence level implies a greater margin of error.

Worked Example 5.8

A random sample of 40 women was selected from the population and their pulse rates measured. The mean pulse rate of the sample was 76.3 bpm. Assume that σ, the population standard deviation, is known to be 12.5 bpm.

(i) Construct a 95% confidence interval for μ, the mean pulse rate of the population.

(ii) If the margins of error for a 90% and 99% confidence level are $E_{90} = 1.645\dfrac{\sigma}{\sqrt{n}}$ and $E_{99} = 2.575\dfrac{\sigma}{\sqrt{n}}$ respectively, construct a 90% and 99% confidence interval for μ, the mean pulse rate of the population. Comment on your results.

Solution

(i) The 95% confidence interval for μ is:

$$\bar{x} - 1.96\frac{\sigma}{\sqrt{n}} \leqslant \mu \leqslant \bar{x} + 1.96\frac{\sigma}{\sqrt{n}}$$

$$76.3 - 1.96\left(\frac{12.5}{\sqrt{40}}\right) \leqslant \mu \leqslant 76.3 + 1.96\left(\frac{12.5}{\sqrt{40}}\right)$$

$$72.43 \leqslant \mu \leqslant 80.17$$

(ii) The 90% confidence interval for μ is:

$$\bar{x} - 1.645\frac{\sigma}{\sqrt{n}} \leqslant \mu \leqslant \bar{x} + 1.645\frac{\sigma}{\sqrt{n}}$$

$$76.3 - 1.645\left(\frac{12.5}{\sqrt{40}}\right) \leqslant \mu \leqslant 76.3 + 1.645\left(\frac{12.5}{\sqrt{40}}\right)$$

$$73.05 \leqslant \mu \leqslant 79.55$$

The 99% confidence interval for μ is:

$$\bar{x} - 2.575\frac{\sigma}{\sqrt{n}} \leqslant \mu \leqslant \bar{x} + 2.575\frac{\sigma}{\sqrt{n}}$$

$$76.3 - 2.575\left(\frac{12.5}{\sqrt{40}}\right) \leqslant \mu \leqslant 76.3 + 2.575\left(\frac{12.5}{\sqrt{40}}\right)$$

$$71.21 \leqslant \mu \leqslant 81.39$$

A greater confidence level implies a wider confidence interval (see table below). This is because a larger confidence level results in a larger margin of error.

Confidence level	Level of significance	Confidence interval
90%	10%	[73.05, 79.55]
95%	5%	[72.43, 80.17]
99%	1%	[71.21, 81.39]

Exercise 5.2

1. A population has a mean μ and a standard deviation of 10. A random sample of 800 from this population has a mean of 63. Construct a 95% confidence interval for μ.

2. A normally distributed population has a standard deviation of 12 and a mean μ. A random sample of 400 from this population has a mean of 110. Form a 95% confidence interval for μ.

3. A population has a mean μ and a standard deviation of 20. A random sample of 900 from this population has a mean of 172. Construct a 95% confidence interval for μ.

4. The pulse rates of a random sample of 36 teenagers were measured. The mean was found to be 68.8 beats per minute with a standard deviation of 4.75. Form a 95% confidence interval for the mean of the population.

5. When people smoke, the nicotine they absorb is converted to cotinine, which can be measured. A sample of 100 smokers has a mean cotinine level of 173. Assuming that σ, the standard deviation of the population, is known to be 120.5, construct a 95% confidence interval for the mean cotinine level of all smokers.

6. A random sample of 250 cars was taken. The mean age of the cars was 4.5 years and the standard deviation was 2.2 years.

   (a) Construct a 95% confidence interval for the mean age of all cars.

   (b) What sample size is required to estimate the mean age with 95% confidence to ±0.3 years?

7. On a tree farm 6,000 Christmas trees are ready to be cut and sold. Fifty of the trees are randomly selected and their heights measured. The heights in centimetres of each of the fifty trees is given in the table.

163	135	144	170	155	160	185	155	163	160
110	143	130	115	135	175	145	178	188	140
120	123	123	148	185	128	120	155	130	125
158	183	143	108	170	145	123	143	138	165
178	185	113	120	173	173	143	163	123	108

   (i) Calculate the mean of the sample.

   (ii) Construct a 95% confidence interval for the mean height of all 6,000 trees. The standard deviation of the population is known to be 23.

   (iii) If the trees sell for €3.50 per 30 cm, give a lower and upper bound on the value of the 6,000 trees.

8. A survey was carried out to estimate the weekly rental costs of holiday apartments in a certain country. A random sample of 400 apartments was taken. The mean of the sample was €400 and the standard deviation was €50. Form a 95% confidence interval for the mean weekly rental costs of apartments in this country.

9. Farmers measure daily milk production in pounds. Ayrshire cows average 47 pounds of milk per day with a standard deviation of 6 pounds. Jersey cows average 43 pounds of milk per day with a standard deviation of 5 pounds. Assume that milk production is normally distributed for all cow breeds.

   (a) What is the probability that a randomly selected Ayrshire cow produces more than 45 pounds of milk per day?

   (b) Twenty Jersey cows are selected at random. What is the probability that two or more of these cows will produce more than 54 pounds of milk per day? [Hint: Binomial distribution]

   (c) Four hundred Friesian cows are randomly selected. The mean production of this sample was an average of 47 pounds of milk per day with a standard deviation of 6.5 pounds.
   Find a 95% confidence interval for the mean production per day of this breed.

10. The IQs of 400 randomly selected students showed a mean of 107. The standard deviation of the population is known to be 15.

   (i) Calculate a 95% confidence interval for the mean IQ of this population.

   (ii) If the margins of error for a 90% and a 99% confidence level are $E_{90} = 1.645\frac{\sigma}{\sqrt{n}}$ and $E_{99} = 2.575\frac{\sigma}{\sqrt{n}}$ respectively, construct 90% and 99% confidence intervals for the mean of the population. Comment on your results.

11. Data collected by child development researchers produced this confidence interval for the mean age at which babies begin to crawl, where ages are measured in weeks:

$$29.202 < \mu < 31.844$$

The confidence level for this interval is 95%.

   (i) What is the margin of error for this interval?

   (ii) If the researcher had calculated a 90% confidence interval, would the margin of error be larger or smaller? Explain.

5.3 Estimating a Population Proportion

We are usually unable to collect information about a total population, so we have to rely on a sample to draw conclusions about the population.

We use a sample proportion to estimate the population proportion. When a sample from a population is selected, we hope that the data we get represents the population as a whole.

To ensure this:

● The sample must be random.

● Every member of the population must have an equal chance of being included.

The sample proportion $\hat{p}$ (pronounced 'p hat') is the best point estimate of the population proportion p.

> p = population proportion
>
> $\hat{p} = \dfrac{x}{n}$ = sample proportion of x successes in a sample of size n
>
> $\hat{q} = 1 - \hat{p}$ = the proportion of failures in the sample

For example, if in a random selection of 400 students, 180 said they owned a smartphone, then the best point estimate of the proportion of students in the whole population who own a smartphone is:

$$\hat{p} = \frac{180}{400} = \frac{9}{20} = 0.45$$

Just before the 2000 US presidential election, an NBC news poll asked 1,000 randomly selected voters whom they would vote for in the election. Of the sample, 430 said they would vote for George W. Bush; the remainder of the sample chose other candidates. In a CNN poll taken at the same time, 460 voters out of 1,000 randomly selected voters said they would vote for Bush.

The best point estimate from the NBC poll that people would vote for Bush is 0.43, while the best point estimate from the CNN poll is 0.46. The two proportions are different. Proportions vary from sample to sample because the samples are composed of different people. This variation is known as **sampling variability**.

If it were possible to collect every sample of size 1,000, the distribution of the sample proportions would be normal. The mean of the distribution would be p, and the standard deviation would be:

> $\sigma_{\hat{p}} = \sqrt{\dfrac{p(1-p)}{n}}$
>
> p is the population proportion, $\hat{p}$ is the sample proportion and n is the sample size.
>
> $\sigma_{\hat{p}}$ is also known as the standard error of the proportion.

$\sigma_{\hat{p}}$ is stated on page 34 of *Formulae and Tables*.

The sampling distribution of the sample proportions is approximately normal if the sample size is large enough. While we don't have to worry about this detail on our course, one common test that is used is to check that np and nq are both greater than or equal to 15.

Confidence Interval for a Proportion

In the preceding example, 0.43 was our best estimate from the NBC poll, but how good is this estimate? A point estimate does not reveal how good the estimate is. Instead of the point estimate, statisticians usually use confidence intervals, as discussed in the previous section.

The confidence interval for a population proportion with a confidence level of 95% is given by

$$\hat{p} - E < p < \hat{p} + E$$

where $E = 1.96\sqrt{\dfrac{p(1-p)}{n}}$ and $E = 1.96\sqrt{\dfrac{\hat{p}(1-\hat{p})}{n}}$

if p is known   if p is unknown

where $\hat{p}$ is the sample proportion and n is the sample size. We use $\hat{p}$ instead of p in the formula, as p is unknown to begin with. Confidence intervals at other confidence levels (say, 90% or 99%) could also be constructed in the same way that we constructed differing confidence intervals for the population mean in Worked Example 5.8.

Worked Example 5.9

In the example from the US presidential elections above, find confidence intervals for both the NBC and CNN polls at a 95% confidence level. Interpret the results. (In the actual election Bush won 48% of the vote.)

Solution

NBC: $E = 1.96\sqrt{\dfrac{0.43(1-0.43)}{1,000}}$ CNN: $E = 1.96\sqrt{\dfrac{0.46(1-0.46)}{1,000}}$

      $= 0.031$ $= 0.031$

     $0.399 < p < 0.461$ $0.429 < p < 0.491$

The actual proportion that Bush received is not within the NBC interval, but it is within the CNN interval. However, the true proportion that would have voted for Bush on the day the poll was carried out may not be the proportion that voted for him in the election. Many voters often change their mind on the day of an election. Therefore, we cannot say that the NBC poll got it wrong.

Worked Example 5.10

In a survey of n voters, 0.7 of the sample said they voted in a recent referendum. A 95% confidence interval for the proportion of voters who said they voted in the referendum was given as: $0.6716 \leqslant p \leqslant 0.7284$

(i) How many voters were surveyed?

(ii) If the margin of error for a 90% confidence level is given by

$$E = 1.645\sqrt{\dfrac{\hat{p}(1-\hat{p})}{n}}$$

construct a 90% confidence interval for the proportion of voters who said they voted in the referendum.

(iii) If the pollsters wanted to cut the margin of error in part (i) in half, then how many voters should be surveyed at a 95% confidence level, assuming the proportion in the new sample remains the same as in the smaller sample?

What do you notice?

Solution

(i) $\hat{p} + E = 0.7284$

    $0.7 + 1.96\sqrt{\dfrac{(0.7)(0.3)}{n}} = 0.7284$

    $1.96\sqrt{\dfrac{(0.7)(0.3)}{n}} = 0.7284 - 0.7$

    $1.96\sqrt{\dfrac{0.21}{n}} = 0.0284$

    $\sqrt{\dfrac{0.21}{n}} = 0.014489745$

    $\dfrac{0.21}{n} = 0.000209954$

    $n = \dfrac{0.21}{0.000209954}$

    $n = 1,000$ (to the nearest whole number)

(ii) A 90% confidence interval for the proportion is given by:

$$0.7 - 1.645\sqrt{\frac{0.21}{1,000}} \leqslant p \leqslant 0.7 + 1.645\sqrt{\frac{0.21}{1,000}}$$

$$0.6762 \leqslant p \leqslant 0.7238$$

(iii) From part (i), the existing margin of error is 0.0284 (0.7284 − 0.7). Therefore, we now require a margin of error equal to 0.0142 (0.0284 ÷ 2).

$$1.96\sqrt{\frac{(0.7)(0.3)}{n}} = 0.0142$$

$$\sqrt{\frac{0.21}{n}} = 0.007244897$$

$$\frac{0.21}{n} = 0.000052488$$

$$n = \frac{0.21}{0.000052488}$$

$$n = 4,001 \quad \text{(to the nearest whole number)}$$

Note how we need to multiply the sample size by 4 (2^2) if we wish to divide the margin of error by 2. Similarly, you would need to multiply the sample size by 9 (3^2) to divide the margin of error by 3.

At the 95% confidence level the margin of error is given by

$$E = 1.96\sqrt{\frac{\hat{p}(1 - \hat{p})}{n}}$$

where $\hat{p}$ is the sample proportion and n is the size of the sample. As $\hat{p}(1 - \hat{p})$ is a quadratic expression with a negative square term, the expression will have a maximum value. It can be shown using calculus that $\hat{p} = \frac{1}{2}$ maximises the expression $\hat{p}(1 - \hat{p})$. Therefore, at the 95% confidence level the maximum possible margin of error is:

$$E = 1.96\sqrt{\frac{\frac{1}{2}\left(1 - \frac{1}{2}\right)}{n}}$$

$$= 1.96\sqrt{\frac{1}{4n}}$$

$$= \frac{1.96}{2}\left(\frac{1}{\sqrt{n}}\right)$$

$$= 0.98\left(\frac{1}{\sqrt{n}}\right)$$

In fact $0.98\left(\frac{1}{\sqrt{n}}\right) < \frac{1}{\sqrt{n}}$. We can say that at the 95% confidence level, the margin of error for a population proportion will not exceed $\frac{1}{\sqrt{n}}$, where n is the sample size. While this approximation gives wider confidence intervals, it is easy to construct. On our course we will use the margin of error $E = 1.96\sqrt{\frac{\hat{p}(1 - \hat{p})}{n}}$ unless specifically asked to use the $\frac{1}{\sqrt{n}}$ margin of error for the population proportion.

Exercise 5.3

1. Express the following confidence intervals in the form $\hat{p} \pm E$; where E is the margin of error:

   (a) $0.333 < p < 0.555$

   (b) $0.7 < p < 0.9$

   (c) $0.233 < p < 0.621$

   (d) $0.607 < p < 0.713$

2. A sample is used to estimate a population proportion p. Find the margin of error E that corresponds to the given statistics and confidence level.

   (a) $n = 500$, $x = 150$, 95% confidence level

   (b) $n = 1,000$, $x = 800$, 95% confidence level

   (c) $n = 600$, $x = 300$, 95% confidence level

   (d) $n = 1,600$, $x = 20$, 95% confidence level

STATISTICS III

3. In a survey of 1,000 voters, 690 said they voted in a recent general election. Voting records show that 63% of eligible voters actually did vote.

   (a) Find a 95% confidence interval estimate of the proportion of people who said they voted.

   (b) Are the survey results consistent with the actual voter turnout of 63%?

4. An insurance company checks Garda records on 500 randomly selected car accidents and notes that teenagers were at the wheel in 82 of them.

   (a) Construct a 95% confidence interval for the percentage of all car accidents that involve teenagers.

   (b) Explain what your interval means.

5. Gregor Mendel (1822–84) is usually considered to be the founder of modern genetics. When Mendel conducted genetics experiments with peas, one sample of offspring consisted of 428 green peas and 152 yellow peas.

   (a) Form a 95% confidence interval for the percentage of yellow peas in the population.

   (b) Based on his theories, Mendel expected that 25% of the offspring peas would be yellow. Given the percentage of yellow peas in the sample, do the results contradict Mendel's theory? Explain.

6. SeaFerry Ltd. is exploring the possibility of offering a ferry service between two coastal towns, provided there is sufficient demand. The company randomly interviews 200 commuters from the two towns and 130 of them indicate that they would use the ferry service rather than the present bus service.

   (a) Estimate the population proportion p of commuters who would use the ferry service.

   (b) Construct a 95% confidence interval for p.

7. A newspaper reports that the government's approval rating is at 61%. The paper states that the poll is based on a random sample of 900 voters and that the margin of error is 3.2%. Show that the pollsters used a 95% level of confidence.

8. Suppose a sociologist wants to determine the percentage of Irish households using email. How many households must be surveyed in order to be 95% confident that the sample percentage is in error by no more than 4 percentage points?

9. Wildlife biologists inspect 180 deer shot by hunters and find 44 of them carrying ticks that test positive for Lyme disease.

   (a) Construct a 95% confidence interval for the percentage of deer that may carry such ticks.

   (b) If the scientists wanted to cut the margin of error in half, how many deer must they inspect?

   (c) Do you have any concerns about this sample? Explain.

10. (a) A newspaper states that the results of a poll of voters has a margin of error of plus or minus 3%. Explain carefully what that means.

    (b) A TV talk show asks viewers to register their opinion on school uniforms by logging on to a website. Of the 610 who voted, 480 favoured a uniform.

       (i) Identify the sample and the population in this survey.

       (ii) What is $\hat{p}$, the sample proportion?

       (iii) The TV show wishes to estimate the level of support among the general public for school uniforms. Identify possible sources of bias in the poll.

11. In a survey of 900 voters, 400 said they voted in a recent General Election.

    (i) Construct a 95% confidence interval for the proportion of people who actually voted in the election.

    (ii) If the margin of error for a 99% confidence level is given by

    $$E_{99} = 2.575\sqrt{\frac{\hat{p}(1-\hat{p})}{n}}$$

    construct a 99% confidence interval for the proportion.

    (iii) A 99% confidence interval is wider than a 95% confidence interval. What factor other than increasing the confidence level would increase the width of a confidence interval?

12. In a survey of n students, 600 said they owned a smartphone. A 95% confidence interval for the proportion of students owning a smartphone was given as [0.35128, 0.39872].

   (i) How many students were surveyed?

   (ii) If the margin of error for a 99% confidence interval is given by

   $$E_{99} = 2.575\sqrt{\frac{\hat{p}(1 - \hat{p})}{n}}$$

   construct a 99% confidence interval for the proportion of students owning a smartphone.

13. A 95% confidence interval for a proportion is given by:

   $$\hat{p} - 1.96\sqrt{\frac{\hat{p}(1 - \hat{p})}{n}} \leqslant p \leqslant \hat{p} + 1.96\sqrt{\frac{\hat{p}(1 - \hat{p})}{n}}$$

   Another method approximates a 95% confidence interval for a proportion as

   $$\hat{p} - \frac{1}{\sqrt{n}} \leqslant p \leqslant \hat{p} + \frac{1}{\sqrt{n}}$$

   where $\hat{p}$ is the sample proportion and n the sample size.

   (i) Construct 95% confidence intervals using both methods for a sample of size 400 with sample proportion $\frac{1}{10}$.

   (ii) Construct 95% confidence intervals for both methods for a sample of size 400 and sample proportion $\frac{1}{2}$.

   (iii) Comment on how the intervals are related as the sample proportion increases towards $\frac{1}{2}$.

   (iv) Investigate how the intervals are related as the sample proportion increases from $\frac{1}{2}$ towards 1.

   (v) Which is the more useful of the two methods?

14. Companies often send junk mail to thousands of potential customers in the hope that some will buy the company's product. The response rate is usually low. Suppose a company wants to test a response to a new product and sends a flyer to 1,000 people randomly selected from its mailing list of over 100,000 people. The company gets orders from 112 people.

   (a) Create a 95% confidence interval for the percentage of people the company contacts who may buy something.

   (b) Explain what this interval means.

   (c) The company must now decide whether to do a mass mailing. The mailing won't be cost-effective unless it produces at least a 5% return. What does your confidence interval suggest?

5.4 Hypothesis Testing

Hypothesis testing is an important aspect of statistics.

> In statistics, an hypothesis is a claim or statement about a population.

> An hypothesis test is a procedure for testing a claim about a parameter of a population.

Here are some examples of hypotheses that can be tested.

- Medical researchers claim that the mean body temperature of healthy adults is equal to 37 °C.
- 50% of car crashes occur within 10 km of home.
- The mean weight of an airline passenger with carry-on baggage is 84 kg.

Components of a Formal Hypothesis Test

- The **null hypothesis** (denoted by H_0) is a statement that the value of a population parameter (such as proportion or mean) is equal to some claimed value. Of course, it could also be that it is $>, \geqslant, <, \leqslant$ some value. In the examples above, we could use $H_0: \mu = 37$ °C, $H_0: p = 0.5$ and $H_0: \mu = 84$ kg. We test the null hypothesis directly in the sense that we assume it is true and reach a conclusion to reject H_0 or fail to reject H_0.

- The **alternative hypothesis** (denoted by H_1 or H_A) is a statement that the population parameter has a value that is different from that assumed under the null hypothesis. In the examples above, $H_1: \mu \neq 37$ °C, $H_1: p \neq 0.5$, $H_1: \mu \neq 84$ kg.

- When testing hypotheses about proportions, we set up a confidence interval for the population proportion at a given confidence level. If the proportion stated in the null hypothesis is within the confidence interval, then we **fail to reject** the null hypothesis. If the proportion stated in the null hypothesis is outside the confidence interval, then we **reject** the null hypothesis in favour of the alternative hypothesis.

> Note that we say, 'Fail to reject the null hypothesis'. You should not say, 'Accept the null hypothesis'.

Worked Example 5.11

It is thought that 30% of a certain kind of apple seed will germinate. In an experiment, 85 out of 300 seeds germinated. What conclusion can be reached at the 95% confidence level about the true population proportion of seeds that will germinate?

Solution

Step 1 State the null and alternative hypotheses.

$H_0: p = 0.3$ $\qquad$ $H_1: p \neq 0.3$

Step 2 Calculate the sample proportion.

$$\hat{p} = \frac{85}{300}$$

$$= \frac{17}{60}$$

Step 3 Set up the confidence interval at the 5% level of significance. (Note: 95% confidence level $\Rightarrow$ 5% significance level)

Margin of error: $1.96 \sqrt{\dfrac{0.28\dot{3}(1 - 0.28\dot{3})}{300}} \approx 0.051$

Confidence interval: $\hat{p} - E < p < \hat{p} + E$

$0.28\dot{3} - 0.051 < p < 0.28\dot{3} + 0.051$

$0.232 < p < 0.334$

0.3 is within this interval, so we fail to reject the null hypothesis. Therefore, we conclude that 30% of all seeds will germinate.

STATISTICS III

- The **test statistic** is a value used in making a decision about the null hypothesis. It is found by converting the sample statistic (such as the sample proportion $\hat{p}$ or the sample mean $\bar{x}$) to a z-score with the assumption that the null hypothesis is true. Since we will be using a confidence interval to test hypotheses about proportions, the only test statistic we will need is the test statistic for a mean. The test statistic for a mean is:

$$z = \frac{\bar{x} - \mu}{\frac{\sigma}{\sqrt{n}}}$$

This formula appears on page 35 of *Formulae and Tables*.

- If the z-score obtained is within the region known as the **critical region**, we reject the null hypothesis. The critical region depends on the level of confidence that we require. The critical values bound the critical region. For a 95% confidence level, the critical values for a two-tailed test are ±1.96. If $|z| \geqslant 1.96$ (i.e. if $z \leqslant -1.96$ or if $z \geqslant 1.96$), then the

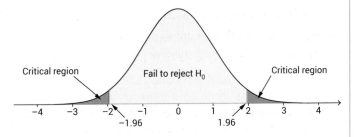

z-score is in the critical region, and the null hypothesis is rejected. If $|z| < 1.96$, we fail to reject the null hypothesis.

- The **significance level** is the probability that the test statistic will fall in the critical region given that the null hypothesis is actually true. Therefore, for a 95% confidence level, the significance level is 5%. If a test statistic falls in the critical region, we reject the null hypothesis. Therefore, the significance level is the probability of rejecting a null hypothesis, given that it is true. In statistics, such an error is known as a 'Type 1 Error'.

Worked Example 5.12

The manufacturers of 'Durabeat' batteries claim that they have a mean lifetime of 86 hours. A random sample of 200 'Durabeat' batteries has a mean lifetime of 87.5 hours and a standard deviation of 11 hours. Does this provide evidence at the 5% level of significance that the 'Durabeat' batteries have a different mean lifetime to that claimed by the manufacturer?

Solution

Step 1 State the null and alternative hypotheses. The null hypothesis is that there is no difference.

$$H_0: \mu = 86 \qquad H_1: \mu \neq 86$$

Step 2 Calculate the test statistic.

$$z = \frac{\bar{x} - \mu}{\left(\frac{\sigma}{\sqrt{n}}\right)}$$

$$= \frac{87.5 - 86}{\left(\frac{11}{\sqrt{200}}\right)}$$

$$= \frac{15\sqrt{2}}{11}$$

 For a large enough sample (generally $n \geqslant 30$), we can use the sample standard deviation s in place of the unknown population standard deviation σ when constructing our confidence interval for the population mean μ.

$$\therefore z = 1.93 \quad \text{(correct to 2 decimal places)}$$

Since $|z| < 1.96$, the result is not significant and we fail to reject the null hypothesis that 'Durabeat' batteries have a mean lifetime of 86 hours. We do so with 95% confidence.

p-Values

The p-value is the probability that the test statistic or a more extreme value could occur if the null hypothesis is correct. If the p-value is small enough, then we reject the null hypothesis. To be more specific, if the p-value is smaller than the significance level, we reject the null hypothesis. Otherwise, we fail to reject the null hypothesis.

Worked Example 5.13

The mean systolic blood pressure for adult males aged 30–45 is 128. Airport authorities in the UK are concerned about the effects of stress on male air traffic controllers. A random sample of 100 male air traffic controllers in this age group is selected. Their mean systolic blood pressure is 132 with a standard deviation of 15.

(i) Construct a 95% confidence interval for the mean systolic blood pressure for the air traffic controllers. Interpret this interval.

(ii) Carry out an hypothesis test at the 5% level of significance to find out if there is evidence to suggest that the mean systolic blood pressure for male air traffic controllers in the UK (aged 30–45) is different to the global average.

(iii) Give a p-value for this hypothesis test and interpret this p-value.

Solution

(i) Let μ be the mean systolic blood pressure for air traffic controllers.

The 95% confidence interval for μ is:

$$\bar{x} - 1.96\frac{\sigma}{\sqrt{n}} \leqslant \mu \leqslant \bar{x} + 1.96\frac{\sigma}{\sqrt{n}}$$

$$132 - 1.96\frac{15}{\sqrt{100}} \leqslant \mu \leqslant 132 + 1.96\frac{15}{\sqrt{100}}$$

$$129.06 \leqslant \mu \leqslant 134.94$$

We can be 95% confident that the mean systolic blood pressure for the population of male air traffic controllers aged 30–45 working in the UK lies in the interval [129.06, 134.94]. This is different from the mean pressure of 128 for the global population of 30–45-year-old males. This supports the idea that these UK-based air traffic controllers have higher mean systolic blood pressure than males of the same age globally.

(ii) The null hypothesis is that the mean systolic blood pressure for the UK-based male air traffic controllers is 128, the same as the national average for males aged 30–45: $H_0: \mu = 128$.

The alternative hypothesis is that mean systolic blood pressure for the air traffic controllers is not equal to 128: $H_1: \mu \neq 128$.

We now find the test statistic.

$$z = \frac{\bar{x} - \mu}{\left(\frac{\sigma}{\sqrt{n}}\right)}$$

We use the known sample standard deviation value of 15 in place of the unknown σ.

$$= \frac{132 - 128}{\left(\frac{15}{\sqrt{100}}\right)}$$

$$= 2.67 \quad \text{(to 2 decimal places)}$$

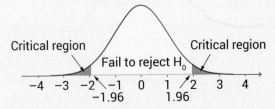

Critical region   Critical region

Fail to reject H_0

−4 −3 −2 −1   0   1   2   3   4
        −1.96   1.96

As 2.67 is in the critical region at the 5% level of significance, we reject the null hypothesis and conclude that the mean systolic blood pressure for the air traffic controllers is different to the global average for males aged 30–45.

(iii) The probability of getting a z-score ≥ 2.67 is found in the z-tables.

$$P(z \geq 2.67) = 1 - P(z < 2.67)$$

$$= 1 - 0.9962$$

$$= 0.0038$$

As this is a two-tailed test, we require the probability of z being greater than 2.67 or less than −2.67. This means we have to multiply 0.0038 by 2.

$$P(|z| \geq 2.67) = 2(0.0038) = 0.0076$$

This number is the p-value.

The significance level is 0.05.

As the p-value is less than the significance level ($0.0076 < 0.05$), we reject $H_0: \mu = 128$. So the mean systolic blood pressure for UK-based male air traffic controllers is significantly different to the mean pressure for the global population of males aged 30–45.

Exercise 5.4

1. Write the null and alternative hypotheses you would use to test each of the following situations:

   (a) Is a coin fair?

   (b) Only 20% of people who quit smoking succeed. Sellers of a motivational DVD claim that listening to the DVD can help people quit.

   (c) In the 1970s, only 30% of young people who graduated from second-level education went on to third level. Has the percentage changed since then?

2. The editor of a weekly magazine is concerned about typographical errors and believes that about 1.5% of the number of lines printed will have one error. An examination of 650 randomly selected lines revealed 11 lines that had one error. Does the sample support the editor's belief? Use a 5% level of significance.

3. In a study of 8,000 car crashes, it was found that 4,200 of them occurred within 5 miles of home. Use a 0.05 significance level to test the claim that 50% of car crashes occur within 5 miles of home.

4. Suppose you interview 1,000 randomly selected exiting voters following a Presidential election. Of the 1,000 voters, 550 reported that they voted for John F. Murphy. Assuming that there were only two candidates in the race, is there sufficient evidence to suggest that Mr. Murphy will be the next President? Use a 5% level of significance.

5. A biologist was interested in determining whether sunflower seedlings treated with a chemical designed to prevent disease, resulted in a different mean height of sunflower seedlings than the standard height of 15.7 cm. The biologist treated a random sample of $n = 33$ seedlings with the chemical. Subsequently, the seedlings were measured and the mean height of the sample was 13.66 cm with a standard deviation of 2.54 cm. Has the mean height of the seedlings changed? Use a 5% level of significance.

6. The following z-scores were obtained in a selection of two-tailed hypothesis tests. Give a p-value for each test.

   (i) 1.98   (iv) 2.92   (vii) 1.67

   (ii) 2.45   (v) 3.04   (viii) 1.82

   (iii) 2.58   (vi) 1.15

7. A particular machine produces metal rods that are normally distributed with a mean length of 210 cm and a standard deviation of 6 cm. The machine is serviced. Following the service, a random sample of 100 rods is taken and the mean length of the sample is found to be 211.5 cm with a standard deviation also of 6 cm. Is there evidence at the 5% level of significance of a change in the mean length of the bars produced? Give a p-value for this hypothesis test and interpret this p-value.

8. The mean mark for all students taking a certain Leaving Certificate subject at Higher Level in 2012 was 67.5 with a standard deviation of 10. A random sample of 100 students who sat the Leaving Certificate exam in the same subject in 2013 revealed a sample mean of 69. Is there evidence to conclude that the students have improved in a year? (Assume the 2012 and 2013 exams were of equal difficulty.)

9. A random sample of 106 body temperatures has a mean of 98.2 °F and a standard deviation of 0.62 °F. Use a 0.05 significance level to test the claim that the mean body temperature is not 98.6 °F. Give a p-value for this hypothesis test and interpret this p-value.

Revision Exercises

1. (a) What is inferential statistics?

   (b) Explain the following terms:

      (i) census   (iv) parameter

      (ii) sample   (v) statistic

      (iii) random sample

2. Suppose we draw all possible samples of size 400 from a given population. Suppose further that we compute the mean of each sample.

   (i) What is the name given to the distribution of these sample means?

   (ii) What is the shape of this distribution?

   (iii) If μ is the population mean and λ is the mean of the distribution, how are μ and λ related?

   (iv) If σ is the population standard deviation and α the standard deviation of the distribution, how are σ and α related?

3. A simple random sample of size 100 is chosen from a population that is known to be normal. The mean of the population is 120 with a standard deviation of 15. Find the probability that the sample mean is greater than 124.

4. A simple random sample of size 64 is chosen from a population that is known to be normal. The mean of the population is 175 with a standard deviation of 4. Find the probability that the sample mean is less than 172.

5. A random sample of 900 oranges was taken from a large consignment. The mean weight, μ, of the oranges in the consignment is unknown. The mean weight of the sample was 82.4 grams and the standard deviation of the sample was 12 grams. Construct a 95% confidence interval for the mean weight of the oranges in the consignment.

6. A population has a mean μ and a standard deviation of 15. A random sample of 400 from this population has a mean of 95.

   (i) Construct a 95% confidence interval for μ.

   (ii) If the margin of error for a 90% confidence level is $E_{90} = 1.645\frac{\sigma}{\sqrt{n}}$, construct a 90% confidence interval for μ.

   (iii) If the margin of error for a 99% confidence level is $E_{99} = 2.575\frac{\sigma}{\sqrt{n}}$, construct a 99% confidence level for μ.

7. A newspaper reports that the government's approval rating has improved. In a random sample of 900 voters, 480 voters approved of the government. Construct a 95% confidence interval for the approval rating of the government.

8. In 2007, 24% of Irish consumers purchased organic food products. In a recent random sample of 900 Irish consumers, 120 consumers reported regularly purchasing organic food products. Does this provide evidence at the 5% level of significance that the proportion has changed from 2007?

9. A vegetable grower packages carrots in bags with a nominal weight of 5 kg. The grower claims that the mean weight of all bags packed is 5 kg. A random sample of 64 bags was selected. These had a mean weight of 4.9 kg with a standard deviation of 0.25 kg. Does this provide evidence at the 5% level of significance that the mean weight is not 5 kg?

10. ABC Ltd is exploring the possibility of offering a new product to its customers, provided there is sufficient demand for the product. The company randomly interviews 300 customers and 200 of them indicate that they would switch to the new product.

    (a) Estimate the population proportion p of customers who would buy the new product.

    (b) Construct a 95% confidence interval for p.

11. 'Dowsing' is a type of divination employed in attempts to locate groundwater, buried metals or ores, gemstones, oil, grave sites, etc.

A person who practices dowsing is known as a dowser. Dowsers claim that the forked stick they carry vibrates when something of interest, such as groundwater, is located directly below.

In a rural area, about 30% of the wells drilled find adequate water at a depth of 35 m or less. A local dowser claims that he is able to find water with a forked stick. A survey of 80 randomly selected customers of his reveals that 27 have wells less than 35 m in depth.

Test the hypothesis that the dowser has a different success rate to the water drillers.

12. According to a National Business Travel Association 2008 survey, the average salary of a travel management professional is $97,300. Assume that the standard deviation of such salaries is $30,000. Consider a random sample of 50 travel management professionals.

    (a) What is the mean of the sampling distribution of the sample mean with sample size 50?

    (b) What is the standard deviation of the same sampling distribution?

    (c) Describe the shape of this sampling distribution.

    (d) Sketch this sampling distribution.

    (e) Find the z-score for a value of $89,500 for the sample mean.

    (f) What is the probability that a random sample of size 50 will have a sample mean of less than $89,500?

STATISTICS III

Exam Questions

1. The distribution of the hourly earnings of all employees in Ireland in October 2009 is shown in the diagram. It can be seen that the distribution is positively skewed.

   - The mean is €22.05.
   - The median is €17.82.
   - The standard deviation is €10.64.
   - The lower quartile is €12.80.
   - The upper quartile is €26.05.

   (i) If six employees are selected at random from this population, what is the probability that exactly four of them had hourly earnings of more than €12.80?

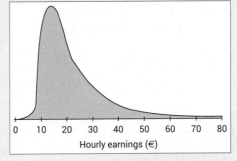

Hourly earnings (€)

Source: Adapted from: CSO. *National Employment Survey 2008 and 2009*

In a computer simulation, random samples of size 200 are repeatedly selected from this population and the mean of each sample is recorded. A thousand such sample means are recorded.

(ii) Describe the expected distribution of these sample means. Your description should refer to the shape of the distribution and to its mean and standard deviation.

(iii) How many of the sample means would you expect to be greater than €23?

SEC Leaving Certificate Higher Level, Project Maths Sample Paper 2, 2012

2. Some research was carried out into the participation of girls and boys in sport. The researchers selected a simple random sample of 50 male and 50 female teenagers enrolled in GAA clubs in the greater Cork area. They asked the teenagers the question: How many sports do you play?

The data collected were as follows:

Boys	Girls
0, 4, 5, 1, 4, 1, 3, 3, 3, 1,	3, 3, 3, 1, 1, 3, 3, 1, 3, 3,
1, 2, 2, 2, 5, 3, 3, 4, 1, 2,	2, 2, 4, 4, 4, 5, 5, 2, 2, 3,
2, 2, 2, 3, 3, 3, 4, 5, 1, 1,	3, 3, 4, 1, 6, 2, 3, 3, 3, 4,
1, 1, 1, 2, 2, 2, 2, 2, 3, 3,	4, 5, 3, 4, 3, 3, 3, 4, 4, 3,
3, 3, 3, 3, 3, 3, 3, 3, 3, 3	1, 1, 3, 2, 1, 3, 1, 3, 1, 3

(a) Display the data in a way that gives a picture of each distribution.

(b) State **one difference** and **one similarity** between the distributions of the two samples.

(c) Do you think that there is evidence that there are differences between the two populations? Explain your answer.

(Note: you are not required to conduct a formal hypothesis test.)

(d) The researchers are planning to repeat this research on a larger scale. List **two** improvements they could make to the design of the research in order to reduce the possibility of bias in the samples. Explain why each improvement you suggest will reduce the likelihood of bias.

NCCA Pre-Leaving Certificate Project Maths Paper 2, February 2010

3. A factory manufactures aluminium rods. One of its machines can be set to produce rods of a specified length. The lengths of these rods are normally distributed with mean equal to the specified length and standard deviation equal to 0.2 mm.

The machine has been set to produce rods of length 40 mm.

(a) What is the probability that a randomly selected rod will be less than 39.7 mm in length?

(b) Five rods are selected at random. What is the probability that at least two of them are less than 39.7 mm in length?

(c) The operators want to check whether the setting on the machine is still accurate. They take a random sample of ten rods and measure their lengths. The lengths in millimetres are:

39.5   40.0   39.7   40.2   39.8

39.7   40.2   39.9   40.1   39.6

Conduct a hypothesis test at the 5% level of significance to decide whether the machine's setting has become inaccurate. You should start by clearly stating the null hypothesis and the alternative hypothesis, and finish by clearly stating what you conclude about the machine.

SEC Leaving Certificate Higher Level, Project Maths Paper 2, 2010

4. A generic drug used to treat a particular condition has a success rate of 51%. A company is developing two new drugs, *A* and *B*, to treat the condition. They carried out clinical trials on two groups of 500 patients suffering from the condition. The results showed that Drug *A* was successful in the case of 296 patients. The company claims that Drug *A* is more successful in treating the condition than the generic drug.

(i) Use a hypothesis test at the 5% level of significance to decide whether there is sufficient evidence to justify the company's claim. State the null hypothesis and state your conclusion clearly.

(ii) The null hypothesis was accepted for Drug *B*. Estimate the greatest number of patients in that trial who could have been successfully treated with Drug *B*.

SEC Leaving Certificate Higher Level, Paper 2, 2014

5. A survey of 100 shoppers, randomly selected from a large number of Saturday supermarket shoppers, showed that the mean shopping spend was €90.45. The standard deviation of this sample was €20.73.

(a) Find a 95% confidence interval for the mean amount spent in a supermarket on that Saturday.

(b) A supermarket has claimed that the mean amount spent by shoppers on a Saturday is €94. Based on the survey, test the supermarket's claim using a 5% level of significance. Clearly state your null hypothesis, your alternative hypothesis, and your conclusion.

(c) Find the *p*-value of the test you performed in part (b) above and explain what this value represents in the context of the question.

SEC Leaving Certificate Higher Level, Paper 2, 2015

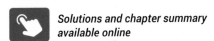
Solutions and chapter summary available online

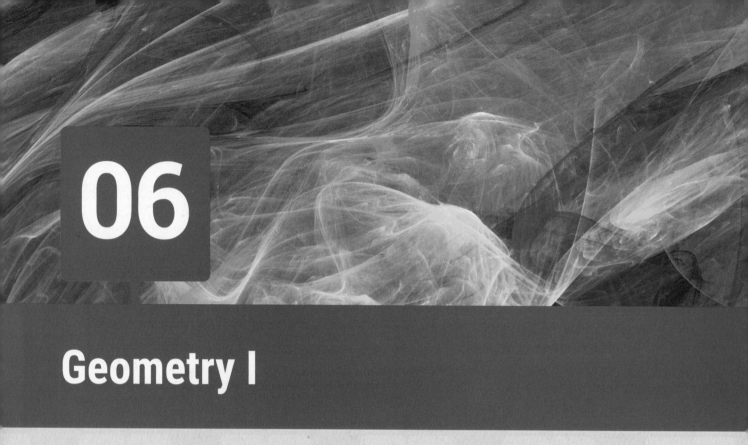

06

Geometry I

 In this chapter you will learn about:

- The basic concepts of geometry and geometry notation

- What an axiom is and how to use axioms to solve problems

- Theorem 1. Vertically opposite angles are equal in measure.

- Theorem 2. In an isosceles triangle the angles opposite the equal sides are equal. Conversely, if two angles are equal, then the triangle is isosceles.

- Theorem 3. If a transversal makes equal alternate angles on two lines then the lines are parallel (and converse).

- Theorem 4. The angles in any triangle add to 180°.

- Theorem 5. Two lines are parallel if, and only if, for any transversal, the corresponding angles are equal.

- Theorem 6. Each exterior angle of a triangle is equal to the sum of the interior opposite angles.

- Theorem 7. In a triangle, the angle opposite the greater of two sides is greater than the angle opposite the lesser side. Conversely, the side opposite the greater of two angles is greater than the side opposite the lesser angle.

- Theorem 8. Two sides of a triangle are together greater than the third.

- Theorem 9. In a parallelogram, opposite sides are equal and opposite angles are equal.

- Corollary 1. A diagonal divides a parallelogram into two congruent triangles.

- Theorem 10. The diagonals of a parallelogram bisect each other.

- Theorem 11. If three parallel lines cut off equal segments on some transversal line, then they will cut off equal segments on any other transversal.

- Theorem 12. Let ABC be a triangle. If a line l is parallel to BC and cuts $[AB]$ in the ratio $m:n$, then it also cuts $[AC]$ in the same ratio.

- Theorem 13. If two triangles are similar, then their sides are proportional, in order.

- Theorem 14. The theorem of Pythagoras: In a right-angled triangle the square of the hypotenuse is the sum of the squares of the other two sides.

- Theorem 15. The converse to the theorem of Pythagoras: If the square of one side of a triangle is the sum of the squares of the other two sides, then the angle opposite the first side is a right angle.

- Theorem 16. For a triangle, base times height does not depend on the choice of base.

- Theorem 17. A diagonal of a parallelogram bisects the area.

- Theorem 18. The area of a parallelogram is the base times the height.

- Theorem 19. The angle at the centre of a circle standing on a given arc is twice the angle at any point of the circle standing on the same arc.

- Corollary 2. All angles at points of a circle, standing on the same arc, are equal.

- Corollary 3. Each angle in a semicircle is a right angle.

- Corollary 4. If the angle standing on a chord [BC] at some point of the circle is a right angle, then [BC] is a diameter.

- Corollary 5. If ABCD is a cyclic quadrilateral, then opposite angles sum to 180°.

- Theorem 20. Each tangent is perpendicular to the radius that goes to the point of contact. If P lies on s, and a line l is perpendicular to the radius to P, then l is a tangent to s.

- Corollary 6. If two circles intersect at one point only, then the two centres and the point of contact are collinear.

- Theorem 21. (i) The perpendicular from the centre to a chord bisects the chord. (ii) The perpendicular bisector of a chord passes through the centre.

You should remember...

- Geometry notation
- Types of angles
- Types of triangles
- Parallel
- Perpendicular
- Junior Certificate geometry theorems
- How to deal with fractions

Key words

- Axiom
- Theorem
- Corollary
- Converse
- Vertically opposite
- Alternate
- Corresponding
- Isosceles triangle
- Interior angle
- Exterior angle
- Quadrilateral
- Parallelogram
- Similar triangle
- Ratio
- Pythagoras
- Area
- Circle
- Diameter
- Chord
- Perpendicular
- Tangent

6.1 Geometry

When we study figures and their properties in two- or three-dimensional space, we are studying geometry. We encounter geometrical shapes everywhere in our daily lives – in buildings, in works of art and in countless other objects.

Geometry comes from the Greek word meaning 'earth measurement' (γεωμετρία; *geo* = earth, *metria* = measure). Many of the theorems and proofs that we use today were first recorded by Euclid of Alexandria, a Greek mathematician. His book *The Elements*, written about 300 BC, is one of the most famous mathematics textbooks ever written and is still in use more than 2,000 years later!

We encounter geometry in many aspects of everyday life, and a knowledge of geometry is essential in many careers. Carpenters, engineers and architects, to name but a few, must have a knowledge of geometry to do their jobs.

6.2 Basic Concepts

The Plane

> A **plane** is a flat two-dimensional surface. It has length and width, but it has no thickness.

A **plane** stretches on to infinity. Points and lines are shown on a plane.

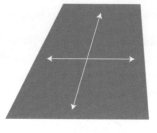

Points on the Plane

> A **point** is a position on a plane. It has no dimensions.

A **point** is denoted by a capital letter and a dot.

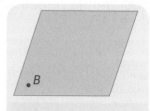

This is the point *B*.

> If points lie on the same plane they are said to be **coplanar**.

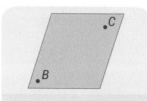

Here, *B* and *C* are **coplanar**.

Lines

A **line** can be named by any two points on the line or by a lower-case letter. It has an infinite number of points on it.

> A **line** is a straight, infinitely thin one-dimensional figure that continues forever in both directions; it has no endpoints.

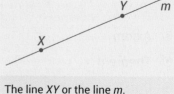

The line *XY* or the line *m*.

> Points that lie on the same line are called **collinear points**.

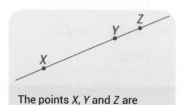

The points *X*, *Y* and *Z* are **collinear**.

The points *A*, *B* and *C* are not collinear.

Perpendicular and Parallel Lines

The line *a* is **perpendicular** to the line *b*.

We denote this as $a \perp b$.

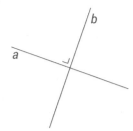

Perpendicular lines are lines that are at right angles or 90° to each other.

The line *d* is **parallel** to the line *e*.

We denote this as $d \parallel e$.

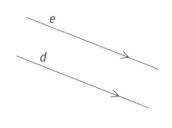

Parallel lines are lines that are the same distance apart. They never meet.

Line Segment

The **line segment** shown has one endpoint *A* and another endpoint *B*. This is the line segment [AB] or [BA].

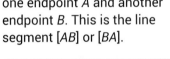

A line segment is part of a straight line. It has two endpoints and can be measured using a ruler.

When we write an actual measurement, we use the | | symbols to show this.

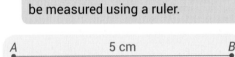

|AB| = 5 cm

Ray

A ray is part of a line that originates at a point and goes on forever in only one direction.

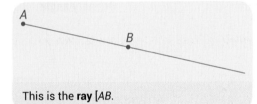

This is the **ray** [AB.

The other end goes on to infinity. It is sometimes called a half-line.

A single square bracket is used to denote from where the ray originates.

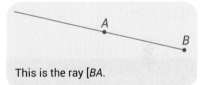

This is the ray [BA.

6.3 Angles

Angle Notation

When two rays meet at a point called the vertex, they make an angle.

There are many different ways to label an angle.

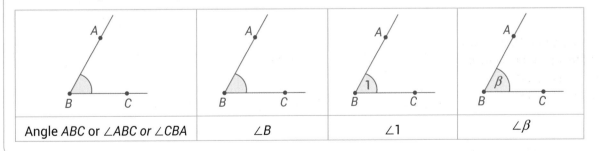

| Angle *ABC* or ∠*ABC* or ∠*CBA* | ∠*B* | ∠1 | ∠*β* |

Identifying Different Types of Angles

Angles can be divided into many different types.

Null angle	Acute angle	Right angle
Angle = 0°	An angle that measures more than 0° but less than 90°	Angle = 90°
Obtuse angle	**Straight angle**	**Reflex angle**
An angle that measures more than 90° but less than 180°	180° Angle = 180°	An angle that measures more than 180° but less than 360°
Full angle	**Ordinary angle**	**Supplementary angles**
360° Full rotation, angle = 360°	An angle that measures more than 0° but less than 180°	1 2 Two angles whose measures add up to 180° $|\angle 1| + |\angle 2| = 180°$

> Supplementary angles do not need to be beside or adjacent to each other.

For example, the two angles shown are supplementary.

Measuring Angles

Angles on our course are usually measured in degrees or radians.

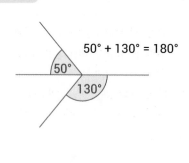

50° + 130° = 180°

50°

130°

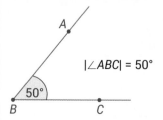

$|\angle ABC| = 50°$

We use a protractor to measure angles accurately.
A protractor has two scales, a centre point and a baseline.

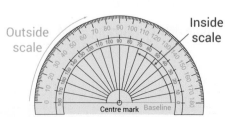

Outside scale

Inside scale

Centre mark   Baseline

6.4 Axioms

An axiom is a statement that we accept **without any proof**. Knowing axioms is essential to understanding geometry and proving geometry theorems.

Axiom 1 (Two Points Axiom)
There is exactly one line through any two given points.

We can draw only one line through the points *A* and *B*.

Axiom 2 (Ruler Axiom)
The properties of the distance between points.

1. Distance is never a negative number.

2. |AB| = |BA|.

3. If *C* lies on *AB*, between *A* and *B*, then |AB| = |AC| + |CB|.

4. Given any ray from the point *X* and a distance *d* ⩾ 0, there is exactly one point *Y* on the ray whose distance from *X* is *d*. This property means that we can mark off a distance of, say, 4 cm on a ray from a point *X* and call this point *Y*. The length of the line segment [XY] will also be 4 cm.

Axiom 3 (Protractor Axiom)
The properties of the degree measure of an angle.

The number of degrees in an angle is always a number between 0 and 360. This axiom has the following properties:

1. A straight angle has 180°.

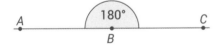

All the angles at a point add up to 360°.

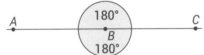

2. Given a ray [AB and a number between 0 and 180, there is exactly one ray from *A*, on each side of the line *AB*, that makes an (ordinary) angle having *d* degrees with the ray [AB.

This property of the protractor axiom means that there is, for example, only one 60° angle on each side of the line *AB*.

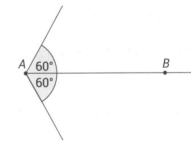

3. If an angle is divided into two smaller angles, then these two angles add up to the original angle.

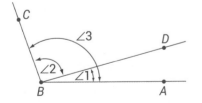

|∠1| + |∠2| = |∠3|

Axiom 5 (Axiom of Parallels)
Given any line *l* and a point *P*, there is exactly one line through *P* that is parallel to *l*.

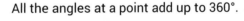

Only one line can be drawn through the point *P* that is parallel to the line *l*.

6.5 Angles and Lines

In the previous sections, we looked at the different concepts, types of angle and axioms from our geometry course. We can now investigate certain properties, rules or theorems associated with various geometrical shapes.

Let us begin by investigating the relationships between angles and certain lines.

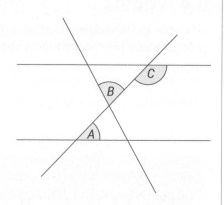

> Given two intersecting lines, **vertically opposite angles** are angles that have the same vertex and are not adjacent to each other.

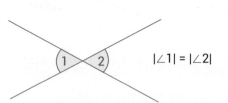

$|\angle 1| = |\angle 2|$

> **Theorem 1**
> Vertically opposite angles are equal in measure.

To spot **vertically opposite angles,** we look for the **X shape**.

When a line cuts across two or more other lines, certain angles are formed.

> A line that cuts two or more lines (usually parallel) is called a **transversal**.

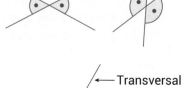
← Transversal

> **Alternate angles** are on opposite sides of the transversal that cuts two lines but are between the two lines.

> **Theorem 3**
> If a transversal makes equal alternate angles on two lines then the lines are parallel (and converse).

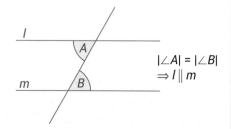

$|\angle A| = |\angle B|$
$\Rightarrow l \parallel m$

> The **converse** of a theorem is formed by swapping the order of the hypothesis and conclusion. The conditional statement 'if A then B' has an hypothesis (A) and a conclusion (B). In general, the converse of 'if A then B' is 'if B then A'. Converses may or may not be true.

Remember to look for the **Z shape**.

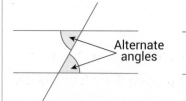
Alternate angles

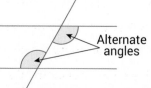
Alternate angles

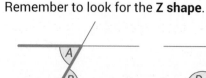

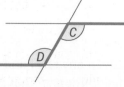

Corresponding angles are on the same side of the transversal that cuts two lines. One angle is between the lines, and the other angle is outside the lines.

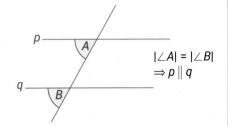

$|\angle A| = |\angle B|$
$\Rightarrow p \parallel q$

Theorem 5

Two lines are parallel if, and only if, for any transversal, the corresponding angles are equal.

Remember to look for the **F shape**.

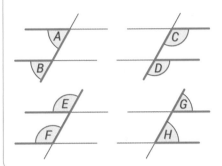

Corresponding angles

Corresponding angles

Corresponding angles

Corresponding angles

Interior angles between two parallel lines add up to 180°.

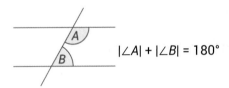

$|\angle A| + |\angle B| = 180°$

Worked Example 6.1

Without measuring, find the value of $|\angle A|$, $|\angle B|$, $|\angle C|$ and $|\angle D|$.

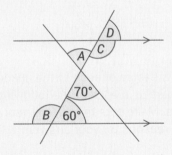

Solution

$|\angle A| = 70°$ (vertically opposite angle)

$|\angle B| = 180° - 60°$ (straight angle)

$\Rightarrow |\angle B| = 120°$

$|\angle C| = 120°$ (equal alternate angle to B)

$|\angle D| = 60°$ (equal corresponding angle)

Remember: Most questions have more than one way in which to find the measure of the required angle.

Give reasons for your answers.

Exercise 6.1

1. On a plane, plot the points A, B, C, D, E, F, G and H. Using these points, draw:

   (i) A line AB

   (ii) A line segment $[DE]$

   (iii) A line segment $[FH]$

   (iv) A ray $CD]$

   (v) A ray $[FG$

   (vi) A line parallel to AB, which passes through another point

   (vii) A line perpendicular to AC and passing through the point B

   (viii) State, using an axiom, why $|EF|$ and $|FE|$ are equal.

   (ix) Find $|AB|$. Explain why you cannot measure the length of line AB.

2. (a) On a plane, plot the points *P* and *Q*.

    (i) How many lines can be drawn through the point *P*?

    (ii) Draw a line through the points *P* and *Q*. How many lines can be drawn through the points *P* and *Q*?

(b) (i) Draw a line segment [*RS*] where |*RS*| = 10 cm.

    (ii) Mark any point on the line segment [*RS*] and label as the point *X*.

    (iii) Show that |*RX*| + |*SX*| = |*RS*|.

3. Explain each of the following terms used to describe angles. Construct an example of each angle, giving the measure of the angle.

    (i) Obtuse angle   **(iv)** Straight angle

    (ii) Ordinary angle   **(v)** Reflex angle

    (iii) Acute angle   **(vi)** Full angle

4. Use a protractor to draw the following angles:

    (i) 35°   **(iii)** 235°   **(v)** 350°

    (ii) 165°   **(iv)** 180°   **(vi)** 275°

5. Classify each of the following pairs of angles using the diagram below:

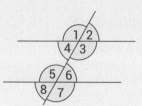

(i)	∠1 and ∠2	Supplementary
(ii)	∠3 and ∠5	
(iii)	∠4 and ∠8	
(iv)	∠4 and ∠2	
(v)	∠1 and ∠5	

6. Using the diagram, list:

    (i) Two pairs of equal corresponding angles

    (ii) Two pairs of equal alternate angles

    (iii) Two pairs of vertically opposite angles

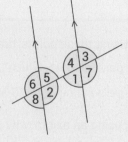

7. Consider the following diagram:

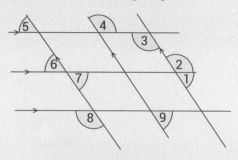

If |∠1| = 63°, find the measure of all the angles numbered. Give reasons for your answers.

8. Solve for *x* in each of the following diagrams:

    (i)

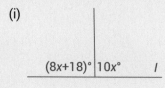

    (ii)

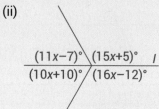

    (iii)

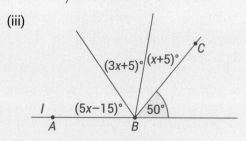

9. Find the measure of each of the unknown angles marked in each of the following diagrams. Make sure to show all your work and give reasons for your answers.

    (i)

    (ii)

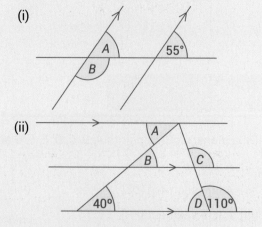

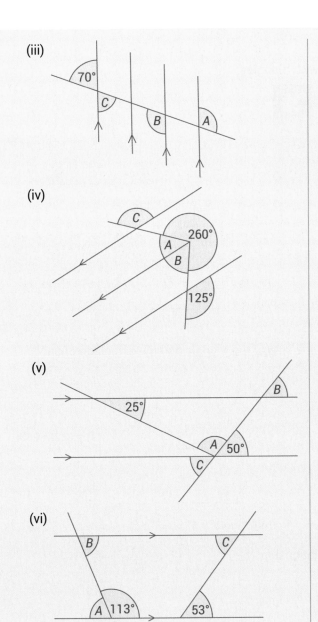

(iii) 70° C B A

(iv) C 260° A B 125°

(v) 25° B A 50° C

(vi) B C A 113° 53°

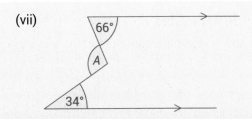

(vii) 66° A 34°

10. Find the measure of the unknown variable in each of the following diagrams. Show all necessary workings and give reasons for your answers.

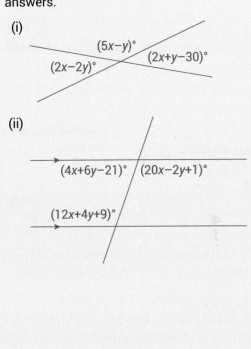

(i) $(5x-y)°$ $(2x-2y)°$ $(2x+y-30)°$

(ii) $(4x+6y-21)°$ $(20x-2y+1)°$ $(12x+4y+9)°$

6.6 Triangles I

When investigating triangles, we must first be aware of the different types of triangles and the notation used to describe them.

Equilateral	Isosceles	Scalene
60° 60° 60°		
All sides the same length	At least two sides the same length	No sides the same length
All angles the same size (60°)	At least two angles the same size	No angles the same size

An equilateral triangle is also considered to be an isosceles triangle. This is because **at least two** sides or angles are equal.

Angles in Triangles

We can now investigate some theorems associated with triangles.

Theorem 2

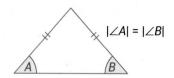

In an isosceles triangle the angles opposite the equal sides are equal in measure. Conversely, if two angles in a triangle are equal in measure, then the triangle is isosceles.

$|\angle A| = |\angle B|$

Theorem 4

The angles in any triangle add to 180°.

$|\angle 1| + |\angle 2| + |\angle 3| = 180°$

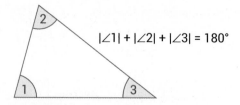

An **exterior angle** of a triangle is the angle between one side of the triangle and the extension of an adjacent side.

Theorem 6

Each exterior angle of a triangle is equal to the sum of the interior opposite angles.

$|\angle 1| = |\angle 2| + |\angle 3|$

More Triangles

We will now deal with one property concerning the relationship between the angles and sides of triangles.

In any triangle:
- The largest angle is opposite the largest side.
- The smallest angle is opposite the smallest side.

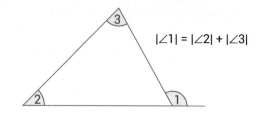

The converse is also true.

In any triangle:
- The largest side is opposite the largest angle.
- The smallest side is opposite the smallest angle.

Theorem 7

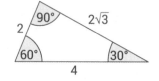

The angle opposite the greater of two sides is greater than the angle opposite the lesser side. Conversely, the side opposite the greater of two angles is greater than the side opposite the lesser angle.

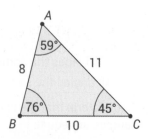

$|AC| > |BC|,$

$\therefore |\angle ABC| > |\angle BAC|$

Another property of triangles can help determine if three lengths can form the three sides of a triangle.

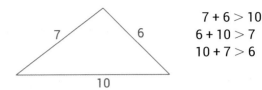

$7 + 6 > 10$
$6 + 10 > 7$
$10 + 7 > 6$

The sum of the lengths of any two sides of a triangle have to be greater than the length of the third side.

This allows us to state the following theorem:

Theorem 8

Two sides of a triangle are together greater than the third. This theorem is sometimes referred to as the **triangle inequality theorem**.

$a + b > c$
$a + c > b$
$b + c > a$

This theorem implies that one side of a triangle must be smaller than the sum of the other two sides.

Worked Example 6.2

Find, without measuring the angles:

(i) $|\angle A|$

(ii) $|\angle B|$

(iii) $|\angle C|$

(iv) $|\angle D|$

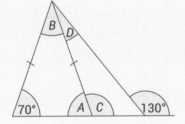

Solution

(i) $|\angle A| = 70°$ (isosceles triangle)

(ii) $|\angle B| + |\angle A| + 70° = 180°$ (angles in a triangle)

$\Rightarrow |\angle B| + 70° + 70° = 180°$

$|\angle B| = 180° - 70° - 70°$

$|\angle B| = 40°$

(iii) $|\angle C| = 180° - 70°$ (straight angle)

$|\angle C| = 110°$

(iv) $|\angle C| + |\angle D| = 130°$ (exterior angle)

$110° + |\angle D| = 130°$

$|\angle D| = 20°$

Worked Example 6.3

Determine if the following triangles with the given side lengths can be constructed:

(i) 9, 4 and 3 cm   (ii) 4, 8 and 11 cm

Solution

(i) Sides of 9, 4 and 3 cm

It is a good idea to draw out a table and to start with the smaller sides first.

$3 + 4 = 7$	$7 \not> 9$	∴ Triangle can't be constructed.

(ii) Sides of 4, 8 and 11 cm

The two sides must add to a value greater than (and not equal to) the other side.

$4 + 8 = 12$	$12 > 11$	
$8 + 11 = 19$	$19 > 4$	∴ Triangle can be constructed.
$4 + 11 = 15$	$15 > 8$	

Sometimes, we might be asked to find the range of values that a side of a triangle could have, when the other two sides are given.

Worked Example 6.4

The sides of a triangle are 6.1, 7.2 and n, where $n \in N$.

Find:

(i) The minimum possible value of n

(ii) The maximum possible value of n

(iii) The range of possible values of n

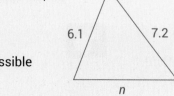

Solution

(i) The minimum possible value of n:

n and the smallest side given, when added together, must be greater than the given larger side.

$n + 6.1 > 7.2$

$n > 7.2 - 6.1$

> Minimum possible value of triangle side > Largest side given − smallest side given.

$\Rightarrow n > 1.1$

As $n \in N$, the minimum value of n is the smallest natural number greater than 1.1.

$\therefore n = 2$

(ii) The maximum possible value of n:

The two sides given, when added together, must be greater than n. This means that n must be smaller than the sum of the two sides.

$n < 7.2 + 6.1$

> Maximum possible value of triangle side < Sum of other two sides.

$\Rightarrow n < 13.3$

As $n \in N$, the largest value of n is the largest natural number less than 13.3.

$\therefore n = 13$

(iii) The range of the possible values of n:

Minimum possible value of triangle side is $n = 2$.

Maximum possible value of triangle side is $n = 13$.

$\therefore 2 \leq n \leq 13, n \in N$

> When writing a range of values for the sides of the triangle, we usually write it in the form min $\leq n \leq$ max.

Exercise 6.2

1. Find the size of each of the unknown angles marked in the following diagrams. Make sure to show all your work and give reasons for your answers.

(i)

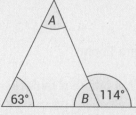

(ii)

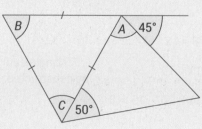

(iii)

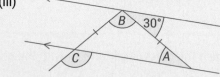

(iv)

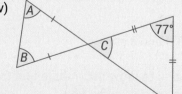

(v)

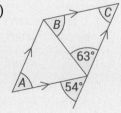

(vi)

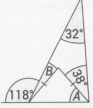

(vii)

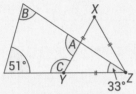

ΔXYZ is equilateral

2. Find the measure of the unknowns in each of the following diagrams:

(i)

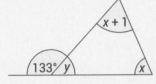

(ii)

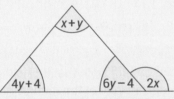

3. In each of the following polygons, **either**:

(a) Identify the smallest and largest angles (if sides are given).

OR

(b) Identify the smallest and largest sides (if angles are given).

(i)

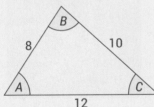

(ii)

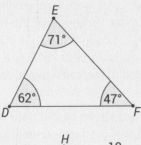

(iii)

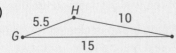

(iv)

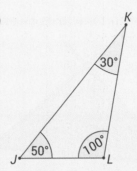

4. Explain, in each case, if it is possible to construct triangles with sides of the following lengths:

(i) 2, 3, 6

(ii) 40, 50, 15

(iii) 8, 9, 10

(iv) 6, 3, 3

(v) 3, 4, 4

(vi) $x + 1$, x, $x - 3$, where $x \geqslant 5$, $x \in N$

5. The sides of a triangle are of lengths 2.9, 11.4 and a, where $a \in N$. What is the:

(i) Smallest possible value of a

(ii) Largest possible value of a

(iii) Range of the possible values of a

6. The sides of a triangle are of lengths 4, 12.3 and b, where $b \in N$. What is the:

(i) Smallest possible value of b

(ii) Largest possible value of b

(iii) Range of the possible values of b

7. Consider the diagram below.

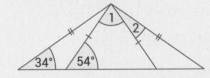

Find:

(i) $|\angle 1|$

(ii) $|\angle 2|$

8. This is the side view of a planned dormer extension to the roof of a house.

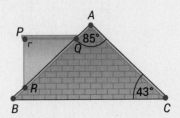

Assuming $PQ \parallel BC$, calculate:

(i) $|\angle ABC|$ (ii) $|\angle PQR|$ (iii) $|\angle PRQ|$

GEOMETRY I

9. A diagram where three roads intersect is shown.

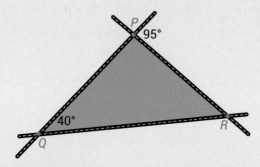

Which intersection, P or Q, is closer to R?

10.

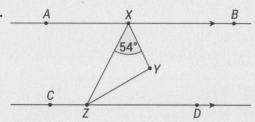

A triangle XYZ is drawn between two parallel lines AB and CD as shown.

XZ bisects ∠BXZ.

ZY bisects ∠DYX.

If |∠YXZ| = 54°, find:

(i) |∠BXZ| (iii) |∠XYZ|

(ii) |∠AXY| (iv) |∠XZY|

11. The straight line distance between Town A and Town B is 200 km. The straight line distance between Town B and Town C is 350 km. Calculate, to the nearest km:

(i) The maximum possible straight line distance between towns A and C

(ii) The minimum possible straight line distance between towns A and C

12. Consider the following diagram:

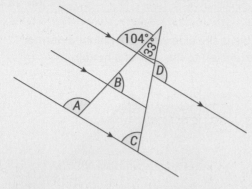

Find:

(i) |∠A| (ii) |∠B| (iii) |∠C| (iv) |∠D|

13. Consider the following diagram. (The diagram is not to scale.)

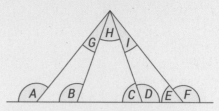

List all the angles that measure:

(i) Less than ∠A   (iii) Greater than ∠C

(ii) Less than ∠F   (iv) Greater than ∠E

14. The incentre of the triangle ABC is the point D.

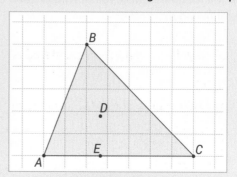

E is a point on [AC] such that |DE| is the radius length of the incircle of the triangle ABC.

|∠ADE| = 55° and |∠CDE| = 68°.

Find:

(i) |∠BAC| (ii) |∠ACB| (iii) |∠ABC|

15. Two groups of scientists are trying to locate an Asian tiger they are studying.

The tiger is fitted with a radio collar that the two groups are using to find the tiger's location in the jungle. Group A measure the direction of the radio signal to be S 76° E, Group B measure the direction of the radio signal to be N 48° E. Group A is N 30° W of Group B.

(i) Draw a diagram to illustrate the location of the two groups and the tiger.

(ii) Which group is closest to the tiger? Give a reason for your answer.

16. The side lengths of a quadrilateral are 5, 8, 10 and c, where c ∈ N. Find all the possible values of c.

17. The sides of a triangle are of lengths $2x$, $3x + 4$, and 30, where 30 is the longest side.

   If a triangle is an acute triangle (all interior angles less than 90), then $a^2 + b^2 > c^2$, where c is the longest side of the triangle.

   Calculate the range of values of x that will produce an acute triangle.

18. The sides of a triangle are of lengths $7x + 2$, $11x - 13$ and $2x + 21$, where $x \in N$. Find the smallest and largest possible values of x.

6.7 Quadrilaterals

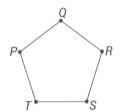

> A polygon is a closed shape (without gaps or openings) with straight sides. A polygon has at least three sides.
>
> A regular polygon has equal sides and equal angles.

One type of **polygon** commonly encountered is the parallelogram.

Parallelograms

A **parallelogram** is a quadrilateral for which both pairs of opposite sides are parallel.

There are different types of parallelograms, each with their own properties.

Type of quadrilateral	Sides	Parallel sides	Angles	Diagonals
Parallelogram	Opposite sides are equal	Opposite sides are parallel	Opposite angles are equal	Bisect each other
Rhombus	Four equal sides	Opposite sides are parallel	Opposite angles are equal	Bisect each other – angle of 90° formed
Rectangle	Opposite sides are equal	Opposite sides are parallel	All angles the same size (90°)	Bisect each other
Square	Four equal sides	Opposite sides are parallel	All angles the same size (90°)	Bisect each other – angle of 90° formed

A square, rectangle and rhombus could all be described as being parallelograms.

We can now state specific theorems related to parallelograms.

> **Theorem 9**
>
> In a parallelogram, opposite sides are equal and opposite angles are equal.
>
> Conversely, if the opposite angles of a convex quadrilateral are equal, then it is a parallelogram. Also, if the opposite sides of a convex quadrilateral are equal, then it is a parallelogram.

A convex quadrilateral has both diagonals completely contained within the shape. Each interior angle is less than 180°.

Corollary 1

A diagonal divides a parallelogram into two congruent triangles.

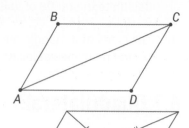

$\triangle ABC \equiv \triangle ADC$ (SAS)

Theorem 10

The diagonals of a parallelogram bisect each other.

Worked Example 6.5

In the following parallelogram, find:

(i) $|\angle 1|$ (ii) $|\angle 2|$ (iii) $|\angle 3|$

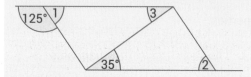

Solution

(i) $|\angle 1| = 180° - 125°$ (straight angle)

$|\angle 1| = 55°$

(ii) $|\angle 2| = 55°$ ($\angle 2$ is opposite $\angle 1$)

(iii) $|\angle 3| = 35°$ (equal alternate angle)

6.8 Area of a Triangle and Area of a Parallelogram

Area of a Triangle

We should remember the formula for the area of a triangle:

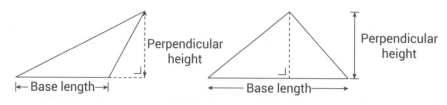

Area of a triangle = $\frac{1}{2}$ (base length) × perpendicular height

It is also clear that in calculating the area of a triangle:

It does not matter which base of the triangle we choose, as long as we know the perpendicular height from the corresponding base.

This is stated as:

Theorem 16

For a triangle, base times height does not depend on the choice of base.

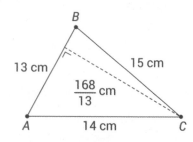

Area $\triangle ABC$

$= \frac{1}{2}(14)(12)$

$= 84 \text{ cm}^2$

Area $\triangle ABC$

$= \frac{1}{2}(13)\left(\frac{168}{13}\right)$

$= 84 \text{ cm}^2$

GEOMETRY I

Area of a Parallelogram

We can now consider how to find the area of a parallelogram.

Theorem 17

A diagonal of a parallelogram bisects the area.

From Theorem 17, a parallelogram can be cut into two triangles of equal area.

Area triangle Ⓐ = $\frac{1}{2}$ base × height

$\quad\quad = \frac{1}{2} \times 8 \times 5 = 20$ cm²

Area triangle Ⓑ = $\frac{1}{2}$ base × height

$\quad\quad = \frac{1}{2} \times 8 \times 5 = 20$ cm²

Area of parallelogram = Area of triangles Ⓐ + Ⓑ

Area of parallelogram = 20 cm² + 20 cm² = 40 cm² (= 8 × 5)

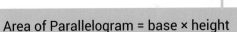

Theorem 18

The area of a parallelogram is the base times the height.

Area of Parallelogram = base × height

Worked Example 6.6

Find the value of *x* in the following triangle:

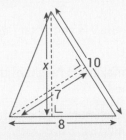

Solution

Area of triangle = $\frac{1}{2}$(base length) (perpendicular height)

$\Rightarrow \frac{1}{2}(10)(7) = \frac{1}{2}(8)(x)$

$\quad\quad 35 = 4x$

$\quad\quad \therefore 8.75 = x$

Exercise 6.3

1. Find the measure of the unknown angles labelled in each of the parallelograms. Show as much work as possible.

(i)

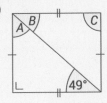

(ii)

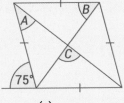

(iii)

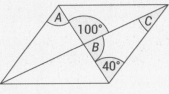

(iv)

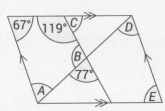

(v)

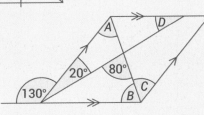

GEOMETRY I

2. Find the value of *x* and *y* in each of the following parallelograms:

(i)

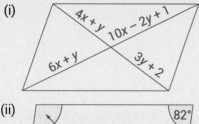

(ii)

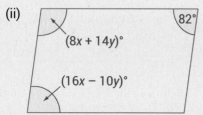

3. Find the area of each of the following triangles and parallelograms:

(i)

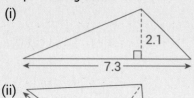

(ii)

(iii)

(iv)

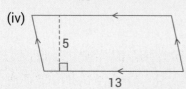

(v)

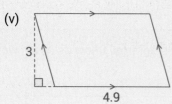

(vi)

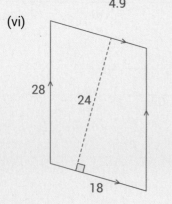

4. Find the value of *x* in each of the following shapes:

(i)

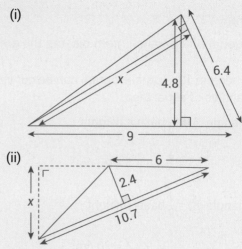

(ii)

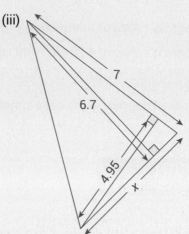

(iii)

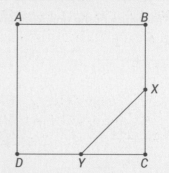

5. A parallelogram *ABCD* is such that |*AB*| = 5 cm and |*BC*| = 3 cm.

(i) What is the maximum height of this parallelogram?

(ii) What is the maximum area of this parallelogram?

6. A square *ABCD* is shown. *Y* is the midpoint of [*DC*] and *X* is the midpoint of [*BC*].

What is the ratio of the area of the square to the triangle *XYC*?

7. The circumcentre of the triangle *ABC* is the point *F*. The points *D* and *E* are the midpoints of [*AC*] and [*BC*] respectively. |∠*DFG*| = 83° and |∠*FGH*| = 56°.

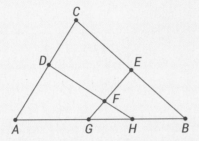

Find:

(i) |∠*DFE*|

(ii) |∠*ACB*|

(iii) |∠*ABC*|

(iv) |∠*BAC*|

8. (a) Consider the following quadrilateral:

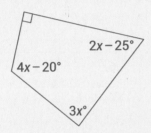

(i) Explain why the sum of the interior angles is 360°.

(ii) Find the value of the 3 unknown angles in the quadrilateral.

(b) A regular pentagon is shown. Calculate the size of the interior angle *A*.

(c) A regular hexagon is shown. Calculate the size of the interior angle *B*.

(d) What is the size of an interior angle of a regular octagon (8 sides)?

(e) Can a regular polygon have an interior angle of 155°? Give a reason for your answer.

(f) Two sides, [*QP*] and [*PR*], of a regular polygon are shown.

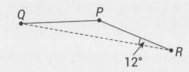

Given that |∠*PRQ*| = 12°, calculate:

(i) The size of the interior angle *QPR*

(ii) The number of sides of this polygon

6.9 Triangles II

We will now study more properties associated with triangles.

Students are required to prove theorems 11, 12 and 13. This will be covered in Chapter 10 Geometry II.

Parallel Lines and Triangles

We will now consider:

(a) what happens when three parallel lines intersect a transversal and, specifically,

(b) what happens when that transversal is cut into two equal segments.

We can state that:

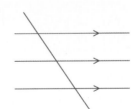

If a transversal is cut into two equal parts by three parallel lines, then any other transversal drawn between these parallel lines will also be cut into two equal parts.

GEOMETRY I

We can now state this as a theorem.

> **Theorem 11**
> If three parallel lines cut off equal segments on some transversal line, then they will cut off equal segments on any other transversal.

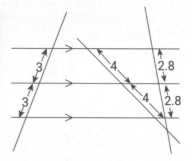

When a line is parallel to one side of a triangle, it divides another side of the triangle in a certain ratio.

> A line that is parallel to one side of a triangle cuts the other two sides of the triangle in the same ratio. This ratio is often referred to as *m:n*.

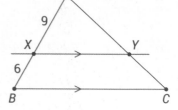

$m:n = s:t$

Consider the triangle shown on the right.

If the ratio |AX|:|XB| is equal to 3:2, then the ratio |AY|:|YC| is also 3:2.

This can be written more formally as:

> **Theorem 12**
> Let *ABC* be a triangle. If a line *l* is parallel to *BC* and cuts [AB] in the ratio *m : n*, then it also cuts [AC] in the same ratio.

Ratios can be written as fractions. So, this theorem can also be written as:

$$\frac{|AX|}{|XB|} = \frac{|AY|}{|YC|} \quad \text{or} \quad \frac{\text{Top length}}{\text{Bottom length}} = \frac{\text{Top length}}{\text{Bottom length}}$$

It is important to realise that all of these ratios can be inverted or turned upside down.

$$\frac{|XB|}{|AX|} = \frac{|YC|}{|AY|} \quad \text{or} \quad \frac{\text{Bottom length}}{\text{Top length}} = \frac{\text{Bottom length}}{\text{Top length}}$$

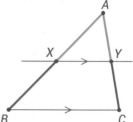

The theorem means that the following is also true:

$$\frac{|AB|}{|XB|} = \frac{|AC|}{|YC|} \quad \text{or} \quad \frac{\text{Overall length}}{\text{Bottom length}} = \frac{\text{Overall length}}{\text{Bottom length}}$$

And:

$$\frac{|AB|}{|AX|} = \frac{|AC|}{|AY|} \quad \text{or} \quad \frac{\text{Overall length}}{\text{Top length}} = \frac{\text{Overall length}}{\text{Top length}}$$

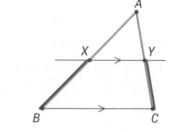

The converse of Theorem 12 can be used to show that two lines are parallel.

> If a line cuts two sides of a triangle in the same ratio, then the line is parallel to the side not cut by the line.

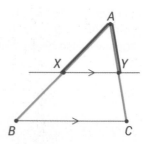

Worked Example 6.7

Find the value of x.

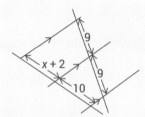

Solution

We can see that the transversal is cut into even parts. Therefore, all the other transversals will be cut into equal parts as well.

To find x:

$x + 2 = 10$

$x = 8$

Worked Example 6.8

Find the length of x, given that $DE \parallel BC$.

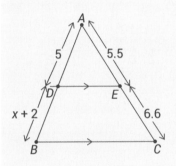

Solution

We will use |BD| to find x, so we must identify which ratio we are using.

We start with the side we are looking for when writing the ratio, as this makes our calculations much easier.

$$\frac{\text{Bottom length}}{\text{Top length}} = \frac{\text{Bottom length}}{\text{Top length}}$$

$$\frac{x+2}{5} = \frac{6.6}{5.5}$$

$5.5(x + 2) = 5(6.6)$ (Cross-multiply.)

$5.5x + 11 = 33$

$5.5x = 22$

$\therefore x = 4$

Similar Triangles

An important relationship that two triangles can have is that of similarity.

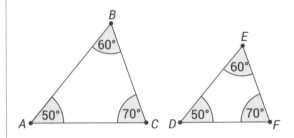

In **similar** or **equiangular** triangles, all three angles in one triangle have the same measurement as the corresponding three angles in the other triangle.

It is clear that when we have two **similar** triangles:

The corresponding sides of similar triangles are in the same ratio.

In the similar triangles *ABC* and *DEF* shown:

$$\frac{|AB|}{|DE|} = \frac{|BC|}{|EF|} = \frac{|AC|}{|DF|}$$

$$\left(\text{that is, } \frac{5}{10} = \frac{7}{14} = \frac{9}{18}\right)$$

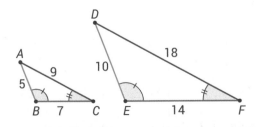

This now allows us to state the following theorem:

Theorem 13

If two triangles are similar, then their sides are proportional, in order.

In the following similar triangles, the corresponding sides are proportional (in order):

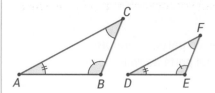

$$\frac{|AB|}{|DE|} = \frac{|AC|}{|DF|} = \frac{|BC|}{|EF|} \quad \text{or} \quad \frac{|DE|}{|AB|} = \frac{|DF|}{|AC|} = \frac{|EF|}{|BC|}$$

Usually, we only need to use two of the ratios to determine the missing side.

The converse of Theorem 13 also applies.

> If, in any two triangles, the sides are proportional (in order), then the two triangles are similar to each other.

It is also apparent that:

> If a triangle is cut by a line parallel to one of its sides, this line divides the triangle into two similar triangles.

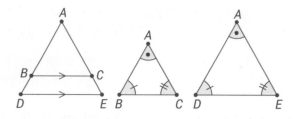

Worked Example 6.9

In the similar triangles shown, find the value of:

(i) $|AC|$　(ii) $|DE|$

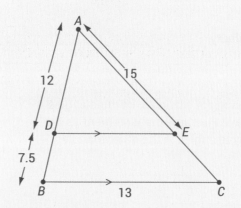

Solution

(i) To find $|AC|$:

We can use Theorem 12 to find $|AC|$.

$$\frac{|AC|}{15} = \frac{19.5}{12}$$

$$12|AC| = 19.5 \times 15$$

$$12|AC| = 292.5$$

$$|AC| = \frac{292.5}{12}$$

$$\therefore |AC| = 24.375$$

(ii) **Method 1**

To find $|DE|$:

It is a good idea to redraw the triangles, but this time into two separate similar triangles.

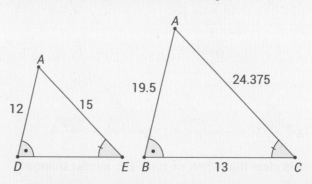

$$\frac{|DE|}{13} = \frac{12}{19.5}$$

$$19.5\,|DE| = 12 \times 13$$

$$19.5\,|DE| = 156$$

$$|DE| = \frac{156}{19.5}$$

$$\therefore |DE| = 8$$

GEOMETRY I

Method 2

We could also find |DE| by finding how many times bigger or smaller one side of the similar triangle is when compared to the corresponding side.

$$\frac{|AD|}{|AB|} = \frac{12}{19.5} = \frac{8}{13}$$

|AD| is $\frac{8}{13}$ times smaller than the corresponding side |AB|.

△ABC and △ADE are similar triangles.

∴ |DE| is $\frac{8}{13}$ times smaller than the corresponding side |BC|.

$$13 \times \frac{8}{13} = 8$$

∴ |DE| = 8

The factor by how much bigger or smaller one similar triangle is to another is called the scale factor. We will encounter this again in enlargements in Chapter 12.

Worked Example 6.10

A scale model of a triangular section for a building is shown. If the length of the longest side of the actual triangular section is $37\frac{1}{3}$ m, find, to the nearest cm, the dimensions of the other two sides of the section.

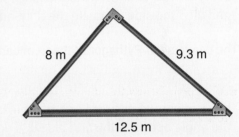

Solution

When faced with geometry problems dealing in real-life settings, it helps if we:

● Draw a diagram to represent the problem.

● Fill in as much information on the diagram as possible, checking both the diagram and text given in the question.

● Identify and then label on the diagram what we are asked to find (in this case x and y).

Using similar triangles we solve for x.

$$\frac{x}{8} = \frac{37\frac{1}{3}}{12.5} \qquad x = \frac{8\left(37\frac{1}{3}\right)}{12.5}$$

$$x = 23.8933...$$

$$x \approx 23.89 \text{ m}$$

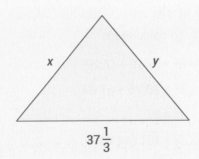

Now solve for y.

$$\frac{y}{9.3} = \frac{37\frac{1}{3}}{12.5} \qquad y = \frac{9.3\left(37\frac{1}{3}\right)}{12.5}$$

$$y = 27.776$$

$$y \approx 27.78 \text{ m}$$

GEOMETRY 1

The Theorem of Pythagoras

One of the best-known theorems concerns the properties of right-angled triangles.

While this theorem is named after the Greek mathematician Pythagoras of Samos, who lived in the sixth century BC, it was widely known before then.

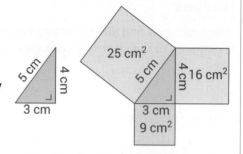

In the given right-angled triangle, it was noticed that $5^2 = 25$ and also that $3^2 + 4^2 = 25$.

We can show that:

> **Theorem 14: The theorem of Pythagoras**
>
> In a right-angled triangle the square of the hypotenuse is the sum of the squares of the other two sides.

This leads to the equation:

$$c^2 = a^2 + b^2$$

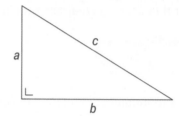

c is the hypotenuse: this is the longest side and also the side opposite the right angle.

The converse of Pythagoras' theorem can be used to investigate if a triangle is right-angled.

> **Theorem 15**
>
> If the square of one side of a triangle is equal to the sum of the squares of the other two sides, then the angle opposite the first side is a right angle.

GEOMETRY I

Worked Example 6.11

Calculate the value of x and the value of y in the given diagram.

Solution

(i) To calculate x:

$x^2 = (5.4)^2 + (7.2)^2$

$x^2 = 29.16 + 51.84$

$x^2 = 81$

$x = \sqrt{81}$ (as $x > 0$)

$x = 9$

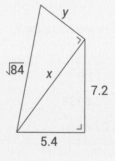

(ii) To calculate y:

$(\sqrt{84})^2 = (9)^2 + y^2$ OR

$84 = 81 + y^2$ $y = \sqrt{(\sqrt{84})^2 - 9^2}$

$y^2 = 3$ $= \sqrt{84 - 81}$

$y = \sqrt{3}$ (as $y > 0$) $y = \sqrt{3}$

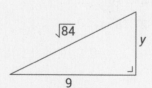

Exercise 6.4

1. In each of the following diagrams, find the value of *x* and *y*:

   (i)

   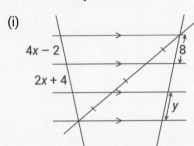

   (ii)

   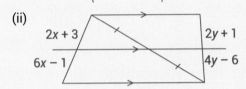

   (iii)

   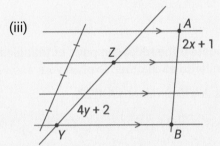

   |AB| = 15 cm and |YZ| = 12 cm.

2. In the triangle *ABC*, *PQ* ∥ *BC*.

   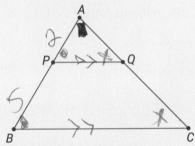

   (i) If $\frac{|AP|}{|PB|} = \frac{2}{5}$, then $\frac{|AQ|}{|QC|} = $ _____

   (ii) If $\frac{|AP|}{|PB|} = \frac{1}{3}$, then $\frac{|AP|}{|AB|} = $ _____

   (iii) If $\frac{|AC|}{|QC|} = \frac{4}{3}$, then $\frac{|AB|}{|AP|} = $ _____

   (iv) If $\frac{|AQ|}{|AC|} = \frac{3}{7}$, then $\frac{|AP|}{|AB|} = $ _____

3. In the diagram, *ST* ∥ *QR*.
   |PS| : |PQ| = 3 : 5.

   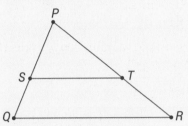

   Find the following ratios:

   (i) |PT| : |PR|

   (ii) |PS| : |SQ|

   (iii) |PR| : |TR|

4. Find the value of *x* in each case.

   (i)

   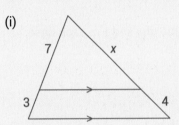

   (ii)

   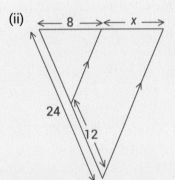

5. Investigate if *AB* ∥ *DE*.

   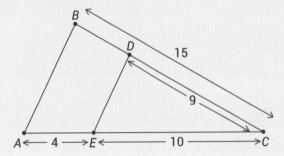

6. Find the value of *y* in each case.

(i)

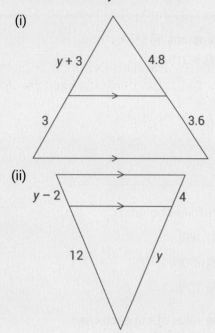

(ii)

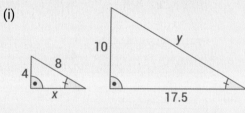

7. Find the value of *x* and *y* in each case.

(i)

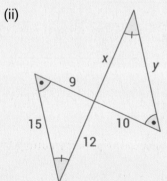

(ii)

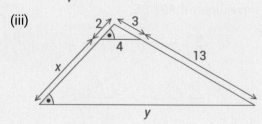

(iii)

(iv)

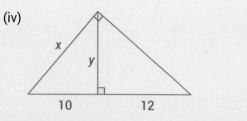

(v)

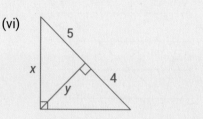

(vi)

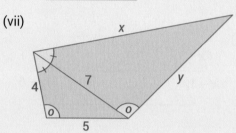

(vii)

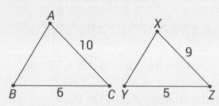

8. Investigate if the following pairs of triangles are similar to each other. Explain your answer.

(i) Is △*ABC* similar to △*XYZ*?

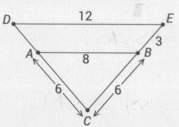

(ii) Is △*CDE* similar to △*ABC*?

9. Find the length of *x* and *y* in each of the following triangles. Leave your answers in surd form where appropriate.

(i)

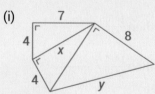

(ii)

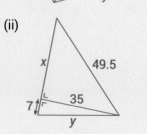

(iii)

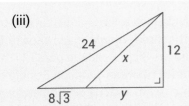

(iv)

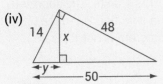

10. In the given diagram, $AB \perp BC$ and $EC \perp ED$.

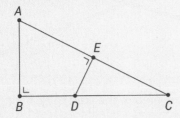

(i) Show that the two triangles *ABC* and *EDC* are similar.

Given that $|ED| = 6$, $|AB| = 12$ and $|DC| = 10$, find:

(ii) $|AC|$ (iii) $|BC|$ (iv) $|EC|$

11. *ABCD* is a parallelogram. (The diagram is not to scale.)

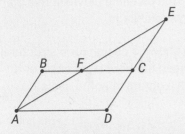

(i) Prove that $\triangle ABF$ and $\triangle EFC$ are similar.

(ii) If $|BF|:|FC| = 3:5$, $|DC| = 16$ and $|FE| = 32$, find $|ED|$.

12. The two triangles *ABC* and *DEF* are similar.

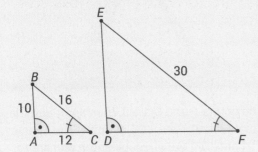

Find, correct to 2 decimal places:

(i) $|ED|$ (ii) $|DF|$

(iii) The area of $\triangle ABC$

(iv) The area of $\triangle DEF$

(v) The perimeter of $\triangle DEF$

What do you notice about the relationship between the perimeters of the two triangles?

13. A rectangular box is shown.

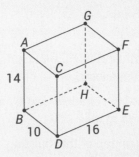

Find:

(i) $|AD|$ (ii) $|DF|$ (iii) $|AE|$

14. A square-based pyramid is shown. Its sides are four identical triangles.

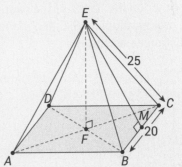

(i) Find $|AC|$.

(ii) Find $|FE|$.

(iii) If *M* is the midpoint of $[BC]$, calculate $|EM|$.

15. In the triangle *PQR*, $AB \parallel CD \parallel QR$.

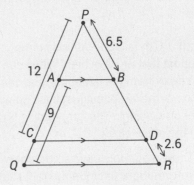

Find:

(i) $|BD|$ (ii) $|CQ|$ (iii) $|AC|$

16. A building with a height of 5 m casts a shadow 28 m long on the ground.

(i) How high is another building that casts a shadow that is 49 m long?

(ii) Find the length of the shadow cast by a nearby building 75 m tall.

(iii) A man standing on top of this building casts a 10 m shadow. Find the height of the man.

17. Megan wishes to find the width of the river that runs through her town. She finds a beech tree and an ash tree that sit directly across from each other on the banks of the river. She places three stakes at points *P*, *Q* and *R* and records the distances as shown.

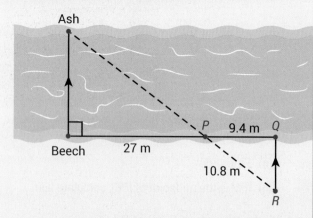

Determine the width of the river, to the nearest metre.

18. Jane is 1.6 m tall. She stands in front of a lamppost that is 3.2 m high. When she stands 14 m away from the lamppost, she can see that the top of the lamppost just lines up with the top of her office block. The lamppost is 90 m away from the office block.

(i) Draw a suitable diagram to show the above information. (Include the fact that she is 1.6 m tall.)

(ii) Hence, find the height of the office block (to the nearest metre).

19. A new park is planned to be built within the area enclosed by the three straight roads shown. The Cork Road and the Sligo Road run parallel. The shortest distance between Junction *Z* and the Sligo Road is 0.75 km and the length between Junctions *X* and *Y* is 1.5 km. The shortest distance between Junction *Z* and the Cork Road is 1.6 km. (The diagram is not to scale.)

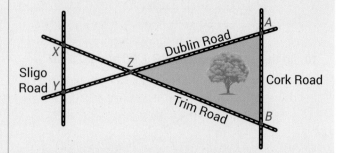

Find the area of the park to be built.

20. Two buildings are 70 m apart. One building is 10 m tall, the other is 15 m tall. A line can be drawn from the top of each building to the bottom of the other. These two lines intersect at a point *B*, 0.6 m above the ground.

(i) Draw a suitable diagram to show the above information.

(ii) Calculate the distance between this point and the two buildings.

21. The diagram shows a design for a structural support between the floor and ceiling of a building. (The diagram is not to scale.)

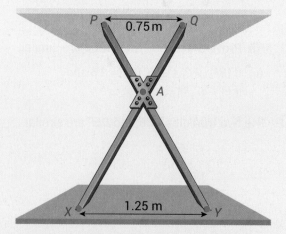

The points *P* and *Q* are 0.75 m apart and the points *X* and *Y* are 1.25 m apart. The beams [PY] and [QX] are of equal length and are to be bolted together at the point *A*. The height between the floor and ceiling is 2.8 m.

(i) Calculate the distance between point *A* and the floor.

(ii) Calculate the length of [PY].

22. A red and grey squirrel are at the top of two washing line poles 30 m apart.

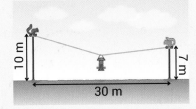

The red squirrel sits on a 10 m high pole while the grey squirrel's pole is 7 m high. A squirrel feeder is attached to the washing line at a height of 2 m. Assuming that the washing line is rigid, how far is the squirrel feeder from each pole so that both squirrels are equal distances away?

23. A spider and fly are in a rectangular room as shown.

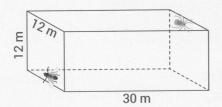

The spider is sitting 1 m down from the ceiling and in the centre of the end wall of the room. The fly is sitting on the opposite wall, 1 m up from the floor and in the centre of that wall.

(i) Calculate, to the nearest cm, the distance between the spider and fly.

(ii) What is the shortest distance that the spider must crawl in order to reach the fly?

24. In the given diagram, $AB \perp BE$ and $DE \perp BE$.

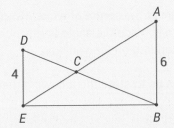

Find the perpendicular distance from C to $[EB]$.

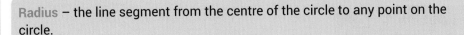

6.10 Circles

A **circle** is a very common shape found in all aspects of everyday life.

Some common terms associated with circles:

> A **circle** is a set of points in a plane that are all equidistant from a fixed point, its centre.

> **Radius** – the line segment from the centre of the circle to any point on the circle.

The centre of a circle is usually marked with a dot and sometimes the letter O.

> The plural of radius is **radii**.

> **Chord** – any segment that joins two points on a circle.

> **Diameter** – a chord that passes through the centre of a circle. The diameter is twice the radius in length. The diameter is the longest chord of a circle.

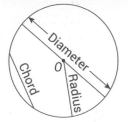

> **Circumference** – the perimeter or length of the circle.

> **Arc** – any part of the circumference of the circle.

> **Tangent** – a line that touches the circle at only one point. Where the tangent touches the circle is called the point of contact, or point of tangency.

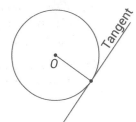

Sector – the region of the circle enclosed by two radii and the arc between these radii.

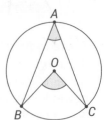
Arc / Sector / Radius / Radius

Circle Properties

We can now investigate some properties of circles.

(a) Angle at the Centre of a Circle Compared with the Angle at the Circle

The circle in the diagram contains the angles *BOC* (angle at the centre) and *BAC* (angle at the circle).

The angle at the centre of a circle standing on a given arc is twice the angle at any point of the circle standing on the same arc.

$|\angle BOC| = 2|\angle BAC|$

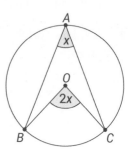

This leads us to state the following theorem:

Theorem 19

The angle at the centre of a circle standing on a given arc is twice the angle at any point of the circle standing on the same arc.

(b) Two Angles in a Circle Standing on the Same Arc

In the diagram, both angles at *B* and *D* stand on the same arc, *AC*.

Corollary 2

All angles at a point of a circle, standing on the same arc, are equal in measure.

The converse of this corollary also applies.

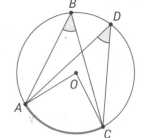

If the angles at points of the circle are equal in measure, then they must be standing on the same arc.

$|\angle B| = |\angle D|$ as the two angles are both standing on arc *AC*.

Worked Example 6.12

Consider the following diagram of a circle with centre *O* and diameter [*AB*]:

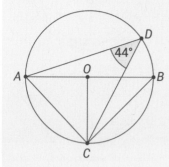

Find:

(i) $|\angle ABC|$

(ii) $|\angle AOC|$

(iii) $|\angle OCA|$

Solution

(i) $|\angle ABC| = 44°$ (angle on same arc)

(ii) $|\angle AOC| = 88°$ (angle at centre of circle is twice the measure of angle at arc)

(iii) $|\angle OCA| = (180° - 88°) \div 2$ ($\triangle AOC$ is an isosceles triangle)

$= 46°$

(c) Cyclic Quadrilaterals

A quadrilateral in which all four vertices (corners) are points of a circle is referred to as a cyclic quadrilateral.
Opposite angles in a cyclic quadrilateral add up to 180°.

$|\angle A| + |\angle C| = 180°$. Also, $|\angle B| + |\angle D| = 180°$.

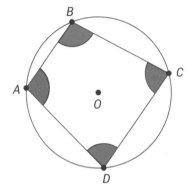

From this, we can state the following corollary:

Corollary 5
If *ABCD* is a cyclic quadrilateral, then opposite angles sum to 180°.

The converse of this corollary states:

If the opposite angles of a quadrilateral sum to 180°, then it is cyclic, i.e. the vertices of the quadrilateral will lie on the circle.

(d) Angles in a Semicircle

The angle opposite the diameter in a circle is a right angle or 90°.

This can be stated as:

Corollary 3
Each angle in a semicircle is a right angle.

From this corollary, we can also show another property of a circle:

Corollary 4
If the angle standing on a chord [*BC*] at some point of the circle is a right angle, then [*BC*] is a diameter.

This corollary could be considered the converse of Corollary 3.

(e) Tangents

Another important theorem based on a circle concerns the properties of a **tangent** to the circle.

A tangent to a circle is at a right angle to the radius at the point of contact.

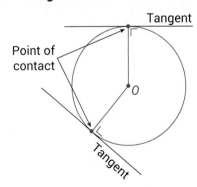

This is more formally stated as:

Theorem 20
Each tangent is perpendicular to the radius that goes to the point of contact.

The converse of Theorem 20 is:

> If a point *P* lies on a circle *s* and a line *l* that passes though the point *P* is perpendicular to the radius, then this line is a tangent to the circle at the point *P*.

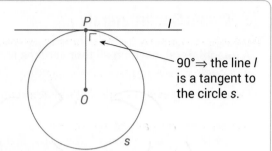

90° ⟹ the line *l* is a tangent to the circle *s*.

This can be more formally stated as:

> If *P* lies on *s*, and a line *l* is perpendicular to the radius at *P*, then *l* is tangent to *s*.

Circles touch when they intersect at one point only. They therefore have a single point in common with each other. Circles can touch both externally and internally, as shown.

External:

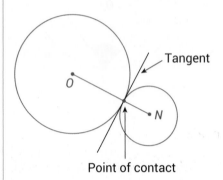

Tangent

Point of contact

Internal:

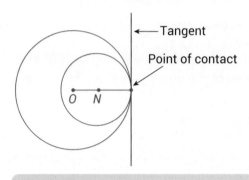

Tangent

Point of contact

Tangents can also be found when two circles meet at one point only.

Corollary 6

If two circles intersect at one point only, then the two centres and the point of contact are collinear.

Worked Example 6.13

A circle, with centre *O* and radius [*OP*] is shown. *t* is a tangent to the circle with a point of contact *P*.

$|OP|$ = 7 cm and $|PS|$ = $\sqrt{15}$ cm.

Find:

(i) $|OS|$ (ii) $|RS|$

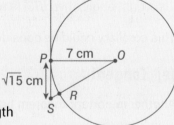

Solution

(i) To find $|OS|$:

Δ*OPS* is a right-angled triangle, and [*OS*] is the hypotenuse.

$$|OS|^2 = 7^2 + \left(\sqrt{15}\right)^2$$
$$= 49 + 15$$
$$= 64$$
$$\therefore |OS| = 8 \text{ cm}$$

(ii) To find $|RS|$:

Remember that the radius length $|OP|$ = 7 = $|OR|$.

$$\therefore |RS| = 8 - 7$$
$$|RS| = 1 \text{ cm}$$

(f) Perpendicular to a Chord

We can also consider the relationship between any chord of a circle and the centre of the circle.

> If a line is drawn at right angles to a chord and this line goes through the centre of the circle, it will cut the chord into two equal segments.

This can more formally be written as:

Theorem 21 Part (i)

The perpendicular from the centre to a chord bisects the chord.

Perpendicular bisector of [AB]
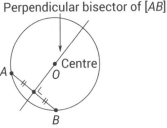

Theorem 21 Part (ii)

The perpendicular bisector of a chord passes through the centre.

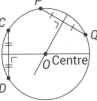

By constructing the perpendicular bisectors of two chords, we can use this theorem to find the centre of a given circle.

Worked Example 6.14

[AB] is the diameter of a circle with centre O.
[CD] is a chord with a midpoint M.

AB ⊥ CD

|CD| = 64 cm and
|OM| = 24 cm.

Find:

(i) |OC|

(ii) |BC| in simplest surd form

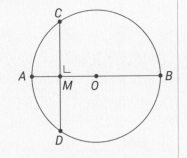

Solution

(i) To find |OC|:

|CM| = 32 cm (the perpendicular from the centre to a chord bisects the chord)

△CMO is a right-angled triangle.

Using the theorem of Pythagoras:

$$|OC|^2 = |CM|^2 + |OM|^2$$
$$= (32)^2 + (24)^2$$
$$|OC|^2 = 1,600$$
$$\therefore |OC| = 40 \text{ cm}$$

(ii) To find |BC|:

△CMB is a right-angled triangle.

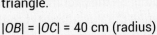

|OB| = |OC| = 40 cm (radius)

|CM| = 32 cm and |MB| = 64 cm (24 + 40)

Using the theorem of Pythagoras, |BC| = 32√5 cm.

Exercise 6.5

1. Find |∠A| and |∠B| in each of the following diagrams.
   Remember to show as much work as possible. O is the centre in each case.

(i)

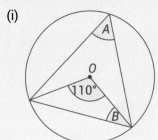

(ii)

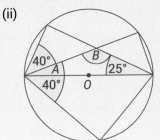

(iii)

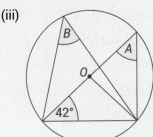

GEOMETRY I

(iv)

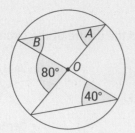

(v)

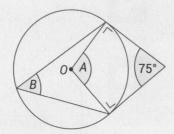

(vi)

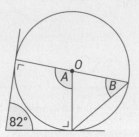

(vii)

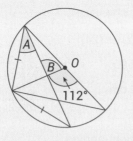

2. *A*, *B* and *C* are points on the circumference of a circle with a centre *O*. *AP* is a tangent to this circle and *P*, *B* and *O* are collinear.

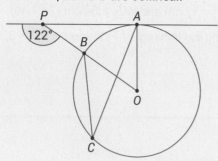

Find:

(i) |∠APC|

(ii) |∠AOP|

(iii) |∠ACB|

3. The points *C*, *D*, *E* and *F* are points on a circle with a centre *O*. |∠BCF| = 75°.

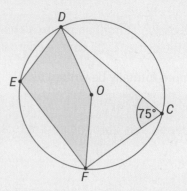

Find:

(i) |∠DOF| (obtuse)   (ii) |∠DEF|

4. *P*, *Q* and *R* are points on a circle with a centre *O*. *RS* and *QS* are tangents to this circle.

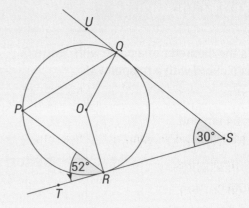

Find:

(i) |∠ROQ| (obtuse)   (iii) |∠PRO|

(ii) |∠QPR| (iv) |∠PQU|

5. Consider the following circle with centre *O*:

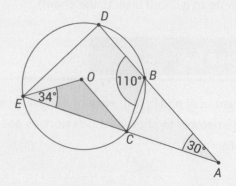

Find:

(i) |∠EOC| (iii) |∠ECB|

(ii) |∠BCA| (iv) |∠EDA|

6. In the diagram below, *C* is the the centre of the circle and *XT* is a tangent.

$|\angle XTQ| = 50°$ and $|\angle PCT| = 140°$.

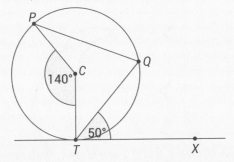

Write down the value of the following angles:

(i) $|\angle CTX|$ (iv) $|\angle CQT|$

(ii) $|\angle CTQ|$ (v) $|\angle CQP|$

(iii) $|\angle PQT|$ (vi) $|\angle QPC|$

7. *PQRS* are points on a circle with centre *C*.

Name an angle equal in measure to:

(i) $2|\angle RPS|$

(ii) $|\angle QSP|$

(iii) A right angle

8. The vertices of the isosceles triangle *ABC* lie on a circle with centre *O* as shown.

$|AB| = |AC|$ and *DC* is a tangent to the circle. $|\angle BCD| = 26°$.

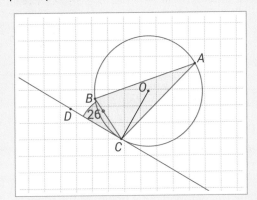

Find:

(i) $|\angle BOC|$

(ii) $|\angle BAC|$

(iii) $|\angle OCA|$

9. *AB* and *CD* are two chords of a circle as shown.

$|AB| = 3.4$, $|CD| = 4$ and $|BE| = 3.8$. Find, to one decimal place, $|DE|$.

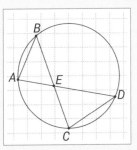

10. *ABC* is a triangle with vertices on a circle with a centre *O*. The point *D* lies on the same circle. *BE* is a tangent to this circle.

$|\angle ABO| = 41°$ and $|\angle BAD| = 27°$.

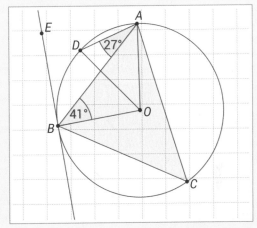

Find:

(i) $|\angle BOD|$ (iv) $|\angle ACB|$

(ii) $|\angle AOB|$ (v) $|\angle ABD|$

(iii) $|\angle ADO|$

11. *Q*, *S*, *T* and *V* are points on a circle. *PR* is a tangent to this circle at the point *V*.

ST ‖ *PR* and $|SV| = |VT|$. *S* is on the line *PQ* and *T* is on the line *QR*.

$|\angle QPR| = 70°$ and $|\angle RQV| = 36°$.

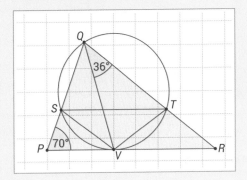

Find:

(i) $|\angle TSV|$ (iv) $|\angle SQV|$

(ii) $|\angle PSV|$ (v) $|\angle VTR|$

(iii) $|\angle SVT|$

GEOMETRY I

12. In each diagram, O is the centre of the circle. P is the point of contact between a tangent and the circle. Find the value of x in each case.

(i)

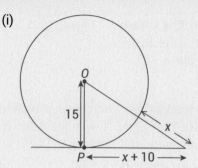

(ii)

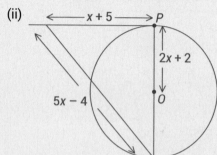

13. A circle with centre O has a radius of 25 cm. The chord $[RS]$ has length 14 cm and $RS \perp PQ$.

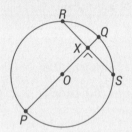

Find:

(i) $|RX|$

(ii) $|QX|$

(iii) $|PX|$

(iv) $|PS|$

14. A circle with centre O of radius 25 cm has two chords $[AB]$ and $[CD]$.

$OM \perp AB$ and $ON \perp CD$.

$|OM| = 24$ cm $|ON| = 20$ cm

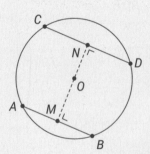

Find:

(i) $|CD|$

(ii) $|AB|$

15. The circle s with centre O and the circle p with centre C are shown. AB is a tangent to both circles. $|OA| = 12$ cm and $|BC| = 3$ cm.

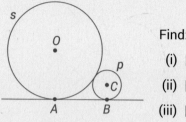

Find:

(i) $|AB|$

(ii) $|AC|$

(iii) $|OB|$

16. The circles x, y and z are shown, with centres O, P and R respectively.

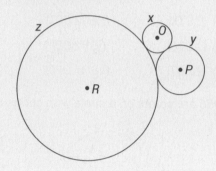

The radius length of circle x is 12 cm, and the radius length of circle y is 20 cm.

If $|\angle ROP| = 90°$, find the radius length of circle z.

> We sometimes encounter geometry questions that require the use of trigonometry as well.

17. A circle with centre O is inscribed in triangle ABC as shown.

$|AB| = |BC| = 92$ mm and $|AC| = 120$ mm.

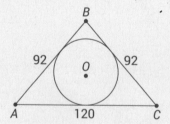

Find:

(i) $|\angle BAC|$

(ii) The radius of the circle

(iii) The perpendicular height of the triangle

Revision Exercises

1. Consider *ABCD* and the rhombus *CEFG*.

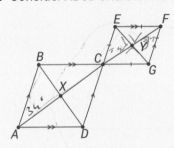

   If |∠*BAC*| = 34°, find:

   (i) |∠*CEF*| (v) |∠*CGE*|

   (ii) |∠*BCD*| (vi) |∠*BXC*|

   (iii) |∠*BCA*| (vii) |∠*EYF*|

   (iv) |∠*DAC*| (viii) |∠*DCG*|

2. Consider the following diagram:

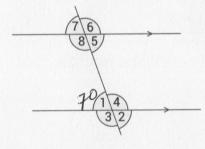

   (a) If |∠1| = 70°, find:

   (i) |∠2| (iii) |∠5|

   (ii) |∠4| (iv) |∠6|

   (b) If |∠4| = (7x + 10)° and
   |∠8| = (8x − 5)°, find |∠6|.

3. (a) Consider the diagram below.

   |∠2| = (10x + 2y)°, |∠5| = (5x + 5y)° and |∠6| = (15x + 7y)°

   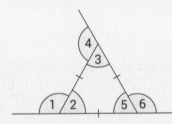

   (i) Find the value of *x* and *y*.

   (ii) Hence, find the measure of each of the angles.

   (b) The following diagram shows a regular seven-sided polygon (i.e. equal side lengths):

   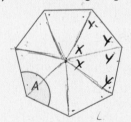

   (i) Explain what is meant by the term 'polygon'.

   (ii) Show that the sum of the interior angles of any seven-sided polygon is equal to 900°.

   (iii) Deduce the measure of angle *A*, correct to the nearest degree.

   (c) A regular *n*-agon has *n* sides of equal length.

   Explain why the angle at each vertex is $\left(\dfrac{n-2}{n}\right)180°$.

4. Consider the parallelogram *ABCD*.

   (a) If |∠*CAD*| = 27°, |∠*AXB*| = 66° and |∠*ACD*| = 42°, find:

   (i) |∠*ABD*| (iii) |∠*ADB*|

   (ii) |∠*BXC*| (iv) |∠*ACB*|

   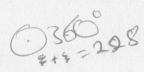
   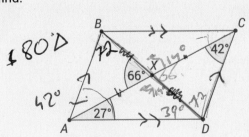

   (b) |*AB*| = 4x + 2y + 2, |*DC*| = 7x + $\dfrac{3}{2}$y,

   |*BC*| = 8x + 4y − 5 and |*AD*| = 4x + 6y − 5.

   (i) Find the value of *x* and *y*.

   (ii) Hence, find the measure of each of the sides.

GEOMETRY I

5. Three roads are all parallel to each other. Ann Street and Bee Street intersect these three roads at junctions *P*, *Q*, *R*, *S*, *T* and *V* as shown on the diagram.

Find the distance between Main Road and Town Road on Ann Street.

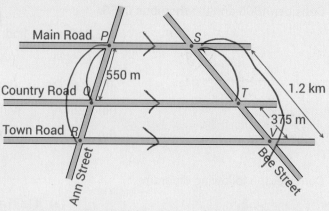

---

6. (a) In the diagram, *XZ* ∥ *AB*.

Also, |*XC*| : |*AX*| = 4 : 3.

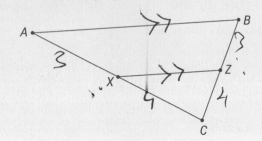

Write down the following ratios:

(i) $\dfrac{|XA|}{|AC|}$

(ii) $\dfrac{|BZ|}{|BC|}$

(iii) $\dfrac{|BC|}{|CZ|}$

(b) Investigate if *XY* ∥ *PR*.

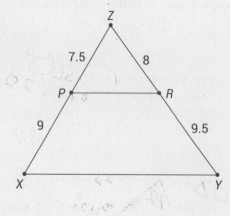

(c) Find the value of *x* in each case.

(i)

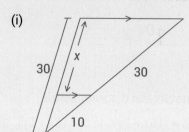

(ii)

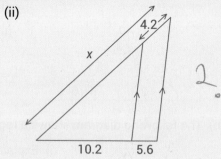

(iii)

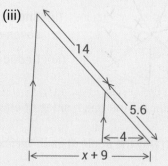

(iv)

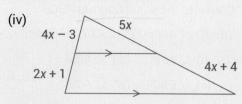

7. (a) A sail boat has two similar sails as shown.

(i) Find the height of the mast.

(ii) Find the total area of the sails.

(b) Two circles with centres O and M are shown. AC and EC are tangents to both circles. The points A, B, D and E are points of tangency. (Diagram is not to scale.)

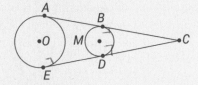

If $|AB|:|BC|$ is $1:4$ and $|EC| = 25$ cm, find $|ED|$.

(c) Consider the triangles XYZ and AYB.

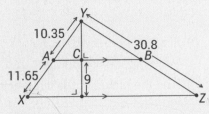

Find:

(i) $|BZ|$

(ii) $|YC|$ correct to the nearest whole number

(iii) Hence, find $|XZ|$ correct to two decimal places.

8. (a) A person 1.4 m high measures the length of her shadow and the length of a tree shadow on a sunny day. She records the results as shown on the diagram.

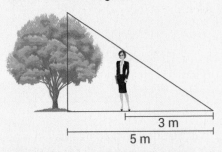

Calculate the height of the tree (to the nearest centimetre).

(b) A building is 6 m from the point B as shown in the diagram. (The diagram is not to scale.)

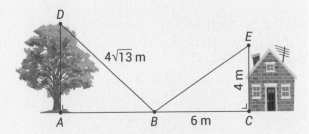

If $|\angle DBA| = |\angle EBC|$, find:

(i) The height of the tree

(ii) The distance from the bottom of the tree (A) to the house (C)

(c) Two pylons A and B are 100 m apart and connected by supporting cables.

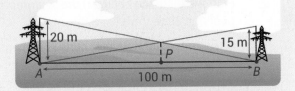

To increase stability, it is decided to put another smaller pylon between the two at the point P, the point of intersection of the two cables.

Find, to the nearest centimetre:

(i) The height of this smaller pylon

(ii) The distance from the smaller pylon to pylons A and B

9. (a) A river 5 m wide with two parallel sides AB and CD is shown. A boat can moor at points A, B, C or D.

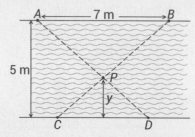

It is decided to place a buoy at a point P, the intersection of $[AB]$ and $[CD]$. The perpendicular distance between P and $[CD]$ is y. Find $|CD|$ in terms of y.

(b) The triangle PQR is shown. If $|PQ| = 35$ cm and $|QR| = 12$ cm, find the ratio of the shaded area to the unshaded area.

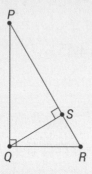

10. (a) A council wishes to build a new swimming pool that will service three towns A, B and C. The distance between each town is 24 km.

The swimming pool will be located at an equal distance from all three towns. Find the distance between the swimming pool and each town.

(b) A truncated right-circular cone is shown.

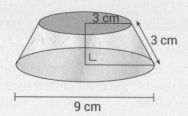

Find the height of the original cone.

11. (a) (i) Construct the circumcentre of an equilateral triangle. Label as in the diagram shown.

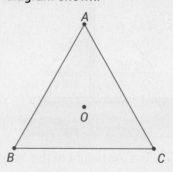

(ii) Let the length of $[AB] = y$. Find the shortest distance between O and $[AB]$ in terms of y and r, where r is the radius of the circumcircle.

(b) An equilateral triangle of side length x is inscribed in a circle as shown.

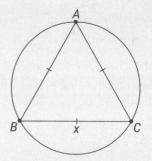

(i) Find the perpendicular height of the triangle in terms of x.

(ii) Find the radius of the circumcircle in terms of x.

The incircle of the triangle is then drawn as shown.

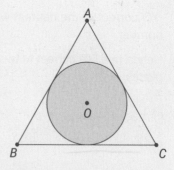

(iii) Find the radius of the incircle in terms of x.

(iv) Find the ratio of the area of the incircle to the area of the circumcircle.

Solutions and chapter summary available online

07

Trigonometry

✱ In this chapter you will learn to:

- ⊙ Apply the result of the theorem of Pythagoras to solve right-angled triangle problems of a simple nature involving heights and distances

- ⊙ Use the trigonometric ratios sin, cos and tan to solve problems

- ⊙ Define $\sin x$ and $\cos x$ for all values of x

- ⊙ Define $\tan x$

- ⊙ Find trigonometric ratios in surd form for angles 30°, 45° and 60°

- ⊙ Calculate the area of a triangle

- ⊙ Use the Sine and Cosine Rules to solve problems

- ⊙ Calculate the area of a sector of a circle and the length of an arc of a circle

- ⊙ Graph the trigonometric functions sine, cosine, tangent

- ⊙ Graph trigonometric functions of type
  - ⊙ $f(\theta) = a + b \sin c\theta$
  - ⊙ $g(\theta) = a + b \cos c\theta$

  for $a, b, c \in R$

- ⊙ Solve trigonometric equations such as $\cos n\theta = \dfrac{1}{2}$ and $\sin n\theta = 0$ giving all solutions

- ⊙ Use the radian measure of angles

- ⊙ Derive the trigonometric formulae 1, 2, 3, 4, 5, 6, 7, 9

- ⊙ Apply the trigonometric formulae 1–24

❗ You should remember...

- ⊙ The angles in a triangle sum to 180°.

- ⊙ Angles at the base of an isosceles triangle are equal in measure.

- ⊙ All angles in an equilateral triangle measure 60°.

- ⊙ Distance = Speed × Time.

Key words

- Right-angled triangle
- Pythagoras' theorem
- Opposite, adjacent, hypotenuse
- sin, cos, tan

- Radian measure
- Unit circle
- Reference angle
- Surd form
- Sector

- Period
- Range
- Sine Rule
- Cosine Rule
- Proof

Trigonometry is the study of triangles, their angles, areas and lengths. It is not the work of any one mathematician or nation. Its history dates back thousands of years. Archaelogical evidence dating to 2150 BC suggests that the ancient Egyptians had a knowledge of trigonometry.

Much of the technology that we use in today's highly developed world would not be possible without trigonometry. There are numerous applications of trigonometry. Astronomers use trigonometry to calculate distances to nearby stars. Engineers use trigonometry to construct bridges and build giant skyscrapers. Seismologists use trigonometry to study earthquakes. Here is a list of just some of the other areas to which trigonometry has been applied: navigation, medical imaging (MRI scans), computer graphics, electrical engineering, biology and economics.

7.1 Right-Angled Triangles and Pythagoras' Theorem

Pythagoras, an ancient Greek mathematician, is credited with first proving a very famous feature of right-angled triangles. Today, this feature is known as **Pythagoras' theorem**.

In a right-angled triangle, the area of the square on the hypotenuse is equal to the sum of the areas of the squares on the other two sides.

$c^2 = a^2 + b^2$

This can be found on page 16 of *Formulae and Tables*.

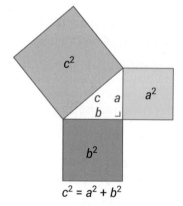

$c^2 = a^2 + b^2$

Worked Example 7.1

Use the theorem of Pythagoras to find the value of x.

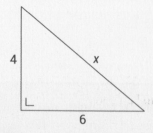

Solution

$x^2 = 4^2 + 6^2$ (Pythagoras)

$x^2 = 16 + 36$

$x^2 = 52$

$x = \sqrt{52} = \sqrt{4}\sqrt{13} = 2\sqrt{13}$

This answer is exact and in surd form.

TRIGONOMETRY

Worked Example 7.2

A mast on a sailing boat is held in place by steel wires called stays. The mast is 12 m tall. The stay is 13 metres long. What is the width of the deck between the base of the mast and the stay?

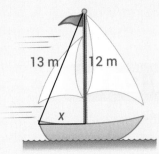

Solution

Let the distance between the base and the stay be x.

$$13^2 = 12^2 + x^2$$
$$169 = 144 + x^2$$
$$169 - 144 = x^2$$
$$25 = x^2$$
$$x = 5 \text{ m}$$

7.2 Right-Angled Triangles and the Trigonometric Ratios

In a right-angled triangle, we have the following special ratios:

$$\sin A = \frac{\text{opposite}}{\text{hypotenuse}}$$

$$\cos A = \frac{\text{adjacent}}{\text{hypotenuse}}$$

$$\tan A = \frac{\text{opposite}}{\text{adjacent}}$$

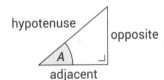

These ratios can be found on page 16 of *Formulae and Tables*.

Worked Example 7.3

In the following right-angled triangle, write down the value of each of the following ratios:
$\sin A$, $\cos A$ and $\tan A$; also $\sin B$, $\cos B$ and $\tan B$

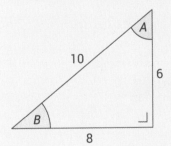

Solution

$$\sin A = \frac{8}{10} = \frac{4}{5} \qquad \sin B = \frac{6}{10} = \frac{3}{5}$$

$$\cos A = \frac{6}{10} = \frac{3}{5} \qquad \cos B = \frac{8}{10} = \frac{4}{5}$$

$$\tan A = \frac{8}{6} = \frac{4}{3} \qquad \tan B = \frac{6}{8} = \frac{3}{4}$$

7.3 Calculator Work

Worked Example 7.4

Use your calculator to find the value of each of the following, correct to four decimal places:

(i) $\sin 32.4°$ (ii) $\cos 45.6°$ (iii) $\tan 22.5°$

Solution

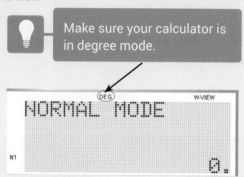

Make sure your calculator is in degree mode.

(i) On the calculator, press:

$$\boxed{\text{sin}} \; \boxed{\text{32.4}} \; \boxed{=}$$

The answer should be 0.5358 corrected to four decimal places.

(ii)

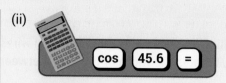

$$\boxed{\text{cos}} \; \boxed{\text{45.6}} \; \boxed{=}$$

Answer is 0.6997.

(iii)

$$\boxed{\text{tan}} \; \boxed{\text{22.5}} \; \boxed{=}$$

Answer is 0.4142.

How can we find the measure of the angle A in the diagram shown?

From the diagram, we know that:

$\sin A = \dfrac{11}{61}$

We can now use the calculator to find A.

Key in the following:

$$\boxed{\text{2nd F}} \; \boxed{\text{sin}} \; \boxed{\tfrac{11}{61}} \; \boxed{=}$$

This gives an answer of 10.39° (to two decimal places).

This is written as:

$\sin A = \dfrac{11}{61}$

$\therefore A = \sin^{-1} \dfrac{11}{61}$

$\therefore A = 10.39°$

Always use the fraction button or brackets to avoid errors.

$\sin^{-1}\left(\dfrac{11}{61}\right) \neq \sin^{-1} 11 \div 61$

Individual calculators may differ from what is shown next.

Worked Example 7.5

Change 35.6° to degrees and minutes.

Solution

$$\boxed{\text{35.6}} \; \boxed{\text{2nd F}} \; \boxed{\text{D°M'S}} \; \boxed{=}$$

The answer 35° 36' 0" is displayed.
Therefore, 35.6° = 35° 36'.

On some calculators, $\boxed{\text{D°M'S}}$ is replaced with $\boxed{\text{° ' "}}$.

1° = 60' and 1' = 60"

This is to some extent equivalent to 1 hr = 60' and 1' = 60" in the measurement of time.

Worked Example 7.6

Change 64° 45′ to degrees.

Solution

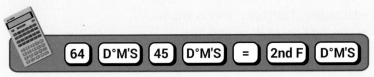

The answer $64\frac{3}{4}$ is displayed.

$\Rightarrow$ 64° 45′ = 64.75°

Worked Example 7.7

If $\cos A = 0.2183$, then, using your calculator, find:

(i) The measure of the angle A to two decimal places

(ii) The measure of the angle A to the nearest minute

Solution

(i) $\cos A = 0.2183$

$\Rightarrow A = \cos^{-1} 0.2183$

Key in the following:

$\therefore A = 77.39°$ (to two decimal places)

(ii) Key in the following:

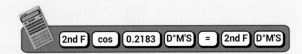

This gives the answer 77° 23′
(to the nearest minute).

Worked Example 7.8

Consider the triangle ABC with $|\angle BAC| = 90°$. If $|AB| = 9$ cm and $|\angle ABC| = 50°$, find the lengths of the remaining two sides of the triangle correct to two decimal places.

 Draw and label diagrams – they could get you partial credit. It will also be easier to answer these types of questions with a diagram.

Solution

Let $|BC| = x$.

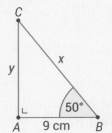

$\cos 50° = \dfrac{9}{x}$

$x \cos 50° = 9$ (Multiply both sides by x.)

$x = \dfrac{9}{\cos 50°}$ (Divide both sides by $\cos 50°$.)

$x = 14.00$ (correct to two decimal places)

$\therefore |BC| = 14.00$ cm

Let $|AC| = y$.

$\tan 50° = \dfrac{y}{9}$

$9 \tan 50° = y$ (Multiply both sides by 9.)

$y = 10.73$ (to two decimal places)

$\therefore |AC| = 10.73$ cm

7.4 Using Trigonometry to Solve Practical Problems

Compass Directions

The diagram shows the four main compass directions: North, South, East and West.

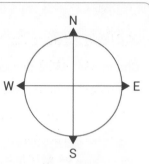

For all other compass directions, we can begin by looking North or South and then turning either East or West through the required number of degrees. This is shown in the diagrams below. One could also begin by looking East or West and then turning North or South through the required angle.

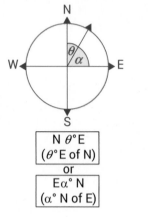

N θ°E
(θ°E of N)
or
Eα° N
(α° N of E)

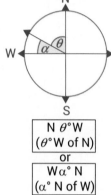

N θ°W
(θ°W of N)
or
Wα° N
(α° N of W)

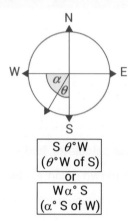

S θ°W
(θ°W of S)
or
Wα° S
(α° S of W)

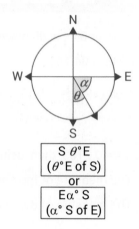

S θ°E
(θ°E of S)
or
Eα° S
(α° S of E)

Angles of Elevation and Depression

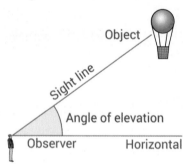

If you look up at a tall building or object, the angle that your line of vision makes with the horizontal is called the **angle of elevation**.

> The **angle of elevation** is the angle above the horizontal.

If you stand on top of a cliff and observe a swimmer out at sea, the angle that your line of vision makes with the horizontal is called the **angle of depression**.

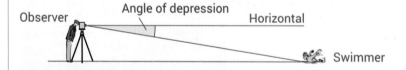

> The **angle of depression** is the angle below the horizontal.

Worked Example 7.9

Ger is out playing golf. As he approaches the ninth tee his friend tells him the hole is 310 m from the tee (*A*) to the hole (*C*).

On the first stroke the ball travels a distance of 225 m in the direction N 40° E. Ger then takes his second shot (from *B*) and the ball travels in the direction S 50° E and rolls onto the green and into the hole.

(i) How far did Ger hit the ball on his second shot? Give your answer to the nearest metre.

(ii) Find |∠*ACB*| to the nearest degree.

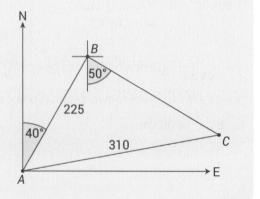

TRIGONOMETRY

Solution

(i) $|\angle ABC| = 40° + 50° = 90°$

$|AC| = 310$

$|AC|^2 = |AB|^2 + |BC|^2$ (Pythagoras)

$310^2 = 225^2 + |BC|^2$

$|BC|^2 = 45475$

$|BC| = \sqrt{45475}$

$\therefore |BC| \approx 213$ m

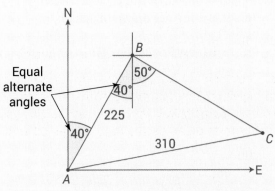

(ii) $\sin|\angle ACB| = \dfrac{225}{310}$

$|\angle ACB| = \sin^{-1}\left(\dfrac{225}{310}\right)$

$\therefore |\angle ACB| \approx 47°$

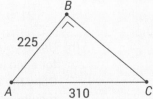

> 💡 Draw the triangle you are dealing with separately.

Exercise 7.1

1. Find the value of x in each case:

(i)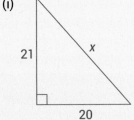

(ii)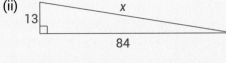

(iii)

(iv)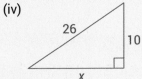

(v)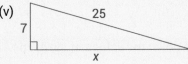

(vi)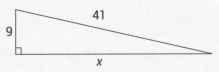

2. Find the value of x in each case (leave your answers in surd form):

(i)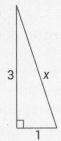

(ii)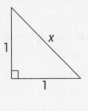

(iii)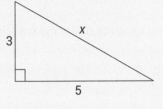

(iv)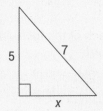

3. A ladder is 6.5 m long and rests against a vertical wall. The top of the ladder reaches a point on the wall that is 6 m above the ground. Find the distance from the wall to the foot of the ladder.

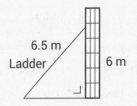

4. Find the value of *x* and *y* in each case (diagrams are not drawn to scale):

(i)
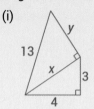

(ii)
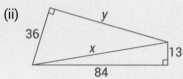

(iii)
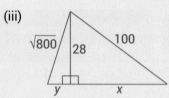

(iv)
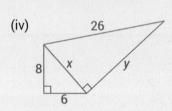

5. The perimeter of a rectangle is 280 cm. The length of the longest side is 80 cm. Find:

(i) The length of the shortest side

(ii) The length of a diagonal of the rectangle

(iii) The area of the rectangle

6. (a) Copy the table below. Use the pattern to complete the table.

Side *a*	Side *b*	Hypotenuse *c*
3	4	5
6	8	10
9	12	15
12		
	20	
		30
21		

(b) Using your calculator, check if $a^2 + b^2 = c^2$ for each row of the completed table. Copy the table below and show your results.

a^2	b^2	c^2	$a^2 + b^2 = c^2$ Tick if true
9	16	25	✓
36			

7. For each of the following triangles, write down the values of sin *A*, cos *A* and tan *A*:

(i)
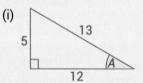

(ii)
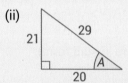

8. For each of the following triangles, write down the values of sin *A*, cos *A*, tan *A*, sin *B*, cos *B* and tan *B*:

(i)
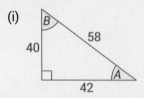

(ii)
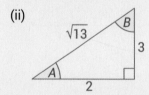

(iii)
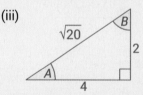

9. Use your calculator to find the value of each of the following, correct to four decimal places:

(i) sin 15° (v) tan 42° (ix) tan 80° (xiii) sin 31.4° (xvii) sin 63.3°

(ii) cos 30° (vi) cos 85° (x) tan 25.6° (xiv) tan 15.8° (xviii) tan 82.4°

(iii) tan 75° (vii) tan 12° (xi) cos 43.8° (xv) cos 30.9° (xix) cos 88.24°

(iv) sin 14° (viii) sin 30° (xii) sin 79.2° (xvi) cos 56.7° (xx) sin 63.16°

10. Use your calculator to find the measure of the angle A, $0° \leqslant A \leqslant 90°$. Give your answers to two decimal places.

(i) $\sin A = 0.6192$ (v) $\tan A = 0.3762$ (ix) $\tan A = 2.1375$

(ii) $\cos A = 0.8694$ (vi) $\cos A = 0.1246$ (x) $\cos A = 0.4523$

(iii) $\tan A = 0.3592$ (vii) $\tan A = 1.6347$ (xi) $\sin A = 0.1436$

(iv) $\sin A = 0.4375$ (viii) $\sin A = 0.7221$ (xii) $\tan A = 0.8777$

11. Change each of the following to degrees and minutes. Give your answers to the nearest minute.

(i) $2.5°$ (iii) $2.75°$ (v) $1.2°$

(ii) $2.25°$ (iv) $25.4°$ (vi) $\frac{1}{3}$ of a degree

12. Change the following to degrees. Give your answers correct to two decimal places.

(i) $2° 31'$ (ii) $10° 40'$ (iii) $25° 50'$ (iv) $70° 22'$ (v) $11° 37'$ (vi) $33° 33'$

13. Use your calculator to find the measure of the angle B, $0° \leqslant B \leqslant 90°$. Give your answers to the nearest minute.

(i) $\sin B = 0.9701$ (v) $\tan B = 0.3193$ (ix) $\tan B = 0.4080$

(ii) $\cos B = 0.6661$ (vi) $\cos B = 0.8925$ (x) $\cos B = 0.5297$

(iii) $\tan B = 0.9628$ (vii) $\tan B = 3.4650$ (xi) $\sin B = 0.4321$

(iv) $\sin B = 0.6635$ (viii) $\sin B = 0.2411$ (xii) $\cos B = 0.9201$

14. Calculate, to the nearest degree, the value of the angle B.

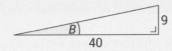

15. Calculate, to the nearest minute, the value of the angle C.

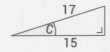

16. Find the value of x in the following triangles (answers to two decimal places where necessary):

(i)

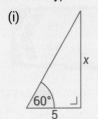

(ii)

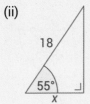

(iii)

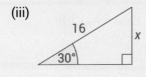

(iv)

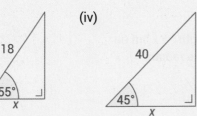

(v)   (vii)

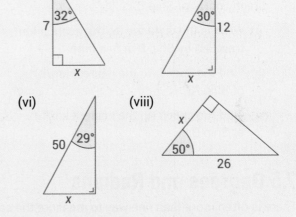

(vi)   (viii)

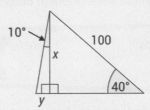

17. Solve for x and y to two decimal places.

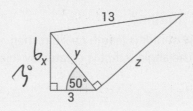

18. Solve for x, y and z to two significant figures.

19. A ship leaves a port *A* and sails a distance of 4 km in the direction N 30° E. The ship then changes direction and sails for a further 6 km in the direction S 60° E to a point *C* (see diagram).

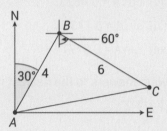

(i) Calculate the distance from the ship's present position at point *C* to port *A*. Give your answer to one decimal place.

(ii) Find $|\angle BCA|$, to the nearest degree.

(iii) Hence, find the direction of *C* **from** *A*.

20. Two ships A and B leave the same harbour. Ship A travels due west and Ship B travels 67° south of west. After two hours, Ship A has travelled 46 km and is directly north of Ship B.

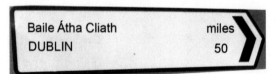

(i) What is the distance (to the nearest km) travelled by Ship B in this time?

(ii) Find the speed (to the nearest km/h) of Ship A.

(iii) Find the speed (to the nearest km/h) of Ship B.

21. The Empire State Building pictured below is one of New York's tallest buildings. Using the information given, calculate the height of the building.

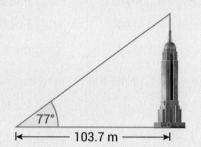

22. John is standing on a cliff top and observes a boat drifting towards the base of the cliff. He decides to call the emergency services and give them the position of the boat. He measures the angle of depression of the boat from the cliff top to be 30°, and he knows the cliff top is 200 m above sea level. How far is the boat from the base of the cliff?

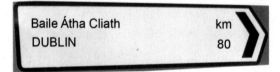

23. David wants to measure the height of a tree. He walks exactly 15 metres from the base of the tree and looks up. The angle from eye level to the top of the tree is 33°. If David is 1.7 metres tall, calculate the height of the tree.

7.5 Degrees and Radians

There is often more than one way to measure the same thing. For example, it is only since January 2005 that distances on Irish road signs have been given in kilometres – up to then distances were given in miles. Changing the unit of measurement does not change the distance between towns.

Baile Átha Cliath — DUBLIN — miles 50

Baile Átha Cliath — DUBLIN — km 80

The same applies to angles. Angles can be measured in degrees or in radians. Radian measure is essential in Higher Level mathematics, particularly for calculus.

What is a Radian?

Draw a circle of radius length $r = x$ cm, then mark an arc of length $l = x$ cm on this circle. The angle θ that is created by this arc measures **one radian**.

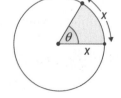

One **radian** is the measure of the angle at the centre of a circle when the length of the arc is equal to the length of the radius.

If you marked an arc of length $l = 2x$ cm on a circle with radius length $r = x$ cm, the angle θ that is created is **two radians** in measure.

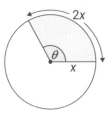

$l = r\theta$ (when θ is in radians)

This formula appears on page 9 of *Formulae and Tables*.

How Many Radians are in a Full Revolution?

$l = r\theta$ (when θ is in radians)

In a full revolution $l = 2\pi r$.

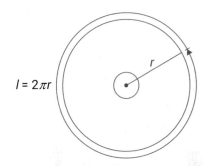

$l = 2\pi r$

But $l = r\theta$.

So, $r\theta = 2\pi r$

$\theta = \dfrac{2\pi r}{r}$

$\theta = 2\pi$ (radians in a full revolution)

From this, we can say the following:

2π radians = 360°   (360° in a full revolution)

π radians = 180°

$1 \text{ radian} = \dfrac{180°}{\pi} \approx 57.296°$

$1° = \dfrac{\pi}{180} \approx 0.01745 \text{ radians}$

Both of these definitions are on page 13 of *Formulae and Tables*.

Converting Degrees to Radians and Radians to Degrees

The following examples show how we can convert degrees to radians and radians to degrees.

Worked Example 7.10

Convert 135° to radians.

Solution

$180° = \pi$ radians

$1° = \dfrac{\pi}{180}$ radians

$1° \times 135 = \dfrac{\pi}{180} \times 135$ radians

$135° = \dfrac{135\pi}{180}$ radians

$\therefore 135° = \dfrac{3\pi}{4}$ radians

Worked Example 7.11

Convert $\dfrac{7\pi}{9}$ radians to degrees.

Solution

π radians = 180°

$\dfrac{7\pi}{9}$ radians $= \dfrac{7(180°)}{9}$

$= 7(20°)$

$\therefore \dfrac{7\pi}{9}$ radians = 140°

7.6 Angles of Different Sizes

There are many situations where angles measure much more than 360° or 2π radians (rads).

In a day, the hands on a clock turn through a lot more than 360°. The minute hand on a clock turns through 8640° (360 × 24 = 8640°) in one day.

Determining Where an Angle Terminates

The following example shows how to find where an angle terminates. The x- and y-axes divide the plane into four quadrants. Angles are measured from the positive sense of the x-axis.

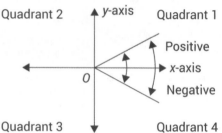

- Positive is an anticlockwise direction.
- Negative is a clockwise direction.

An angle can be of any size, positive or negative.

Worked Example 7.12

Dan is a member of a dance club.

During a routine he spins on his head, turning a total of 960°.

(i) In which quadrant would an angle of 960° terminate?

(ii) What is the measure of this angle in radians?

Solution

(i) To answer this question, reduce the angle by as many full revolutions as possible.

960° − 360° = 600°

600° − 360° = 240°

So 960° is two complete revolutions plus 240°.

960° = 360° + 360° + 240°

This angle would terminate in the third quadrant.

(ii)   180° = π radians

$1° = \dfrac{\pi}{180}$ rads

$1° \times 960 = \dfrac{960\pi}{180}$ rads

$960° = \dfrac{16\pi}{3}$ rads

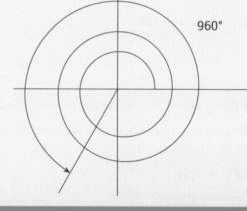

 We could use Modular Arithmetic as in Book 1 Chapter 8.

$\dfrac{960}{360} = 2\dfrac{2}{3}$ (i.e. 2R240)

$\dfrac{2}{3}$ of 360 = 240

Exercise 7.2

1. Copy and complete the following table:

Degrees	90°	180°	270°			45°	
Radians		π		2π	$\dfrac{\pi}{6}$		$\dfrac{\pi}{3}$

TRIGONOMETRY

2. Convert the following angles (given in radians) to degrees:

(i) $\dfrac{\pi}{2}$ (iii) $\dfrac{5\pi}{2}$ (v) $\dfrac{5\pi}{4}$ (vii) 4π (ix) $\dfrac{3\pi}{4}$ (xi) $\dfrac{4\pi}{9}$

(ii) $\dfrac{3\pi}{2}$ (iv) $\dfrac{4\pi}{3}$ (vi) $\dfrac{5\pi}{18}$ (viii) 6π (x) $\dfrac{11\pi}{6}$ (xii) $\dfrac{4\pi}{5}$

3. Convert to radians, leaving your answer in terms of π.

(i) 90°   (iii) 45°   (v) 540°   (vii) 432°   (ix) 75°   (xi) 210°

(ii) 270°   (iv) 15°   (vi) 30°   (viii) 450°   (x) 37.5°   (xii) 980°

4. In which quadrants do these angles terminate?

(i) 110°   (iii) 50°   (v) $\dfrac{8\pi}{6}$ rads   (vii) −60°   (ix) 460°   (xi) 1010°

(ii) $\dfrac{\pi}{4}$ rads   (iv) 185°   (vi) $-\dfrac{15\pi}{6}$ rads   (viii) $\dfrac{9\pi}{4}$ rads   (x) 840°   (xii) $\dfrac{36\pi}{5}$ rads

7.7 The Unit Circle

The unit circle has its centre at (0,0) and has a radius length of 1 unit.

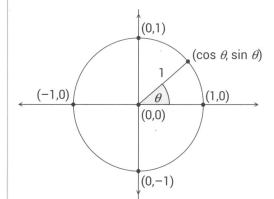

$\cos\theta = x$ co-ordinate
$\sin\theta = y$ co-ordinate
Also, $\tan\theta = \dfrac{\sin\theta}{\cos\theta}$

All of these definitions are on page 13 of *Formulae and Tables*.

7.8 Evaluating the Trigonometric Ratios of All Angles between 0° and 360°

Reference Angles

Consider an angle *AOB*, where $|\angle AOB| = 140°$.

$\angle AOB$ will lie in the second quadrant of the unit circle.

$|\angle AOB| = 140°$
Reference angle
$\quad = 180° - 140°$
$\quad = 40°$

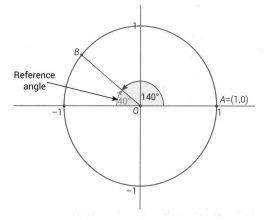

The acute angle formed by the terminal side of $\angle AOB$ (i.e. where the angle ends) and the *x*-axis is called the reference angle of $\angle AOB$. In this case, the reference angle measures 40°.

Here are similar examples for angles that lie in the third and fourth quadrants respectively.

$|\angle AOB| = 250°$

Reference angle

$= 250° - 180°$

$= 70°$

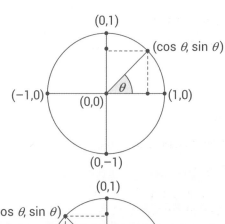

$|\angle AOB| = 330°$

Reference angle

$= 360° - 330°$

$= 30°$

The Sign of the Ratios in Each Quadrant

First Quadrant ($0° < \theta < 90°$)

In the first quadrant, all three ratios are positive.

- $\cos \theta$ is positive, as its value lies on the positive x-axis.

- $\sin \theta$ is positive, as its value lies on the positive y-axis.

- $\tan \theta = \dfrac{\sin \theta}{\cos \theta} = \dfrac{+}{+} = +$ Hence, $\tan \theta$ is positive.

Second Quadrant ($90° < \theta < 180°$)

In the second quadrant, sin is positive; cos and tan are negative.

- $\cos \theta$ is negative, as its value lies on the negative x-axis.

- $\sin \theta$ is positive, as its value lies on the positive y-axis.

- $\tan \theta = \dfrac{\sin \theta}{\cos \theta} = \dfrac{+}{-} = -$ Hence, $\tan \theta$ is negative.

Third Quadrant ($180° < \theta < 270°$)

In the third quadrant, tan is positive; sin and cos are negative.

- $\cos \theta$ is negative, as its value lies on the negative x-axis.

- $\sin \theta$ is negative, as its value lies on the negative y-axis.

- $\tan \theta = \dfrac{\sin \theta}{\cos \theta} = \dfrac{-}{-} = +$ Hence, $\tan \theta$ is positive.

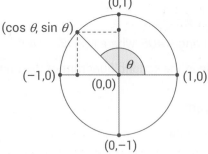

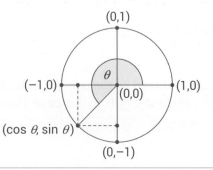

Fourth Quadrant (270° < θ < 360°)

In the fourth quadrant, cos is positive; sin and tan are negative.

- cos θ is positive, as its value lies on the positive *x*-axis.
- sin θ is negative, as its value lies on the negative *y*-axis.
- $\tan \theta = \dfrac{\sin \theta}{\cos \theta} = \dfrac{-}{+} = -$ Hence, tan θ is negative.

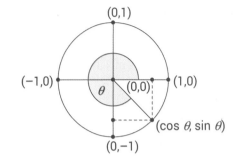

CAST

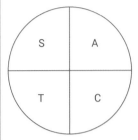

The diagram on the left summarises this section.

(a) In the first quadrant, all three ratios (A) are positive.

(b) In the second quadrant, only sin (S) is positive.

(c) In the third quadrant, only tan (T) is positive.

(d) In the fourth quadrant, only cos (C) is positive.

Worked Example 7.13

When asked to give an answer in surd form, the sine, cosine and tangent ratios can be read easily for the angles 30°, 45° and 60°.

Example: tan 60° = √3 in surd form
                tan 60° ≈ 1.7321 in decimal form

See page 13 of *Formulae and Tables*.

Write in surd form:

(i) cos 225°   (ii) tan 330°   (iii) sin 135°

Solution

(i) cos 225°

Step 1

Draw an angle of 225°.

Step 2

The angle is in the third quadrant, so its cosine is negative.

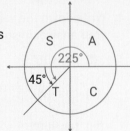

Step 3

The reference angle is 45° (225° − 180°).

$$\cos 45° = \frac{1}{\sqrt{2}}$$

Step 4

$$\therefore \cos 225° = -\frac{1}{\sqrt{2}}$$

(ii) tan 330°

Step 1

Draw an angle of 330°.

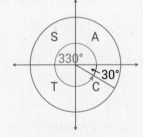

Step 2

The angle is in the fourth quadrant, so its tangent is negative.

Step 3

The reference angle is 30° (360° − 330°).

$$\tan 30° = \frac{1}{\sqrt{3}}$$

Step 4

$$\therefore \tan 330° = -\frac{1}{\sqrt{3}}$$

(iii) $\sin 135°$

Step 1

Draw an angle of 135°.

Step 2

The angle is in the second quadrant, so its sine is positive.

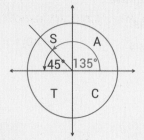

Step 3

The reference angle is 45° (180° − 135°).

$\sin 45° = \dfrac{1}{\sqrt{2}}$

Step 4

$\therefore \sin 135° = \dfrac{1}{\sqrt{2}}$

Exercise 7.3

1. In the following questions, use the unit circle to find the answer:

(i) $\cos 270°$

(ii) $\sin 270°$

(iii) $\cos 90°$

(iv) $\sin 90°$

(v) $\tan 180°$

(vi) $\cos 180°$

(vii) $\sin 180°$

(viii) $\cos 0°$

(ix) $\sin 0°$

(x) $\tan 0°$

(xi) $\cos 360°$

(xii) $\sin 360°$

(xiii) $\tan 360°$

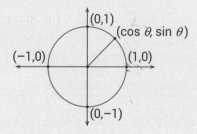

2. Fill in the tables below.

(a)

Angle	Quadrant	Reference Angle
210°		
	4th	20°
	3rd	45°
280°		

(b)

Angle	Quadrant	Reference Angle
315°		
	2nd	45°
	3rd	30°
240°		

3. (a) For the following questions, write your answer in surd form:

(i) $\cos 135°$

(ii) $\sin 150°$

(iii) $\cos 240°$

(iv) $\sin 330°$

(v) $\tan 210°$

(vi) $\cos 315°$

(vii) $\sin 120°$

(viii) $\cos 210°$

(ix) $\tan 300°$

(x) $\tan 60°$

(b) For the following questions, use your calculator and give your answer correct to two decimal places:

(i) $\cos 145°$

(ii) $\sin 160°$

(iii) $\cos 230°$

(iv) $\sin 355°$

(v) $\tan 220°$

(vi) $\cos 325°$

(vii) $\sin 140°$

(viii) $\cos 230°$

(ix) $\tan 350°$

(x) $\tan 160°$

4. Write down the values of the following, giving your answer in surd form where appropriate:

(i) $\sin 405°$

(ii) $\cos 420°$

(iii) $\tan 960°$

(iv) $\cos \dfrac{11\pi}{6}$

(v) $\sin 660°$

(vi) $\cos \dfrac{9\pi}{2}$

(vii) $\tan 1020°$

7.9 Graphing Trigonometric Functions

We recall from our investigations of the unit circle that:

- $\cos\theta = x$ co-ordinate
- $\sin\theta = y$ co-ordinate

These definitions are used when graphing the sine and cosine functions.

- Period: the horizontal distance required for the graph to complete one cycle
- Range: the set of all actual outputs of the function
- Amplitude: the number of units the graph goes up or down from the midline of the graph

Graphing the Sine Function ($y = \sin \theta$)

θ	0	$\dfrac{\pi}{4}$	$\dfrac{\pi}{2}$	$\dfrac{3\pi}{4}$	π	$\dfrac{5\pi}{4}$	$\dfrac{3\pi}{2}$	$\dfrac{7\pi}{4}$	2π
$y = \sin \theta$ to 1 d.p.	0	0.7	1	0.7	0	−0.7	−1	−0.7	0

- $\sin 0 = 0$, so the curve passes through the origin (0,0).
- The maximum value of $\sin \theta$ is 1.
- The minimum value of $\sin \theta$ is −1.
- The graph repeats itself every 2π radians, so it is a **periodic function**.

Period = 2π

Range = [−1, 1]

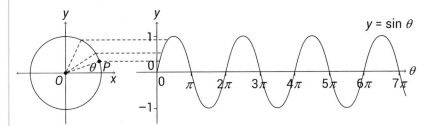

Rotating [OP] through θ and plotting the y co-ordinate for P for each value of θ gives the sine curve.

Graphing the Cosine Function ($y = \cos \theta$)

Graphing the cosine function can be done in a similar way to the sine function.

As $\cos \theta = x$ co-ordinate, it is necessary to **rotate the axes in the unit circle diagram counter-clockwise by 90°.**

Rotating [OP] through θ and plotting the x co-ordinate for P for each value of θ gives the cosine curve.

θ	0	$\dfrac{\pi}{4}$	$\dfrac{\pi}{2}$	$\dfrac{3\pi}{4}$	π	$\dfrac{5\pi}{4}$	$\dfrac{3\pi}{2}$	$\dfrac{7\pi}{4}$	2π
$y = \cos \theta$ to 1 d.p.	1	0.7	0	−0.7	−1	−0.7	0	0.7	1

- $\cos 0 = 1$ so, the curve cuts the y-axis at (0,1).
- The maximum value of $\cos \theta$ is 1.
- The minimum value of $\cos \theta$ is −1.
- The graph repeats itself every 2π radians, so it is a **periodic function**.

Period = 2π

Range = [−1, 1]

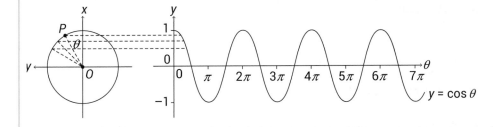

Graphing the Tangent Function ($y = \tan \theta$)

θ	0	$\frac{\pi}{8}$	$\frac{\pi}{4}$	$\frac{3\pi}{8}$	$\frac{\pi}{2}$	$\frac{5\pi}{8}$	$\frac{3\pi}{4}$	$\frac{7\pi}{8}$	π	$\frac{9\pi}{8}$	$\frac{5\pi}{4}$	$\frac{11\pi}{8}$	$\frac{3\pi}{2}$
$y = \tan \theta$ to 1 d.p.	0	0.4	1	2.4	——	−2.4	−1	−0.4	0	0.4	1	2.4	——

- $\tan 0 = 0$ so, the curve passes through the origin (0,0).
- There are no maximum and minimum values.
- The graph repeats itself every π radians, so it is a **periodic function**.
- There are **asymptotes** at $\theta = \pm \frac{\pi}{2}, \pm \frac{3\pi}{2}, \pm \frac{5\pi}{2}, \dots$ [θ given in radians] (at all odd multiples of $\frac{\pi}{2}$ radians).

Period = π

Range = $(-\infty, \infty)$

An **asymptote** is a line the curve will approach but never meet.

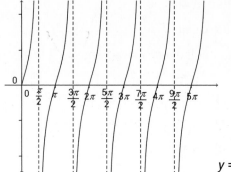

$y = \tan \theta$

Using Graphs to Find a Number of Angles with the Same Trigonometric Ratio

Worked Example 7.14

(i) Find three angles with the same sine value as $\frac{\pi}{4}$ radians.

(ii) Find three angles with the same cosine value as π radians.

(iii) Find three angles with the same tangent ratio as $\frac{\pi}{5}$ radians.

Solution

(i)

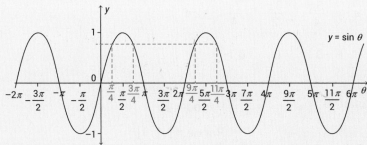

- By symmetry, $\sin \frac{3\pi}{4}$ has the same value as $\sin \frac{\pi}{4}$ (as period = 2π).

- The sine graph repeats every 2π radians.

  So $\sin \frac{\pi}{4} = \sin\left(\frac{\pi}{4} + 2\pi\right) = \sin \frac{9\pi}{4}$.

  $\sin \frac{3\pi}{4} = \sin\left(\frac{3\pi}{4} + 2\pi\right) = \sin \frac{11\pi}{4}$

  Answer: $\frac{3\pi}{4}, \frac{9\pi}{4}, \frac{11\pi}{4}$

(ii)

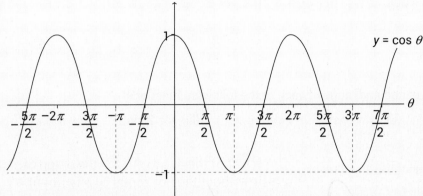

A function $y = f(x)$ is even if $f(x) = f(-x)$ for all $x \in R$.

For example, $f(x) = x^2 + 3$ is even since $f(x) = f(-x) = x^2 + 3$ for all $x \in R$.

- The cosine graph is symmetrical about the y-axis. This makes the cosine function an EVEN function.
  So $\cos \pi = \cos(-\pi)$.

- The cosine graph repeats every 2π radians (as period $= 2\pi$).
  So $\cos \pi = \cos(\pi + 2\pi) = \cos 3\pi$.
  $$\cos 3\pi = \cos(3\pi + 2\pi) = \cos 5\pi$$

  Answer: $-\pi, 3\pi, 5\pi$

(iii) The tangent graph repeats itself every π radians (as period $= \pi$). So if one angle is known, others can be found by adding or subtracting π.

$$\tan \frac{\pi}{5} = \tan\left(\frac{\pi}{5} + \pi\right) = \tan \frac{6\pi}{5}$$

$$\tan \frac{\pi}{5} = \tan\left(\frac{\pi}{5} - \pi\right) = \tan\left(-\frac{4\pi}{5}\right)$$

$$\tan \frac{6\pi}{5} = \tan\left(\frac{6\pi}{5} + \pi\right) = \tan \frac{11\pi}{5}$$

Answer: $-\dfrac{4\pi}{5}, \dfrac{6\pi}{5}, \dfrac{11\pi}{5}$

Worked Example 7.15

(i) Find $\sin 9\pi$. (ii) Find $\sin 105\pi$ (without using a calculator).

Solution

(i) We could use a graph here.

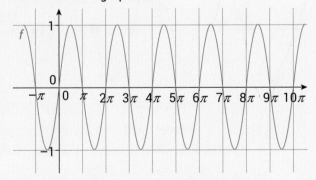

It is easy to see that $\sin 9\pi = 0$.

Alternative Method

$\sin \pi = 0$

The period of the sine function is 2π.

$$\sin \pi = \sin(\pi + 4(2\pi))$$
$$= \sin 9\pi$$

$\therefore \sin 9\pi = 0$

(ii) Here it is too awkward to graph the function up to 105π so we do the following:

The sine function repeats every 2π radians.

To find $\sin 105\pi$ subtract multiples of 2π radians.

$$\sin(105\pi - 2\pi - 2\pi - 2\pi - 2\pi - 2\pi - 2\pi...) = \sin \pi$$

$\therefore \sin \pi = 0$ (from page 13 of *Formulae and Tables*)

We can use the period of a trigonometric ratio to help us find the sine, cosine or tangent of a large positive or negative angle without the use of a calculator. Simply subtract or add multiples of the period from the angle.

Graphing Functions of the Form $a \sin n\theta$ and $a \cos n\theta$ for $a, n \in N$

Worked Example 7.16

Sketch the graphs and state the period and range of each of the following functions:

(i) $y = 4 \sin \theta$ $0 \leqslant \theta \leqslant 2\pi$ (ii) $y = \cos 3\theta$ $-\pi \leqslant \theta \leqslant \pi$ (iii) $y = 2 \sin 2\theta$ $-\pi \leqslant \theta \leqslant \pi$

Solution

(i) Recall the important features of the sine graph:

- It passes through the origin.
- The shape of the graph

θ	$\sin\theta$	$4\sin\theta$	y	Points to graph
0	0	0	0	$(0,0)$
$\frac{\pi}{2}$	1	4	4	$\left(\frac{\pi}{2},4\right)$
π	0	0	0	$(\pi,0)$
$\frac{3\pi}{2}$	-1	-4	-4	$\left(\frac{3\pi}{2},-4\right)$
2π	0	0	0	$(2\pi,0)$

> The effect of the 4 is to stretch the graph of $y = \sin\theta$ about the horizontal by a factor of 4. The range becomes $[-4, 4]$ while the period remains unchanged at 2π.

Plot the points and connect with a smooth curve.

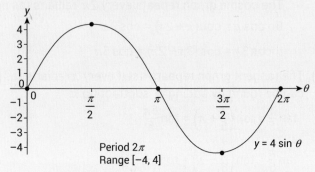

Period 2π
Range $[-4, 4]$
$y = 4\sin\theta$

(ii) Recall the important features of the cosine graph:

- It passes through $(0,1)$.
- The shape of the graph

θ	3θ	$\cos 3\theta$	y	Points to graph
$-\pi$	-3π	-1	-1	$(-\pi,-1)$
$-\frac{5\pi}{6}$	$-\frac{15\pi}{6}$	0	0	$\left(-\frac{5\pi}{6},0\right)$
$-\frac{4\pi}{6}$	$-\frac{12\pi}{6}$	1	1	$\left(-\frac{4\pi}{6},1\right)$
$-\frac{3\pi}{6}$	$-\frac{9\pi}{6}$	0	0	$\left(-\frac{3\pi}{6},0\right)$
$-\frac{2\pi}{6}$	$-\frac{6\pi}{6}$	-1	-1	$\left(-\frac{2\pi}{6},-1\right)$
$-\frac{\pi}{6}$	$-\frac{3\pi}{6}$	0	0	$\left(-\frac{\pi}{6},0\right)$
0	0	1	1	$(0,1)$
$\frac{\pi}{6}$	$\frac{3\pi}{6}$	0	0	$\left(\frac{\pi}{6},0\right)$
$\frac{2\pi}{6}$	$\frac{6\pi}{6}$	-1	-1	$\left(\frac{2\pi}{6},-1\right)$
$\frac{3\pi}{6}$	$\frac{9\pi}{6}$	0	0	$\left(\frac{3\pi}{6},0\right)$
$\frac{4\pi}{6}$	$\frac{12\pi}{6}$	1	1	$\left(\frac{4\pi}{6},1\right)$
$\frac{5\pi}{6}$	$\frac{15\pi}{6}$	0	0	$\left(\frac{5\pi}{6},0\right)$
π	3π	-1	-1	$(\pi,-1)$

> The effect of the 3 is to reduce the period of the graph of $y = \cos\theta$. The period becomes $\frac{2\pi}{3}$. The range remains unchanged at $[-1, 1]$.

Plot the points and connect with a smooth curve.

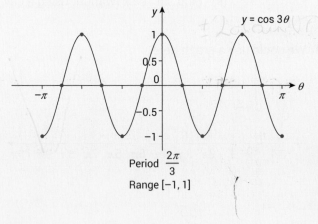

$y = \cos 3\theta$

Period $\frac{2\pi}{3}$
Range $[-1, 1]$

(iii) $y = 2 \sin 2\theta \quad -\pi \leqslant \theta \leqslant \pi$

Recall the important features of the sine graph:

- It passes through (0,0).
- The shape of the graph

θ	2θ	$\sin 2\theta$	$2 \sin 2\theta$	y	Points to graph
$-\pi$	-2π	0	0	0	$(-\pi, 0)$
$-\frac{3\pi}{4}$	$-\frac{3\pi}{2}$	1	2	2	$\left(-\frac{3\pi}{4}, 2\right)$
$-\frac{\pi}{2}$	$-\pi$	0	0	0	$\left(-\frac{\pi}{2}, 0\right)$
$-\frac{\pi}{4}$	$-\frac{\pi}{2}$	-1	-2	-2	$\left(-\frac{\pi}{4}, -2\right)$
0	0	0	0	0	$(0, 0)$
$\frac{\pi}{4}$	$\frac{\pi}{2}$	1	2	2	$\left(\frac{\pi}{4}, 2\right)$
$\frac{\pi}{2}$	π	0	0	0	$\left(\frac{\pi}{2}, 0\right)$
$\frac{3\pi}{4}$	$\frac{3\pi}{2}$	-1	-2	-2	$\left(\frac{3\pi}{4}, -2\right)$
π	2π	0	0	0	$(\pi, 0)$

The effect of the 2 in front of θ is to reduce the period of the graph $y = \sin \theta$. The period becomes π. The effect of the 2 in front of $\sin 2\theta$ is to stretch the graph of $y = \sin \theta$ about the horizontal by a factor of 2. The range becomes $[-2, 2]$.

Plot the points and connect with a smooth curve.

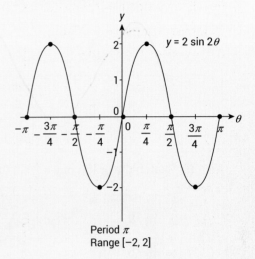

Period π
Range $[-2, 2]$

If $a, n \in N$ then:

- $a \sin n\theta$ has period $\frac{2\pi}{n}$ and range $[-a, a]$.
- $a \cos n\theta$ has period $\frac{2\pi}{n}$ and range $[-a, a]$.
- $a \tan n\theta$ has period $\frac{\pi}{n}$ and range $(-\infty, \infty)$.

Exercise 7.4

1. (a) (i) Sketch the graph of $y = \sin x$, for $-\pi \leqslant x \leqslant \pi$.

x	$-\pi$	$-\frac{3\pi}{4}$	$-\frac{\pi}{2}$	$-\frac{\pi}{4}$	0	$\frac{\pi}{4}$	$\frac{\pi}{2}$	$\frac{3\pi}{4}$	π
$y = \sin x$									
(x, y)									

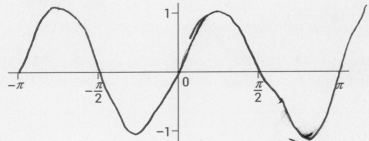

(ii) Range = ± 1 around 0

(iii) Period = $\dfrac{2\pi}{\cancel{1}}$

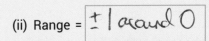

(b) (i) Sketch the graph of $y = \sin 2x$, for $-\pi \leqslant x \leqslant \pi$.

x	$-\pi$	$-\dfrac{3\pi}{4}$	$-\dfrac{\pi}{2}$	$-\dfrac{\pi}{4}$	0	$\dfrac{\pi}{4}$	$\dfrac{\pi}{2}$	$\dfrac{3\pi}{4}$	π
$2x$									
$y = \sin 2x$									
(x,y)									

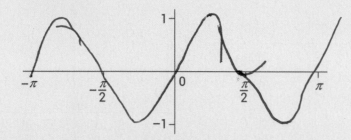

(ii) Range = ±1 around 0

(iii) Period = $\dfrac{2\pi}{2}$

(c) (i) Sketch the graph of $y = 2 \sin 2x$, for $-\pi \leqslant x \leqslant \pi$.

x	$-\pi$	$-\dfrac{3\pi}{4}$	$-\dfrac{\pi}{2}$	$-\dfrac{\pi}{4}$	0	$\dfrac{\pi}{4}$	$\dfrac{\pi}{2}$	$\dfrac{3\pi}{4}$	π
$2x$									
$\sin 2x$									
$y = 2 \sin 2x$									
(x,y)									

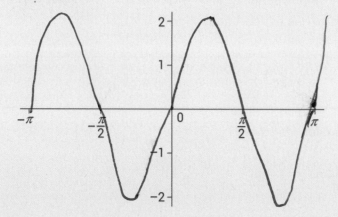

(ii) Range = ±2 around 0

(iii) Period = $\dfrac{2\pi}{2} = \pi$

(iv) What conclusions can be reached about the period and range of the function $y = a \sin bx$ where $a, b \in N$?

2. (a) (i) Sketch the graph of $y = \cos x$, for $-\pi \leqslant x \leqslant \pi$.

x	$-\pi$	$-\dfrac{3\pi}{4}$	$-\dfrac{\pi}{2}$	$-\dfrac{\pi}{4}$	0	$\dfrac{\pi}{4}$	$\dfrac{\pi}{2}$	$\dfrac{3\pi}{4}$	π
$y = \cos x$									
(x,y)									

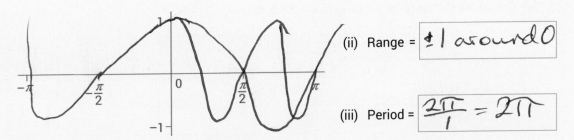

(ii) Range = ±1 around 0

(iii) Period = $\frac{2\pi}{1}$ = 2π

(b) (i) Sketch the graph of $y = \cos 2x$, for $-\pi \leq x \leq \pi$.

x	$-\pi$	$-\frac{3\pi}{4}$	$-\frac{\pi}{2}$	$-\frac{\pi}{4}$	0	$\frac{\pi}{4}$	$\frac{\pi}{2}$	$\frac{3\pi}{4}$	π
2x									
$y = \cos 2x$									
(x,y)									

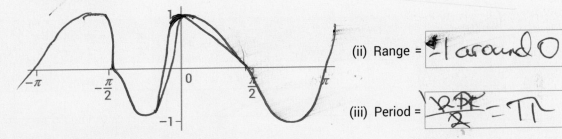

(ii) Range = ±1 around 0

(iii) Period = $\frac{2\pi}{2}$ = π

(c) (i) Sketch the graph of $y = 2\cos 2x$, for $-\pi \leq x \leq \pi$.

x	$-\pi$	$-\frac{3\pi}{4}$	$-\frac{\pi}{2}$	$-\frac{\pi}{4}$	0	$\frac{\pi}{4}$	$\frac{\pi}{2}$	$\frac{3\pi}{4}$	π
2x									
$\cos 2x$									
$y = 2\cos 2x$									
(x,y)									

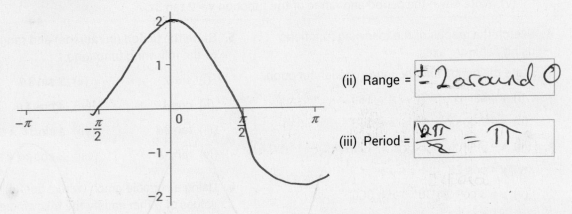

(ii) Range = ±2 around 0

(iii) Period = $\frac{2\pi}{2}$ = π

(iv) What conclusions can be reached about the period and range of the function $y = a\cos bx$ where $a, b \in N$?

3. (a) (i) Sketch the graph of $y = \tan x$, for $-\pi \leqslant x \leqslant \pi$.

x	$-\pi$	$-\dfrac{3\pi}{4}$	$-\dfrac{\pi}{2}$	$-\dfrac{\pi}{4}$	0	$\dfrac{\pi}{4}$	$\dfrac{\pi}{2}$	$\dfrac{3\pi}{4}$	π
$y = \tan x$									
(x,y)									

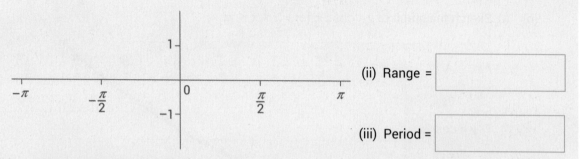

(ii) Range = [   ]

(iii) Period = [   ]

(b) (i) Sketch the graph of $y = \tan 2x$, for $-\pi \leqslant x \leqslant \pi$.

x	$-\pi$	$-\dfrac{3\pi}{4}$	$-\dfrac{\pi}{2}$	$-\dfrac{\pi}{4}$	0	$\dfrac{\pi}{4}$	$\dfrac{\pi}{2}$	$\dfrac{3\pi}{4}$	π
$2x$									
$y = \tan 2x$									
(x,y)									

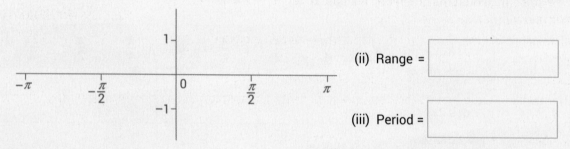

(ii) Range = [   ]

(iii) Period = [   ]

(iv) What can be concluded about the period of the function $y = \tan bx$ where $b \in N$?

(v) Write down the period and range of the function $y = 2 \tan 3x$.

4. Sketch the graphs of the following functions using separate axes.

State the period and the range of each function.

(i) $y = \sin 4x$ $0° \leqslant x \leqslant 180°$

(ii) $y = 2 \cos x$ $0° \leqslant x \leqslant 360°$

(iii) $y = 3 \sin x$ $-2\pi \leqslant x \leqslant 2\pi$

(iv) $y = \cos 2x$ $-\pi \leqslant x \leqslant \pi$

(v) $y = 3 \cos 2x$ $0° \leqslant x \leqslant 360°$

(vi) $y = 2 \sin 4x$ $0° \leqslant x \leqslant 90°$

(vii) $y = \tan 2x$ $0° \leqslant x \leqslant 180°$

5. State the period (in radians) and range for each of the following functions:

(i) $\sin \theta$ (v) $2 \sin 3\theta$

(ii) $\cos 4\theta$ (vi) $4 \cos 4\theta$

(iii) $\tan 2\theta$ (vii) $a \sin 3\theta, a \in N$

(iv) $\tan 3\theta$ (viii) $3 \cos k\theta, k \in N$

6. Using a suitable graph (where useful), find all values of θ that satisfy the following equations:

(i) $\tan \theta = \tan \dfrac{\pi}{7}$ $-2\pi \leqslant \theta \leqslant 2\pi$

(ii) $\sin \theta = \sin 60°$ $0° \leqslant \theta \leqslant 720°$

(iii) $\sin \theta = \sin\left(-\dfrac{\pi}{3}\right)$ $0 \leqslant \theta \leqslant 4\pi$

7. Sketch the following three functions on the **same axes** for $-\pi \leqslant x \leqslant \pi$:

$f(x) = \sin 3x$

$g(x) = 3 \sin 2x$

$h(x) = 2 \sin 3x$

   (i)   Which function has the greatest range?

  (ii)   Which function has the greatest period?

 (iii)   Explain why these functions are periodic.

 (iv)   Do all three functions intersect at any point? If so, explain why this is the case.

8. Sketch the graphs of the following functions on the **same axes** for $-\pi \leqslant x \leqslant \pi$:

$f(x) = \cos 2x$

$g(x) = \sin x$

   (i)   From the graph, write down the points of intersection of the two functions.

  (ii)   Explain how your answers could be verified.

9.

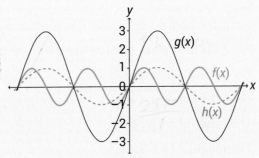

   (i)   The green graph is $f(x) = \sin x$ (x in radians).

      (a)   Identify the co-ordinates where it crosses the x-axis.

      (b)   What are its maximum and minimum values?

  (ii) $y = h(x)$ is the graph of what function?

 (iii) $y = g(x)$ is the graph of what function?

 (iv)   What is the period and range of $g(x)$?

  (v)   Describe how to make the graph of $f(x)$ from the graph of $h(x)$.

7.10 Graphing Functions of the Form $a + b \sin c\theta$ and $a + b \cos c\theta$ for a, b and $c \in R$

$y = a$ is the horizontal midway line. This line is midway between the max and min values of the function.

$|b|$ is the amplitude. This is the greatest height or distance the graph is above or below the midway line.

$\sin c\theta$ and $\cos c\theta$ have period $\dfrac{2\pi}{|c|}$.

As the value of c changes, the period of the function changes.

The graphs of functions of this form are very similar to those studied in the previous section. The main differences are:

1. The a value causes the function to shift vertically.

2. Changing the b value from positive to negative and vice versa causes the function to be reflected about the line $y = a$.

3. Changing the c value from positive to negative and vice versa causes the function to be reflected about the y-axis. This has no effect in this case on $y = a + b \cos c\theta$ since the cosine function is even.

Worked Example 7.17

Consider the functions f and g below.

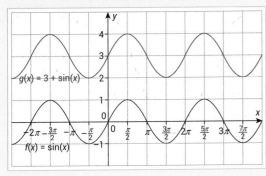

   (i)   What is the horizontal midway line of each graph?

  (ii)   What is the maximum value of each function?

 (iii)   What is the range of each function?

 (iv)   What is the amplitude of each graph?

  (v)   What is the period of each function?

 (vi)   Describe the transformation from $f(x)$ to $g(x)$.

 (vii)   Define a function h in x that represents the function that results from stretching $\sin(x)$ horizontally by a scale factor of 4 and shifting vertically by 3 units.

Solution

(i) For g, the horizontal midway line is the line $y = 3$.

For f, the horizontal midway line is the line $y = 0$ (the x-axis).

(ii) For g, the maximum is 4.

For f, the maximum is 1.

(iii) The range of $g = [2, 4]$.

The range of $f = [-1, 1]$.

(iv) The amplitude of $g = 4 - 3 = 1$.

The amplitude of $f = 1 - 0 = 1$.

(v) The period of both functions is 2π.

(vi) The graph of $y = f(x)$ is shifted vertically by 3 units.

(vii) $h(x) = 3 + \sin\left(\frac{1}{4}x\right)$

Worked Example 7.18

Using the graph below of functions of the form $a + b \sin cx$, where $a, b, c, \in R$, identify:

(i) A function with an amplitude of 2

(ii) Two functions that have the same period

(iii) A function that is a transformation of $\sin x$, stretched vertically

(iv) Two graphs that are images of each other by reflection

(v) A graph that represents $4 + 2 \sin x$

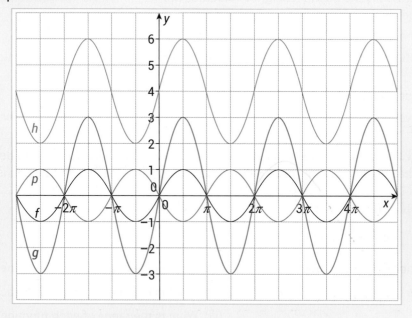

Solution

(i) h has an amplitude of 2. The greatest height of the graph above its midway line is 2.

(ii) f and p or g and h. Both sets of functions have a period of 2π.

(iii) g is $\sin x$ stretched vertically by a scale factor of 3.

(iv) f and p. f and p are reflections of each other about the x-axis, so $f(x) = -p(x)$.

(v) $h(x) = 4 + 2 \sin x$

Worked Example 7.19

A pendulum in a grandfather clock swings back and forth. The distance the pendulum moves to the left (negative) and right (positive) of its resting position with respect to time is represented by the graph.

(i)   What is the period of the pendulum's motion? Explain your answer.

(ii) What is the equation of the horizontal midway line of the curve and what does it represent?

(iii) What is the amplitude of the pendulum's motion? What does the amplitude represent in terms of the motion of the pendulum?

(iv) How many complete swings will the pendulum make in 6 minutes?

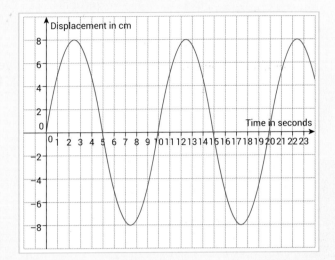

Solution

(i)   The period is 10 seconds. It is the time taken for the pendulum to complete a full swing from extreme left to extreme right and back to extreme left again.

(ii) The equation of the horizontal midway line is $y = 0$. This represents the resting position of the pendulum.

(iii) The amplitude is 8 cm. It represents the maximum distance the pendulum swings to the left or right of its resting position.

(iv) 6 minutes = 360 seconds

Period = 10 seconds

$\frac{360}{10} = 36$

∴ 36 full swings

A simple pendulum exhibits a phenomenon known as **simple harmonic motion**. Such motion is also seen in the rise and fall of sea tides and the hours of daylight during the course of a year. A simple harmonic motion can be represented by functions of the form $a + b \sin cx$ or $a + b \cos cx$ where $a, b, c \in R$.

Exercise 7.5

1. Complete the table below.

	Curve	Horizontal Midway Line	Amplitude	Range
A	$h(x) = 1 + \sin x$	$y = 1$	1	[0, 2]
B	$h(x) = 3 + \cos x$			
C	$h(x) = -1 + \cos x$			
D	$h(x) = -2 + \sin x$			
E	$h(x) = 2 + \cos x$			
F	$h(x) = -3 + \sin x$			
G	$h(x) = 1 + \cos x$			

2. Complete the table below.

	Curve	Vertical Translation	Vertical Shape	Amplitude	Range	Period
(a)	$g(x) = 2 + 3 \sin 4x$	Shifted 2 units upwards	Stretched vertically by a factor of 3	3	$[-1, 5]$	$\dfrac{\pi}{2}$
(b)	$g(x) = 3 - 4 \cos 2x$					
(c)	$g(x) = -4 - 2 \sin 3x$					
(d)	$g(x) = -1 + 5 \sin 2x$					
(e)	$g(x) = 5 - \cos \dfrac{x}{2}$					
(f)	$g(x) = 3 \sin 3x$					
(g)	$g(x) = 1 + \cos 4x$					
(h)	$g(x) = \dfrac{1}{2} + 5 \cos x$					
(i)	$g(x) = 3 - 3 \sin 3x$					
(j)	$g(x) = \dfrac{1}{4} - \dfrac{1}{2} \sin \dfrac{1}{3}x$					

3. Identify the two functions given in each of the parts below.

(a)

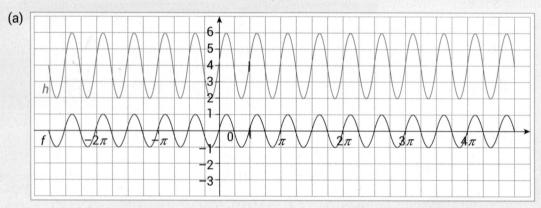

(b)

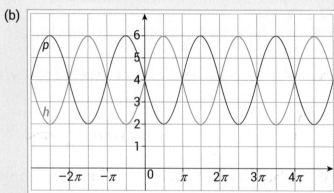

4. The depth of water in a water tank continually varies between a minimum 20 cm below a specified mark and a maximum of 20 cm above this mark over a 24-hour period.

(a) Construct a formula involving a trigonometric function to describe this situation.

(b) If water is added to the tank and the height of the water in the tank rises by 6 cm, construct the formula that now represents the situation, given that the water continues to vary.

TRIGONOMETRY

5. A dog jumps up and down inside the front window of a house waiting for his owner to return. He jumps to a height of 0.4 metres above the window sill and lands back on the ground, which is 0.4 metres below the window sill. He does this in a regular motion (simple harmonic motion). A passer-by using a stopwatch and starting it just as the dog is at the window sill, determines that the dog completes one cycle every 6 seconds.

(a) Construct a formula involving a trigonometric function to describe the displacement of the dog relative to the window sill 1 m above the floor.

(b) Sketch the graph of the function constructed in part (a).

(c) After five seconds how high above the sill is the dog?

(d) Is the dog above or below the window sill after 37 seconds?

6. The table below shows the dates and times of the equinoxes and solstices for the eleven years 2010–2020.

Event	Equinox		Solstice		Equinox		Solstice	
Month	March		June		September		December	
Year	Day	Time	Day	Time	Day	Time	Day	Time
2010	20	17:32	21	11:28	23	03:09	21	23:38
2011	20	23:21	21	17:16	23	09:04	22	05:30
2012	20	05:14	20	23:09	22	14:49	21	11:12
2013	20	11:02	21	05:04	22	20:44	21	17:11
2014	20	16:57	21	10:51	23	02:29	21	23:03
2015	20	22:45	21	16:38	23	08:20	22	04::48
2016	20	04:30	20	22:34	22	14:21	21	10:44
2017	20	10:28	21	04:24	22	20:02	21	16:28
2018	20	16:15	21	10:07	23	01:54	21	22:23
2019	20	21:58	21	15:54	23	07:50	22	04:19
2020	20	03:50	20	21:44	22	13:31	21	10:02

The equinox is the moment the plane of the Earth's equator passes the centre of the Sun.

For northern hemisphere countries such as Ireland, the day on which the spring equinox falls is the day from which the number of hours of daylight begin to exceed the number of hours of darkness. The autumn equinox is the date from which the number of hours of darkness begin to exceed the number of hours of daylight. The solstices are the longest and shortest days (in terms of hours of daylight) respectively.

(In fact, this information is slightly inaccurate but we will assume it is correct for the purposes of this question.)

At a certain latitude, the number of hours of daylight (d) in each day is given by the equation $d = A + B \sin(kt)$ where A and B are positive constants and t is the time in days since the spring equinox.

(i) Given the fact that it takes the Earth 365.25 days to complete one orbit of the Sun, show that the value of k to three significant figures is 0.0172.

(ii) A town at this latitude called Andvari has a weather station that records exactly 6 hours of daylight on the shortest day and 18 hours of daylight on the longest day of 2014.

Using this information, calculate the values of the constants A and B.

(iii) Calculate the amount of daylight in hours and minutes that the town of Andvari will have on New Year's Eve in December 2014.

(iv) Andvari holds a traditional town fair called Staralfur on the two days on which there are 10 hours of daylight. On what two dates in 2014 will Andvari hold this fair?

As part of the Staralfur fair, a banner depicting the earth and the sun is hung from the front of the town hall. The banner's design is shown here.

The banner consists of a larger circle enclosing a smaller circle. The circles share a common centre. The line segment *EF* measures 12 metres and is tangential to the smaller circle.

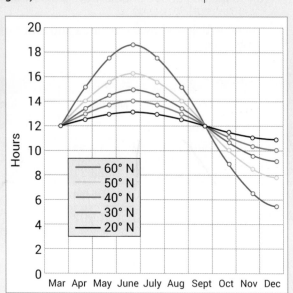

(v) Calculate the area of the annulus (the shaded region).

The diagram below shows the relationship between the number of hours of daylight and the northern latitude of a location on the Earth's surface for a range of different latitudes.

(vi) Given that the town of Andvari has 18 hours of sunshine on the longest day, estimate from the diagram its latitude.

Another town called Ísjaki, also in the northern hemisphere, lies on the same **line of longitude** as Andvari. Its longest day only has 14 hours of daylight. It is possible to fly directly from Andvari to Ísjaki.

(vii) If an airplane making this journey travels along the shortest route, how far does it fly? Answer correct to the nearest kilometre. Assume the radius of the Earth is 6,371 kilometres.

7.11 Special Angles 30°, 45° and 60°

Special Angles 30° and 60°

A 60° angle can be constructed as follows, with just a ruler and a compass:

(a) Construct an equilateral triangle with sides of length 2 units.

(b) Bisect one of the angles in the triangle.

(c) Let *x* be the shortest distance from the vertex of the bisected angle to the opposite side.

(d) Use the theorem of Pythagoras to find *x*.

$x^2 + 1^2 = 2^2$

$\quad x^2 = 4 - 1$

$\quad x^2 = 3$

$\quad\; x = \sqrt{3}$

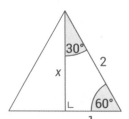

From the triangle, we have:

- $\sin 60° = \dfrac{\sqrt{3}}{2}$

- $\cos 60° = \dfrac{1}{2}$

- $\tan 60° = \sqrt{3}$

Also:

- $\sin 30° = \dfrac{1}{2}$

- $\cos 30° = \dfrac{\sqrt{3}}{2}$

- $\tan 30° = \dfrac{1}{\sqrt{3}}$

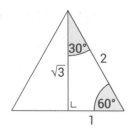

Special Angle 45°

A 45° angle can also be constructed with just a ruler and a compass:

(a) Construct a right-angled isosceles triangle with equal sides of 1 unit in length.

(b) Let x be the length of the hypotenuse.

(c) Use the theorem of Pythagoras to find x.

$$1^2 + 1^2 = x^2$$
$$2 = x^2$$
$$\sqrt{2} = x$$

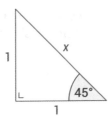

From the triangle, we have:

- $\sin 45° = \dfrac{1}{\sqrt{2}}$

- $\cos 45° = \dfrac{1}{\sqrt{2}}$

- $\tan 45° = 1$

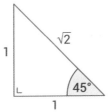

These ratios for 30°, 45° and 60° appear on page 13 of *Formulae and Tables*.

Exercise 7.6

1.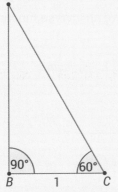

(i) What is the measure of $\angle BAC$?

(ii) Find $|AB|$ in surd form.

(iii) Use the theorem of Pythagoras to find $|AC|$.

2.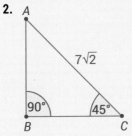

(i) Find the measure of $\angle BAC$.

(ii) Find $|BC|$.

3.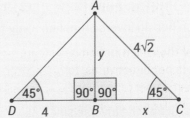

(i) Find the values of x and y.

(ii) What is the measure of $\angle DAB$?

4. Using the trigonometric ratios for 30°, 45° and 60° stated on page 13 of *Formulae and Tables*, manually evaluate each of the following:

(i) $\cos 135°$

(ii) $\sin 330°$

(iii) $\tan 120°$

(iv) $\cos 150°$

(v) $\sin 135°$

(vi) $\sin 225°$

(vii) $\cos \dfrac{3\pi}{4}$

(viii) $\sin\left(-\dfrac{7\pi}{4}\right)$

(ix) $\tan(-150°)$

(x) $\sin 405°$

(xi) $\sin 660°$

(xii) $\cos 540°$

(xiii) $\tan \dfrac{16\pi}{3}$

(xiv) $\sec \dfrac{7\pi}{6}$

(xv) $\operatorname{cosec} 330°$

$$\sec A = \frac{1}{\cos A}$$
$$\operatorname{cosec} A = \frac{1}{\sin A}$$

See page 13 of *Formulae and Tables*.

Questions 5–8 should be done with manual calculations (no calculator) using *Formulae and Tables*.

5. Evaluate $\sin^2 45° + \cos^2 45°$.

$$\sin^2 45° = (\sin 45°)^2$$

6. Evaluate $\sin^2 60° + \cos^2 60° + \tan^2 60°$.

7. Evaluate $\tan^2 30° + \sin^2 30° + \cos^2 30°$.

8. Show that $\dfrac{\sin 30°}{\cos 30°} = \tan 30°$.

9. Using page 13 of *Formulae and Tables*, evaluate the following:

(i) $\dfrac{\sin^2 270° + \cos^2 180°}{2 \cos 0°}$

(ii) $\dfrac{\cos \dfrac{11\pi}{6} + \sin \dfrac{11\pi}{6}}{\sin 150°}$

(iii) $\dfrac{\csc 330°}{\tan 240°}$

7.12 Solving Trigonometric Equations

The solutions to trigonometric equations are used in many professions. Engineers and carpenters make frequent use of these solutions in the design of roofs, bridges and many other structures.

One solution to a trigonometric equation can be found either by using a calculator or by using the special angles. From this one solution, other solutions can be found using the graph of the trigonometric function given in the question (as seen previously) or by considering the quadrant in which the angle lies.

Inverse Trigonometric Functions and Principal Values

Not every function has an inverse function. Only functions that are bijections can have an inverse function.

From the graph of the sine function it is clear that the function is not bijective as, for example, it is not injective (one to one).

How, then, can we define the inverse sine function? To do this we must consider the sine function on a restricted domain, where the function is injective. By convention we choose the domain $\left[-\dfrac{\pi}{2}, \dfrac{\pi}{2}\right]$.

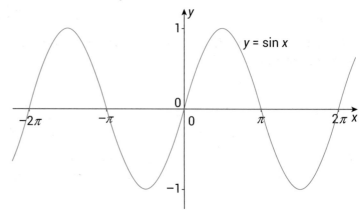

One of the reasons why the domain $\left[-\dfrac{\pi}{2}, \dfrac{\pi}{2}\right]$ is chosen is that angles within this domain produce all possible sine values (i.e. values in the interval $[-1, 1]$).

The function $g: \left[-\dfrac{\pi}{2}, \dfrac{\pi}{2}\right] \to [-1, 1]: x \mapsto \sin x$ is a bijection and, hence, has an inverse. This inverse function is called the arcsine function and is written as $\arcsin x$ or $\sin^{-1} x$.

We can carry out a similar analysis for the cosine and tangent functions.

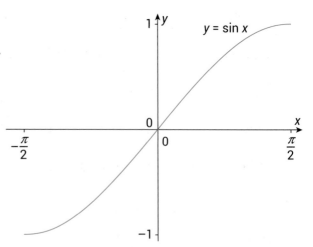

This is the graph of $y = \sin^{-1} x$.

This is the graph of $y = \cos^{-1} x$.

This is the graph of $y = \tan^{-1} x$.

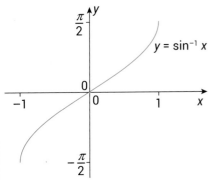

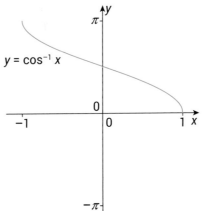

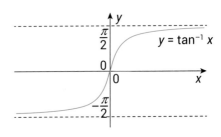

The inverse function
$g^{-1}(x) = \sin^{-1} x$
has domain $[-1, 1]$
and range $\left[-\dfrac{\pi}{2}, \dfrac{\pi}{2}\right]$.

The inverse function
$g^{-1}(x) = \cos^{-1} x$
has domain $[-1, 1]$
and range $[0, \pi]$.

The inverse function
$g^{-1}(x) = \tan^{-1} x$
has domain $(-\infty, \infty)$
and range $\left(-\dfrac{\pi}{2}, \dfrac{\pi}{2}\right)$.

The ranges of the inverse trigonometric functions are known as **principal values**.

When we use our calculator to find the inverse trigonometric functions the answer will always be within the range of the principal values.

For example: Find $\cos^{-1} \dfrac{1}{2}$.

Our calculator will give an answer of $\theta = 60°$ or $\theta = \dfrac{\pi}{3}$ radians.

Even though we know from the unit circle that $\cos 300°$ or $\cos \dfrac{5\pi}{3}$ would also give an answer of $\dfrac{1}{2}$.

If we used a range of values for θ that included $300°$, for example, $0 \leqslant \theta \leqslant 360°$, then the function would no longer be bijective and so it would not have an inverse function.

Principal Values of Inverse Functions

Trig Ratio	Principal Values	
$\sin^{-1}$	$-90° \leqslant \theta \leqslant 90°$ or	$-\dfrac{\pi}{2} \leqslant \theta \leqslant \dfrac{\pi}{2}$
$\cos^{-1}$	$0° \leqslant \theta \leqslant 180°$ or	$0 \leqslant \theta \leqslant \pi$
$\tan^{-1}$	$-90° < \theta < 90°$ or	$-\dfrac{\pi}{2} < \theta < \dfrac{\pi}{2}$

Worked Example 7.20

Solve for θ in each of the following:

(i) $\cos\theta = -\dfrac{\sqrt{3}}{2}$ for $0° \le \theta \le 360°$

(iii) $\tan\theta = -\dfrac{1}{\sqrt{3}}$ for $0 \le \theta \le 2\pi$

(ii) $\sin\theta = \dfrac{1}{4}$ for $0° \le \theta \le 360°$

(iv) $\cos\theta = -\dfrac{1}{2}$ for $\theta \in R$, where θ is in radians

Solution

(i) $\cos\theta = -\dfrac{\sqrt{3}}{2}$ for $0° \le \theta \le 360°$

> Make sure that you set your calculator to the correct mode (Degree or Radian) for each part.

Step 1   Find the reference angle. Ignore the minus sign and find $\cos^{-1}\dfrac{\sqrt{3}}{2}$.

$$\cos^{-1}\dfrac{\sqrt{3}}{2} = 30°$$

> We could also have found a reference angle value of 30° from page 13 of *Formulae and Tables*.

Step 2   Establish where cos is negative, i.e. in the second and third quadrants.

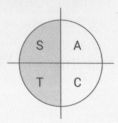 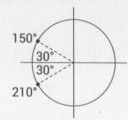

Thus, $\theta = 180° - 30° = 150°$

or $\theta = 180° + 30° = 210°$

Answer: 150°, 210°

(ii) $\sin\theta = \dfrac{1}{4}$ for $0° \le \theta \le 360°$

Step 1   Find the reference angle: $\sin^{-1}\dfrac{1}{4} \approx 14.5°$

Step 2   Establish where sin is positive, i.e. in the first and second quadrants.

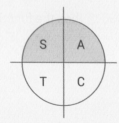 

$\theta = 14.5°$

or $\theta = 180° - 14.5° = 165.5°$

Answer: 14.5°, 165.5°

(iii) $\tan\theta = -\dfrac{1}{\sqrt{3}}$ for $0 \le \theta \le 2\pi$

Step 1   Find the reference angle: $\tan^{-1}\dfrac{1}{\sqrt{3}} = \dfrac{\pi}{6}$

> We could have used page 13 of *Formulae and Tables* here as well.

Step 2   Establish where tan is negative, i.e. in the second and fourth quadrants.

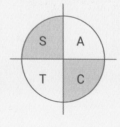 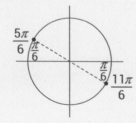

Thus, $\theta = \pi - \dfrac{\pi}{6} = \dfrac{5\pi}{6}$

or $\theta = 2\pi - \dfrac{\pi}{6} = \dfrac{11\pi}{6}$

Answer: $\dfrac{5\pi}{6}, \dfrac{11\pi}{6}$

(iv) $\cos\theta = -\dfrac{1}{2}$ for $\theta \in R$, where θ is in radians

Step 1 Find the reference angle: $\cos^{-1}\dfrac{1}{2} = \dfrac{\pi}{3}$

> We could have used page 13 of *Formulae and Tables* here as well.

Step 2 Establish where $\cos$ is negative, i.e. in the second and third quadrants.

> In this question, we are not using a finite domain (as $\theta \in R$), so it will be necessary to give a general solution.

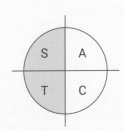 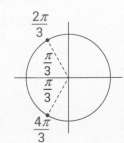

Thus, $\theta = \pi - \dfrac{\pi}{3} = \dfrac{2\pi}{3}$

or $\theta = \pi + \dfrac{\pi}{3} = \dfrac{4\pi}{3}$

Step 3 With every full rotation, the same ratio is given: $\cos\dfrac{4\pi}{3} = \cos\left(\dfrac{4\pi}{3} \pm 2\pi\right) = \cos\left(\dfrac{4\pi}{3} \pm 4\pi\right)$, etc.

$\therefore \theta = \dfrac{2\pi}{3} + 2n\pi$ **or** $\theta = \dfrac{4\pi}{3} + 2n\pi$, where $n \in Z$

> Z is used, as we have to allow for anti-clockwise and clockwise revolutions around the unit circle.

Worked Example 7.21

Solve $\cos 2\theta = \dfrac{\sqrt{3}}{2}$, for $\theta \in R$.

Solution

Step 1 $\cos^{-1}\dfrac{\sqrt{3}}{2} = \dfrac{\pi}{6}$ or $-\dfrac{\pi}{6}$

$2\theta = \dfrac{\pi}{6}$ or $-\dfrac{\pi}{6}$

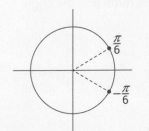

Step 2 As the domain is the set of real numbers, we need to use the general form.

$2\theta = \dfrac{\pi}{6} + 2n\pi$ or $2\theta = -\dfrac{\pi}{6} + 2n\pi$

$\therefore \theta = \dfrac{\pi}{12} + n\pi$ or $\theta = -\dfrac{\pi}{12} + n\pi$

where $n \in Z$

Exercise 7.7

1. Solve each of the following equations for $0° \leq \theta \leq 360°$:

   (i) $\cos\theta = 0.5$

   (ii) $\tan\theta = 1$

   (iii) $\sin\theta = -\dfrac{\sqrt{3}}{2}$

   (iv) $\cos\theta = -\dfrac{1}{\sqrt{2}}$

   (v) $\sin\theta = \dfrac{\sqrt{3}}{2}$

   (vi) $\sec\theta = -\sqrt{2}$

   (vii) $2\sin^2\theta = 1$

   (viii) $\cot\theta = -1$

   (ix) $4\cos^2\theta - 1 = 0$

> $\sec\theta = \dfrac{1}{\cos\theta}$
>
> $\cot\theta = \dfrac{\cos\theta}{\sin\theta}$
>
> $\cos^2\theta = (\cos\theta)^2$

2. Solve each of the following equations for $0 \leqslant x \leqslant 2\pi$ (give answers in radians):

   (i) $\sin x = \dfrac{1}{2}$

   (ii) $\tan x = \dfrac{1}{\sqrt{3}}$

   (iii) $\cos x = \dfrac{1}{\sqrt{2}}$

   (iv) $\sin x = -\dfrac{1}{\sqrt{2}}$

   (v) $\sin x = 0$

   (vi) $\cos x + 1 = 0$

3. Find, correct to one decimal place, the two values of A, where $0° \leqslant A \leqslant 360°$.

   (i) $5 \sin A = 2$

   (ii) $7 \cos A + 3 = 0$

   (iii) $2 \tan A = -7$

   (iv) $3 \sec A = 5$

   (v) $2 \operatorname{cosec} A - 11 = 0$

   (vi) $17 \cot A + 23 = 1$

4. Find, without using a calculator, the values of:

   (i) $\sin \theta$ and $\tan \theta$, if $\cos \theta = \dfrac{4}{5}$ and θ is acute

   (ii) $\cos \theta$ and $\tan \theta$, if $\sin \theta = \dfrac{5}{13}$ and θ is obtuse

5. For $0° \leqslant \theta \leqslant 360°$, find values of θ for the following (correct to one decimal place where necessary):

   (i) $\sin 2\theta = \dfrac{1}{2}$

   (ii) $\cos 2\theta = 0.5$

   (iii) $\tan 3\theta = -0.1$

   (iv) $\sin 3\theta = -1$

   (v) $\cos \dfrac{\theta}{2} = -\dfrac{\sqrt{3}}{2}$

6. Solve for $\theta \in R$ (θ in radians).

   (i) $\sin \theta = 1$

   (ii) $\cos \theta = -\dfrac{1}{\sqrt{2}}$

   (iii) $\cos \theta = 0$

   (iv) $2 \sin \theta = \sqrt{2}$

   (v) $\sin 3\theta = -1$

7. Derek is an engineer and part of his job is to design the ramps used in multi-storey car parks. Regulations state that there must be a 2.0 m clearance from the level below to the top of the ramp and the angle of elevation of the ramp must not exceed 15°.

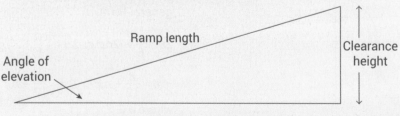

He designs two ramps. In his first design, the ratio of clearance height to ramp length is 2 : 8. In his second design, the ratio is 2 : 6.

Are his designs in line with the regulations specified? Explain why or why not.

8. When erecting a roof, it is more economical to have the pitch of the roof between 15° and 40°. However, trusses for support may be supplied at additional cost if a customer wishes to build outside this range.

   The following plans were drawn up by an architect.
   Is this an economical design for the roof?
   (Note: Pitch = $\theta°$)

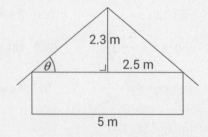

7.13 Using the Sine Rule

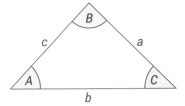

$$\frac{a}{\sin A} = \frac{b}{\sin B} = \frac{c}{\sin C}$$

OR

$$\frac{\sin A}{a} = \frac{\sin B}{b} = \frac{\sin C}{c}$$

You can find this formula on page 16 of *Formulae and Tables*.

To use the sine rule you need:

two angles and one side (opposite one of the angles)

OR

two sides and one angle (opposite one of the sides)

Worked Example 7.22

Find the values of the unknown sides and angles correct to one decimal place.

Solution

$|\angle BAC| = 180° - 48° - 75.5° = 56.5°$

$|AC|: \dfrac{|AC|}{\sin 75.5°} = \dfrac{5.6}{\sin 56.5°}$

$|AC| = \dfrac{5.6 \sin 75.5°}{\sin 56.5°}$

$\therefore |AC| \approx 6.5$ cm

$|AB|: \dfrac{|AB|}{\sin 48°} = \dfrac{5.6}{\sin 56.5°}$

$|AB| = \dfrac{5.6 \sin 48°}{\sin 56.5°}$

$\therefore |AB| \approx 5.0$ cm

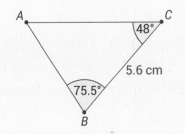

Worked Example 7.23

Find the value of the remaining side and angles to two decimal places.

Solution

$\dfrac{\sin B}{9} = \dfrac{\sin 60°}{10}$

$\sin B = \dfrac{9 \sin 60°}{10}$

$\sin B = \dfrac{9\sqrt{3}}{20}$

$\Rightarrow B = \sin^{-1}\left(\dfrac{9\sqrt{3}}{20}\right)$

$\therefore B \approx 51.21°$

So, $C = 180° - 51.21° - 60° = 68.79°$

$\dfrac{|AB|}{\sin 68.79°} = \dfrac{10}{\sin 60°}$

$|AB| = \dfrac{10 \sin 68.79°}{\sin 60°}$

$\therefore |AB| \approx 10.76$ cm

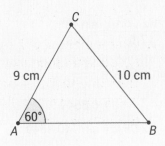

Worked Example 7.24

An exit sign is suspended from the ceiling of a concert venue by two chains.

One chain is 46 cm long and makes an angle of 60° with the ceiling. The other chain is 64 cm long.
What angle does the longer chain make with the ceiling? Answer correct to one decimal place.

TRIGONOMETRY

Solution

Label the required angle X.

As we are looking for an angle, use $\dfrac{\sin A}{a} = \dfrac{\sin B}{b}$.

$$\dfrac{\sin X}{46} = \dfrac{\sin 60°}{64}$$

$$\sin X = \dfrac{46 \sin 60°}{64}$$

$$X = \sin^{-1}\left(\dfrac{46 \sin 60°}{64}\right)$$

$X = 38.5°$ or $X \approx 180 - 38.5°$

$\qquad\qquad = 141.5°$

Reject, since $141.5° + 60° = 201.5° > 180°$.

$X \approx 38.5°$

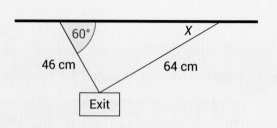

7.14 The Ambiguous Case

If you are given two sides and an angle, more than one triangle may satisfy the data.

This is called the **ambiguous case**.

Worked Example 7.25

Find the values of the unknown sides and angles to the nearest metre and degree.

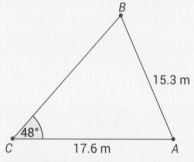

Solution

$$\dfrac{\sin|\angle CBA|}{17.6} = \dfrac{\sin 48°}{15.3}$$

$$\sin|\angle CBA| = \dfrac{17.6 \sin 48°}{15.3}$$

$$= 0.8549\ldots$$

$$|\angle CBA| = \sin^{-1}(0.8549\ldots)$$

$$\approx 59°$$

But $\sin|\angle CBA| = 0.8549\ldots$ could also give an angle in the second quadrant.

So, $|\angle CBA| = 180° - 59° = 121°$.

This is a feasible value for $\angle CBA$ as $48° + 121° = 169°$, and $169° < 180°$ (angles of a triangle).

So we need to allow for both possible triangles:

Δ1 $|\angle CBA| = 59°$ Δ2 $|\angle CBA| = 121°$

Here are the two possible triangles:

$$\dfrac{|BC|}{\sin 73°} = \dfrac{15.3}{\sin 48°}$$

$$|BC| = \dfrac{15.3 \sin 73°}{\sin 48°}$$

$$\approx 20 \text{ m}$$

$$\dfrac{|BC|}{\sin 11°} = \dfrac{15.3}{\sin 48°}$$

$$|BC| = \dfrac{15.3 \sin 11°}{\sin 48°}$$

$$\approx 4 \text{ m}$$

7.15 Using the Cosine Rule

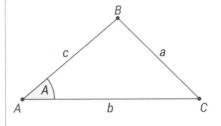

 There is no ambiguity with the Cosine Rule, as the cosine is positive in the first quadrant and negative in the second quadrant, giving acute and obtuse angles respectively.

$$a^2 = b^2 + c^2 - 2bc \cos A$$

OR

$$\cos A = \frac{b^2 + c^2 - a^2}{2bc}$$

You can find this formula on page 16 of *Formulae and Tables*.

If the lengths of two sides of a triangle and the angle between these sides are known, then we can use the Cosine Rule to find the length of the third side in the triangle.

If we know the lengths of all three sides in a triangle, then we can use the Cosine Rule to find the measure of any angle in the triangle.

Worked Example 7.26

Find x, the distance from A to B. Give your answer correct to three significant figures.

Solution

$$a^2 = b^2 + c^2 - 2bc \cos A$$
$$\Rightarrow x^2 = 6^2 + 8^2 - 2(6)(8) \cos 40°$$
$$x^2 = 26.4597\ldots$$
$$x = 5.1439\ldots$$
$$\therefore x \approx 5.14$$

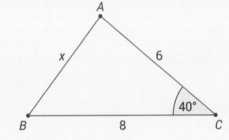

Worked Example 7.27

Calculate the measure of the angle A.

Solution

Method 1

$$a^2 = b^2 + c^2 - 2bc \cos A$$
$$7^2 = 5^2 + 8^2 - 2(5)(8) \cos A$$
$$49 = 25 + 64 - 80 \cos A$$
$$80 \cos A = 89 - 49$$
$$80 \cos A = 40$$
$$\cos A = \frac{40}{80} = \frac{1}{2}$$
$$\Rightarrow A = \cos^{-1} \frac{1}{2} \quad \therefore A = 60°$$

Method 2

$$\cos A = \frac{b^2 + c^2 - a^2}{2bc}$$
$$\cos A = \frac{(5)^2 + (8)^2 - (7)^2}{2(5)(8)}$$
$$\cos A = \frac{40}{80} = \frac{1}{2}$$
$$\Rightarrow A = \cos^{-1} \frac{1}{2}$$
$$\therefore A = 60°$$

Exercise 7.8

1. Use the Sine Rule to find the values of the unknown sides and angles to one decimal place where necessary. In any ambiguous case, give both solutions.

   (i)

   (ii)

   (iii)

2. Find the values of the unknowns in these triangles without using a calculator:

   (i)

   (ii)

3. Use the Cosine Rule to find the value of *a*. Write each answer correct to two decimal places.

   (i)
   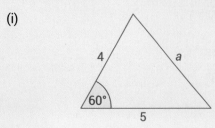

   (ii)
   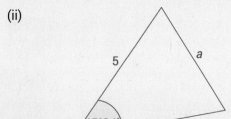

4. Use the Cosine Rule to find the value of *A*. Give your answers to the nearest degree.

   (i)

   (ii)
   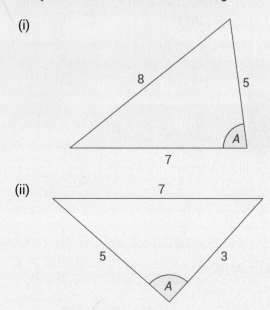

5. Find to the nearest integer |*AC*| and |*AD*|, given that *B*, *C* and *D* are collinear.

   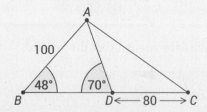

6. The sides of a triangle have lengths 10 cm, 8 cm and 4 cm. Find the measure of the largest angle to the nearest degree.

7. Construct the two possible triangles *ABC*, given the following information:
   a = 8, *b* = 9 and *A* = 60°

8. In the diagram, Y is the midpoint of $[XZ]$. $|\angle WXY| = 48°$, $|WX| = 10$ and $|WY| = 11$.

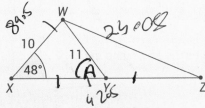

Find, correct to one decimal place:

(i) $|\angle WYX|$ (ii) $|XY|$ (iii) $|WZ|$

9. ABC is a triangle and D is a point on $[BC]$. The lengths $|AB|$, $|AD|$, $|AC|$ and $|BD|$ are as shown in the diagram.

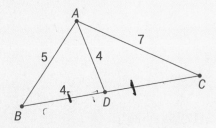

Find $|DC|$, correct to one decimal place.

10. John is standing at a point P on the southern bank of a river. He wants to swim across to the northern bank. There are just two landing points, Q and R, on the northern bank. R is 80 m downstream from Q. The path $[PQ]$ makes an angle of 50° with the bank, and the path $[PR]$ makes an angle of 60° with the bank. The situation is shown in the diagram below.

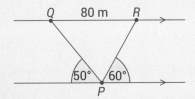

Using the Sine Rule, calculate $|PQ|$ and $|PR|$.

11. A boat is anchored at sea. Alice wants to find out the distance from the boat to the shore. She measures the distance between two points, A and B, on the shore. She then measures the angles CAB and CBA.

(i) Calculate $|\angle ACB|$.

(ii) Using the Sine Rule, calculate $|AC|$.

(iii) Now find $|CD|$, the distance from the boat to the shore. Give your answer to one decimal place.

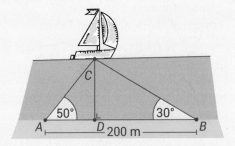

12. Using the Sine Formula, prove that:

(i) $a \sin B = b \sin A$

(ii) $a(\sin B - \sin C) + b(\sin C - \sin A) + c(\sin A - \sin B) = 0$

13. Consider the diagram below.

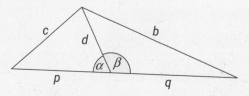

(i) Express $\cos \alpha$ and $\cos \beta$ in terms of the labelled lengths.

(ii) Show that:
$pb^2 + qc^2 = (p + q)(pq + d^2)$

7.16 Area of a Triangle

Derivation of Area

The sine ratio can be used to derive a formula for the area of a triangle.

Step 1   Write down $\sin C$ in term of a and h.

$$\sin C = \frac{h}{a}$$

Step 2   Using the answer to step 1, write h in terms of a and $\sin C$.

$$h = a \sin C$$

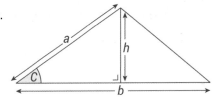

Step 3 Now, using the formula 'Area of a Triangle = $\frac{1}{2}$ Base × Perpendicular height', write down the area of the area of the triangle in terms of b and h.

Area = $\frac{1}{2}bh$

Step 4 Using steps 2 and 3, write down the area of the triangle in terms of a, b and sin C.

Area = $\frac{1}{2}bh$

$= \frac{1}{2}(b)(a \sin C)$

$= \frac{1}{2}ab \sin C$

This formula is also given on page 16 of *Formulae and Tables*.

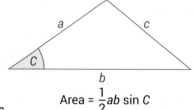

Area = $\frac{1}{2}ab \sin C$

To use this formula, we need to know the lengths of two sides of the triangle and the angle **between** these two sides.

Worked Example 7.28

Find the area of △ABC.

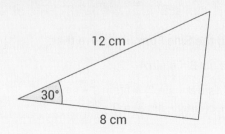

Solution

Area = $\frac{1}{2}ab \sin C$

$= \frac{1}{2}(12)(8)(\sin 30°)$

$= \frac{1}{2} \times 12 \times 8 \times \frac{1}{2}$

Area = 24 cm²

Worked Example 7.29

In the given triangle the area is 13.6 cm².

Find the measure of the angle A to the nearest degree. (The diagram is not to scale.)

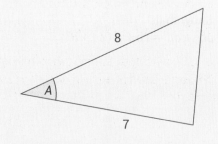

Solution

$\frac{1}{2}(8)(7) \sin A = 13.6$

$28 \sin A = 13.6$

$\sin A = \dfrac{13.6}{28}$

$A = \sin^{-1}\dfrac{13.6}{28}$

$\therefore A \approx 29°$ or $A \approx 151°$

7.17 Length of an Arc and Area of a Sector

Length of an arc of a circle: $l = (2\pi r)\left(\dfrac{\theta}{360}\right)$, where θ is measured in degrees

Area of a sector of a circle: $A = (\pi r^2)\left(\dfrac{\theta}{360}\right)$, where θ is measured in degrees

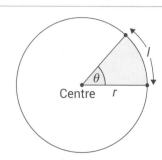

Centre r

TRIGONOMETRY

We also have two formulae for finding the area and length when using radian measure.

Length of an arc: $l = r\theta$ (θ in radians)

Area of a sector: $A = \frac{1}{2}r^2\theta$ (θ in radians)

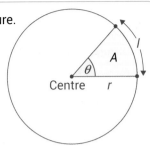

These formulae appear on page 9 of *Formulae and Tables*.

Worked Example 7.30

The minor arc AB subtends an angle $\frac{\pi}{4}$ at the centre, O, of a circle with radius 8 cm.

(i) Find the length of the arc AB.

(ii) Find the area of the sector OAB.

Solution

(i) Length of the arc AB:

$l = r\theta$

$= 8\left(\frac{\pi}{4}\right)$

Length of arc $= 2\pi$ cm

(ii) Area of the sector OAB:

Area $= \frac{1}{2}r^2\theta$

$= \frac{1}{2}(8)^2\left(\frac{\pi}{4}\right)$

$= 32\left(\frac{\pi}{4}\right)$

$= 8\pi$ cm^2

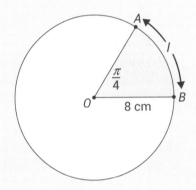

Exercise 7.9

Find the area of the following triangles (answers correct to two decimal places):

1.

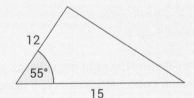

2.

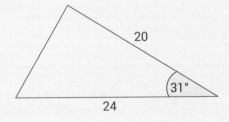

3.

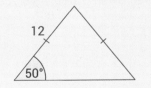

4. Find the area of the triangle ABC in which:

(i) $A = 90°$ $\quad$ $B = 27°$ $\quad$ $a = 15$ cm

(ii) $a = b = 12$ cm $\quad$ $c = 4$ cm

(iii) $a = b = 12$ cm $\quad$ $A = 80°$

5. Solve for x in each of the following triangles (to the nearest centimetre or degree where necessary):

(i)

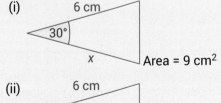

Area $= 9$ cm^2

(ii)

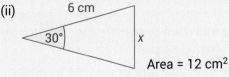

Area $= 12$ cm^2

(iii)

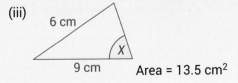

Area $= 13.5$ cm^2

TRIGONOMETRY

6. Find the area and the length of the arc of each of the following sectors. (Angles given in radians.)

    (i)

    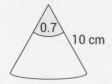

    (ii)

    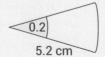

    (iii)

    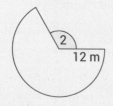

7. A pizza with a 30 cm diameter is shared equally between six people. Find the perimeter and the area of each slice.

8. The diameter of a circle is 16 cm long. Find the angle in radians at the centre that is subtended by an arc of length 12 cm.

9. The arc AB of a sector of a circle, centre O, radius 3 cm, is 6 cm long. Find:

    (i) The area of the sector AOB

    (ii) The area of the triangle AOB

    (iii) The area of the minor segment cut off by the line AB

10. The diagram shows the cross-section of a table-tennis ball, radius r cm, floating in water. The surface of the ball touches the water at A and B. AB subtends an angle of $\frac{2\pi}{3}$ at the centre of the ball.

    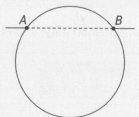

    (i) Find the length of the chord AB in terms of r.

    (ii) Hence, find, in terms of r, the circumference of the circle where the ball crosses the surface of the water.

11. Three bottles of perfume come in a special gift set. Each bottle is in its own individual canister. Then the three canisters are placed in a gift box as shown.

    Each canister has a radius of 5 cm, and all three canisters touch each other in the gift box.

    What is the area of the space between the canisters?

    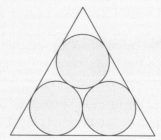

7.18 Three-Dimensional (3D) Problems

To solve a three-dimensional (3D) problem, it is important to be able to identify the right-angled triangles in the question. Then, redraw these right-angled triangles and use appropriate trigonometric ratios or Pythagoras' theorem to solve them. It is also often important to identify the shape of the base of the 3D object in question.

Worked Example 7.31

A vertical tower stands 91 metres tall on a horizontal plane. A tourist is standing at a point C on the horizontal plane. From C, the angle of elevation to the top of the tower, A, is 32°. The tourist's husband is standing at a point D, which is 235 metres from the base, B, of the tower. Given $|\angle CBD| = 49°$, calculate (to two decimal places):

(i) $|BC|$ (ii) $|CD|$

Solution

(i) **Step 1** Draw a diagram representing the problem.

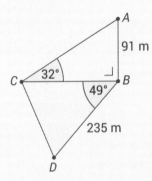

Step 2 Draw triangle ABC to find $|BC|$.

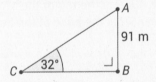

Solve for $|BC|$.

$$\tan 32° = \frac{91}{|BC|}$$

$$|BC| = \frac{91}{\tan 32°}$$

$$= 145.60344...$$

$$\therefore |BC| \approx 145.63 \text{ m}$$

(ii) **Step 1** Draw triangle BCD.

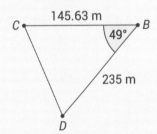

Step 2 Using the Cosine Rule:

$$a^2 = b^2 + c^2 - 2bc \cos A$$

$$|CD|^2 = (145.63)^2 + (235)^2 - 2(145.63)(235) \cos 49°$$

$$|CD|^2 = 31,528.415$$

$$|CD| = 177.5624...$$

$$\therefore |CD| \approx 177.56 \text{ m}$$

Worked Example 7.32

The diagram below shows a rectangular box with top $ABCD$ and base $EFGH$. The dimensions of the box are as indicated on the diagram. From the diagram find:

(i) $|BH|$ to 1 d.p.   (ii) $|\angle FHB|$

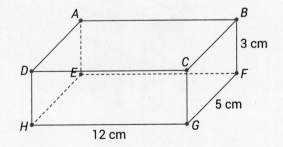

Solution

(i) Find FH first then find BH.

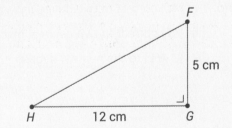

$[FG] \perp [GH]$ on the base of the rectangular box.

$$|FH|^2 = 12^2 + 5^2 \text{ (by Pythagoras)}$$

$$|FH| = \sqrt{(12^2 + 5^2)}$$

$$= 13 \text{ cm}$$

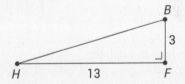

$[BF] \perp [HF]$ as $[BF]$ is a vertical hitting the base at a right angle.

$$|BH|^2 = 13^2 + 3^2$$

$$|BH| = \sqrt{(13^2 + 3^2)}$$

$$= 13.3 \text{ cm (to 1 d.p.)}$$

(ii) From triangle FHB:

$$\tan \angle FHB = \frac{3}{13}$$

$$|\angle FHB| = 13°$$

Exercise 7.10

1. The diagram below shows a wedge in which rectangle *ABCD* is perpendicular to rectangle *CDEF*. The distances are as indicated on the diagram. From the diagram find:

   (a) |*BE*| (to 1 d.p.) (b) |∠*CEB*| (to 1 d.p.)

   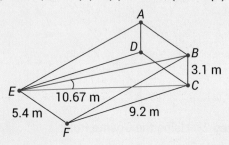

2. The diagram below shows a rectangular box with top *ABCD* and base *EFGH*. The distances are as indicated on the diagram. From the diagram find:

   (a) |*AG*|

   (b) |∠*EGA*| (to 1 d.p.)

   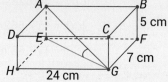

3. Shown is a cube with side length 5 cm.

   Calculate |∠*CAG*|.

   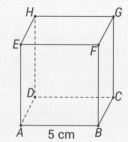

4. Shown here is a cuboid.

   |*AG*| = 16 cm.

   |∠*CAG*| = 35°.

   Calculate |*EG*|.

   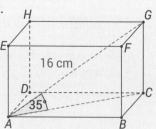

5. A tree is located in the corner of a rectangular field.

   The field is 15 metres long and 12 metres wide.

   The tree is 5 metres tall.

   Calculate |∠*CAE*|.

6. [*SP*] and [*TQ*] are vertical poles each of height 10 m. *P*, *Q*, *R* are points on level ground. Two wires of equal length join *S* and *T* to *R*, i.e. |*SR*| = |*TR*|.

   If |*PR*| = 8 m and |∠*PRQ*| = 120°, calculate:

   (i) |*PQ*| to the nearest metre

   (ii) |*SR*| in surd form

   (iii) |∠*SRT*| to the nearest degree

   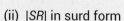
   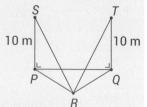

7. The diagram shows a rectangular box. Rectangle *ABCD* is the top of the box and rectangle *EFGH* is the base of the box.

   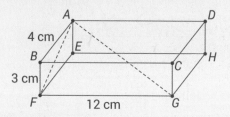

   |*AB*| = 4 cm, |*BF*| = 3 cm and |*FG*| = 12 cm.

   Find:

   (i) |*AF*| (iii) |∠*AGE*|

   (ii) |*AG*| (iv) |∠*AGF*|

   Give angles correct to two decimal places.

8.

   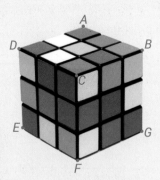

   A Rubik cube has the dimensions 5.75 cm × 5.75 cm × 5.75 cm.

   Find: (i) |*AC*| correct to two decimal places

   (ii) |*AF*| correct to two decimal places

   (iii) |∠*AFE*| to the nearest degree

9. The diagram shows an international squash singles court. All measurements are in millimetres.

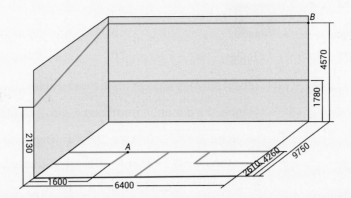

If Carol is standing at the point *A* when she hits the ball, what is the angle of elevation from this point to the point *B*?

10.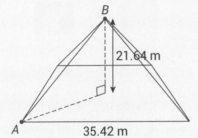

The Louvre Pyramid, is a square based pyramid and has the following dimensions:

Width 35.42 m   Height 21.64 m

(i) What is the slant height *AB* of the pyramid?

(ii) What is the angle of elevation from the point *A* to the top, *B*?

11. A vertical radio mast [*PQ*] stands on flat horizontal ground. It is supported by three cables that join the top of the mast *Q* to the points *A*, *B* and *C* on the ground. The foot of the mast *P* lies inside the triangle *ABC*.

Each cable is 52 m long and the mast is 48 m high.

(i) Find the (common) distance from *P* to each of the points *A*, *B* and *C*.

(ii) Given that |*AC*| = 38 m and |*AB*| = 34 m, find |*BC*| correct to one decimal place.

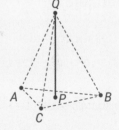

7.19 Derivation of Trigonometric Formulae 1, 2, 3, 4, 5, 6, 7 and 9

With any proof, always consider the tools available:

- The Sine Rule
- The Cosine Rule
- The Area of a Triangle Formula
- The Distance Formula
- Any previous proof may also be used.

Students must be able to derive the formulae proved overleaf in examination.

Formula 1

$\cos^2 A + \sin^2 A = 1$

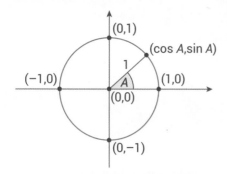

Proof

$(\cos A, \sin A)$ is a point on the unit circle.

Hence, the distance from $(\cos A, \sin A)$ to $(0,0)$ is one unit.

$\Rightarrow \sqrt{(\cos A - 0)^2 + (\sin A - 0)^2} = 1$ (Distance Formula)

$(\cos A - 0)^2 + (\sin A - 0)^2 = 1$ (Square both sides.)

$\therefore \cos^2 A + \sin^2 A = 1$

Formula 2

Sine Formula: $\dfrac{a}{\sin A} = \dfrac{b}{\sin B} = \dfrac{c}{\sin C}$

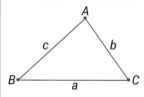

$\dfrac{1}{2} ac \sin B = \dfrac{1}{2} ab \sin C$ (Area of a Triangle Formula)

Divide by $\dfrac{1}{2} abc$ on both sides.

$\dfrac{\sin B}{b} = \dfrac{\sin C}{c} \Rightarrow \dfrac{b}{\sin B} = \dfrac{c}{\sin C}$

Similarly, $\dfrac{a}{\sin A} = \dfrac{b}{\sin B}$.

Therefore, $\dfrac{a}{\sin A} = \dfrac{b}{\sin B} = \dfrac{c}{\sin C}$.

Formula 3

Cosine Formula:
$a^2 = b^2 + c^2 - 2bc \cos A$

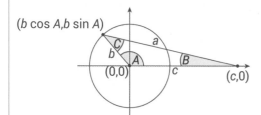

Proof

Consider a circle with centre $(0,0)$ and radius b.

Any point on this circle can be written as $(b \cos A, b \sin A)$, where A is the positive angle opened by the radius to the point $(b \cos A, b \sin A)$ and the x-axis.

Based on the co-ordinate geometry distance formula, the distance between the vertices containing angles B and C is:

$d = \sqrt{(x_2 - x_1)^2 + (y_2 - y_1)^2}$

$\Rightarrow a = \sqrt{(b \cos A - c)^2 + (b \sin A - 0)^2}$

$a^2 = b^2 \cos^2 A - 2bc \cos A + c^2 + b^2 \sin^2 A$

$a^2 = b^2 (\cos^2 A + \sin^2 A) + c^2 - 2bc \cos A$

$\therefore a^2 = b^2 + c^2 - 2bc \cos A$ (since $\cos^2 A + \sin^2 A = 1$)

Formula 4

$$\cos(A - B) = \cos A \cos B + \sin A \sin B$$

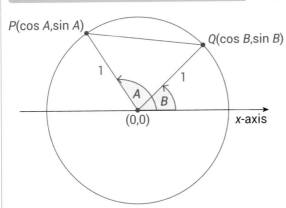

Let $P(\cos A, \sin A)$ and $Q(\cos B, \sin B)$ be two points on the unit circle.

Using the Cosine Rule:

$$|PQ|^2 = 1^2 + 1^2 - 2(1)(1)\cos(A - B)$$
$$= 1 + 1 - 2\cos(A - B)$$
$$\therefore |PQ|^2 = 2 - 2\cos(A - B) \ .....\textcircled{1}$$

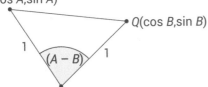

Using the distance formula:

$$|PQ| = \sqrt{(\cos A - \cos B)^2 + (\sin A - \sin B)^2}$$
$$|PQ|^2 = (\cos A - \cos B)^2 + (\sin A - \sin B)^2$$
$$= \cos^2 A - 2\cos A \cos B + \cos^2 B + \sin^2 A - 2\sin A \sin B + \sin^2 B$$
$$= \cos^2 A + \sin^2 A + \cos^2 B + \sin^2 B - 2\cos A \cos B - 2\sin A \sin B$$
$$= 1 + 1 - 2\cos A \cos B - 2\sin A \sin B \quad \text{(by Formula 1)}$$
$$\therefore |PQ|^2 = 2 - 2(\cos A \cos B + \sin A \sin B) .....\textcircled{2}$$

$$\textcircled{1} = \textcircled{2}$$

$$\cancel{2} - 2\cos(A - B) = \cancel{2} - 2(\cos A \cos B + \sin A \sin B)$$
$$\therefore \cos(A - B) = \cos A \cos B + \sin A \sin B$$

Formula 5

$$\cos(A + B) = \cos A \cos B - \sin A \sin B$$

Use the same proof as for Formula 4. Then replace B with $-B$ on both sides.

$$\cos(A - (-B)) = \cos A \cos(-B) + \sin A \sin(-B)$$
$$\therefore \cos(A + B) = \cos A \cos B - \sin A \sin B$$
$$[\text{as } \cos(-B) = \cos B \text{ and } \sin(-B) = -\sin B]$$

These rules appear on page 13 of *Formulae and Tables*.

Formula 6

$$\cos 2A = \cos^2 A - \sin^2 A$$

Given: $\cos(A + B) = \cos A \cos B - \sin A \sin B$

Proof: $\cos(A + A) = \cos A \cos A - \sin A \sin A$

$$\therefore \cos 2A = \cos^2 A - \sin^2 A$$

Formula 7

$$\sin(A + B) = \sin A \cos B + \cos A \sin B$$

Given: $\cos(A - B) = \cos A \cos B + \sin A \sin B$

Proof: Replace A with $\left(\dfrac{\pi}{2} - A\right)$ on both sides.

$$\Rightarrow \cos\left[\left(\frac{\pi}{2} - A\right) - B\right] = \cos\left(\frac{\pi}{2} - A\right)\cos B + \sin\left(\frac{\pi}{2} - A\right)\sin B$$

But $\cos\left(\dfrac{\pi}{2} - A\right) = \sin A.$ (proof not needed for this course)

Also, $\sin\left(\dfrac{\pi}{2} - A\right) = \cos A.$ (proof not needed for this course)

$$\Rightarrow \cos\left(\frac{\pi}{2} - A - B\right) = \sin A \cos B + \cos A \sin B$$

$$\cos\left(\frac{\pi}{2} - (A + B)\right) = \sin A \cos B + \cos A \sin B$$

$$\therefore \sin(A + B) = \sin A \cos B + \cos A \sin B$$

Formula 9

$$\tan(A + B) = \frac{\tan A + \tan B}{1 - \tan A \tan B}$$

Given: $\tan A = \dfrac{\sin A}{\cos A}$

Proof: $\tan(A + B) = \dfrac{\sin(A + B)}{\cos(A + B)}$

$$= \frac{\sin A \cos B + \cos A \sin B}{\cos A \cos B - \sin A \sin B}$$

Divide above and below by $\cos A \cos B$.

$$\tan(A + B) = \frac{\dfrac{\sin A \cos B + \cos A \sin B}{\cos A \cos B}}{\dfrac{\cos A \cos B - \sin A \sin B}{\cos A \cos B}}$$

$$= \frac{\dfrac{\sin A \cos B}{\cos A \cos B} + \dfrac{\cos A \sin B}{\cos A \cos B}}{\dfrac{\cos A \cos B}{\cos A \cos B} - \dfrac{\sin A \sin B}{\cos A \cos B}}$$

$$\therefore \tan(A + B) = \frac{\tan A + \tan B}{1 - \tan A \tan B}$$

7.20 Application of Formulae 1–24

1. $\cos^2 A + \sin^2 A = 1$	13. $\cos 2A = \dfrac{1 - \tan^2 A}{1 + \tan^2 A}$
2. Sine Formula: $\dfrac{a}{\sin A} = \dfrac{b}{\sin B} = \dfrac{c}{\sin C}$	14. $\tan 2A = \dfrac{2 \tan A}{1 - \tan^2 A}$
3. Cosine Formula: $a^2 = b^2 + c^2 - 2bc \cos A$	15. $\cos^2 A = \frac{1}{2}(1 + \cos 2A)$
4. $\cos(A - B) = \cos A \cos B + \sin A \sin B$	16. $\sin^2 A = \frac{1}{2}(1 - \cos 2A)$
5. $\cos(A + B) = \cos A \cos B - \sin A \sin B$	17. $2 \cos A \cos B = \cos(A + B) + \cos(A - B)$
6. $\cos 2A = \cos^2 A - \sin^2 A$	18. $2 \sin A \cos B = \sin(A + B) + \sin(A - B)$
7. $\sin(A + B) = \sin A \cos B + \cos A \sin B$	19. $2 \sin A \sin B = \cos(A - B) - \cos(A + B)$
8. $\sin(A - B) = \sin A \cos B - \cos A \sin B$	20. $2 \cos A \sin B = \sin(A + B) - \sin(A - B)$
9. $\tan(A + B) = \dfrac{\tan A + \tan B}{1 - \tan A \tan B}$	21. $\cos A + \cos B = 2 \cos \dfrac{A + B}{2} \cos \dfrac{A - B}{2}$
10. $\tan(A - B) = \dfrac{\tan A - \tan B}{1 + \tan A \tan B}$	22. $\cos A - \cos B = -2 \sin \dfrac{A + B}{2} \sin \dfrac{A - B}{2}$
11. $\sin 2A = 2 \sin A \cos A$	23. $\sin A + \sin B = 2 \sin \dfrac{A + B}{2} \cos \dfrac{A - B}{2}$
12. $\sin 2A = \dfrac{2 \tan A}{1 + \tan^2 A}$	24. $\sin A - \sin B = 2 \cos \dfrac{A + B}{2} \sin \dfrac{A - B}{2}$

Worked Example 7.33

Express, in surd form: (i) $\cos 15°$ (ii) $\tan 105°$

Solution

(i) $\cos 15° = \cos(45° - 30°)$

$\cos(A - B) = \cos A \cos B + \sin A \sin B$

$\therefore \cos 15° = \cos 45 \cos 30 + \sin 45 \sin 30$

$= \left(\dfrac{1}{\sqrt{2}}\right)\left(\dfrac{\sqrt{3}}{2}\right) + \left(\dfrac{1}{\sqrt{2}}\right)\left(\dfrac{1}{2}\right)$

$= \dfrac{\sqrt{3}}{2\sqrt{2}} + \dfrac{1}{2\sqrt{2}}$

$= \dfrac{\sqrt{3} + 1}{2\sqrt{2}}$

$= \left(\dfrac{\sqrt{3} + 1}{2\sqrt{2}}\right)\left(\dfrac{\sqrt{2}}{\sqrt{2}}\right)$

$= \dfrac{\sqrt{6} + \sqrt{2}}{4}$

(ii) $\tan 105° = \tan(60° + 45°)$

$\tan(A + B) = \dfrac{\tan A + \tan B}{1 - \tan A \tan B}$

$\therefore \tan 105° = \dfrac{\tan 60 + \tan 45}{1 - \tan 60 \tan 45}$

$= \dfrac{\sqrt{3} + 1}{1 - (\sqrt{3})(1)}$

$= \dfrac{\sqrt{3} + 1}{1 - \sqrt{3}}$

$= \left(\dfrac{\sqrt{3} + 1}{1 - \sqrt{3}}\right)\left(\dfrac{1 + \sqrt{3}}{1 - \sqrt{3}}\right)$

$= \dfrac{\sqrt{3} + 3 + 1 + \sqrt{3}}{1 - 3}$

$= \dfrac{4 + 2\sqrt{3}}{-2}$

$= -2 - \sqrt{3}$

Worked Example 7.34

If $\tan(A + B) = 4$ and $\tan B = 3$, find the value of $\tan A$.

Solution

$\tan(A + B) = \dfrac{\tan A + \tan B}{1 - \tan A \tan B}$

Let $\tan A = t$.

Substitute what you know.

$4 = \dfrac{t + 3}{1 - 3t}$

Multiply both sides by $(1 - 3t)$.

$4(1 - 3t) = t + 3$

$4 - 12t = t + 3$

$1 = 13t$

$t = \dfrac{1}{13}$

$\therefore \tan A = \dfrac{1}{13}$

Worked Example 7.35

If $\cos 2A = \dfrac{1}{49}$, find two values of $\cos A$ without using a calculator.

Solution

$\cos 2A = \dfrac{1 - \tan^2 A}{1 + \tan^2 A}$

Let $\tan A = t$.

$\dfrac{1}{49} = \dfrac{1 - t^2}{1 + t^2}$

$1 + t^2 = 49 - 49t^2$

$50t^2 = 48$

$t^2 = \dfrac{48}{50}$

$t = \pm\sqrt{\dfrac{48}{50}} = \pm\sqrt{\dfrac{24}{25}} = \pm\dfrac{\sqrt{24}}{5}$

$\tan A = \pm\dfrac{\sqrt{24}}{5}$

$\therefore \cos A = \dfrac{5}{7} \text{ or } -\dfrac{5}{7}$

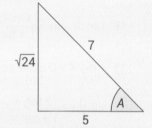

Assume that A is an acute angle. However, A could be in any quadrant. Therefore, $\tan A$ could be positive or negative, hence the final answer form $\pm$.

Worked Example 7.36

Write: (i) $\cos 5x \cos x$ as a sum

       (ii) $\sin 6x + \sin 4x$ as a product

Solution

(i) $2\cos A \cos B = \cos(A + B) + \cos(A - B)$

$\therefore \cos A \cos B = \dfrac{1}{2}[\cos(A + B) + \cos(A - B)]$

$\therefore \cos 5x \cos x = \dfrac{1}{2}[\cos(5x + x) + \cos(5x - x)]$

$= \dfrac{1}{2}[\cos 6x + \cos 4x]$

(ii) $\sin A + \sin B = 2\sin\dfrac{A + B}{2}\cos\dfrac{A - B}{2}$

$\therefore \sin 6x + \sin 4x = 2\sin\dfrac{6x + 4x}{2}\cos\dfrac{6x - 4x}{2}$

$= 2\sin 5x \cos x$

See page 15 of *Formulae and Tables*.

Exercise 7.11

1. Write the following in surd form:

   (i) $\sin 15°$ (v) $\sin 165°$

   (ii) $\sin 105°$ (vi) $\cos 240°$

   (iii) $\cos 75°$ (vii) $\sin 75°$

   (iv) $\tan 75°$ (viii) $\sec 120°$

   (ix) $\cos 25° \cos 20° - \sin 25° \sin 20°$

   (x) $\sin 12° \cos 18° + \cos 12° \sin 18°$

2. A and B are acute angles such that $\tan A = \frac{3}{4}$ and $\tan B = \frac{1}{4}$. Find $\tan(A + B)$.

3. If $\tan A = \frac{1}{5}$, find the value of $\tan 2A$.

4. A and B are acute angles such that $\cos A = \frac{3}{5}$ and $\cos B = \frac{12}{13}$.

    Draw right-angled triangles to allow for calculation of ratios in parts (i) to (iv).

   Find the value of:

   (i) $\sin A$ (iii) $\sin B$ (v) $\cos(A + B)$

   (ii) $\tan A$ (iv) $\tan B$ (vi) $\tan(A + B)$

5. If $\tan 2A = \frac{4}{3}$, find two possible values for $\tan A$.

6. If $\cos 2A = \frac{12}{13}$, find two possible values of $\tan A$.

7. If $\tan A = \frac{1}{4}$ and $\tan(A + B) = 1$, find $\tan B$.

8. Write the following as sums:

   (i) $2 \sin 6\theta \cos 2\theta$ (vi) $\sin 6x \cos 2x$

   (ii) $\cos 3\theta \cos \theta$ (vii) $-2 \sin 4\theta \sin \theta$

   (iii) $\cos 3A \sin A$ (viii) $2 \cos \frac{1}{2}\theta \sin \frac{1}{2}\theta$

   (iv) $\sin 5x \sin 3x$ (ix) $\cos x \sin 5x$

   (v) $2 \cos 4\theta \cos \theta$ (x) $2 \cos\left(x + \frac{\pi}{2}\right) \cos\left(x - \frac{\pi}{2}\right)$

9. Find the exact value of:

   (i) $\cos 75° \cos 15°$ (ii) $2 \sin 75° \sin 105°$

10. Write the following as products:

    (i) $\sin 4x + \sin 2x$

    (ii) $\sin 3x - \sin x$

    (iii) $\cos 9x + \cos 3x$

    (iv) $\sin x + \sin 3x$

    (v) $\sin 2x - \sin x$

    (vi) $\sin 10x + \sin 2x$

    (vii) $\cos 8\theta - \cos 2\theta$

    (viii) $\cos x - \cos 5x$

    (ix) $\cos(30° + x) - \cos(30° - x)$

    (x) $\sin(x + 60°) + \sin(x - 60°)$

11. Find the exact value of:

    (i) $\sin 75° - \sin 15°$ (ii) $\cos 75° - \cos 15°$

12. Show that $\dfrac{\cos 80° - \cos 40°}{\sin 80° - \sin 40°} = -\sqrt{3}$.

13. If $\tan A = \frac{1}{3}$, $\tan B = \frac{1}{5}$, $\tan C = \frac{1}{7}$ and $\tan D = \frac{1}{8}$, find:

    (i) $\tan(A + B)$

    (ii) $\tan(C + D)$

    (iii) $\tan(A + B + C + D)$

    Deduce that $A + B + C + D = \frac{\pi}{4}$.

14. Prove that $\dfrac{\sin 3A + \sin A}{\cos 3A + \cos A} = \tan 2A$.

15. Prove that $\tan 3\theta = \dfrac{3 \tan \theta - \tan^3 \theta}{1 - 3 \tan^2 \theta}$.

16. Prove that $\sin 3\theta + \sin \theta = 4 \sin \theta \cos^2 \theta$.

Revision Exercises

1. Find the value of x and complete the tables below.

$\sin \alpha$	$\cos \alpha$	$\tan \alpha$

$\sin \beta$	$\cos \beta$	$\tan \beta$

   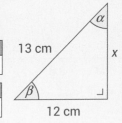

   13 cm   12 cm

2. Copy and complete the table below.

Degrees	90°	180°		360°	120°	45°	
Radians			$\frac{3\pi}{2}$				$\frac{\pi}{3}$

3. Convert to degrees:

  (i) $\dfrac{6\pi}{5}$ rads   (ii) $\dfrac{2\pi}{10}$ rads   (iii) $\dfrac{5\pi}{3}$ rads

4. Convert to radians:

  (i) $150°$ (ii) $288°$ (iii) $108°$

5. A department store has the space *PQRS* available for two new departments. The store manager provides the following measurements to two potential clients:

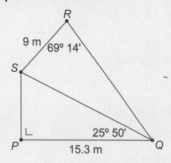

More details are required before a decision can be reached by the clients. You have been asked to provide the following:

  (i) $|SQ|$ correct to the nearest metre

  (ii) $|\angle SQR|$ to the nearest degree

6. A triangle has sides of lengths *a*, *b* and *c*. The angle opposite the side of length *a* is *A*. Prove the following:

  (i) $a^2 = b^2 + c^2 - 2bc \cos A$

  (ii) $\dfrac{a}{\sin A} = \dfrac{b}{\sin B} = \dfrac{c}{\sin C}$

7. (a) Study the unit circle below. Then complete the table in terms of *P* and *Q*.

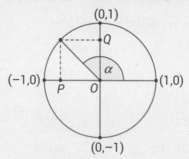

sin α	cos α	tan α

(b)

The area of the triangle shown above is 15 square units.

  (i) Find the value of *x*, correct to two decimal places.

  (ii) Using the Cosine Rule, find the value of *y*.

8. Write down the values of each of the following. Give your answer in surd form where appropriate.

  (i) $\sin 45°$ (iv) $\sin 102°$

  (ii) $\cos \dfrac{11\pi}{6}$ (v) $\cos \dfrac{6\pi}{7}$

  (iii) $\tan 94°$

9. (a) Sketch the graphs of the following functions for $-2\pi \leqslant x \leqslant 2\pi$:

  (i) $\cos x$ (iii) $2 \cos x$ (v) $3 \sin 2x$

  (ii) $\sin x$ (iv) $\tan 2x$ (vi) $2 \cos 3x$

(b) Complete the table below.

	Curve	Horizontal Midway Line	Amplitude	Range
(i)	$h(x) = 3 + \sin x$			
(ii)	$h(x) = -1 + \sin x$			
(iii)	$h(x) = -2 + \cos x$			

10. (a) Write down the functions *f* and *g* (shown below).

  (i)

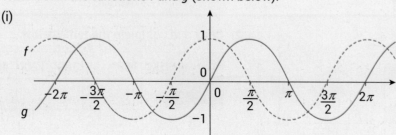

(ii)

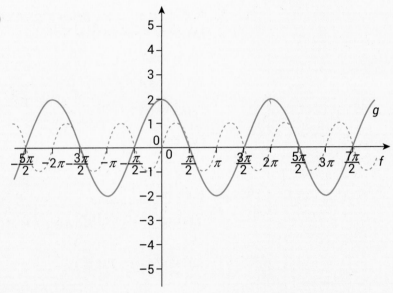

(iii)

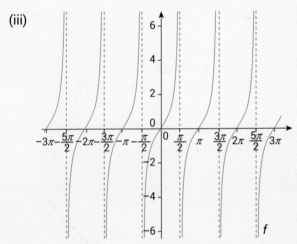

(iv)

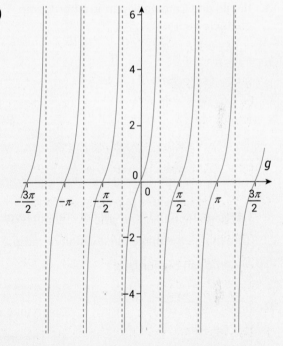

(b) Complete the table below.

	Curve	Vertical Translation	Vertical Shape	Amplitude	Range	Period
(i)	$g(x) = 1 + 3\cos x$					
(ii)	$g(x) = 4 + 3\cos \frac{1}{2}x$					
(iii)	$g(x) = 5\sin x + 1$					

11. Prove that $\cos 2A = \cos^2 A - \sin^2 A$.

12. Prove that $\tan(A + B) = \dfrac{\tan A + \tan B}{1 - \tan A \tan B}$.

13. Show that $\dfrac{\sin 2A}{1 + \cos 2A} = \tan A$.

14. Show that $(\cos A + \sin A)^2 = 1 + \sin 2A$.

15. Using $\cos 2A = \cos^2 A - \sin^2 A$, or otherwise, prove that $\cos^2 A = \frac{1}{2}(1 + \cos 2A)$.

16. (i) Prove that $\cos 2A = \cos^2 A - \sin^2 A$.

    (ii) Deduce that $\cos 2A = 2\cos^2 A - 1$.

17. Express each of the following as a product of two trigonometric functions:

    (i) $\sin 5x - \sin 3x$ (ii) $\cos x + \cos 7x$

18. Find the exact value of $\cos 37.5° \sin 7.5°$.

19. Copy and complete the table below (entries in surd form, where necessary).

A	30°	45°	60°
sin A			
cos A			
tan A			

Using the given table, solve the following equations for A, B, C and D:

(i) $\sin A = \cos 60°$

(ii) $\tan B = 1$

(iii) $\sin C = \cos C$

(iv) $\sin D \cos 30° = \dfrac{3}{4}$

20. (a) Find, correct to one decimal place, the two values of A where $0° \leqslant A \leqslant 360°$.

(i) $5 \sin A = 2$

(ii) $7 \cos A + 3 = 0$

(iii) $2 \tan A + 7 = 0$

(iv) $\cos A = -\dfrac{1}{2}$

(v) $2 \sin A - \sqrt{3} = 0$

(b) Solve the equations:

(i) $\cos 3\theta = \dfrac{1}{2}$, $\theta \in R$ (where θ is in radians)

(ii) $\sin 2\theta = \dfrac{\sqrt{3}}{2}$, $\theta \in R$

21. Nicola and Carol took part in a bootcamp. There were two different ramps, A and B, side by side on the obstacle course.

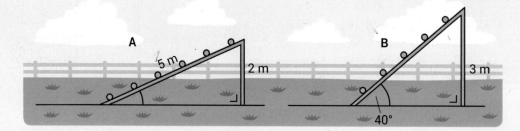

Carol ran up ramp A and Nicola ran up ramp B.

(i) What is the angle of elevation of ramp A (to the nearest degree)?

(ii) Who ran the furthest?

22.

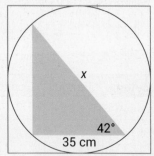

Given that x is the diameter, find:

(i) The area of the circle that is not covered by the triangle

(ii) The area of the square that is not covered by the circle

23. The diagram shows a blueprint for a house. All measurements are in metres.

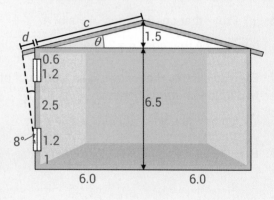

(i) Find the pitch of the roof (θ).

(ii) Find the sloping distance, c, from the top of the roof to the top of the walls.

(iii) The overhang of the roof is a distance d. The angle between the base of the bottom window and the overhang is 8°.

Find the length of the overhang, d.

24. A helicopter pilot has plotted her route on a map. She plans to fly from Dublin to Limerick, from Limerick on to Waterford and, finally, from Waterford back to Dublin. She knows that the flying distance between Dublin and Limerick is 176 km and that the distance between Waterford and Dublin is 135 km. She also has the measure of one angle on the triangular route.

(i) Find the flying distance between Limerick and Waterford.

(ii) If the helicopter has an average flying speed of 280 kmh⁻¹ and the pilot stops over in Limerick for 1 hour and in Waterford for 2 hours, find to the nearest minute the time taken for the pilot to complete the trip.

(iii) An Internet route planner gives the road distance between Limerick and Waterford as 127 km. As the helicopter takes off from Dublin, a driver begins his journey from Limerick to Waterford travelling at an average speed of 50 kmh⁻¹. He has scheduled a meeting with the pilot. What is the maximum time the meeting can last if the pilot has to stick with the 2-hour stopover?

(iv) Suggest another method for finding the flying distance between Limerick and Waterford.

25. This is the new company logo for ABC Ltd. The logo is made by removing two equal sectors from an equilateral triangle. The sectors have their centres, respectively, on two vertices of the equilateral triangle. On the logo there are three straight edges, two measuring 10 cm and one measuring 6 cm.

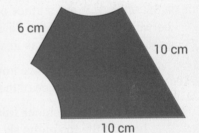

(i) Find the radius length of one of the sectors that have been removed.

(ii) Find the area of the sectors that were removed.

(iii) Find the area of the equilateral triangle from which the logo has been taken.

(iv) Find the area of the logo.

26. *QRST* is a vertical rectangular wall of height *h* on level ground.
P is a point on the ground in front of the wall.
The angle of elevation of *R* from *P* is *θ*, and the angle of elevation of *S* from *P* is 2*θ*. |*PQ*| = 3|*PT*|.
Find the measure of *θ*.

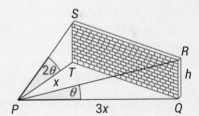

27. A rectangular swimming pool has the dimensions 18 m × 6 m × 1.8 m as shown.

(i) Find the length of the diagonal [*EB*].

(ii) What is the angle formed between the bottom of the pool and the line [*EB*]?

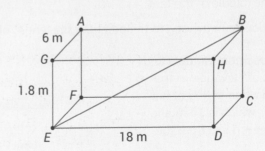

TRIGONOMETRY

28. A Fifth Year maths class has been asked to find the width and height of a soccer goal. The students are equipped with just a clinometer. Any measurements have to be taken from the point P. The teacher has already given the class the distance from P to the foot of both uprights and also the measure of the angle at P, formed by the two uprights and the point P.

The students decide to measure the angle of elevation from P to the top of one of the uprights. They find the angle of elevation to be 22°.

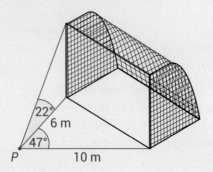

(i) Find the width of the goal.
Give your answer to two decimal places.

(ii) Find the height of the goal.
Give your answer to the nearest centimetre.

(iii) If the class had chosen to measure the angle of elevation of the other upright from P, then what measurement should they have found? Give your answer to the nearest degree.

29. Paul is water skiing on a calm, flat river. His body forms a 55° angle with the surface of the water. The angle formed between his legs and the ski is 105°. From the foot-hold to the top of the ski measures 0.7 m. Paul is 1.6 m tall.

(i) Estimate the distance from the top of Paul's head to the surface of the water.

(ii) Estimate the distance from the top of Paul's head to the top of the ski.

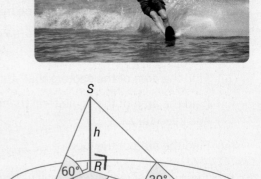

30. P, Q and R are three points on horizontal ground.

$[SR]$ is a vertical pole of height h metres.

The angle of elevation of S from P is 60°, and the angle of elevation of S from Q is 30°.

$|PQ| = c$ metres.

Given that $3c^2 = 13h^2$, find $|\angle PRQ|$.

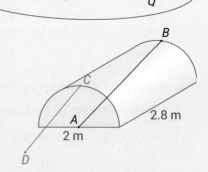

31. Niall and Barry buy a half cylinder pop-up tent for the Oxegen music festival. The dimensions of the tent are as shown.

(i) What is the height of the tent?

(ii) What is the length of the diagonal $[AB]$?

During the weekend the tent is damaged. Niall uses the laces from his runners to form a support. He connects the end of his laces to point C and pegs it to point D as shown. Points B and C are exactly in the middle of the tent.

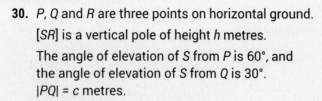

(iii) What is the angle of elevation from the peg to the point C if the length of the support line is 1.2 m?

32. Ahmad is sitting beside the classroom window and sees a bird in a tree. The angle of elevation to the bird is 36°. Ahmad is 1.5 m tall when sitting at his desk. He is on the second floor, which is 10 m above the ground. The base of the tree is 16 m from the wall of the building.

At what height from the ground is the bird in the tree?

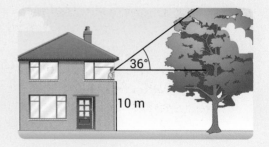

33. The Titanium Building in Santiago, Chile, was completed in 2009 and is the third tallest building in South America.

Two engineering students from the Universidad de Chile, Fernando and Alejandra, were asked to use a clinometer, tape measure and calculator to estimate the height of the tower to the nearest centimetre, as the first part of their final exam in trigonometry.

They decided to take three measurements at different times on the same day and to use the average of these as their estimate of the building's height.

The method they decided to use was to measure the length of the shadow of the building on the ground in the afternoon sun, along with the corresponding angle of inclination from the end of the shadow to the top of the building. The building is situated in a very flat part of the city, so the two students were able to neglect changes in elevation as they took their measurements.

Fernando measured the shadow lengths while Alejandra measured the angles of inclination. These measurements are presented here.

Time	Shadow length	Angle of inclination
12:07	56.38 m	73.68°
13:25	72.07 m	69.47°
15:56	164.29 m	49.52°

Fernando determined that Alejandra held the clinometer 1.62 m above the ground when taking each clinometer reading.

(a) Draw a suitable diagram representing the taking of the first reading. (The diagram should include the unknown building height, the measured shadow length, the measured angle of inclination and the measured height above the ground of the clinometer.)

(b) With the aid of this diagram, calculate the first estimate of the building's height by the two students. Give your answer in metres, correct to four decimal places.

(c) Calculate the second estimate and the third estimate of the building's height. Give your answers in metres, correct to four decimal places.

(d) What was the final estimate of the building's height that the students arrived at? Give your answer correct to the nearest centimetre.

The second part of the two students' trigonometry exam involved investigating the oscillation of the range of the tide at the nearby port of Valparaiso on the Pacific coast.

The range of a tide is defined as the difference between high and low tides. For example, if on a particular day, the high tide is measured as 4.2 m and the low tide as 1.7 m, then the tidal range for that day is 4.2 − 1.7 = 2.5 m.

The students were presented with the following table showing the recorded tidal ranges for a three-week period (tidal range is given in metres):

(e) The students were then asked to draw a graph of Tidal Range (on the vertical axis) against Day (on the horizontal axis). Draw the graph that the students would have drawn.

(f) Fernando estimates the period of the above graphed function to be 13 days. Explain how you think he came to this conclusion.

Day	Tidal range	Day	Tidal range	Day	Tidal range
1	4.3	8	5.7	15	3.7
2	3.8	9	6.3	16	3.0
3	3.3	10	6.6	17	2.8
4	3.0	11	6.5	18	3.1
5	3.2	12	6.0	19	3.7
6	4.0	13	5.5	20	4.3
7	4.9	14	4.6	21	4.7

(g) What estimate do you think the students got for the range of the above graphed function? Explain how you arrived at your answer.

TRIGONOMETRY

Exam Questions

1. Windows are sometimes in the shape of a pointed arch, like the one shown in the picture.

   A person is designing such an arched window. The outline is shown in the diagram.

   The centre for the arc *AB* is *C*, and the centre for the arc *AC* is *B*. |*BD*| = 2.4 metres and |*DE*| = 1.8 metres.

   (a) Show that |∠*ABC*| = 60°.

   (b) Find the length of the arc *AB*. Give your answer in metres, correct to three decimal places.

   (c) Find the length of the perimeter of the window. Give your answer in metres, correct to two decimal places.

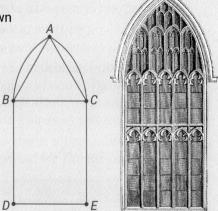

SEC Leaving Certificate Higher Level, Project Maths Paper 2, 2010

2. Roofs of buildings are often supported by frameworks of timber called roof trusses.

   A quantity surveyor must find the total length of timber needed in order to make the triangular truss shown below.

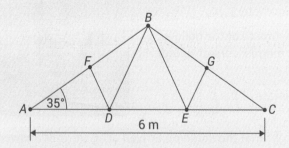

   The length of |*AC*| is 6 metres, and the pitch of the roof is 35°, as shown.

   |*AD*| = |*DE*| = |*EC*| and
   |*AF*| = |*FB*| = |*BG*| = |*GC*|

   (i) Calculate the length of [*AB*] in metres, correct to two decimal places.

   (ii) Calculate the total length of timber required to make the truss.

SEC Leaving Certificate Higher Level, Project Maths Paper 2, 2010

3. Two surveyors want to find the height of an electricity pylon. There is a fence around the pylon that they cannot cross for safety reasons. The ground is inclined at an angle. They have a clinometer and a 100 metre tape measure. They have already used the clinometer to determine that the ground is inclined at 10° to the horizontal.

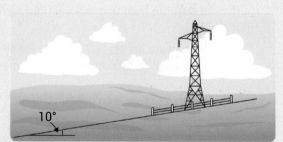

   (a) Explain how they could find the height of the pylon.

   Your answer should be illustrated on the diagram. Show the points where you think they should take measurements, and write down clearly what measurements they should take.

   (b) Write down possible values for the measurements taken, and use them to show how to find the height of the pylon. (That is, find the height of the pylon using your measurements, and showing your work.)

SEC Leaving Certificate Higher Level, Project Maths Sample Paper 2, 2010

4. A tower that is part of a hotel has a square base of side 4 m and a roof in the form of a pyramid. The owners plan to cover the roof with copper. To find the amount of copper needed, they need to know the total area of the roof.

A surveyor stands 10 m from the tower, measured horizontally, and makes observations of angles of elevation from the point O as follows:

The angle of elevation of the top of the roof is 46°.

The angle of elevation of the closest point at the bottom of the roof is 42°.

The angle of depression of the closest point at the bottom of the tower is 9°.

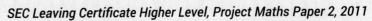

   (i)   Find the vertical height of the roof.

   (ii) Find the total area of the roof.

   (iii) If all of the angles observed are subject to a possible error of ±1°, find the range of possible areas for the roof.

SEC Leaving Certificate Higher Level, Project Maths Paper 2, 2011

5. (a) Solve the equation $\cos 3\theta = \frac{1}{2}$, for $\theta \in R$ (where θ is in radians).

   (b) The graphs of three functions are shown on the diagram below. The scales on the axes are not labelled. The three functions are:

$$x \rightarrow \cos 3x$$

$$x \rightarrow 2\cos 3x$$

$$x \rightarrow 3\cos 2x$$

Identify which function is which, and write your answers in the spaces below the diagram.

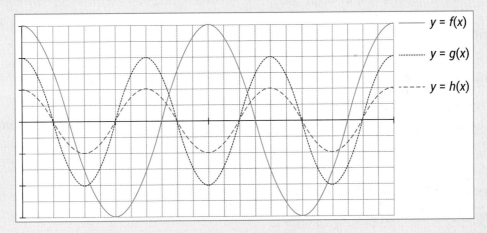

f: x→ _____   g: x→ _____   h: x→ _____

   (c) Label the scales on the axes in the diagram in part (b).

SEC Leaving Certificate Higher Level, Project Maths Paper 2, 2010

 Solutions and chapter summary available online

TRIGONOMETRY

08

Co-ordinate Geometry: The Line

 In this chapter you will learn to:

- Calculate the distance between two points

- Calculate the slope of a line through two points and consolidate the understanding of the concept of slope

- Find the equation of a line, given the slope and a point

- Find the equation of a line, given two points

- Calculate the area of a triangle

- Recognise the fact that the relationships $y = mx + c$ and $y - y_1 = m(x - x_1)$ are linear and use these relationships to solve problems

- Find the equation of lines parallel to and perpendicular to a given line and through a given point

- Find the point of intersection of two lines

- Recognise the fact that $ax + by + c = 0$ represents a linear relationship and use this relationship to solve problems

- Calculate the length of the perpendicular from (x_1, y_1) to $ax + by + c = 0$

- Calculate the angle θ between two lines with slopes of m_1 and m_2 using

$$\tan \theta = \pm \frac{m_1 - m_2}{1 + m_1 m_2}$$

- Divide a line segment internally in a given ratio $m : n$

! **You should remember...**

- The theorem of Pythagoras

- How to find the area of a parallelogram

- How to find the area of a triangle

- How to find the area of a rectangle

- A circle is the set of all points that are a fixed distance from a given point

- Distance = Speed × Time

Key words

- Distance
- Midpoint
- Slope of a line
- Equation of a line
- Parallel
- Perpendicular
- Internal divisor
- Intercept

Modern co-ordinate geometry dates back to the French mathematician and philosopher René Descartes (1596–1650). It is sometimes called Cartesian geometry in his honour. Co-ordinate geometry has applications in such diverse areas as geography, astronomy, engineering and economics. For example, when you look up the location of a place on a map, it is usually given as a set of co-ordinates.

Co-ordinate geometry is used by accountants and business managers regularly when they calculate break-even points and profit margins.

In co-ordinate geometry, we refer to the plane on which we work as the *xy*-plane, or the Cartesian plane.

René Descartes

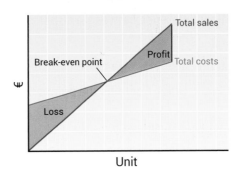

8.1 Revision of Formulae

1. **Distance between two points**

   Finding the distance between two points P and Q is the equivalent of finding the length of the line segment $[PQ]$.

   The formula for calculating the length of the line segment derives from Pythagoras' theorem.

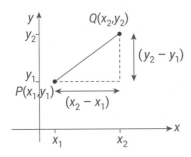

$$|PQ| = \sqrt{(x_2 - x_1)^2 + (y_2 - y_1)^2}$$

This formula appears on page 18 of *Formulae and Tables*.

$$|PQ|^2 = (x_2 - x_1)^2 + (y_2 - y_1)^2$$
$$\text{So } |PQ| = \sqrt{(x_2 - x_1)^2 + (y_2 - y_1)^2}$$

2. **Midpoint of a line segment**

   The point that bisects a line segment is called the midpoint of the line segment. If C is the midpoint of $[AB]$, then $|AC| = |CB|$.

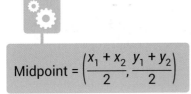

$$\text{Midpoint} = \left(\frac{x_1 + x_2}{2}, \frac{y_1 + y_2}{2}\right)$$

If C is the midpoint of $[AB]$, then $\vec{AC} = \vec{CB}$.

This formula appears on page 18 of *Formulae and Tables*.

3. Slope of a line given two points

The slope of a line is a measure of the 'steepness' of the line. We measure the slope of a line by finding how much the line rises or falls as we move from left to right along it.

Consider the line *l*, which contains the points $A(1,1)$ and $B(4,3)$.

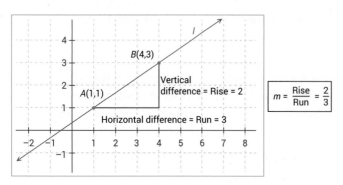

A slope is a 'rate of change'. How much does *y* change for every one unit change in *x*?

m is often used to denote slope.

Run: The horizontal difference between *A* and *B* is 3.

Rise: The vertical difference between *A* and *B* is 2.

- The slope of *l* is $\frac{\text{rise}}{\text{run}} = \frac{2}{3}$.
- For every three steps right we move two steps up.

Consider the line *k*, which contains the points $C(-2,3)$ and $D(2,1)$.

- The slope of *k* is: $m = \frac{\text{rise}}{\text{run}} = \frac{-2}{4} = -\frac{1}{2}$.
- For every two steps right we move one step down.
- As a rate of change, we say for every one unit change in *x*, *y* changes by −0.5 units.
- Horizontal line: Vertical line:
  slope = 0   no defined slope

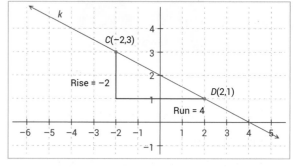

Given two points (x_1,y_1) and (x_2,y_2), the slope of the line containing both points can be found using a formula.

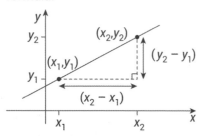

$$\text{Slope} = m = \frac{y_2 - y_1}{x_2 - x_1}$$

This formula appears on page 18 of *Formulae and Tables*.

4. Equation of a line

The equation of a line tells us how the *x* co-ordinate and the *y* co-ordinate of every point on the line are related to each other.

For example, consider the line containing the points (1,4), (2,3), ..., (6,−1).
Do you notice a pattern? For each point on this line, the sum of the *x*- and *y*-co-ordinates is always 5. So the equation of this line is $x + y = 5$.

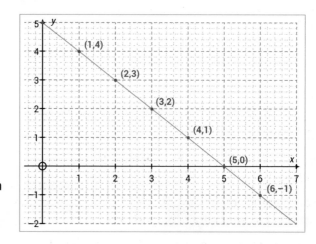

Equations of lines are written in three main forms:

  (i) $y - y_1 = m(x - x_1)$ [(x_1, y_1) is a specific point on the line; m is the slope]

  (ii) $y = mx + c$ [m = slope; c is called the y-intercept – this is where the line cuts the y-axis]

  (iii) $ax + by + c = 0$ [a, b and c are coefficients]

5. Slope of a line, given its equation

  (i) $y - y_1 = m(x - x_1)$ slope is m

  (ii) $y = mx + c$ slope is m

  (iii) $ax + by + c = 0$ slope is $\dfrac{-a}{b}$

6. Point of intersection of a line with the x- and y-axes

  • When a line cuts the x-axis, the value of the y co-ordinate is 0.
  • When a line cuts the y-axis, the value of the x co-ordinate is 0.

7. Point of intersection of two lines

Use the method of solving simultaneous equations to find the point of intersection.
Points of intersection can also be located graphically.

8. Slope of parallel and perpendicular lines

If two lines a and b have defined slopes m_1 and m_2 respectively, then:

$a \parallel b \Leftrightarrow m_1 = m_2$

$a \perp b \Leftrightarrow m_1 . m_2 = -1$

> To find the slope of a perpendicular line, invert the slope and change the sign!

Suppose the lines j and k, with slopes m_1 and m_2, are parallel.

This means they make equal angles A with the positive sense of the x-axis. (A = the angle of inclination)

Then $m_1 = \tan A = m_2$.

Thus parallel lines have equal slopes.

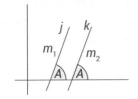

Worked Example 8.1

The line k: $6x - 8y - 71 = 0$ and the points $A(8,-6)$ and $B(5,-2)$ are shown.

  (i) Find $|AB|$.

  (ii) Find the midpoint of $[AB]$.

  (iii) Show that the line k contains the midpoint of $[AB]$.

  (iv) Find the slope of AB.

  (v) Find the slope of the line k: $6x - 8y - 71 = 0$.

  (vi) Find the point of intersection of the line k and the x-axis.

  (vii) From the graph, find the intersection of AB and the line k.

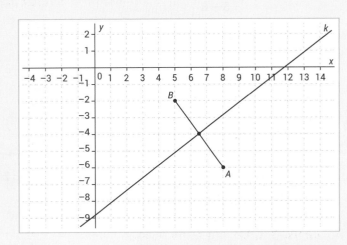

  (viii) Given that the equation of AB is $4x + 3y = 14$, verify the point of intersection found in part (vii).

  (ix) What can you conclude about AB and the line k?

Solution

(i) $A(8,-6)$ $B(5,-2)$
 $x_1\ y_1x_2\ y_2$

$|AB| = \sqrt{(x_2 - x_1)^2 + (y_2 - y_1)^2}$

$ = \sqrt{(5 - 8)^2 + (-2 + 6)^2}$

$ = \sqrt{(-3)^2 + (4)^2}$

$ = \sqrt{9 + 16}$

$ = \sqrt{25}$

$\therefore |AB| = 5$

(ii) Midpoint of $[AB]$:

$\text{Midpoint} = \left(\dfrac{x_1 + x_2}{2}, \dfrac{y_1 + y_2}{2}\right)$

$\phantom{\text{Midpoint}} = \left(\dfrac{8 + 5}{2}, \dfrac{-6 - 2}{2}\right)$

$\phantom{\text{Midpoint}} = \left(\dfrac{13}{2}, -\dfrac{8}{2}\right)$

$\phantom{\text{Midpoint}} = (6.5, -4)$

(iii) $(6.5, -4) \in 6x - 8y - 71 = 0$?

$6(6.5) - 8(-4) - 71 = 0$

$39 + 32 - 71 = 0$

$71 - 71 = 0$

$0 = 0 \quad \text{True}$

$\therefore (6.5, -4)$ is on the line k.

(iv) Slope of AB:

$m = \dfrac{y_2 - y_1}{x_2 - x_1}$

$ = \dfrac{-2 + 6}{5 - 8}$

$ = -\dfrac{4}{3}$

$\therefore$ Slope of $AB = -\dfrac{4}{3}$

(v) k: $\boxed{6}\,x\ \boxed{-8}\,y\ \boxed{-71} = 0$
 $\ abc$

$m = \dfrac{-a}{b} = \dfrac{-6}{-8} = \dfrac{3}{4}$

(vi) $y = 0$

$\therefore 6x - 8(0) - 71 = 0$

$\therefore 6x = 71$

$\therefore x = \dfrac{71}{6}\qquad \left(\dfrac{71}{6}, 0\right)$

(vii) $(6.5, -4)$ is the midpoint of $[AB]$, and from part (iii), it also lies on k.

$\therefore$ Point of intersection $= (6.5, -4)$

(viii)
$$4x + 3y = 14 \cdots\cdots ①$$
$$6x - 8y = 71 \cdots\cdots ②$$
$$\underline{}$$
$$12x + 9y = 42 \qquad ① \times 3$$
$$-(12x - 16y = 142) \qquad ② \times 2$$
$$\underline{}$$
$$25y = -100$$
$$y = -4$$

$①\quad 4x + 3(-4) = 14$

$\quad 4x - 12 = 14$

$\quad 4x = 26$

$\quad x = 6.5 \qquad (6.5, -4)$

$\therefore$ Point of intersection is verified.

(ix) Slope of $AB = -\dfrac{4}{3}\ (m_1)$

 Slope of $k = \dfrac{3}{4}\ (m_2)$

$m_1 \times m_2 = -\dfrac{4}{3} \times \dfrac{3}{4} = -1$

$\therefore AB \perp k$

Exercise 8.1

1. (i) Find $|AB|$ for each of these pairs of points:

 (a) $A(3,2)$ and $B(8,14)$

 (b) $A(-6,-1)$ and $B(3,-4)$

 (c) $A(6,9)$ and $B(6,12)$

 (d) $A(-4,-2)$ and $B(3,-7)$

 (ii) Find the midpoint of $[AB]$ for each line segment in part (i).

2. l: $2x - y = 12$. Find:

 (i) The slope of l

 (ii) The point of intersection of l and

 (a) the x-axis (b) the y-axis

3. Find the point of intersection of lines l and k.

 l: $2x - y - 10 = 0$

 k: $2x = 14y - 146$

4. *P*, *Q* and *R* are the points (3,−3), (−5,1) and (1,3) respectively.

   (i) Show that the triangle *PQR* is isosceles.

   (ii) Find the co-ordinates of *S*, the midpoint of [*QP*].

   (iii) Show that *SR* ⊥ *QP*.

5. Find *a* and *b* if the point (6,3) is the midpoint of the line joining (2*a*,2*a* − *b*) and (*a* − 2*b*,4*a* + 3*b*).

6. *l*: 2*x* − 3*y* + 4 = 0 and *k*: 3*x* + 2*y* − 6 = 0 are two lines. Prove that *l* ⊥ *k*.

7. *a*: 2*x* + 3*y* − 8 = 0 and *b*: 4*x* + 6*y* − 9 = 0 are two lines. Prove that *a* ∥ *b*.

8. *m*: 3*x* − 4*y* = 8 and *n*: *ax* − 8*y* = 12 are two lines. If *m* ∥ *n*, find the value of *a*.

9. *A*(2,−2) and *B*(4,4) are two points.

   (i) Find |*AB*|.

   (ii) Find *C*, the midpoint of [*AB*].

   The equation of *AB* is 3*x* − *y* − 8 = 0.

   (iii) Verify that (3,1) is on *AB*.

   l: *x* + 3*y* = 14

   (iv) Find the point of intersection of *l* and *AB*.

   (v) Find the slope of *l* and the slope of *AB*.

   What can you conclude about the lines *l* and *AB*?

10. The points *B*(10,4), *C*(2,*t*) and *D*(*q*,0) lie on the circle with centre (4,2).
   Find the radius and the possible values for *t* and *q*.

11. *A*(1,3) and *B*(*x*,*y*) are two points.
   The slope of *AB* is $\frac{1}{2}$ and |*AB*| = $\sqrt{20}$.
   Find two possible points *B*.

12. Three points (*x*,1), (1,3) and (5,5) are collinear. Find the value of *x* ∈ *Z*.

13. The charge for repairing a washing machine is made up of a fixed charge and a fee that depends on the time taken to repair the machine.

   (i) What is the fixed charge for a repair?

   (ii) What is the charge for a repair that takes 40 minutes?

   (iii) Calculate the slope of the line.

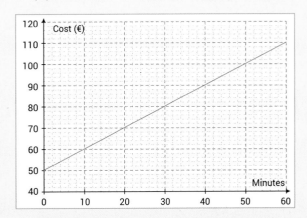

   (iv) What does the slope represent in the context of this question?

   (v) Find the equation of the line.

   (vi) Use your equation to find the cost of a repair that takes two hours.

14. Carlos is in a circular pool in a water park at point *A*(6,3). He swims from *A* to the centre of the pool at the point (−3,7). He then continues to swim in a straight line to the other side of the pool to point *B*.

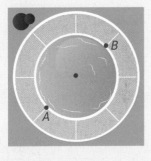

   (i) Find the co-ordinates of the point *B*.

   (ii) If each unit is 1.5 metres, find the diameter of the pool to the nearest metre.

8.2 Derivation of the Divisor of a Line Segment

P(*x*₁,*y*₁), *Q*(*x*₂,*y*₂) and *R*(*x*,*y*) are three points.

Consider the line segment *PQ* to which the point *R* belongs.

R divides [*PQ*] internally in the ratio *a* : *b*.

Drop a perpendicular from *P*, *R* and *Q* to the *x*-axis.

Draw right-angled triangles as shown in the diagram.

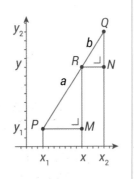

The triangles *PMR* and *RNQ* are similar by our construction, so their sides are in proportion.

$$\frac{PM}{RN} = \frac{a}{b} \quad \text{so} \quad \frac{x - x_1}{x_2 - x} = \frac{a}{b}$$

Make *x* the subject of the formula.

$$bx - bx_1 = ax_2 - ax$$

$$ax + bx = ax_2 + bx_1$$

$$x = \frac{ax_2 + bx_1}{a + b}$$

Also, $\dfrac{RM}{QN} = \dfrac{a}{b}$.

$$\Rightarrow \frac{y - y_1}{y_2 - y} = \frac{a}{b}$$

Make *y* the subject of the formula.

$$by - by_1 = ay_2 - ay$$

$$ay + by = ay_2 + by_1$$

$$y = \frac{ay_2 + by_1}{a + b}$$

> If the ratio was 1:1 we are just talking about the midpoint!

$$R = \left(\frac{bx_1 + ax_2}{b + a}, \frac{by_1 + ay_2}{b + a} \right)$$

This formula appears on page 18 of *Formulae and Tables*.

Worked Example 8.2

A(−5,3) and *B*(3,−1) are two points. Find the co-ordinates of *C*, which divides [*AB*] in the ratio 3:1.

Solution

Method 1

A(−5,3) — 3 — C — 1 — B(3,−1)
$x_1 y_1$ $\quad x_2 y_2$

$$C = \left(\frac{bx_1 + ax_2}{b + a}, \frac{by_1 + ay_2}{b + a} \right) \qquad \begin{matrix} 3:1 \\ a:b \end{matrix}$$

$$= \left(\frac{1(-5) + 3(3)}{1 + 3}, \frac{1(3) + 3(-1)}{1 + 3} \right)$$

$$= \left(\frac{-5 + 9}{4}, \frac{3 - 3}{4} \right)$$

$$\therefore C = (1,0)$$

Method 2

$$A(-5,3) \xrightarrow[\; y - 4 \;]{\; x + 8 \;} B(3,-1)$$

We are told that |*AC*|:|*CB*| = 3:1.

So $\overrightarrow{AC}$ is $\frac{3}{4}$ of +8 and $\frac{3}{4}$ of −4 i.e. +6 and −3.

$$A(-5,3) \xrightarrow[\; y - 3 \;]{\; x + 6 \;} (1,0) = C$$

Worked Example 8.3

Consider the points *A*(4,6), *B*(−4,2) and *C*(*x*, *y*). Given that the point *B* divides the line segment [*AC*] internally in the ratio 2:3, find the co-ordinates of the point *C*.

Solution

Step 1

A(4,6) — 2 — B(−4,2) — 3 — C(x,y)

Draw a quick sketch of the line segment and label the points.

Step 2

Write out the formula and sub in the values.

Ratio = 2:3

$$B = \left(\frac{3(4) + 2(x)}{3 + 2}, \frac{3(6) + 2(y)}{3 + 2} \right)$$

$$(-4,2) = \left(\frac{12 + 2x}{5}, \frac{18 + 2y}{5} \right)$$

Step 3

Set up two equations in terms of *x* and *y*.

$$-4 = \frac{12 + 2x}{5} \qquad\qquad 2 = \frac{18 + 2y}{5}$$

$$-20 = 12 + 2x \qquad\qquad 10 = 18 + 2y$$

$$2x = -32 \qquad\qquad 2y = -8$$

$$x = -16 \qquad\qquad y = -4$$

$$\therefore C = (-16, -4)$$

Exercise 8.2

1. $A(1,-2)$ and $C(-4,8)$ are two points. B divides $[AC]$ internally in the ratio $3:2$. Find the co-ordinates of B.

2. $Q(-2,6)$ and $R(12,27)$ are two points. Find the co-ordinates of P when P is a point on $[QR]$ such that $|QP|:|PR| = 3:4$.

3. $A(-1,4)$ and $B(9,-1)$ are two points and P is a point on $[AB]$. Given that $|AP|:|PB| = 2:3$, find the co-ordinates of P.

4. $P(2,-5)$ and $Q(-5,9)$ are two points. Find the co-ordinates of $K(x,y)$ on the line PQ where $|PK|:|KQ| = 4:3$ if $K \in [PQ]$.

5. $X(-2,-1)$, $Y(2,1)$ and $Z(4,2)$ are three points.

   (i) Prove that X, Y and Z are collinear.

   (ii) Find the ratio by which Y divides $[XZ]$ internally.

6. A is a point on the y-axis and E is a point on the x-axis. $D(2,1)$ divides $[AE]$ internally in the ratio $4:1$.

   Find the co-ordinates of A and E.

7. $A(8,-6)$ and $B(5,-2)$ are two points. In what ratio does the line $6x - 8y - 71 = 0$ divide $[AB]$?

8. $A(x,y)$, $B(0,1)$ and $C(-2,2)$ are three points. B divides $[AC]$ internally in the ratio $5:1$. Find the co-ordinates of A.

8.3 Finding the Equation of a Line

To find the equation of a line, given:

1. A point on the line $[x, y]$

2. The slope

use the formula $y - y_1 = m(x - x_1)$

The general form of the equation of a straight line is $ax + by + c = 0$, where a, b and $c \in R$.

Equation of a line:

$$y - y_1 = m(x - x_1)$$

This formula appears on page 18 of *Formulae and Tables*.

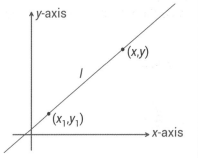

The Equations of Parallel and Perpendicular Lines

Parallel lines have the same slopes, so coefficients of x and y are in the same ratio.

A line parallel to $ax + by + c = 0$ is $ax + by + d = 0$ (where $d \in R$).

Perpendicular lines' slopes multiply to give -1.

A line perpendicular to $ax + by + c = 0$ is $bx - ay + d = 0$ (where $d \in R$).

Equations of the Form $y = mx + c$

Many equations that model or represent real-life situations are of the form $y = mx + c$. So, it makes sense to study equations of the form $y = mx + c$.

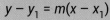

$$y = mx + c$$

↓ ↓

slope y-intercept

When we use equations to solve everyday problems, we usually refer to the equation as a model of the problem.

Equation of a line:

$$y = mx + c$$

where m = slope and c = y-intercept

This formula appears on page 18 of *Formulae and Tables*.

For example, the equation for the total cost of manufacturing a product could be modelled as

$T = 0.5Q + 5$, where Q = Quantity produced (in 10,000 unit batches) and T = Total cost (in €000s).

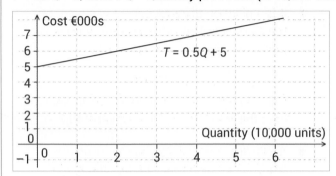

From the graph and equation, $m = 0.5$. This means that for every extra 10,000 units produced, the cost increases by €500 (0.5 × €1,000).

From the graph and equation, $c = 5$. This indicates that, regardless of how many units are produced, there is a fixed cost of €5,000.

Worked Example 8.4

(i) Find the equation of the line that passes through $A(3,4)$ with slope $\frac{1}{2}$.

(ii) Find the equation of the line that passes through $B(-2,0)$ and $C(2,-3)$.

(iii) Find the equation of the line that passes through $(2,3)$ and is parallel to $3x + 4y + 6 = 0$.

(iv) l is the line $4x + 3y + 8 = 0$. The line k contains $(2,-3)$ and is perpendicular to l. Find the equation of k.

Solution

(i) Point $A(3, 4)$ Slope $m = \dfrac{1}{2}$
     $x_1\, y_1$

Equation: $y - y_1 = m(x - x_1)$

$$(y - 4) = \frac{1}{2}(x - 3)$$

$$2(y - 4) = 1(x - 3)$$

$$2y - 8 = x - 3$$

$$x - 2y + 5 = 0$$

(ii) Points $B(-2,0)$ and $C(2,-3)$
        $x_1\, y_1$ $x_2\, y_2$

Slope $m = \dfrac{y_2 - y_1}{x_2 - x_1} = \dfrac{-3 - 0}{2 + 2} = -\dfrac{3}{4}$

Equation: $y - y_1 = m(x - x_1)$

$$y - 0 = -\frac{3}{4}(x + 2)$$

$$4y = -3x - 6$$

$$3x + 4y + 6 = 0$$

(iii) Point $(2, 3)$ | Parallel to $3x + 4y + 6 = 0$
     $x_1\, y_1$

$\Rightarrow$ Slope $m = -\dfrac{a}{b} = -\dfrac{3}{4}$

Equation: $y - y_1 = m(x - x_1)$

$$y - 3 = -\frac{3}{4}(x - 2)$$

$$4y - 12 = -3x + 6$$

$$3x + 4y - 18 = 0$$

(iv) Point $(2,-3)$ | Perpendicular to l: $4x + 3y + 8 = 0$
     $x_1\, y_1$

$\Rightarrow$ Slope $m = \dfrac{b}{a}$

$\therefore m = \dfrac{3}{4}$

Equation: $y - y_1 = m(x - x_1)$

$$y + 3 = \frac{3}{4}(x - 2)$$

$$4(y + 3) = 3(x - 2)$$

$$4y + 12 = 3x - 6$$

$$3x - 4y - 18 = 0$$

$y - y_1 = m(x - x_1)$

Exercise 8.3

1. Find the equations of the lines containing the point A with slope m.

	A	m
(i)	(6,8)	−3
(ii)	(−4,−2)	$\frac{2}{3}$
(iii)	$\left(4, -\frac{1}{2}\right)$	$-\frac{2}{5}$
(iv)	(0,−3)	2

2. Find the equation of the line through the points A and B.

(i) A(2,1); B(3,2)   (iii) A(−5,−1); B(−2,5)

(ii) A(−1,3); B(2,4)

3. Find the equation of the line through the points X and Y.

(i) X(−2,2); Y(−5,3)   (iii) X(6,−5); Y(−3,9)

(ii) X(1,7); Y(−2,4)

4. Find the equation of the line that passes through the origin and has a slope of −1.

5. Find the equation of the lines labelled j, k and l.

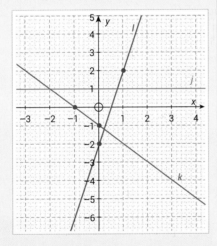

6. Find the equation of the line passing through the point of intersection of $3x + 2y - 1 = 0$ and $5x + 6y + 1 = 0$, and which is perpendicular to $3x - y = 0$.

7. A line crosses the x-axis at x = 3 and the y-axis at y = 2.

Find the equation of the line.

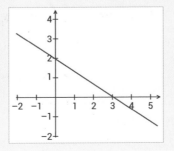

8. l is the line $3x - 2y + 4 = 0$.
The line k contains the point (2,−3) and is parallel to l. Find the equation of k.

9. m is the line $x - 6y + 12 = 0$.
The line n contains the point (−3,2) and is perpendicular to m. Find the equation of n.

10. p is the line $2x - y + 14 = 0$.
The line q contains the point (−1,2) and is parallel to p. Find the equation of q.

11. l is the line $x - y + 2 = 0$.
The line k contains the point (2,2) and is perpendicular to l. Find the equation of k.

12. A(−1,4) and B(5,−4) are two points.
Find the equation of the perpendicular bisector of [AB].

13. Find the equation of the line through the point (1,0) that also passes through the point of intersection of the lines $2x - y + 6 = 0$ and $10x + 3y - 2 = 0$.

14. Find the equation of the straight line joining the origin to the midpoint of the line joining A(3,2) and B(5,−1).

15. One side of a rhombus is the line $y = 2x$ and two opposite vertices are the points (0,0) and (4.5,4.5).

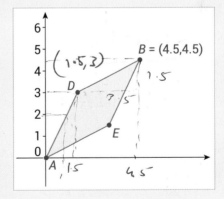

Find:

(i) The equations of the diagonals

(ii) The co-ordinates of the other two vertices

(iii) The length of a side of the rhombus

16. Find the equation of the line l through the point (−4,3) so that the area of the triangle formed by l, the negative x-axis and the positive y-axis, is 24 square units.

CO-ORDINATE GEOMETRY: THE LINE

17. Triangle *ABC* has the vertices *A*(4,−1), *B*(2,1) and *C*(−2,−3).

  (i) Plot the points *A*, *B* and *C*.

  (ii) Construct the circumcircle of the triangle.

  Check the accuracy of your construction by doing the following:

  (iii) Find the equation of the perpendicular bisector of *AB*.

  (iv) Find the equation of the perpendicular bisector of *BC*.

  (v) Hence, using your answers from parts (iii) and (iv), find the co-ordinates of *K*, the circumcentre of triangle *ABC*.

  (vi) Verify that |*AK*| = |*BK*| = |*CK*|.

8.4 The Area of a Triangle

The diagram below shows a triangle with vertices *O*(0,0), *A*(x_1,y_1) and *B*(x_2,y_2).

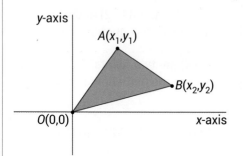

The area of this triangle is given by:

$$\frac{1}{2}|x_1 y_2 - x_2 y_1|$$

This formula appears on page 18 of *Formulae and Tables*.

> To use this formula, one vertex must be (0,0).

> The symbol |...| means take the absolute value of the number inside e.g. |−3| = 3.

Worked Example 8.5

Find the area of the triangle with vertices (0,0), (7,3) and (15,0).

Solution

One of the vertices is at (0,0) so we can use the formula directly.

(0,0) (7,3) (15,0)
        $x_1 y_1$ $x_2 y_2$

$$\text{Area} = \frac{1}{2}|x_1 y_2 - x_2 y_1|$$

$$= \frac{1}{2}|(7)(0) - (15)(3)|$$

$$= \frac{1}{2}|0 - 45|$$

$$= \frac{1}{2}|-45|$$

$$= \frac{1}{2}(45)$$

> |−45| means a 'distance' of −45 from 0 on the number line.
>
> ∴ |−45| = 45

∴ Area = 22.5 sq units

What if there is No Vertex at (0,0)?

We need to:

1. Translate one point to (0,0).
2. Apply the translation to the other two points.

> A translation such as this maintains the size of the triangle and, hence, the area.

Worked Example 8.6

Find the area of the triangle with vertices (−3,4), (4,2) and (6,10).

Solution

Step 1

Translate the triangle so that one vertex is at (0,0).

$$
\begin{array}{ccc}
(-3,\ 4) & (4,\ 2) & (6,\ 10) \\
+3 \downarrow -4 & +3 \downarrow -4 & +3 \downarrow -4 \\
(0,\ 0) & (7,\ -2) & (9,\ 6) \\
 & x_1\ \ y_1 & x_2\ \ y_2
\end{array}
$$

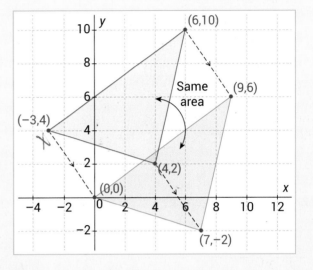

Step 2

Sub into the formula.

Area $= \dfrac{1}{2}|x_1 y_2 - x_2 y_1|$

$= \dfrac{1}{2}|(7)(6) - (9)(-2)|$

$= \dfrac{1}{2}|42 + 18|$

$= \dfrac{1}{2}(60)$

$= 30$ square units

Worked Example 8.7

$A(8,2)$, $B(-3,-4)$, $C(6,k)$ are three vertices of a triangle of area 50 square units.

Find two values of k.

Solution

$$
\begin{array}{ccc}
(8,\ 2) & (-3,\ -4) & (6,\ k) \\
-8 \downarrow -2 & -8 \downarrow -2 & -8 \downarrow -2 \\
(0,\ 0) & (-11,\ -6) & (-2,\ k-2) \\
 & x_1\ \ y_1 & x_2\ \ y_2
\end{array}
$$

Area $= \dfrac{1}{2}|(-11)(k-2) - (-2)(-6)| = 50$

$\Rightarrow |(-11)(k-2) - (-2)(-6)| = 100$

$|-11k + 22 - 12| = 100$

$|-11k + 10| = 100$

Method 1

Square both sides.

$121k^2 - 220k + 100 = 10{,}000$

$121k^2 - 220k - 9900 = 0$

$11k^2 - 20k - 900 = 0$

$(11k + 90)(k - 10) = 0$

$\boxed{k = -\dfrac{90}{11}}$

$\boxed{k = 10}$

Method 2

$$
\begin{array}{ccc}
-11k + 10 = 100 & & -11k + 10 = -100 \\
-11k = 90 & \text{or} & -11k = -110 \\
11k = -90 & & 11k = 110 \\
\boxed{k = -\dfrac{90}{11}} & & \boxed{k = 10}
\end{array}
$$

Exercise 8.4

1. Find the areas of the triangles with vertices:

	A	B	C
(i)	(0,0)	(2,−3)	(3,5)
(ii)	(5,2)	(0,0)	(3,10)
(iii)	(2,2)	(0,0)	(3,7)
(iv)	(−5,6)	(−1,1)	(5,0)
(v)	(1,5)	(−5,−3)	(4,1)
(vi)	(−1,−4)	(−2,3)	(2,−1)
(vii)	(1,3)	(3,4)	(2,6)
(viii)	(−1,−3)	(4,1)	(3,5)

2. A triangle has vertices (−1,−1), (6,1) and (−2.5,−5).

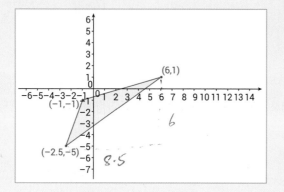

Find the area of the triangle.

3. Find the area of the triangle with vertices (1,1), (8,−5) and (5,−2).

4. X(−3,1), Y(1,3) and Z(3,0) are vertices of a triangle. Find the area of △XYZ.

5. The area of △ABC is 8 square units. A(1,−2), B(8,−3) and C(x,y).

   If C is a point on the x-axis, calculate the two possible sets of co-ordinates for C.

6. Find the area of the quadrilateral ABCD with vertices A(3,3), B(1,4), C(−3,1) and D(3,−5).

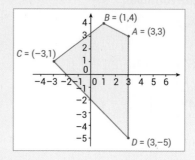

7. (0,0), (6t,t) and (2t,3t) are the vertices of a triangle of area 72 square units.

   Find two possible values of t.

8. A(2,1), B(0,3) and C(2k,−1) are vertices of a triangle of area 4 square units.

   Find the values of k.

8.5 The Perpendicular Distance from a Point to a Line

The shortest distance from a point to a line is the perpendicular distance.

The distance from a point (x_1, y_1) to the line $ax + by + c = 0$ is given by:

$$d = \frac{|ax_1 + by_1 + c|}{\sqrt{a^2 + b^2}}$$

This formula appears on page 19 of *Formulae and Tables*.

In order to use this formula, make sure that the equation of the line is written in the form $ax + by + c = 0$.

This formula is often used in circle questions.

The perpendicular distance from the centre to a tangent is the radius.

Worked Example 8.8

Find the distance from the point (3,1) to the line $4x + 3y + 10 = 0$.

Solution

$\underset{a}{\boxed{4}}\, x\, \underset{b}{\boxed{+3}}\, y\, \underset{c}{\boxed{+10}} = 0$ $(\, \underset{x_1}{\boxed{3}},\, \underset{y_1}{\boxed{1}}\,)$

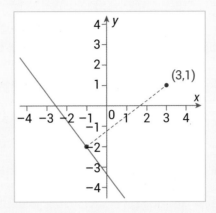

$$d = \frac{|4(3) + 3(1) + 10|}{\sqrt{(4)^2 + (3)^2}}$$

$$= \frac{|12 + 3 + 10|}{\sqrt{16 + 9}}$$

$$= \frac{25}{\sqrt{25}}$$

$$= \frac{25}{5}$$

$$= 5$$

$\therefore d = 5$ units

Worked Example 8.9

Find the equation of two lines that are parallel to the line $x - 2y = 5$ and a distance of $3\sqrt{5}$ from it.

Solution

- Any line parallel to $x - 2y - 5 = 0$ is of the form $x - 2y + c = 0$.
- Any point on $x - 2y - 5 = 0$ will be a distance of $3\sqrt{5}$ from $x - 2y + c = 0$.

  (5,0) is on the line $x - 2y - 5 = 0$.

  $\therefore$ The perpendicular distance from (5,0) to $x - 2y + c = 0$ is equal to $3\sqrt{5}$.

$$\frac{|1(5) - 2(0) + c|}{\sqrt{(1)^2 + (-2)^2}} = 3\sqrt{5}$$

$$\frac{|5 + c|}{\sqrt{5}} = 3\sqrt{5}$$

$$|5 + c| = 3\sqrt{5}\sqrt{5}$$

$$\therefore |5 + c| = 15$$

Square both sides.	**OR**	Put $5 + c = \pm(15)$.
$c^2 + 10c + 25 = 225$		$5 + c = 15$ **or** $5 + c = -15$
$c^2 + 10c - 200 = 0$		$c = 10$ $c = -20$
$(c + 20)(c - 10) = 0$		
$\therefore c = -20$ **or** $c = 10$		

Equations:

$x - 2y - 20 = 0$

$x - 2y + 10 = 0$

Worked Example 8.10

Find the equations of the two lines that pass through the point (3,2) and are at a distance of $\sqrt{5}$ from the point $(-2,-3)$.

Solution

Step 1

Sketch the lines and the points.

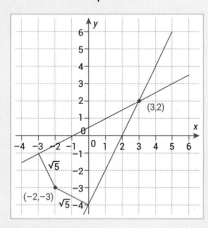

Step 2

We are trying to find the equations of the lines and we need to write the equation in terms of m.

$\qquad$ Point on lines (3,2) $\quad$ Slope = m

$\qquad y - 2 = m(x - 3)$

$\qquad y - 2 = mx - 3m$

$\qquad mx - y - 3m + 2 = 0$

Remember the equation must be in the form $ax + by + c = 0$.

Step 3

$\perp$ distance from $(-2,-3)$ to $mx - y - 3m + 2 = 0$ is equal to $\sqrt{5}$.

$$\frac{|m(-2) - (-3) - 3m + 2|}{\sqrt{m^2 + (-1)^2}} = \sqrt{5}$$

$$\frac{|-5m + 5|}{\sqrt{m^2 + 1}} = \sqrt{5}$$

$$|-5m + 5| = \sqrt{5}\sqrt{m^2 + 1}$$

$$25m^2 - 50m + 25 = 5m^2 + 5$$

$$20m^2 - 50m + 20 = 0$$

$$2m^2 - 5m + 2 = 0$$

$$(2m - 1)(m - 2) = 0$$

$2m - 1 = 0 \quad$ or $\quad m - 2 = 0 \qquad m = \dfrac{1}{2} \quad$ or $\quad m = 2$

Step 4

Substitute each value of m into the line equation.

$m = \dfrac{1}{2}$ $\qquad\qquad\qquad\qquad$ $m = 2$

$\dfrac{1}{2}x - y - 3\left(\dfrac{1}{2}\right) + 2 = 0$ $\qquad$ $2x - y - 3(2) + 2 = 0$

$\qquad\qquad\qquad\qquad\qquad\qquad$ $2x - y - 4 = 0$

$\qquad x - 2y + 1 = 0$

So the equations of the two lines are $x - 2y + 1 = 0$ and $2x - y - 4 = 0$.

Exercise 8.5

1. Find the distance from:

   (i) $(3,-1)$ to $6x + 8y - 31 = 0$

   (ii) $(1,3)$ to $3x + 4y + 10 = 0$

   (iii) $(3,8)$ to $12x - 5y - 9 = 0$

   (iv) $(3,2)$ to $2x - y + 1 = 0$

   (v) $(3,4)$ to $x - y - 1 = 0$

2. Find, in surd form, the perpendicular distance from:

   (i) $(-1,1)$ to $x - 2y = 2$ $\qquad$ (iii) $(10,0)$ to $x = 2y$

   (ii) $(0,0)$ to $x + y - 8 = 0$ $\quad$ (iv) $(11,-10)$ to $x = \dfrac{3y}{2}$

3. Find the perpendicular distance from the point $(5,6)$ to the line $2x + 3y + 4 = 0$.

4. Find the distance from the point $(-3,7)$ to the line $5y = 6x + 2$.

5. Show that $(2,-1)$ is equidistant from the lines with equations $4x + 3y - 20 = 0$ and

   $$y = \frac{12x + 10}{5}.$$

6. Investigate if the point $(3,1)$ is equidistant from $3x - 4y + 5 = 0$ and $12x + 5y - 15 = 0$.

7. The distance from $(0,0)$ to $x + y + k = 0$ is $4\sqrt{2}$. Find two possible values for $k \in R$.

8. The line l has equation $5x - 3y + 10 = 0$.

   The point K has co-ordinates $(6,2)$.

   Show that the perpendicular distance from K to l is $\sqrt{34}$.

9. k is the line $3x - 4y + 9 = 0$.

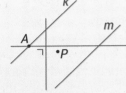

The point $A(-3,0)$ is on k.

The line m is parallel to k.

The point $P(2,-1)$ is midway between k and m.

   (i) Find the equation of m.

   (ii) Calculate the distance between k and m.

> If we only know the equations of two parallel lines, we need to find a point on one first in order to calculate the distance between the lines.

10. Find the shortest distance between the two lines below.

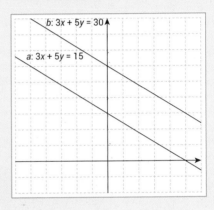

11. (i) Calculate the distance from the point $(-1,-5)$ to the line $3x - 4y - 2 = 0$.

    (ii) The point $(-1,-5)$ is equidistant from the lines $3x - 4y - 2 = 0$ and $3x - 4y + k = 0$, where $k \neq -2$.

    Find the value of k.

12. Find the distance between the parallel lines:

    a: $3x - 4y + 10 = 0$

    b: $3x - 4y + 15 = 0$

13. Find the equations of the lines that pass through the point $(-3,-4)$ and that are a distance of $\sqrt{10}$ from the point $(2,1)$.

14. Find the equations of the lines that are perpendicular to $8x + 15y + 1 = 0$ and that are a distance of 5 units from $(1,1)$.

15. Find the equation of the two lines parallel to $x + 2y = 5$, which are a distance of $7\sqrt{5}$ from it.

16. For what value of m is the point $(7,-5)$ a distance of 8 units from the line $mx - y + (m - 1) = 0$?

8.6 The Angle of Inclination and the Angle Between Two Lines

The Angle of Inclination

> The **angle of inclination** is the anti-clockwise angle formed between a line and the positive sense of the x-axis.

The angle doesn't have to be in the first quadrant.

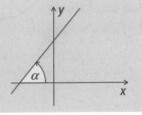

The **angle of inclination** is always between 0° and 180°.

- It is always measured anti-clockwise from the positive sense of the x-axis.

- The slope m of any line is equal to the tangent of its angle of inclination.
  Then $m = \tan \alpha$ (where α = angle of inclination)

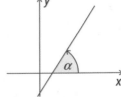 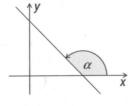

- All horizontal lines have an angle of inclination of 0°.
  Their slopes are zero.

- All vertical lines have an angle of inclination of 90°.
  Their slopes are not defined.

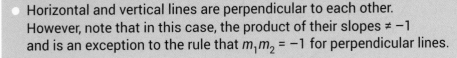

- Horizontal and vertical lines are perpendicular to each other.
  However, note that in this case, the product of their slopes $\neq -1$ and is an exception to the rule that $m_1 m_2 = -1$ for perpendicular lines.

The Angle Between Two Lines

When two lines intersect, the angle between them is defined as the angle through which one of the lines must be rotated to make it coincide with the other line.

Generally, find the acute angle first ($\tan\theta$ is positive) and use $180° - \theta$ to find the obtuse angle.

If two lines p and q have slopes m_1 and m_2 respectively, and θ is the angle between them, then:

$$\tan\theta = \pm\frac{m_1 - m_2}{1 + m_1 m_2}$$

This formula appears on page 19 of *Formulae and Tables*.

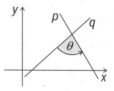

Worked Example 8.11

Find the measure of the angles between the two lines

p: $2x + y - 6 = 0$ and q: $3x - 2y + 2 = 0$.

Solution

Step 1

Find the slope of each line.

$m = -\dfrac{a}{b}$

$2x + y - 6 = 0$ $3x - 2y + 2 = 0$

$a = 2$ $b = 1$ $a = 3$ $b = -2$

$m_1 = \dfrac{-2}{1} = -2$ $m_2 = \dfrac{-3}{-2} = \dfrac{3}{2}$

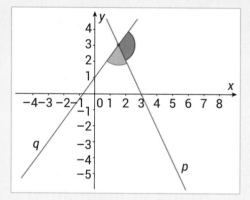

Step 2

Sub into formula.

$\tan\theta = \pm\dfrac{m_1 - m_2}{1 + m_1 m_2}$

$\tan\theta = \pm\dfrac{-2 - \dfrac{3}{2}}{1 + (-2)\left(\dfrac{3}{2}\right)}$

$\quad = \pm\left(\dfrac{-4 - 3}{2 + (-2)(3)}\right)$

$\quad = \pm\left(\dfrac{-7}{-4}\right) = \pm\dfrac{7}{4}$

$\tan\theta = \pm\dfrac{7}{4}$

$\theta = \tan^{-1}\left(\dfrac{7}{4}\right)$ … for acute angle

$\therefore\ \theta = 60.26°$

or $\theta = 180° - 60.26°$ … for obtuse angle

$\therefore\ \theta = 119.74°$

Worked Example 8.12

Find the equations of the lines through the point (4,3) that make an angle of 45° with the line $6x + y - 5 = 0$.

Solution

Step 1

Find the slope of $6x + y - 5 = 0$.

$m_1 = \dfrac{-6}{1} = -6$

Step 2

Let the slope of the line(s) through (4,3) be m.

Step 3

Sub into formula.

$$\tan \theta = \pm \frac{m_1 - m_2}{1 + m_1 m_2}$$

$$= \pm\left(\frac{-6 - m}{1 - 6m}\right)$$

> We use the modulus sign here, as we know that the required angle is acute and so we need the positive value.

But $\tan \theta = \tan 45° = 1$.

$$\Rightarrow 1 = \left|\frac{-6 - m}{1 - 6m}\right|$$

$$1 = \frac{36 + 12m + m^2}{1 - 12m + 36m^2}$$

$$1 - 12m + 36m^2 = 36 + 12m + m^2$$

$$35m^2 - 24m - 35 = 0$$

$$(7m + 5)(5m - 7) = 0$$

$$m = -\frac{5}{7} \quad \text{or} \quad m = \frac{7}{5}$$

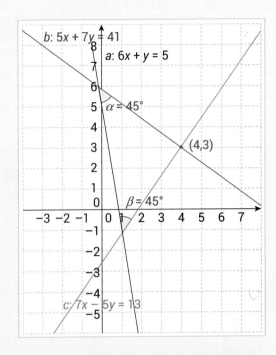

Case 1

Point $(4,3)$

Slope $m = -\frac{5}{7}$

$$y - 3 = -\frac{5}{7}(x - 4)$$

$$7y - 21 = -5x + 20$$

$$\boxed{5x + 7y - 41 = 0}$$

Case 2

Point $(4,3)$

Slope $m = \frac{7}{5}$

$$y - 3 = \frac{7}{5}(x - 4)$$

$$5y - 15 = 7x - 28$$

$$\boxed{7x - 5y - 13 = 0}$$

Lines b and c are perpendicular to each other. This is because they both meet the given line a at an angle of 45°, and therefore the remaining angle at $(4,3)$ must equal 90°.

Exercise 8.6

1. (a) Find the acute angle between the two lines that have the following slopes:

	m_1	m_2
(i)	3	7
(ii)	$\frac{3}{5}$	$-\frac{1}{4}$
(iii)	2	-1
(iv)	$-\frac{1}{2}$	$\frac{1}{3}$
(v)	2	$\frac{1}{3}$

(b) Find the obtuse angle between the two lines that have the following slopes:

	m_1	m_2
(i)	2	6
(ii)	$\frac{4}{5}$	-3
(iii)	-1	$\frac{1}{3}$
(iv)	$\frac{1}{2}$	$\frac{1}{4}$
(v)	$\frac{1}{3}$	3

2. Find, to the nearest degree, the measures of the angles between these pairs of lines:

(i) $2x + y - 6 = 0$ and $3x - 2y + 2 = 0$

(ii) $x + 2y + 7 = 0$ and $2y = 5 - 3x$

(iii) $2x + 5y = 10$ and $5x - 2y = 9$

(iv) $6x - 2y + 5 = 0$ and $2x - 1 = 4y$

(v) $x + y - 5 = 0$ and $2x + y + 3 = 0$

CO-ORDINATE GEOMETRY: THE LINE

3. Find the measure of the acute angle between $x - y - 6 = 0$ and $3x - y + 1 = 0$.

4. Find the measure of the obtuse angle between $3x + y = 0$ and $2x - y = 11$.

5. Part of an obstacle course is called the 'vertical ramp'. If the ramp is on flat ground and its slope is 6, what is the angle of inclination of the ramp?

6. Find the equations of the two lines that pass through the origin and make an angle of 45° with the line $6x - y = 9$.

7. Find the equations of the lines that pass through the point (2,3) and make 45° angles with the line $x - 2y - 1 = 0$.

8. Calculate the measure of the acute angle between AP and k, where:

   $A(-3,0)$, $P(2,-1)$ and k: $3x - 4y + 9 = 0$

   Give your answer correct to the nearest degree.

9. A triangle has vertices (1,−1), (5,1) and (−2.5,−5).

   Calculate the value of the smallest angle in this triangle.

10. A line containing the point (−4,−2) has slope m. This line intercepts the x-axis at $(x_1,0)$ and the y-axis at $(0,y_1)$. Given that $x_1 + y_1 = 3$, find the slopes of the two lines that satisfy this condition, and find the acute angle between these two lines (to the nearest degree).

11. For rain to run off a roof with no risk of water damage, the roof must have a pitch of at least 15°. If the gradient of the roof is 0.25, is there a risk of water damage?

12. An architect is designing a museum for modern art. In keeping with his philosophy, he decides on a very angular building. In the foyer, the wall is at an angle of 55°, while the glass roof is sloped, with a gradient of −0.25.

    Find the interior angle where the wall a and glass roof b meet.

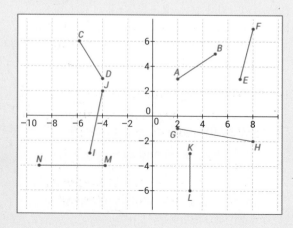

Revision Exercises

1. Using the points given in the table, find:

   (a) The distance between the points

   (b) The midpoint of line segment [AB]

   (c) The equation of line AB

	(i)	(ii)	(iii)	(iv)	(v)
A	(2,1)	(−3,2)	$\left(\frac{1}{2},1\right)$	(−2,0)	$\left(\frac{2}{3},-\frac{1}{3}\right)$
B	(4,5)	(3,−2)	$\left(-\frac{3}{2},-5\right)$	$(0,\sqrt{2})$	$\left(\frac{5}{6},1\right)$

2. Write down the slope of each of the following line segments:

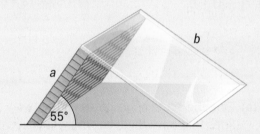

3. $A(2,1)$, $B(10,7)$, $C(14,10)$ and $D(7,3)$ are four points.

   (i) Plot A, B, C and D on the plane.

   (ii) Verify that $|AB| = 2|BC|$ and that $|AB| = 2|BD|$.

4. $A(-2,1)$ and $B(4, -5)$ are two points.

   (i) Plot the two points on graph paper.

   (ii) Find M, the midpoint of $[AB]$.

   (iii) Verify that $|AM| = |MB|$.

   (iv) Find the slope of AB.

   (v) Find the equation of AB.

   (vi) Find the co-ordinates of the point where AB cuts the x-axis.

5. Find two values of x such that the distance between $A(0,0)$ and $B(x,-4)$ is 5.

6. Find two values of y such that the distance between $(5,1)$ and $(5,y)$ is 8.

7. l: $3x + y + 12 = 0$ and k: $x + 2y - 1 = 0$ are two lines. Find:

   (i) The acute angle between them

   (ii) The distance of their point of intersection from the origin

   (iii) The area of the triangle enclosed by l, k and the x-axis

   (iv) The equation of the line m through $(2,3)$ and perpendicular to l

   (v) The perpendicular distance from $(4,4)$ to m

8. The points $A(-3,8)$ and $B(5,-6)$ lie at either end of the diameter of a circle. Find the area of the circle to two decimal places.

9. The line p contains the points $(6,-2)$ and $(-4,10)$. The line q with equation $ax + by + 21 = 0$ is perpendicular to p. Express a in terms of b.

10. Show that the line containing the points $(2,-6)$ and $(-8,12)$ is perpendicular to the line $5x - 9y + 6 = 0$.

11. The equation of the line l is $14x + 6y + 1 = 0$. Find the equation of the line perpendicular to l that contains the point $(5,-3)$.

12. The line l_1: $3x - 2y + 1 = 0$ and the line l_2: $5x + y + 6 = 0$ intersect at the point P. Find the equation of the line through P perpendicular to l_2.

13. (i) The line $3x - 5y + k = 0$ cuts the x-axis at P and the y-axis at Q. Write down the co-ordinates of P and Q in terms of k.

   (ii) The area of the triangle OPQ is 10 square units, where O is the origin. Find the two possible values of k.

14. Find the equations of the two lines that pass through the point $(6,1)$ and make an angle of $45°$ with the line $x + 2y = 0$.

15. Find the area of the triangle with vertices $(5,-3)$, $(-5,-1)$ and $(8,7)$.

16. The line k has a positive slope and passes through the point $P(2,-9)$. k intersects the x-axis at Q and the y-axis at R and $|PQ|:|PR| = 3:1$.

Find the co-ordinates of Q and the co-ordinates of R.

17. The corners of a triangle are the points $P(4,7)$, $Q(-2,5)$ and $R(3,-10)$.

   (a) Find the length of each side of triangle PQR, giving your answers in terms of surds.

   (b) Hence, verify that triangle PQR contains a right-angle.

   (c) Find the area of triangle PQR.

18.

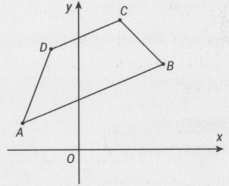

The diagram shows trapezium $ABCD$ in which sides AB and DC are parallel. The point A has co-ordinates $(-4,2)$ and the point B has co-ordinates $(6,6)$.

   (a) Find the equation of the straight line passing through A and B, giving your answer in the form $ax + by + c = 0$, where a, b and c are integers.

Given that the gradient of BC is -1:

   (b) Find the equation of the line passing through B and C.

Given also that the point *D* has co-ordinates (−2,7):

(c) Find the co-ordinates of the point *C*.

(d) Show that |∠*ACB*| = 90°.

(e) Find the area of the quadrilateral *ABCD*.

19. (a) The distance from (5,6) to (*k*,2) is $2\sqrt{5}$. Find two possible values of *k*.

(b) (i) Show that *P*(*k* − 2,7*k* − 7) is on the line *m*: 7*x* − *y* + 7 = 0.

(ii) Find the equation of the line *n*, on which the point *Q*(*t* + 1, 3 − *t*) lies for all values of *t* ∈ R.

20. (4,3) is a point on the line that intersects the *x*-axis at (*A*,0) and the *y*-axis at (0,*B*).

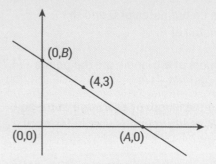

(i) Write down an equation in *A* and *B*.

(ii) If the triangle formed by the points (0,*B*), (*A*,0) and the origin is 24 square units, find the values of *A* and *B*.

21. *l* and *k* are two lines passing through the point of intersection of 2*x* − 3*y* + 1 = 0 and *x* + 2*y* = 3.

(i) If (2,−1) is on *l*, find the equation of *l*.

(ii) If *k* is parallel to 3*x* − *y* = 0, find the equation of *k*.

(iii) Find the angles between the two lines *l* and *k*.

22. Find the value of *b* if the lines *x* + (*b* − 4)*y* = 4 and *bx* + *y* = 18 are perpendicular to each other.

23. (i) Write down the equation of any line parallel to *x* − 2*y* = 4.

(ii) If such a parallel line contains the point (7,−2), find its equation.

24. (i) Write down the equation of any line perpendicular to *x* + 3*y* = 10.

(ii) If such a perpendicular line contains the point (7,−6), find its equation.

25. Two common units of measurement in cooking are the tablespoon and the cup.
The table below gives some conversions.

Tablespoon	4	8	12	16
Cup	$\frac{1}{4}$	$\frac{1}{2}$	$\frac{3}{4}$	1

(i) Using suitable axes and scales, draw a straight line graph of the conversion.

(ii) Using the graph, convert 6 tablespoons to cups.

(iii) Find the slope of the line.

(iv) Hence, write down the equation of the line in the form *y* = *mx*.

(v) Use your equation to convert 50 tablespoons to cups.

26. A car passes a traffic light travelling at a speed of 30 kmh⁻¹. The graph below gives the speed of the car during the 20-second period after passing the traffic light.

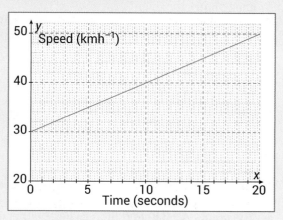

(i) What is the speed of the car 10 seconds after passing the light?

(ii) How many seconds does it take the driver to reach a speed of 48 kmh⁻¹?

(iii) Find the equation of the line.

(iv) What is the *y*-intercept of this line? What value does it represent?

(v) By how many kilometres per hour does the speed change in the 20-second period?

(vi) If the driver continues to change his speed (accelerates) at the same rate over the next 10-second period, then what will the speed of the car be 25 seconds after passing the light?

27. The graph below shows the cost of production for a given product. The total cost of production is made up of fixed costs and variable costs.

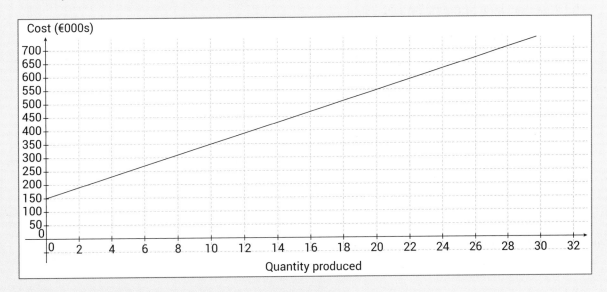

(i) What is the fixed cost associated with this product?

(ii) What is the variable cost per unit produced?

(iii) Find the equation of the line graphed above.

28. The following equation gives the time (T) in minutes for cooking a turkey whose weight (w) is in kilograms:

$T = 44w + 20$

(i) Plot the graph for $0 \leqslant w \leqslant 10$.

(ii) Find the time needed to cook a turkey whose weight is 4.8 kg.

(iii) A turkey was cooked for 5 hours. Using the equation above, find an approximation for its weight in kilograms.

29. A student is asked to design a flag for her team for a school sports day. She has the basic colour scheme for the design. Her teacher told her to get prices on the material needed before she adds any designs.

Below is her basic pattern. Each unit measurement represents 10 cm.

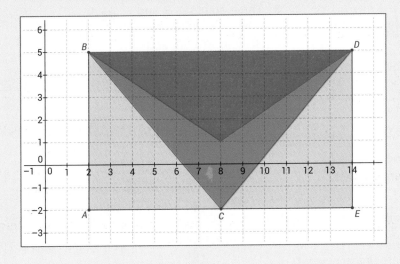

(i) Find, correct to the nearest cm², the amount of coloured material she will need for each section of the flag.

(ii) The budget for material is €70 and the material costs are as follows:

- Blue material 79 cents per 100 cm²

- Green material 64 cents per 100 cm²

- Red material 40 cents per 100 cm²

Does she have enough money for this design?

30. The graph below represents the total sales and total costs of a firm for selling a particular product.

(i) Find the slope of the 'Total sales' line.

Indicate which answer completes this sentence correctly:

The slope of this line gives us ...

(a) Total sales

(b) The selling price per unit

(c) The cost of selling 10,000 shirts

(ii) Find the equation of the 'Total sales' line.

(iii) Find the equation of the 'Total costs' line.

(iv) The break-even point is the level of production at which sales cover costs.

Find the break-even point from the graph, and verify your answer using algebraic methods.

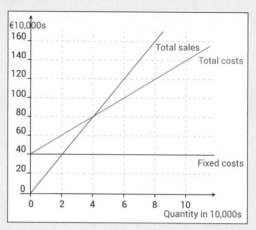

Exam Questions

1. The line l_1 in the diagram has slope 3 and y-intercept 2.

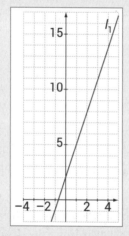

(a) Write down the equation of this line, in the form $y = mx + c$.

(b) On the diagram, draw and label the lines l_2 and l_3, where:

l_2 has slope 3 and y-intercept 7

l_3 has slope 1 and y-intercept 8

(c) On the diagram, draw and label the line l_4, which is perpendicular to l_1 and passes through the point $(0,4)$.

(d) Determine whether l_4 passes through the point $(27,-4)$.

NCCA Pre-Leaving Certificate Higher Level, Project Maths Paper 2, February 2010

2. The co-ordinates of three points A, B, and C are: $A(2,2)$, $B(6,-6)$, $C(-2,-3)$ (see diagram).

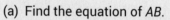
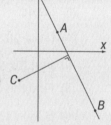

(a) Find the equation of AB.

(b) The line AB intersects the y-axis at D. Find the co-ordinates of D.

(c) Find the perpendicular distance from C to AB.

(d) Hence, find the area of the triangle ADC.

SEC Leaving Certificate Higher Level, Project Maths Sample Paper 2, 2010

3. Three points A, B, and C have co-ordinates: $A(-2,9)$, $B(6,-6)$ and $C(11,6)$.

The line l passes through B and has the equation $12x - 5y - 102 = 0$.

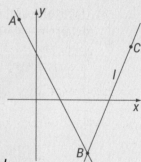

(a) Verify that C lies on l.

(b) Find the slope of AB, and hence, find $\tan(\angle ABC)$, as a fraction.

SEC Leaving Certificate Higher Level, Project Maths Paper 2, 2010

4. In the co-ordinate diagram shown, the lines j, k and l are parallel, and so are the lines m and n. The equations of four of the five lines are given in the table below.

Equation	Line
$x + 2y = -4$	
$2x - y = -4$	
$x + 2y = 8$	
$2x - y = 2$	

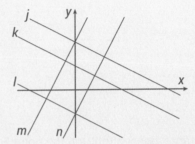

(a) Complete the table by matching four of the lines to their equations.

(b) Hence, insert scales on the x-axis and y-axis.

(c) Hence, find the equation of the remaining line, given that its x-intercept and y-intercept are both integers.

SEC Leaving Certificate Higher Level, Project Maths Paper 2, 2011

5. (a) Given the co-ordinates of the vertices of a quadrilateral $ABCD$, describe **three** different ways to determine, using co-ordinate geometry techniques, whether the quadrilateral is a parallelogram.

(b) Using **one** of the methods you described, determine whether the quadrilateral with vertices $(-4,-2)$, $(21,-5)$, $(8,7)$ and $(-17,10)$ is a parallelogram.

SEC Leaving Certificate Higher Level, Paper 2, 2012

6. The equations of six lines are given:

Line	Equation
h	$x = 3 - y$
i	$2x - 4y = 3$
k	$y = -\frac{1}{4}(2x - 7)$
l	$4x - 2y - 5 = 0$
m	$x + \sqrt{3}y - 10 = 0$
n	$\sqrt{3}x + y - 10 = 0$

(a) Complete the table below by matching each description given to one or more of the lines.

Description	Line(s)
A line with a slope of 2.	
A line which intersects the y-axis at $(0,-2\frac{1}{2})$.	
A line which makes equal intercepts on the axes.	
A line which makes an angle of 150° with the positive sense of the x-axis.	
Two lines which are perpendicular to each other.	

(b) Find the acute angle between the lines m and n.

SEC Leaving Certificate Higher Level, Paper 2, 2013

7. (a) Show that, for all $k \in R$, the point $P(4k - 2, 3k + 1)$ lies on the line $l_1: 3x - 4y + 10 = 0$.

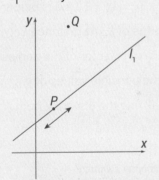

(b) The line l_2 passes through P and is perpendicular to l_1. Find the equation of l_2, in terms of k.

(c) Find the value of k for which l_2 passes through the point $Q(3,11)$.

(d) Hence, or otherwise, find the co-ordinates of the foot of the perpendicular from Q to l_1.

SEC Leaving Certificate Higher Level, Sample Paper 2, 2014

8. The line *RS* cuts the *x*-axis at the point *R* and the *y*-axis at the point *S*(0,10), as shown. The area of the triangle *ROS*, where *O* is the origin, is $\frac{125}{3}$.

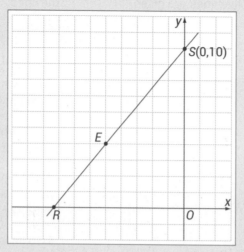

(a) Find the co-ordinates of *R*.

(b) Show that the point *E*(−5,4) is on the line *RS*.

(c) A second line *y* = *mx* + *c*, where *m* and *c* are positive constants, passes through the point *E* and again makes a triangle of area $\frac{125}{3}$ with the axes. Find the value of *m* and the value of *c*.

SEC Leaving Certificate Higher Level, Paper 2, 2014

9. (a) The co-ordinates of two points are *A*(4,−1) and *B*(7,*t*).

The line l_1: 3*x* − 4*y* − 12 = 0 is perpendicular to *AB*. Find the value of *t*.

(b) Find, in terms of *k*, the distance between the point *P*(10,*k*) and l_1.

(c) *P*(10,*k*) is on a bisector of the angles between the lines l_1 and l_2: 5*x* + 12*y* − 20 = 0.

(i) Find the possible values of *k*.

(ii) If *k* > 0, find the distance from *P* to l_1.

SEC Leaving Certificate Higher Level, Paper 2, 2015

Solutions and chapter summary available online

CO-ORDINATE GEOMETRY: THE LINE

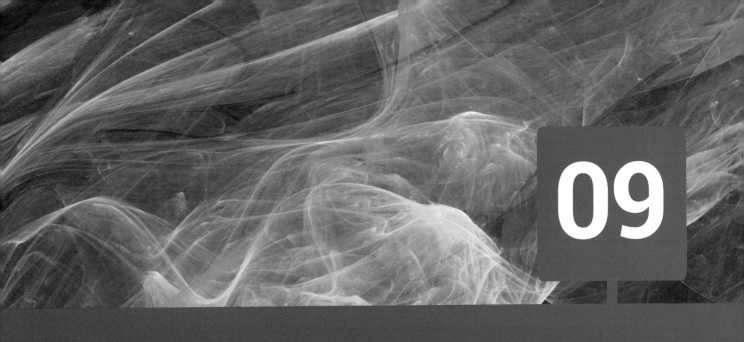

09

Co-ordinate Geometry: The Circle

 In this chapter you will learn to:

- Find the equation of a circle with centre (0,0) and radius length r

- Find the equation of a circle with centre (h,k) and radius length r

- Work with equations of the form $x^2 + y^2 + 2gx + 2fy + c = 0$

- Calculate the points of intersection of a line and a circle

- Prove that a line is a tangent to a circle

- Prove that a line does not intersect a circle

- Show whether a point is inside, outside or on a circle

- Find the equation of tangents to a circle

 You should remember...

- How to find the distance between two points

- How to find the midpoint of two points

- How to find the perpendicular distance of a point from a line

- How to solve quadratic equations

 Key words

- Equation of a circle
- Radius length
- Tangent
- Locus

The ancient Greeks believed that the **circle** was the perfect form, because circular forms occurred so frequently in nature. They also thought that the stars and planets travelled in circular paths around the universe.

> A circle is the set of all points in the plane that are equidistant from a fixed point, the centre. The distance from the centre to any point on the circle is called the radius length of the circle.

An interesting modern-day application of co-ordinate geometry of the circle is the mapping of 'great circle' routes. A great circle of a sphere is a circle that runs along the surface of the sphere so as to cut it into two equal halves. As the earth is almost spherical, we can draw imaginary great circles on the surface of the earth. The shortest route between any two points on the surface of a sphere will lie along a great circle. This is why intercontinental airlines fly along great circle routes – it minimises the distance they have to travel. On the map below we can see examples of three great circle routes: New York to Moscow, Moscow to Tokyo and New York to Tokyo.

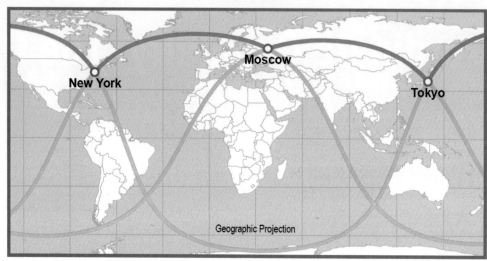

Geographic Projection

9.1 Circles with Centre (0,0) and Radius Length *r*

Consider a circle with centre *O*(0,0) and radius length *r*.

Let *P*(*x*,*y*) be the co-ordinates of any point on the circle.

Using the distance formula we get:

$$|OP| = \sqrt{(x - 0)^2 + (y - 0)^2}$$

$$r = \sqrt{x^2 + y^2}$$

Squaring both sides we get:

$$r^2 = x^2 + y^2$$

∴ $x^2 + y^2 = r^2$ is the equation of a circle with centre (0,0) and radius length *r*.

$$x^2 + y^2 = r^2$$

This formula does not appear in *Formulae and Tables* and should therefore be remembered by students.

Worked Example 9.1

Find the equation of the following circles:

(i) s_1: centre (0,0) and radius length 9   (ii) s_2: centre (0,0) and contains the point (2,3)

Solution

(i) $x^2 + y^2 = r^2$ Given: $r = 9$

$\Rightarrow x^2 + y^2 = 9^2$

$\therefore x^2 + y^2 = 81$ ....$\textcircled{s_1}$

(ii) **Radius length**

$r = \sqrt{(2-0)^2 + (3-0)^2}$

$r = \sqrt{4+9}$

$r = \sqrt{13}$

Equation

$x^2 + y^2 = r^2$

$\therefore x^2 + y^2 = 13$ ....$\textcircled{s_2}$

Worked Example 9.2

Find the centre and radius length of each of the following circles:

(i) $x^2 + y^2 = 169$ (ii) $16x^2 + 16y^2 = 25$

Solution

(i) $x^2 + y^2 = 169$

$\therefore x^2 + y^2 = 13^2$

This equation is of the form $x^2 + y^2 = r^2$.

Therefore, the centre of the circle is (0,0) and the radius length is 13.

(ii) $16x^2 + 16y^2 = 25$

$x^2 + y^2 = \dfrac{25}{16}$ (dividing across by 16)

$\therefore x^2 + y^2 = \left(\dfrac{5}{4}\right)^2$

This equation is of the form $x^2 + y^2 = r^2$.

Therefore, the centre of the circle is (0,0) and the radius length is $\dfrac{5}{4}$.

Worked Example 9.3

Find the equation of the circle, with centre (0,0), which has the line $2x - 3y - 6 = 0$ as a tangent.

Solution

Step 1   A useful approach is to visualise the question by sketching the line (by finding the intercepts) and drawing the circle with this line as tangent.

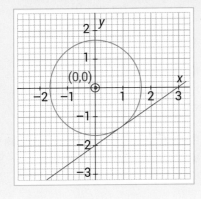

Step 2   We will use the following geometry theorem to find the equation:

The perpendicular distance from the centre of a circle to a tangent of the circle is equal to the radius length of the circle.

Radius length

$$r = \frac{|2(0) - 3(0) - 6|}{\sqrt{2^2 + (-3)^2}}$$

Line $2x - 3y - 6 = 0$ and point $(0,0)$

(using the formula for the perpendicular distance of a point from a line on page 19 of *Formulae and Tables*)

$$r = \frac{6}{\sqrt{13}}$$

Equation

$$x^2 + y^2 = \left(\frac{6}{\sqrt{13}}\right)^2$$

$$x^2 + y^2 = \frac{36}{13}$$

$$\therefore 13x^2 + 13y^2 = 36$$

Exercise 9.1

1. Write down the equation of the circle with centre $O(0,0)$ and radius length:

    (i) 5   (iv) 13   (vii) $\sqrt{3}$ (x) 1.8

    (ii) 8   (v) 17   (viii) $\frac{3}{4}$ (xi) $5\sqrt{3}$

    (iii) 1   (vi) $\sqrt{2}$ (ix) $\frac{1}{2}$ (xii) $3\sqrt{7}$

2. Write down the radius length of each of the following circles:

    (i) $x^2 + y^2 = 64$ (vi) $4x^2 + 4y^2 = 9$

    (ii) $x^2 + y^2 = 81$ (vii) $9x^2 + 9y^2 = 100$

    (iii) $x^2 + y^2 = 4$ (viii) $25x^2 + 25y^2 = 49$

    (iv) $x^2 + y^2 = 49$ (ix) $64x^2 + 64y^2 = 400$

    (v) $x^2 + y^2 = 3$ (x) $3x^2 + 3y^2 = 7$

3. Find the distance from $O(0,0)$ to $B(-6,-8)$ and, hence, write down the equation of the circle with centre O and which contains the point B.

4. A circle with centre $(0,0)$ contains the point $(7,24)$.

    (i) Find the radius length of the circle.

    (ii) Hence, write its equation in the form $x^2 + y^2 = r^2$.

5. The line segment joining $A(-3,4)$ and $B(3,-4)$ is the diameter of a circle.

    (i) Find the centre of this circle.

    (ii) Find the radius length of this circle.

    (iii) Write down the equation of this circle.

6. The line segment joining $A(-6,2)$ and $B(6,-2)$ is the diameter of a circle.

    (i) Find the centre of this circle.

    (ii) Find the radius length of this circle.

    (iii) Write down the equation of this circle.

    (iv) Draw a sketch of the circle.

    (v) Using the formula $C = 2\pi r$, find the circumference of this circle.

    (vi) Using the formula $A = \pi r^2$, find the area of this circle. Give your answer correct to two decimal places.

    (vii) Find the area of the square in which this circle can just be inscribed.

7. Find the area and circumference of each of the following circles.

    Give your answers in terms of π, m, n and a.

    (i) $4x^2 + 4y^2 = 9$

    (ii) $x^2 + y^2 = \frac{1}{a^2}$, $(a > 0)$

    (iii) $x^2 + y^2 = \frac{m^4}{n^4}$, $(m, n > 0)$

    (iv) $x^2 + y^2 = a^2 + 2a + 1$, $(a > 0)$

8. Find the equation of the circle that has centre $(0,0)$ and that touches the line $4x - 3y = 25$ at one point only.

9. Find the equation of the circle that has centre $(0,0)$ and that touches the line $x - 3y - 9 = 0$ at one point only.

10. Find the equation of the circle that has centre (0,0) and that has the line $x - 4y - 1 = 0$ as a tangent.

11. A circle c has equation $x^2 + y^2 = 5$.

   (i) Write down the equation of the circle k, which has its centre at the origin and whose area is 25 times greater than the area of c.

   (ii) If the point $P(t,-2)$ is on k, find the value of t, where $t \in N$.

12.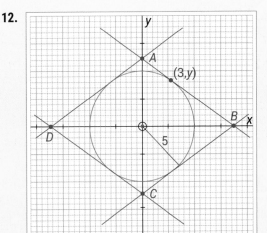

All lines drawn are tangents to the circle.

   (i) Find the value of y.

   (ii) Hence, find the area of the parallelogram $ABCD$.

9.2 Circles with Centre (h,k) and Radius Length r

Consider a circle whose centre is (h,k) and whose radius length is r.

The distance between any point (x,y) on this circle and the centre (h,k) can be expressed using the distance formula:

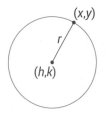

$$r = \sqrt{(x - h)^2 + (y - k)^2}$$

Squaring both sides we get:

$$r^2 = (x - h)^2 + (y - k)^2$$

$\therefore$ $(x - h)^2 + (y - k)^2 = r^2$ is the equation of a circle with centre (h,k) and radius length r.

$(x - h)^2 + (y - k)^2 = r^2$

This formula appears on page 19 of *Formulae and Tables*.

Worked Example 9.4

Find the centre and radius length of the circle $(x - 5)^2 + (y + 3)^2 = 25$.

Solution

Given equation: $(x - 5)^2 + (y + 3)^2 = 25$

General equation: $(x - h)^2 + (y - k)^2 = r^2$

Comparing: $-h = -5$, $-k = 3$, $r^2 = 25$

$\Rightarrow h = 5$, $k = -3$, $r = 5$

$\therefore$ The centre of the circle is $(5,-3)$ and the radius length is 5.

Worked Example 9.5

Find the centre and radius length of the circle:

$$(x + 2)^2 + y^2 = 11$$

Solution

Given equation: $\qquad (x + 2)^2 + y^2 = 11$

$\therefore (x + 2)^2 + (y - 0)^2 = 11$

General equation: $(x - h)^2 + (y - k)^2 = r^2$

Comparing: $\quad -h = 2, \quad -k = -0, \quad r^2 = 11$

$\Rightarrow h = -2, \quad k = 0, \quad r = \sqrt{11}$

$\therefore$ The centre of the circle is $(-2, 0)$ and the radius length is $\sqrt{11}$.

> If the equation is in the form $(x - h)^2 + (y - k)^2 = r^2$, change the signs of the numbers in brackets to get the centre co-ordinates.
>
> E.g. $(x - 2)^2 + (y + 3)^2 = 50$
>
> The centre of this circle is $(2, -3)$.

Worked Example 9.6

The circle shown has a diameter with endpoints $(2, -3)$ and $(6, -8)$. Find:

(i) The centre of the circle

(ii) The radius length of the circle

(iii) The equation of the circle

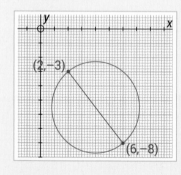

Solution

(i) The centre of the circle is the midpoint of the endpoints of the diameter.

$$\text{Midpoint} = \left(\frac{x_1 + x_2}{2}, \frac{y_1 + y_2}{2} \right)$$

$$\text{Centre} = \left(\frac{2 + 6}{2}, \frac{-3 - 8}{2} \right)$$

$$= \left(\frac{8}{2}, \frac{-11}{2} \right)$$

$$\therefore \text{Centre} = \left(4, \frac{-11}{2} \right)$$

(ii) The radius of the circle is the distance from an endpoint of a diameter to the centre of the circle.

$$\text{Distance} = \sqrt{(x_2 - x_1)^2 + (y_2 - y_1)^2} \qquad \text{Points } (2, -3) \text{ and } \left(4, -\frac{11}{2} \right)$$

$$r = \sqrt{(4 - 2)^2 + \left(-\frac{11}{2} + 3 \right)^2}$$

$$r = \sqrt{4 + \frac{25}{4}} = \sqrt{\frac{41}{4}} \quad \textbf{or} \quad \frac{\sqrt{41}}{2} \qquad \text{(Leave in surd form.)}$$

(iii) Equation:

$$(x - h)^2 + (y - k)^2 = r^2 \qquad \text{Centre} \left(4, -\frac{11}{2} \right), r = \sqrt{\frac{41}{4}}$$

$$(x - 4)^2 + \left(y + \frac{11}{2} \right)^2 = \frac{41}{4}$$

Intercepts on the *x*-Axis and *y*-Axis

The points where a circle crosses the *x*-axis are called the *x*-intercepts of the circle, and the points where a circle crosses the *y*-axis are called the *y*-intercepts of the circle.

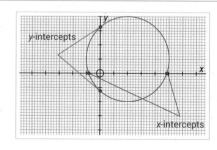

The co-ordinates of points on the *x*-axis are always of the form (*a*,0) and the co-ordinates of points on the *y*-axis are always of the form (0,*b*). Hence:

- We let **y = 0** in the equation of a circle and solve for *x* to find the co-ordinates of the **x-intercepts**.
- We let **x = 0** in the equation of a circle and solve for *y* to find the co-ordinates of the **y-intercepts**.

Worked Example 9.7

Find the *x*-intercepts and the *y*-intercepts of the circle $(x + 3)^2 + (y - 2)^2 = 13$.

Solution

x-intercepts

Let *y* = 0 in the equation of the circle.

$$(x + 3)^2 + (0 - 2)^2 = 13$$
$$(x + 3)^2 + 4 = 13$$
$$(x + 3)^2 = 9$$
$$x + 3 = \pm 3$$
$$x = 0 \quad \text{or} \quad x = -6$$

Therefore, the co-ordinates of the *x*-intercepts are (0,0) and (−6,0).

y-intercepts

Let *x* = 0 in the equation of the circle.

$$(0 + 3)^2 + (y - 2)^2 = 13$$
$$9 + (y - 2)^2 = 13$$
$$(y - 2)^2 = 4$$
$$y - 2 = \pm 2$$
$$y = 4 \quad \text{or} \quad y = 0$$

Therefore, the co-ordinates of the *y*-intercepts are (0,4) and (0,0).

Worked Example 9.8

Find the equation of the circle having the lines $y + 4 = 0$ and $y - 2 = 0$ as tangents and with its centre lying on the line $2x + y = 4$.

Solution

Sketch the lines $y = 2$, $y = -4$ and $2x + y = 4$.

The centre of the circle lies along the line $y = -1$ and also along the line $2x + y = 4$ (given).

Therefore, the centre lies on the intersection of the lines $y = -1$ and $2x + y = 4$.

Substituting $y = -1$ into $2x + y = 4$ gives:

$$2x + (-1) = 4$$
$$2x - 1 = 4$$
$$2x = 5$$
$$x = \frac{5}{2}$$

∴ The centre of the circle is $\left(\frac{5}{2}, -1\right)$.

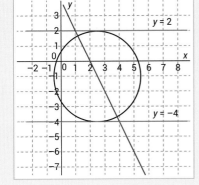

The radius length of the circle is the perpendicular distance from $\left(\frac{5}{2}, -1\right)$ to $y = 2$.

∴ $r = 3$

∴ The equation of the circle is given by:

$$\left(x - \frac{5}{2}\right)^2 + (y + 1)^2 = 3^2$$
$$\therefore \left(x - \frac{5}{2}\right)^2 + (y + 1)^2 = 9$$

Exercise 9.2

1. Find the centre and radius length of each of the following circles:

   (i) $(x - 5)^2 + (y - 2)^2 = 81$

   (ii) $(x + 2)^2 + (y + 5)^2 = 49$

   (iii) $(x - 1)^2 + (y + 3)^2 = 100$

   (iv) $x^2 + (y - 8)^2 = 49$

   (v) $x^2 + y^2 = 100$

   (vi) $x^2 + (y + 3)^2 = 5$

2. Find the equations of the following circles:

   (i) Centre = (3,–5), radius length = 2

   (ii) Centre = (–8,1), radius length = 4

   (iii) Centre = (0,7), radius length = 4

   (iv) Centre = (0,0), radius length = $\sqrt{5}$

   (v) Centre = (–3,–8), radius length = $\frac{1}{2}$

   (vi) Centre = $\left(\frac{1}{2},-\frac{1}{4}\right)$, radius length = 12

   (vii) Centre = (–1,6), radius length = $\frac{7}{2}$

   (viii) Centre = $\left(-2,-\frac{3}{4}\right)$, radius length = $3\sqrt{2}$

3. A circle s with centre (1,1), and which contains the point (5,6), is shown below.

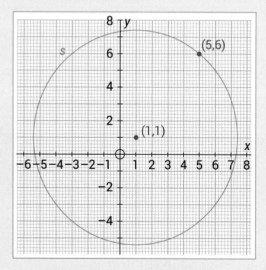

   (i) Find the radius length of s.

   (ii) Write down the equation of s.

4. A circle t with centre (–2,–1), and which contains the point (2,–3), is shown below.

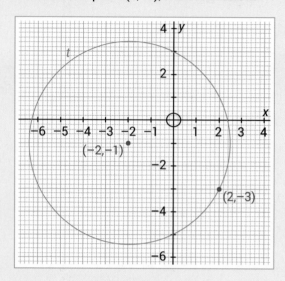

   (i) Find the radius length of t.

   (ii) Write down the equation of t.

5. The circle z shown in the diagram has a diameter with endpoints (–1,4) and (3,–2).

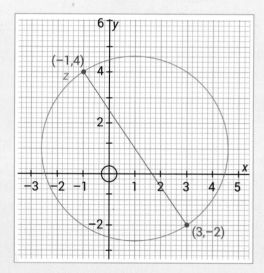

   (i) Find the centre of z.

   (ii) Find the radius length of z.

   (iii) Write down the equation of z.

6. For each of the following circles, find the co-ordinates of the x-intercepts:

   (i) $(x - 2)^2 + (y + 3)^2 = 34$

   (ii) $(x + 3)^2 + (y - 2)^2 = 40$

   (iii) $(x + 5)^2 + (y - 8)^2 = 164$

   (iv) $(x + 1)^2 + (y - 1)^2 = 50$

7. For each of the following circles, find the co-ordinates of the y-intercepts:

   (i) $(x - 3)^2 + (y - 4)^2 = 90$

   (ii) $(x + 2)^2 + (y - 5)^2 = 104$

   (iii) $(x - 6)^2 + (y + 1)^2 = 72$

   (iv) $(x - 1)^2 + (y + 1)^2 = 10$

8. Find the equation of the circle with centre $(-3,2)$ and having the line $x - y + 4 = 0$ as a tangent.

9. Find the equation of the circle having the lines $x + 1 = 0$ and $x - 3 = 0$ as tangents and with its centre lying on the line $y = 3$.

10. Find the equation of the circle with centre $(5,-2)$ and having the line $3x - y + 4 = 0$ as a tangent.

11. The lines k: $2x + 3y - 6 = 0$ and l: $x + \frac{3}{2}y + 12 = 0$ are tangents to the circle s.

    s touches k on the y-axis.

    (i) Sketch k, l and s.

    (ii) Find the equation of s.

12. The centre of a circle s is in the second quadrant. s touches both the x-axis and the y-axis at the points P and Q, respectively. s has a radius length of $5\sqrt{2}$.

    Find the equation of s.

13. The diagram shows four circles, each of radius length 5.

    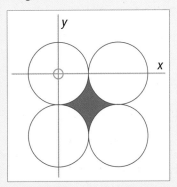

    (i) Find the equation of the circle whose centre lies in the fourth quadrant.

    (ii) Calculate the area of the shaded region. Explain your reasoning.

9.3 Equations of the Form $x^2 + y^2 + 2gx + 2fy + c = 0$

Consider a circle with centre (h,k) and radius length r. The equation of this circle is $(x - h)^2 + (y - k)^2 = r^2$.

Expanding both brackets and simplifying we get:

$x^2 - 2hx + h^2 + y^2 - 2ky + k^2 = r^2$

$x^2 + y^2 - 2hx - 2ky + h^2 + k^2 - r^2 = 0$ (rearranging terms)

Compare this equation form with:

$x^2 + y^2 + 2gx + 2fy + c = 0$

If we assume that these two equations represent the same circle, then:

$-2h = 2g \qquad -2k = 2f \qquad h^2 + k^2 - r^2 = c$

$\Rightarrow h = -g \qquad \Rightarrow k = -f \qquad \Rightarrow g^2 + f^2 - r^2 = c$

$\qquad\qquad\qquad\qquad\qquad\qquad \Rightarrow r^2 = g^2 + f^2 - c$

$\qquad\qquad\qquad\qquad\qquad\qquad \Rightarrow r = \sqrt{g^2 + f^2 - c}$ (as $r > 0$)

$\therefore x^2 + y^2 + 2gx + 2fy + c = 0$ represents a circle with centre, $(-g,-f)$ and radius length $\sqrt{g^2 + f^2 - c}$.

$x^2 + y^2 + 2gx + 2fy + c = 0$ represents a circle with:

- Centre $(-g,-f)$
- Radius length $\sqrt{g^2 + f^2 - c}$

This formula appears on page 19 of *Formulae and Tables*.

Worked Example 9.9

Find the centre and radius length of the circle $x^2 + y^2 - 4x - 6y - 12 = 0$.

Solution

Comparing: $x^2 + y^2 + 2gx + 2fy + c = 0$

and: $x^2 + y^2 - 4x - 6y - 12 = 0$

we get: $2g = -4$ and $2f = -6$

$\Rightarrow g = -2$ and $f = -3$

$\Rightarrow (-g,-f) = (2,3)$

∴ The co-ordinates of the centre are (2,3).

Radius length $= \sqrt{g^2 + f^2 - c}$

$= \sqrt{(-2)^2 + (-3)^2 - (-12)}$

$= \sqrt{25}$

∴ Radius length = 5

> **Quick method to find the co-ordinates of the centre:**
> (−half x-coefficient, −half y-coefficient)
>
> For the example shown:
>
> Centre $= \left(-\dfrac{1}{2}(-4), -\dfrac{1}{2}(-6) \right)$
>
> $= (2, 3)$

Worked Example 9.10

A circle has centre (4,−2) and radius length 5. Find the equation of this circle in the form $x^2 + y^2 + 2gx + 2fy + c = 0$.

Solution

Method 1

$(x - h)^2 + (y - k)^2 = r^2$

$(x - 4)^2 + (y + 2)^2 = 5^2$

$x^2 - 8x + 16 + y^2 + 4y + 4 = 25$

∴ $x^2 + y^2 - 8x + 4y - 5 = 0$

Method 2

$x^2 + y^2 + 2gx + 2fy + c = 0$

$(-g,-f) = (4,-2)$

$\Rightarrow g = -4$ and $f = 2$

$r = \sqrt{g^2 + f^2 - c} = 5$

$\Rightarrow g^2 + f^2 - c = 25$

$(-4)^2 + (2)^2 - c = 25$

$16 + 4 - c = 25$

$20 - c = 25$

$c = -5$

∴ $x^2 + y^2 - 8x + 4y - 5 = 0$

9.4 Points Inside, Outside or On a Circle

Consider the circle $(x - h)^2 + (y - k)^2 = r^2$ with centre (h,k) and radius length r.

This equation form comes from the distance formula

$$\sqrt{(x - h)^2 + (y - k)^2} = r$$

where (x,y) is any point on the circle.

If (x_1,y_1) lies inside the circle, then:

$$\sqrt{(x_1 - h)^2 + (y_1 - k)^2} < r \quad \Leftrightarrow \quad (x_1 - h)^2 + (y_1 - k)^2 < r^2$$

If (x_1,y_1) lies outside the circle, then:

$$\sqrt{(x_1 - h)^2 + (y_1 - k)^2} > r \quad \Leftrightarrow \quad (x_1 - h)^2 + (y_1 - k)^2 > r^2$$

Of course, if (x_1,y_1) lies on the circle, then:

$$\sqrt{(x_1 - h)^2 + (y_1 - k)^2} = r \quad \Leftrightarrow \quad (x_1 - h)^2 + (y_1 - k)^2 = r^2$$

> ⇔ means 'is equivalent to'.

Worked Example 9.11

(a) Investigate if the points (7,–5) and (8,–6) are outside, inside or on the following circle:

$$(x - 4)^2 + (y + 1)^2 = 25$$

(b) Find the range of values of $t \in R$, such that (7,t) lies inside the circle:

$$(x - 4)^2 + (y + 1)^2 = 25$$

Solution

(a) $(x - 4)^2 + (y + 1)^2 = 25$

Substitute (7,–5) into the left-hand side of the equation.

Is $(7 - 4)^2 + (-5 + 1)^2 = 25$?

$$(3)^2 + (-4)^2 = 25$$

$$9 + 16 = 25$$

$$25 = 25 \quad \text{True}$$

Therefore, the point (7,–5) is **on** the circle.

Substitute (8,–6) into the left-hand side of the equation.

Is $(8 - 4)^2 + (-6 + 1)^2 = 25$?

$$(4)^2 + (-5)^2 = 25$$

$$16 + 25 = 25$$

$$41 = 25 \quad \text{False}$$

$$41 > 25$$

Therefore, the point (8,–6) is **outside** the circle.

(b) Let $(7 - 4)^2 + (t + 1)^2 < 25$.

$$(3)^2 + (t + 1)^2 < 25$$

$$9 + (t + 1)^2 < 25$$

$$(t + 1)^2 < 16$$

$$-4 < t + 1 < 4$$

$$\therefore -5 < t < 3, t \in R$$

Worked Example 9.12

Investigate if the point (5,4) lies inside, outside or on the circle $x^2 + y^2 + 2x - 6y - 15 = 0$.

Solution

Step 1

Write the equation in the form $(x - h)^2 + (y - k)^2 = r^2$:

$$x^2 + y^2 + 2x - 6y - 15 = 0$$

$$x^2 + 2x + y^2 - 6y - 15 = 0 \quad \text{(Group together } x\text{-terms and } y\text{-terms.)}$$

$$x^2 + 2x + 1 + y^2 - 6y + 9 - 15 = 1 + 9 \quad \text{(Complete the squares.)}$$

$$(x + 1)^2 + (y - 3)^2 = 10 + 15$$

$$(x + 1)^2 + (y - 3)^2 = 25$$

Step 2

Substitute (5,4) into the modified equation.

Is $(5 + 1)^2 + (4 - 3)^2 = 25$?

$$(6)^2 + (1)^2 = 25$$

$$37 = 25 \quad \text{False}$$

$$37 > 25$$

Therefore, the point (5,4) is **outside** the circle.

Alternative Method

If the equation of a circle is of the form $x^2 + y^2 + 2gx + 2fy + c = 0$, then it can be shown that the point (x_1, y_1) lies:

(i)   Inside the circle if $x_1^2 + y_1^2 + 2gx_1 + 2fy_1 + c < 0$

(ii) Outside the circle if $x_1^2 + y_1^2 + 2gx_1 + 2fy_1 + c > 0$

(iii) On the circle if $x_1^2 + y_1^2 + 2gx_1 + 2fy_1 + c = 0$

$(5)^2 + (4)^2 + 2(5) - 6(4) - 15 = 12 > 0$; therefore, the point $(5,4)$ is **outside** the circle.

Exercise 9.3

1. Find the centre and radius length of each of these circles:

   (i) $x^2 + y^2 - 4x + 6y - 3 = 0$

   (ii) $x^2 + y^2 - 2x - 2y + 1 = 0$

   (iii) $x^2 + y^2 + 2x + 8y + 8 = 0$

   (iv) $x^2 + y^2 + 10x - 8y - 8 = 0$

   (v) $9x^2 + 9y^2 - 12x + 18y + 4 = 0$

   (vi) $x^2 + y^2 - 6x - 7 = 0$

   (vii) $x^2 + y^2 + 10x - 6y + 21 = 0$

   (viii) $y^2 = -x(x - 1)$

   (ix) $x^2 + y^2 + 10y = 0$

   (x) $2x^2 + 2y^2 + 6x - 14y - 3 = 0$

   (xi) $9x^2 + 9y^2 - 24x - 12y + 11 = 0$

   (xii) $9x^2 + 9y^2 - 6x + 18y + 1 = 0$

2. Write down the equation of each of the following circles, giving each equation in the form $x^2 + y^2 + 2gx + 2fy + c = 0$:

Centre	Radius Length
(2,3)	4
(−1,7)	5
(0,3)	2
$\left(-4, \frac{1}{2}\right)$	9
(6,0)	$\sqrt{11}$
(−1.5,−2)	7
(−2,−1)	$\sqrt{3}$

3. Complete the table below by stating whether the points lie inside, outside or on the circle. Show all your workings.

c_1: $(x - 2)^2 + (y - 3)^2 = 9$	$T(2,1)$	Inside
c_2: $(x + 3)^2 + (y - 1)^2 = 25$	$U(0,5)$	
c_3: $x^2 + y^2 = 25$	$V(4,4)$	
c_4: $x^2 + y^2 = 26$	$W(5,1)$	
c_5: $(x - 2)^2 + (y - 3)^2 = 49$	$X(0,0)$	
c_6: $x^2 + y^2 - 4x + 6y - 3 = 0$	$Y(-2,-3)$	
c_7: $x^2 + y^2 - 6x - 7 = 0$	$Z(3,-6)$	

4. For each of the following circles, write down the co-ordinates of the x-intercept:

   (i) $x^2 + y^2 - 4x - 10y + 3 = 0$

   (ii) $x^2 + y^2 + 10x - 16y - 75 = 0$

   (iii) $x^2 + y^2 - 2x - 2y - 3 = 0$

   (iv) $x^2 + y^2 - 2x - 8y - 35 = 0$

5. For each of the following circles, write down the co-ordinates of the y-intercept:

   (i) $x^2 + y^2 - 2x - 4y - 21 = 0$

   (ii) $x^2 + y^2 + 4x - 6y + 5 = 0$

   (iii) $x^2 + y^2 - 6x - 8y = 0$

   (iv) $x^2 + y^2 - 2x + 2y - 8 = 0$

6. The circle $x^2 + y^2 + ax - 2y - 15 = 0$ contains the point $P(-6,5)$. Find the value of a.

7. The circle $x^2 + y^2 - a^2x + ay - 22 = 0$ contains the point $Q(2,4)$. Find the value of a.

8. The circle $x^2 + y^2 + ax + by + 6 = 0$ contains the points $P(1,1)$ and $Q(3,2)$. Find the value of a and the value of b.

9. The circle $x^2 + y^2 - 2x - my - n = 0$ contains the points $A(2,1)$ and $B(-1,2)$.
Find the value of m and the value of n.

10. A circle touches both the x-axis and y-axis.
It has a radius length of 4.

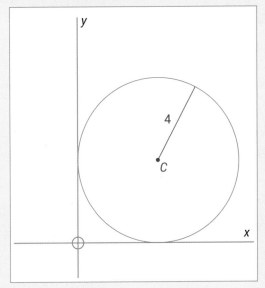

   (i) Write down the co-ordinates of C, the centre of the circle.

   (ii) Hence, find the equation of the circle, writing your answer in the form $x^2 + y^2 + 2gx + 2fy + c = 0$.

11. Find the range of values of a for which the point $P(a,3)$ lies inside the circle $x^2 + y^2 + 6x - 2y - 6 = 0$.
Give your answer in the form $-n - 2\sqrt{n} < a < -n + 2\sqrt{n}$.

12. Show that the point $Q(5,a)$ lies outside the circle $x^2 + y^2 - 5x - y + 4 = 0$, for all $a \in R$.

13. Find the values of b for which the line $5x + by = 169$ is a tangent to $x^2 + y^2 = 169$.

   For $b > 0$, show that this line is also a tangent to the circle $x^2 + y^2 - 20x - 48y + 507 = 0$.

14. Find the value of $t \in R$ such that $(1,t)$ lies on the circle $x^2 + y^2 + 4x - 8y + 11 = 0$.

15. Find the value of $k \in R$ such that $(-2,1)$ lies on the circle $x^2 + y^2 + 3x - ky + 5 = 0$.

16. Find the range of values of $t \in R$ such that $(5, t)$ lies inside the circle $(x - 3)^2 + (y + 2)^2 = 29$.

17. Find the range of values of $k \in R$ such that $(7, k)$ lies outside the circle $(x - 4)^2 + (y + 3)^2 = 45$.

9.5 Intersection of a Line and a Circle

If a line and a circle are drawn on the plane, then the line and the circle may meet at two points or at one point, or they may not meet at all. This is illustrated in the diagrams below.

Two points of intersection

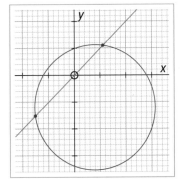

One point of intersection

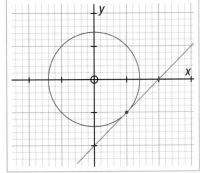

No points of intersection

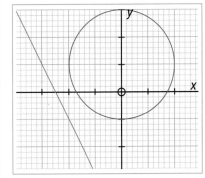

A **tangent** to a circle touches the circle at one point and is perpendicular to the radius that joins the centre of the circle to the point of tangency.

Worked Example 9.13

Find the co-ordinates of the points of intersection of the line l: $5x + y = 24$ and the circle s: $x^2 + y^2 - 4x - 2y - 8 = 0$.

The line is a linear equation and the circle is a non-linear equation. The technique for solving between a linear equation and non-linear equation is covered in Book 1 Chapter 2.

Solution

Step 1 Linear	We start with the linear equation. $5x + y = 24$ $\Rightarrow y = 24 - 5x$ (It is easier to make y the subject of the equation.)
Step 2 Substitution **Always substitute from the linear equation into the equation of the circle.**	$x^2 + y^2 - 4x - 2y - 8 = 0$ Substitute $y = 24 - 5x$ into this equation. $x^2 + (24 - 5x)^2 - 4x - 2(24 - 5x) - 8 = 0$ $x^2 + 576 - 240x + 25x^2 - 4x - 48 + 10x - 8 = 0$ $26x^2 - 234x + 520 = 0$ (Divide by 26.) $x^2 - 9x + 20 = 0$
Step 3 Solving for one variable	$x^2 - 9x + 20 = 0$ $(x - 4)(x - 5) = 0$ $x - 4 = 0$ **OR** $x - 5 = 0$ $\quad x = 4$ **OR** $\quad\quad x = 5$
Step 4 Solving for the other variable. **Always substitute back into the linear. This will avoid obtaining an incorrect solution.**	For the two values of x, now find the corresponding values of y. <table><tr><td colspan="2">$y = 24 - 5x$</td></tr><tr><td>If $x = 4$:</td><td>If $x = 5$:</td></tr><tr><td>$y = 24 - 5(4)$</td><td>$y = 24 - 5(5)$</td></tr><tr><td>$y = 24 - 20$</td><td>$y = 24 - 25$</td></tr><tr><td>$y = 4$</td><td>$y = -1$</td></tr></table>
Step 5 Write answer	The co-ordinates of the points of intersection are $(4,4)$ and $(5,-1)$. Note: Since there are two points of intersection, the line cannot be a tangent to the circle.

Worked Example 9.14

Show that the line $3x - 4y + 10 = 0$ is a tangent to the circle $x^2 + y^2 - 10x = 0$.

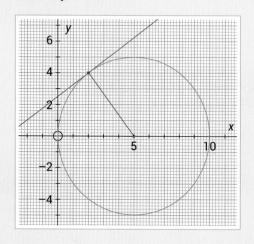

Solution

If the line is a tangent to the circle, then the perpendicular distance from the centre of the circle to the line will be equal to the length of the radius.

Centre $(5,0)$, $r = \sqrt{(5)^2 + (0)^2 - 0} = 5$

Distance from the centre of the circle to the line

$$= \frac{|3(5) - 4(0) + 10|}{\sqrt{3^2 + (-4)^2}}$$

$$= \frac{25}{\sqrt{25}}$$

$$= 5$$

$$= \text{radius length}$$

Therefore, the line is a tangent to the circle.

Worked Example 9.15

Show that the line $x + y = 7$ does not intersect the circle $x^2 + y^2 = 16$.

Solution

Method 1

$x + y = 7$

$\quad y = 7 - x$

Substitute for y into the equation of the circle.

$x^2 + (7 - x)^2 = 16$

$x^2 + 49 - 14x + x^2 = 16$

$2x^2 - 14x + 33 = 0$

Now find the value of the discriminant of this equation.

$b^2 - 4ac = (-14)^2 - 4(2)(33)$

$\quad\quad\quad = -68$

$\quad\quad\quad < 0$

∴ No real solutions to the equation

Therefore, the line $x + y = 7$ does not intersect the circle $x^2 + y^2 = 16$.

Method 2

Find the centre and radius length of the circle $x^2 + y^2 = 16$.

Centre $(0,0)$

Radius $= \sqrt{16}$

$\quad\quad = 4$

Find the perpendicular distance from $(0,0)$ to the line $x + y = 7$.

$\quad\quad x + y = 7$

$\Rightarrow x + y - 7 = 0$

Distance from centre $(0,0)$ to line $x + y - 7 = 0$

$$\frac{|1(0) + 1(0) - 7|}{\sqrt{1^2 + 1^2}} = \frac{7}{\sqrt{2}}$$

$$\approx 4.95$$

$$> 4$$

The distance from the centre to the line is greater than the radius length.

∴ No points of intersection

Worked Example 9.16

Show that the line $l: 5x - y - 20 = 0$ does not intersect the circle $s: x^2 + y^2 - 2x - 2y - 2 = 0$.

Solution

If the line does not intersect the circle, then the perpendicular distance from the centre of the circle to the line will be greater than the length of the radius.

$\quad\quad$ Centre $= (-g, -f)$

$\Rightarrow$ Centre $= (1,1)$

Radius length

$\quad\quad r = \sqrt{g^2 + f^2 - c}$

$\quad \therefore r = \sqrt{1 + 1 + 2} = 2$

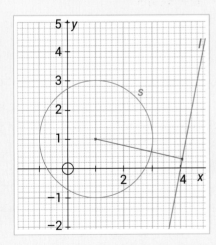

Perpendicular distance

$$\text{Distance from centre to } l = \frac{|5(1) - (1) - 20|}{\sqrt{(5)^2 + (-1)^2}} = \frac{16}{\sqrt{26}} \approx 3.14$$

The distance from the centre to l is greater than the length of the radius; therefore, the line does not intersect the circle.

Locus of a Point

A point A, which moves so that its distance from another fixed point C is always constant, traces out a circle. A mathematician would say that the **locus** of the point A is a circle.

A **locus** is the path traced out by a moving point, satisfying certain given conditions.

Worked Example 9.17

$A(-12,0)$, $B(0,0)$ and $P(x,y)$ are three points. If $|AP| = 5|BP|$, then show that the locus of P is a circle.

Solution

$$|AP| = 5|BP|$$
$$\sqrt{(x+12)^2 + (y-0)^2} = 5\sqrt{(x-0)^2 + (y-0)^2}$$
$$(x+12)^2 + y^2 = 25(x^2 + y^2) \quad \text{(Square both sides.)}$$
$$x^2 + 24x + 144 + y^2 = 25x^2 + 25y^2$$
$$24x^2 + 24y^2 - 24x - 144 = 0$$
$$x^2 + y^2 - x - 6 = 0 \quad \text{(Divide by 24.)}$$

This equation is of the form $x^2 + y^2 + 2gx + 2fy + c = 0$.

Therefore, this is the equation of a circle with centre $\left(\dfrac{1}{2}, 0\right)$ and radius length $\sqrt{\left(\dfrac{1}{2}\right)^2 + (0)^2 + 6} = \sqrt{6.25} = 2.5$.

∴ The locus of P is a circle.

Exercise 9.4

1. Find the points of intersection of the line $x + y = 4$ and the circle $x^2 + y^2 = 10$.

2. Find the points of intersection of the line $x - y = 1$ and the circle $x^2 + y^2 = 13$.

3. l is the line $2x + y - 3 = 0$ and s is the circle $x^2 + y^2 = 26$. Find the points of intersection of l and s.

4. m is the line $x + 7y - 4 = 0$ and n is the circle $x^2 + y^2 = 10$. Find the points of intersection of m and n.

5. Find the co-ordinates of the point or points of intersection of the following lines and circles:

   (i) l: $x + y = 3$ s: $x^2 + y^2 = 5$

   (ii) l: $x - y + 1 = 0$ s: $x^2 + y^2 - 2x + 2y - 3 = 0$

   (iii) l: $x + y - 8 = 0$ s: $x^2 + y^2 + 4x - 8y + 2 = 0$

   (iv) l: $5x + y = 24$ s: $x^2 + y^2 - 4x - 2y - 8 = 0$

   (v) l: $3x + 4y = 25$ s: $x^2 + y^2 = 25$

   (vi) l: $2x + y = 5$ s: $x^2 + y^2 = 5$

   (vii) l: $4x + 5y + 14 = 0$ s: $x^2 + y^2 + 4x - 8y - 17 = 0$

   (viii) l: $2x + 5y = 7$ s: $x^2 + y^2 - 3x + y = 0$

6. Show that the line $x + y = 5$ does not intersect the circle $x^2 + y^2 = 2$.

7. Show that the line $12x + 5y = 169$ is a tangent to the circle $x^2 + y^2 = 169$.

8. Show that the line $x + y = 7$ is a tangent to the circle $x^2 + y^2 - 10x - 12y + 53 = 0$.

9. $A(-3,1)$, $B(0,-5)$ and $P(x,y)$ are three points.

  (i) If $|AP| = 2|BP|$, prove that x and y satisfy the equation $x^2 + y^2 - 2x + 14y + 30 = 0$.

  (ii) Say why this equation represents a circle.

  (iii) Find the centre and radius length of this circle.

10. $A(-3,1)$, $B(0,-5)$ and $P(x,y)$ are three points.

  (i) If $|AP| = 3|BP|$, prove that x and y satisfy the equation $8x^2 + 8y^2 - 6x + 92y + 215 = 0$.

  (ii) Say why this equation represents a circle.

  (iii) Find the centre and radius length of this circle.

11. $A(-3,1)$ and $B(0,-5)$ are two points.
A point $P(x,y)$ moves so that $|AP| = \frac{1}{2}|BP|$.

  (i) Show that the locus of P is a circle.

  (ii) Find the centre and radius length of this circle.

12. A circle s has equation $(x - 2)^2 + (y - 3)^2 = 9$.
$A(-1,3)$ and $B(5,3)$ are the co-ordinates of two points.

  (i) Show that the x-axis is a tangent to s.

  (ii) Prove that $[AB]$ is a diameter of s.

  (iii) If a point $P(x,y)$ moves so that $|AP| = \frac{1}{3}|BP|$, show that the locus of P is a circle. Label this circle t.

  (iv) Find the centre and radius length of t.

  (v) Prove that t does not intersect the x-axis.

  (vi) Using the same axes and scales draw s and t.

13. Find the values of k for which $x + 4y + k = 0$ is a tangent to $x^2 + y^2 - 2x + 2y - 15 = 0$.

9.6 Tangents and Touching Circles

In this section, you will learn:

(1) how to find the equation of a tangent to a point **on** the circle

(2) how to find the equation of a tangent from a point **outside** the circle

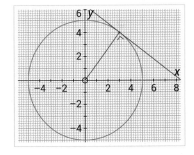

The Equation of a Tangent to a Point On a Circle

Step 1 Find the slope of the radius that contains the point of contact.

Step 2 As the tangent is perpendicular to the radius, it is now possible to find the slope of the tangent.

Step 3 Find the equation of the tangent.

Worked Example 9.18

Find the equation of the tangent to the circle $x^2 + y^2 - 2x + 4y - 20 = 0$ at the point $(-2,2)$.

Solution

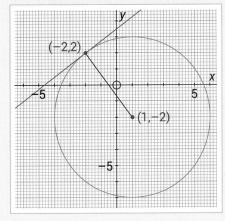

Step 1 The centre of the circle is $(1,-2)$, and the point on the circle is $(-2,2)$.

∴ The slope of this radius is $\dfrac{2 - (-2)}{-2 - 1} = -\dfrac{4}{3}$.

> A rough sketch after this step can help visualise the question and assist with the steps to a solution.

Step 2 ∴ The slope of the tangent is $\dfrac{3}{4}$ (tangent ⊥ radius).

Step 3 Equation of the tangent:

$$y - y_1 = m(x - x_1) \quad \text{Point } (-2,2) \quad m = \frac{3}{4}$$

$$y - 2 = \frac{3}{4}(x + 2)$$

$$4y - 8 = 3x + 6$$

$$3x - 4y + 14 = 0$$

The Equation of a Tangent From a Point Outside a Circle

Step 1 Find the centre and radius length of the circle.

Step 2 Let the slope of the tangent be m.

Step 3 Find the equation of the tangent using m as the slope. (Remember that you will have a point on the tangent.) Write the equation in the form $ax + by + c = 0$.

Step 4 Find, in terms of m, the perpendicular distance from the tangent to the centre of the circle and set this equal to the radius length. Solve for m.

Step 5 Rewrite the equation from Step 3, using the value for m.

Worked Example 9.19

Find the equations of the tangents from $(1,0)$ to the circle $x^2 + y^2 - 12x - 10y + 51 = 0$.

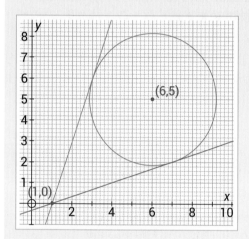

Solution

Step 1

The centre of the circle is $(6,5)$ and the radius length is $\sqrt{36 + 25 - 51} = \sqrt{10}$.

Step 2

Here we are unable to find the slope directly, as we do not have the point of contact. For now, we will let the slope of the tangent be m.

Step 3

Therefore, the equation of the tangent will be of the form:

$y - y_1 = m(x - x_1)$ Point $(1,0)$ Slope $= m$

$y - 0 = m(x - 1)$

$\therefore mx - y - m = 0$

Step 4

The distance from $(6,5)$ to $mx - y - m = 0$ equals $\sqrt{10}$.

$$\frac{|6m - 5 - m|}{\sqrt{m^2 + 1}} = \sqrt{10}$$

$$\frac{|5m - 5|}{\sqrt{m^2 + 1}} = \sqrt{10}$$

$$|5m - 5| = \sqrt{10}\sqrt{m^2 + 1}$$

$\therefore 25m^2 - 50m + 25 = 10m^2 + 10$ (squaring both sides)

You learned about this in Book 1 Chapter 3.

$$15m^2 - 50m + 15 = 0$$

$$3m^2 - 10m + 3 = 0$$

$$(3m - 1)(m - 3) = 0$$

$$\therefore m = \frac{1}{3} \quad \textbf{OR} \quad m = 3$$

Step 5

Therefore, the equations of the tangents are: (1) $\frac{1}{3}x - y - \frac{1}{3} = 0$ (or $x - 3y - 1 = 0$)

and (2) $3x - y - 3 = 0$

Worked Example 9.20

Find the equations of the tangents to the circle $x^2 + y^2 + 6x + 2y - 15 = 0$, which are parallel to the line $3x + 4y + 10 = 0$.

Solution

Step 1

Find the centre and radius length of the circle.

$2g = 6$ and $2f = 2$

$\Rightarrow g = 3$ and $f = 1$

$\therefore$ centre $(-3,-1)$

The radius length is given by $\sqrt{g^2 + f^2 - c}$.

$\therefore r = \sqrt{(3)^2 + (1)^2 + 15}$

$\quad = \sqrt{25}$

$\quad = 5$

Step 2

The equation of any line parallel to $3x + 4y + 10 = 0$ is of the form $3x + 4y + c = 0$, where $c \in R$.

Therefore, the tangents will have equations of the form $3x + 4y + c = 0$.

Step 3

The perpendicular distance from $(-3,-1)$ to the tangents equals the radius length of the circle.

Therefore, we have:

$\dfrac{|3(-3) + 4(-1) + c|}{\sqrt{3^2 + 4^2}} = 5$

$\dfrac{|-9 - 4 + c|}{\sqrt{25}} = 5$

$\dfrac{|c - 13|}{5} = 5$

$|c - 13| = 25$

You learned about this in Book 1 Chapter 3.

$\Rightarrow c - 13 = 25$ **OR** $c - 13 = -25$

$\qquad c = 38$ **OR** $\qquad c = -12$

Step 4

The equations of the two tangents are:
$3x + 4y - 12 = 0$ and $3x + 4y + 38 = 0$

Touching Circles

Two circles s_1 and s_2 have centres c_1 and c_2 and radii lengths r_1 and r_2, respectively.

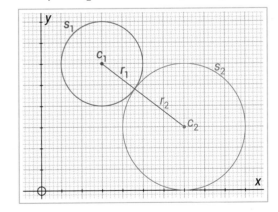

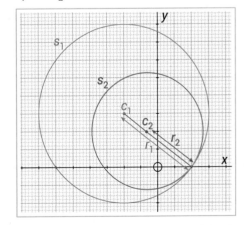

- If the two circles touch externally, then the distance between their centres equals the sum of the two radii.

Two circles touch externally:

$$|c_1 c_2| = r_1 + r_2$$

- If the two circles touch internally, then the distance between their centres equals the difference of the two radii.

Two circles touch internally:

$$|c_1 c_2| = |r_1 - r_2|$$

Worked Example 9.21

Prove that the circles $x^2 + y^2 - 14x - 6y + 49 = 0$ and $x^2 + y^2 - 6x - 12y + 41 = 0$ touch externally.

Solution

$c_1 = (7,3) \qquad r_1 = \sqrt{49 + 9 - 49} = 3$

$c_2 = (3,6) \qquad r_2 = \sqrt{9 + 36 - 41} = 2$ $\Bigg] \quad \therefore r_1 + r_2 = 3 + 2 = 5$

$|c_1 c_2| = \sqrt{(3-7)^2 + (6-3)^2} = \sqrt{16 + 9} = 5$

$r_1 + r_2 = |c_1 c_2|$, therefore the circles touch externally.

Exercise 9.5

1. Find the equations of the tangents to these circles at the points given:

   (i) $x^2 + y^2 = 10$; $(3,1)$

   (ii) $x^2 + y^2 = 20$; $(-4,2)$

   (iii) $(x + 3)^2 + (y + 4)^2 = 25$; $(0,0)$

   (iv) $(x - 6)^2 + (y + 3)^2 = 20$; $(2,-1)$

   (v) $(x - 1)^2 + (y + 2)^2 = 13$; $(3,1)$

   (vi) $x^2 + y^2 - 6x + 4y = 0$; $(6,-4)$

   (vii) $x^2 + y^2 + 2x + 4y - 12 = 0$; $(3,-1)$

2. Find the equations of the tangents from the point P to the given circle.

   (i) $x^2 + y^2 - 2x - 2y + 1 = 0$ $\qquad P(3,4)$

   (ii) $x^2 + y^2 + 2x + 8y + 8 = 0$ $\qquad P(6,-1)$

   (iii) $x^2 + y^2 - 28x - 2y + 172 = 0$ $\qquad P(1,1)$

   (iv) $x^2 + y^2 - 4x - 6y + 4 = 0$ $\qquad P(0,0)$

3. Find the equations of the tangents to the circle $x^2 + y^2 - 4x + 6y - 3 = 0$ from the point $P(6, 7)$.

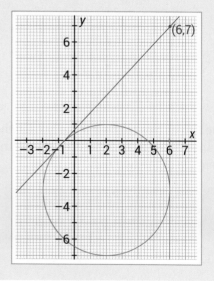

4. Investigate if the circles $x^2 + y^2 - 6x - 16y + 9 = 0$ and $x^2 + y^2 + 4x - 6y + 12 = 0$ touch internally.

5. Sketch the two circles $x^2 + y^2 = 16$ and $x^2 + y^2 - 6x - 8y + 24 = 0$.
   Prove that they touch externally.

6. Draw a rough sketch of the circles $x^2 + y^2 - 2x - 15 = 0$ and $x^2 + y^2 - 14x - 16y + 77 = 0$.
   Prove that they touch externally.

7. Prove that the circles $x^2 + y^2 - 12x + 6y - 76 = 0$ and $x^2 + y^2 + 4x - 6y + 12 = 0$ touch each other, and state whether this is internal or external.

8. s is the circle $x^2 + y^2 = 5$ and P is the point $(2,1)$.

   (i) Verify that P is a point on s.

   (ii) Find the equation of l, the tangent to the circle s at the point P.

   (iii) Find the equation of the tangent to s that is parallel to l.

9. Find the equations of the tangents to the circle $x^2 + y^2 - 8x + 4y + 7 = 0$ that are perpendicular to the line $2x + 3y = 6$.

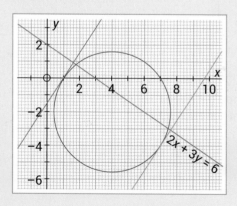

10. s: $x^2 + y^2 = 25$ and
    t: $x^2 + y^2 - 10x + 24y + k = 0$
    touch each other externally.
    Find the value of k.

11. Sketch the circles $x^2 + y^2 = 9$ and
    $x^2 + y^2 - 18x + 72 = 0$. Find the equation of the
    circle whose centre is on the x-axis and which
    touches both of these circles:

    (i) Externally

    (ii) Internally

9.7 Problems in g, f and c

In this section we will be given limited information on a circle. We will then be asked to find the equation
of the circle or to answer some question involving the circle.

Worked Example 9.22

Find the equation of the circle s, which passes through the points $(1,1)$, $(2,3)$ and $(3,-1)$.

Solution
Method 1

Let the equation be $x^2 + y^2 + 2gx + 2fy + c = 0$.

$(1,1)$ is on s	$\therefore 1^2 + 1^2 + 2g(1) + 2f(1) + c = 0$	$\therefore 2g + 2f + c = -2$	**Eq. I**
$(2,3)$ is on s	$\therefore 2^2 + 3^2 + 2g(2) + 2f(3) + c = 0$	$\therefore 4g + 6f + c = -13$	**Eq. II**
$(3,-1)$ is on s	$\therefore 3^2 + (-1)^2 + 2g(3) + 2f(-1) + c = 0$	$\therefore 6g - 2f + c = -10$	**Eq. III**

We have three simultaneous equations. We eliminate c by subtracting Eq. II from Eq. I, and subtracting
Eq. II from Eq. III. This gives us:

$$-2g - 4f = 11 \quad \textbf{Eq. IV}$$

$$2g - 8f = 3 \quad \textbf{Eq. V}$$

Add Eq. IV and Eq. V.

$$-12f = 14 \qquad \therefore f = -\frac{7}{6}$$

Substituting $f = -\frac{7}{6}$ into Eq. IV gives:

$$-2g - 4\left(-\frac{7}{6}\right) = 11 \qquad \therefore g = -\frac{19}{6}$$

Substituting $f = -\frac{7}{6}$ and $g = -\frac{19}{6}$ into Eq. I gives:

$$2\left(-\frac{19}{6}\right) + 2\left(-\frac{7}{6}\right) + c = -2 \qquad \therefore c = \frac{20}{3}$$

We now substitute these values for g, f and c into the general equation.

$$x^2 + y^2 + 2\left(-\frac{19}{6}\right)x + 2\left(-\frac{7}{6}\right)y + \frac{20}{3} = 0 \quad \text{(Multiply across by 6.)}$$

$$6x^2 + 6y^2 - 38x - 14y + 40 = 0 \; ... \text{ equation of circle } s$$

Method 2

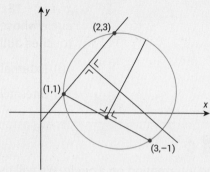

Step 1 Find the equations of the perpendicular bisectors of two chords.

Midpoint [(2,3), (1,1)]:

$$\left(\frac{2+1}{2}, \frac{3+1}{2}\right)$$

$$= \left(\frac{3}{2}, 2\right)$$

Slope [(1,1), (2,3)]:

$$m = \frac{3-1}{2-1}$$

$$= 2$$

$\Rightarrow$ The slope of the
perpendicular bisector is $-\frac{1}{2}$.

Equation of bisector:

$$y - 2 = -\frac{1}{2}\left(x - \frac{3}{2}\right)$$

$$4y - 8 = -2x + 3$$

$$\therefore 2x + 4y = 11$$

Midpoint [(1,1), (3,−1)]:

$$\left(\frac{1+3}{2}, \frac{1-1}{2}\right)$$

$$= (2, 0)$$

Slope [(1,1), (3,−1)]:

$$m = \frac{-1-1}{3-1}$$

$$= -1$$

$\Rightarrow$ The slope of the
perpendicular bisector is 1.

Equation of bisector:

$$y - 0 = 1(x - 2)$$

$$y = x - 2$$

$$\therefore x - y = 2$$

Step 2 Find the point of intersection of the perpendicular bisectors.

$$2x + 4y = 11$$

$$x - y = 2 \qquad \times -2$$

$$\begin{aligned} 2x + 4y &= 11 \\ -2x + 2y &= -4 \\ \hline 6y &= 7 \end{aligned}$$

$$y = \frac{7}{6}$$

$$x - y = 2$$

$$x - \frac{7}{6} = 2$$

$$x = \frac{19}{6}$$

$\therefore \left(\frac{19}{6}, \frac{7}{6}\right)$ is the centre of the circle.

Step 3 Find the length of the radius of the circle.
Radius length = distance from the centre
to a point on the circle $\left(\frac{19}{6}, \frac{7}{6}\right)$ and (1,1).

$$r = \sqrt{\left(1 - \frac{19}{6}\right)^2 + \left(1 - \frac{7}{6}\right)^2}$$

$$= \sqrt{\left(\frac{-13}{6}\right)^2 + \left(-\frac{1}{6}\right)^2}$$

$$= \sqrt{\frac{169}{36} + \frac{1}{36}}$$

$$= \sqrt{\frac{170}{36}}$$

$$= \sqrt{\frac{85}{18}}$$

Step 4 Find the equation of the circle.

$$(x - h)^2 + (y - k)^2 = r^2$$

$$\left(x - \frac{19}{6}\right)^2 + \left(y - \frac{7}{6}\right)^2 = \frac{85}{18}$$

Worked Example 9.23

Find the equation of the circle k, which passes through the points (1,1) and (2,–1) and whose centre lies on the line $3x - y = 7$.

Solution

Let the equation of the circle be $x^2 + y^2 + 2gx + 2fy + c = 0$.

(1,1) is on k $\therefore 1 + 1 + 2g + 2f + c = 0$ $\therefore 2g + 2f + c = -2$ **Eq. I**

(2,–1) is on k $\therefore 4 + 1 + 4g - 2f + c = 0$ $\therefore 4g - 2f + c = -5$ **Eq. II**

($-g,-f$) is on $3x - y = 7$ $\therefore -3g + f = 7$ **Eq. III**

Subtracting Eq. II from Eq. I gives:

$$-2g + 4f = 3 \quad \textbf{Eq. IV}$$

Now solve for g using Eq. III and Eq. IV. Multiply Eq. III by -4.

$$12g - 4f = -28$$
$$-2g + 4f = 3$$

Adding the above equations gives: $10g = -25$ $\therefore g = -\dfrac{5}{2}$

Substituting $g = -\dfrac{5}{2}$ into Eq. III gives: $\dfrac{15}{2} + f = 7$ $\therefore f = -\dfrac{1}{2}$

Putting these values into Eq. I gives: $2\left(-\dfrac{5}{2}\right) + 2\left(-\dfrac{1}{2}\right) + c = -2$

$$-5 - 1 + c = -2$$
$$\therefore c = 4$$

Hence, the equation of the circle k is $x^2 + y^2 - 5x - y + 4 = 0$.

Worked Example 9.24

The line $2x - y - 17 = 0$ is a tangent to the circle k at the point (6,–5). The circle also contains the point (4,1). Find the equation of the circle k.

Solution

Step 1   Let the equation of k be $x^2 + y^2 + 2gx + 2fy + c = 0$.

Step 2   Find the equation of the line through (6,–5) which contains the centre of the circle. This line is perpendicular to $2x - y - 17 = 0$, and therefore its slope is $-\dfrac{1}{2}$.

Equation: $y - y_1 = m(x - x_1)$

$$y + 5 = -\dfrac{1}{2}(x - 6)$$

$$2y + 10 = -x + 6$$

$$\therefore x + 2y + 4 = 0$$

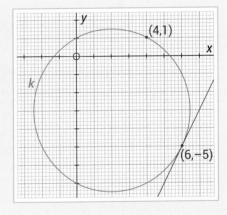

Step 3 $x + 2y + 4 = 0$ contains ($-g,-f$), the centre of the circle: $-g - 2f + 4 = 0$.   **Eq. I**

Step 4   Substitute (4,1) and (6,–5) into the equation of k.

$$(4)^2 + (1)^2 + 8g + 2f + c = 0 \qquad\qquad (6)^2 + (-5)^2 + 12g - 10f + c = 0$$

$$8g + 2f + c = -17 \quad \textbf{Eq. II} \qquad\qquad 12g - 10f + c = -61 \quad \textbf{Eq. III}$$

Eliminate c from Eq. II and Eq. III.

$$4g - 12f = -44 \quad \textbf{Eq. IV}$$

Step 5 Solve for g and f using Eq. I and Eq. IV.

$$-g - 2f = -4$$
$$\underline{4g - 12f = -44}$$
$$-4g - 8f = -16$$
$$\underline{4g - 12f = -44}$$
$$-20f = -60$$
$$\Rightarrow f = 3$$

Substitute $f = 3$ into Eq. IV.

$$4g - 12(3) = -44$$
$$4g = -44 + 36$$
$$4g = -8$$
$$\Rightarrow g = -2$$

Substitute $f = 3$ and $g = -2$ into Eq. II.

$$8(-2) + 2(3) + c = -17$$
$$-16 + 6 + c = -17$$
$$c = -7$$

Therefore, the equation of k is $x^2 + y^2 - 4x + 6y - 7 = 0$.

Worked Example 9.25

(i) Show that if the circle $x^2 + y^2 + 2gx + 2fy + c = 0$ touches the x-axis, then $g^2 = c$.

(ii) Using the result from part (i), find the equations of the two circles that contain the points $A(3,4)$ and $B(5,2)$ and that touch the x-axis.

Solution

(i)

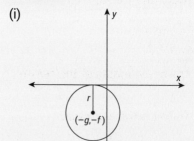

If a circle touches the x-axis, then the length of its radius is given by $r = |-f|$.

> We use the absolute value of $-f$, as length is a non-negative quantity.

Also, $r = \sqrt{g^2 + f^2 - c}$

$\therefore \sqrt{g^2 + f^2 - c} = |-f|$ (Square both sides.)

$$g^2 + f^2 - c = f^2$$
$$g^2 - c = 0$$
$$\therefore g^2 = c$$

(ii) **Step 1**

From part (i) the equations of the circles will be of the form $x^2 + y^2 + 2gx + 2fy + g^2 = 0$.

Step 2

Substitute $A(3,4)$ and $B(5,2)$ into the equation above.

$$(3)^2 + (4)^2 + 2g(3) + 2f(4) + g^2 = 0$$
$$9 + 16 + 6g + 8f + g^2 = 0$$
$$6g + 8f + g^2 = -25 \quad \textbf{Eq. I}$$

$$(5)^2 + (2)^2 + 2g(5) + 2f(2) + g^2 = 0$$
$$25 + 4 + 10g + 4f + g^2 = 0$$
$$10g + 4f + g^2 = -29 \quad \textbf{Eq. II}$$

Step 3

Eliminate f by multiplying Eq. II by -2.

$$6g + 8f + g^2 = -25$$
$$\underline{-20g - 8f - 2g^2 = 58}$$
$$-14g - g^2 = 33$$
$$\therefore g^2 + 14g + 33 = 0$$

Step 4

Solve the resulting quadratic equation in g.

$$g^2 + 14g + 33 = 0$$
$$(g + 3)(g + 11) = 0$$
$$\Rightarrow g = -3 \quad \text{or} \quad g = -11$$

Step 5

Find the corresponding values for *c*.

$g = -3 \Rightarrow c = (-3)^2 = 9$ $\qquad$ $g = -11 \Rightarrow c = (-11)^2 = 121$

Step 6

Find the corresponding values for *f* by substituting into Eq. II (or Eq. I).

$g = -3$	$g = -11$
$10(-3) + 4f + (-3)^2 = -29$	$10(-11) + 4f + (-11)^2 = -29$
$-30 + 4f + 9 = -29$	$-110 + 4f + 121 = -29$
$4f = -8$	$4f = -40$
$f = -2$	$f = -10$

∴ The equations of the circles are:

Circle 1: $g = -3$, $f = -2$, $c = 9$ $\qquad$ and $\qquad$ Circle 2: $g = -11$, $f = -10$, $c = 121$

$\qquad x^2 + y^2 - 6x - 4y + 9 = 0$ $\qquad\qquad\qquad\qquad x^2 + y^2 - 22x - 20y + 121 = 0$

Exercise 9.6

1. Find the equation of the circle that passes through the points *A*, *B* and *C*.

    (i) $A(1,2)$, $B(4,-3)$, $C(0,-2)$

    (ii) $A(3,0)$, $B(4,-3)$, $C(5,-2)$

    (iii) $A(-2,2)$, $B(2,4)$, $C(2,-5)$

    (iv) $A(0,0)$, $B(4,0)$, $C(3,-1)$

    (v) $A(1,2)$, $B(4,5)$, $C(7,-2)$

    (vi) $A(11,2)$, $B(3,-2)$, $C(10,-2)$

2. Find the equation of the circle that contains the two points $O(0,0)$ and $P(4,2)$, and whose centre is on the line $x + y = 3$.

3. Find the equation of the circle that contains the two points $A(0,-1)$ and $B(3,0)$, and whose centre is on the line $x - 3y + 2 = 0$.

4. Find the equation of the circle that contains the two points $Q(0,2)$ and $P(1,5)$, and whose centre is on the line $x + 5y = 15$.

5. (i) Show that if the circle $x^2 + y^2 + 2gx + 2fy + c = 0$ touches the *y*-axis, then $f^2 = c$.

    (ii) Using the result from part (i), find the equation of the circle that contains the points $A(2,3)$ and $B(2,-5)$ and that touches the *y*-axis.

6. Find the equations of the circles that contain the point $(4,3)$, have their centres on the line $3x - 2y = 0$ and touch the *y*-axis.

7. The equation of a circle is $x^2 + y^2 - 4x - 4y + 4 = 0$.

    (i) Write down the co-ordinates of the centre of the circle.

    (ii) Find the radius length of the circle.

    (iii) Draw a sketch of the circle.

    (iv) Explain why the circle touches both axes.

8. There are two circles that have radii lengths of $\sqrt{5}$ and that pass through the points $(-3,1)$ and $(1,1)$. Find their equations.

9. Find the equations of the two circles that contain the point $(2,1)$, have their centres on the line $y = x$ and have radii of length 5 units.

10. Find the equation of the circle that passes through the points $P(-3,-2)$ and $Q(0,-1)$ and has the line $2x - y + 4 = 0$ as a tangent at the point $P(-3,-2)$.

11. Find the equation of the circle that passes through the points $A(-2,2)$ and $B(5,-5)$ and has the line $3x - 4y = 35$ as a tangent at the point $B(5,-5)$.

Revision Exercises

1. The point (1,–7) is on a circle k, which has its centre at $O(0,0)$.

   (a) Sketch the circle k.

   (b) Find the equation of k.

   (c) If (p,p) is a point on k, find two possible values of p.

   (d) If the point $(3,n)$ is inside the circle k, find the greatest possible value of $n \in N$.

2. (a) A circle with centre (1,1) passes through the point (–2,–3). Find the equation of this circle.

   (b) The line $2x + y + k = 0$ is a tangent to the circle $x^2 + y^2 - 6x + 10y + 29 = 0$. Find the two possible values of k.

   (c) A circle has the line $y = 2x$ as a tangent at the point (2,4). The circle also passes through the point (4,–2).
   Find the equation of this circle.

3. (a) Find the centre and radius length of the circle $2x^2 + 2y^2 - 2x + 6y - 1 = 0$.

   (b) Find the equation of the circle that passes through the points (0,–2), (1,1) and (2,2).

   (c) $A(-1,-1)$, $B(2,5)$ and $C(x,y)$ are three points. If $|AC| = 2|BC|$, prove that $x^2 + y^2 - 6x - 14y + 38 = 0$.

4. $A(3,1)$ and $B(-1,-1)$ are points on a circle of centre $(k,-3k)$.

   (a) Find the value of k.

   (b) Find the equation of the circle.

   (c) Find the equations of the two tangents, l and m, to the circle at A and B.

   (d) Find the measure of the acute angle between l and m.

5. (a) The equation of a circle is $(x - 4)^2 + (y - 9)^2 = 80$.

   The line $2x - y + 1 = 0$ intersects the circle at the points A and B.

   Find the co-ordinates of A and B and, hence, investigate if $[AB]$ is a diameter of this circle.

   (b) Find the equation of the circle that passes through (1,0) and (0,2) and has its centre on the line $x + 3y - 11 = 0$.

   Prove that the origin is outside the circle.

6. (a) Prove that the circles
   $x^2 + y^2 + 6x - 8y - 55 = 0$ and
   $x^2 + y^2 + 4y - 1 = 0$ touch internally.

   (b) A line containing the point $P(5,6)$ touches $x^2 + y^2 - 4x - 4y + 4 = 0$ at K. Find $|PK|$.

   (c) If $y = mx + c$ is a tangent to the circle $x^2 + y^2 + 2ax = 0$, prove that $a^2 + 2acm - c^2 = 0$.

7. (a) Find the equation of the tangent to the circle $x^2 + y^2 = 25$ at the point (–3,–4).

   (b) Two circles intersect at $A(1,0)$ and $B(-3,2)$. The distance from the centre of each circle to the chord $[AB]$ is $\sqrt{5}$.
   Find the equation of the two circles.

8. The diagram shows two concentric circles, centred at the origin, of radius length r_1 and r_2, respectively. The area of the shaded region is 144π.

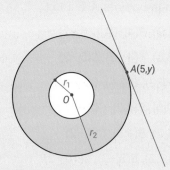

   (i) If $r_2 - r_1 = 8$, find the equation of the larger circle.

   (ii) Find the value of y in the co-ordinate A.

   (iii) Find the equation of the tangent to the larger circle at the point A.

9. (a) A circle has centre (–2,3) and passes through the point (5,6).
   Find the equation of this circle.

   (b) k is the circle $x^2 + y^2 + 2x + 2y - 7 = 0$, and l is the line $4x + 3y = 12$.

   (i) Show that the line l does not intersect the circle k.

   (ii) Find the co-ordinates of the point on k that is closest to l.

(c) The equation of a circle is
$(x + 2)(x - 4) + (y + 1)(y - 1) + 3 = 0$.

   (i) Show that the centre of this circle lies on the x-axis.

   (ii) Find the radius length of this circle.

(d) Show that the equation of the tangent to the circle $x^2 + y^2 = r^2$ at the point (x_1, y_1) is $xx_1 + yy_1 = r^2$.

10. (a) (1,2) and (3,4) are the endpoints of the diameter of a circle.

   (i) Write down the equation of this circle.

   (ii) Construct the circle.

   (iii) Construct the tangent *l* to the circle at the point (3,4).

   (iv) Find the equation of *l*.

(b) Find the equations of the circles that pass through the points (−3,6) and (−6,3) and have the y-axis as a tangent.

(c) (−2,4), (0,−10) and (6,−2) are the vertices of a triangle.

   (i) Plot the vertices of the triangle.

   (ii) Verify that the triangle is right-angled.

   (iii) Construct the circumcircle of the triangle.

   (iv) Find the equation of the circumcircle.

11. (a) Write down the equation of the circle with centre (−3,2) and radius 4.

(b) A circle has equation $x^2 + y^2 - 2x + 4y - 15 = 0$. Find the values of *m* for which the line $mx + 2y - 7 = 0$ is a tangent to this circle.

12. *P* is the point (0,7) and *Q* is the point (8,11).

(a) Find the equation of the circle with diameter [*PQ*].

(b) Find the equation of the tangent at *Q*.

(c) This tangent crosses the x-axis at the point *R*. Find the co-ordinates of *R*.

13. The line $3x - y + 6 = 0$ is a tangent to the circle at the point (−3,−3). The circle also passes through the point (−4,−1).

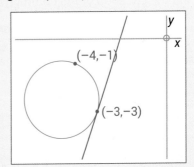

(i) Find the equation of the line, perpendicular to the given tangent, containing the centre of the circle.

(ii) Show that the co-ordinates of the centre of the circle can be written in the form: $\left(a, -4 - \frac{a}{3}\right)$.

(iii) Find the value of *a*.

(iv) Hence, find the equation of this circle.

(v) Find the equation of the tangent to the circle parallel to the tangent through (−3,−3).

Exam Questions

1. (a) The centre of a circle lies on the line $x - 2y - 1 = 0$.
The x-axis and the line $y = 6$ are tangents to the circle.
Find the equation of this circle.

(b) A different circle has equation $x^2 + y^2 - 6x - 12y + 41 = 0$.
Show that this circle and the circle in part (a) touch externally.

SEC Leaving Certificate Higher Level, Project Maths Paper 2, 2010

2. The line $x + 3y = 20$ intersects the circle $x^2 + y^2 - 6x - 8y = 0$ at the points *P* and *Q*.
Find the equation of the circle that has [*PQ*] as diameter.

SEC Leaving Certificate Higher Level, Project Maths Paper 2, 2011

3. The equations of two circles are:

c_1: $x^2 + y^2 - 6x - 10y + 29 = 0$

c_2: $x^2 + y^2 - 2x - 2y - 43 = 0$

(a) Write down the centre and radius length of each circle.

(b) Prove that the circles are touching.

(c) Verify that $(4,7)$ is the point that they have in common.

(d) Find the equation of the common tangent.

SEC Leaving Certificate Higher Level, Project Maths Paper 2, 2012

4. The circle shown in the diagram has, as tangents, the x-axis, the y-axis, the line $x + y = 2$ and the line $x + y = 2k$, where $k > 1$. Find the value of k.

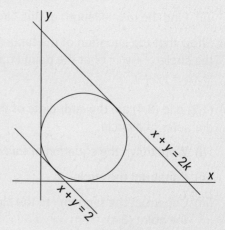

SEC Leaving Certificate Higher Level, Project Maths Paper 2, 2012

5. The circles c_1 and c_2 touch externally as shown.

(a) Complete the following table:

Circle	Centre	Radius	Equation
c_1	$(-3,-2)$	2	
c_2			$x^2 + y^2 - 2x - 2y - 7 = 0$

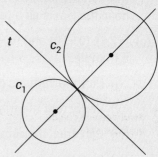

(b) (i) Find the co-ordinates of the point of contact of c_1 and c_2.

(ii) Hence, or otherwise, find the equation of the tangent, t, common to c_1 and c_2.

SEC Leaving Certificate Higher Level, Project Maths Paper 2, 2013

6. Two circles s and c touch internally at B, as shown.

(a) The equation of the circle s is $(x - 1)^2 + (y + 6)^2 = 360$.

Write down the co-ordinates of the centre of s.

Write down the radius of s in the form $a\sqrt{10}$, where $a \in N$.

(b) (i) The point K is the centre of circle c.

The radius of c is one-third the radius of s.

The co-ordinates of B are $(7,12)$.

Find the co-ordinates of K.

(ii) Find the equation of c.

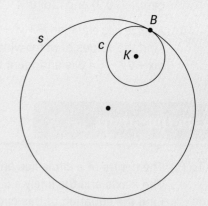

(c) Find the equation of the common tangent at B.

Give your answer in the form $ax + by + c = 0$, where $a, b, c \in Z$.

SEC Leaving Certificate Higher Level, Project Maths Paper 2, 2015

7. The diagram shows a circular clock face, with the hands not shown. The square part of the clock face is glass so that the mechanism is visible. Two circular cogs, *h* and *k*, which touch externally, are shown.

The point *C* is the centre of the clock face. The point *D* is the centre of the larger cog, *h*, and the point *E* is the centre of the smaller cog, *k*.

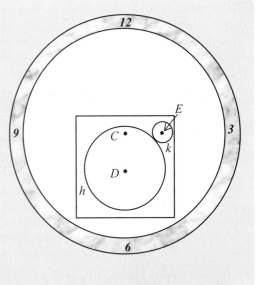

(i) In suitable co-ordinates, the equation of the circle *h* is $x^2 + y^2 + 4x + 6y - 19 = 0$.

Find the radius of *h*, and the co-ordinates of its centre, *D*.

(ii) The point *E* has co-ordinates (3, 2).
Find the radius of the circle *k*.

(iii) Show that the distance from *C*(–2, 2) to the line *DE* is half the length of [*DE*].

(iv) The translation which maps the midpoint of [*DE*] to the point *C* maps the circle *k* to the circle *j*. Find the equation of the circle *j*.

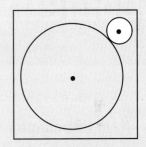

(v) The glass square is of side length *l*. Find the smallest whole number *l* such that the two cogs, *h* and *k*, are fully visible through the glass.

SEC Leaving Certificate Higher Level, Project Maths Paper 2, 2014

Solutions and chapter summary available online

10

Geometry II

In this chapter you will learn about:

- Axiom 4: Congruent triangles (SSS, SAS, ASA and RHS)

- The following terms related to logic and deductive reasoning: *theorem; proof; axiom; corollary; converse; implies; is equivalent to; if and only if; proof by contradiction*

- Theorems from the Junior Certificate course

- Theorems 11, 12 and 13 from the Leaving Certificate course:

  - If three parallel lines cut off equal segments on some transversal line, then they will cut off equal segments on any other transversal

  - Let *ABC* be a triangle. If a line *l* is parallel to *BC* and cuts [*AB*] in the ratio *s* : *t*, then it also cuts [*AC*] in the same ratio

  - If two triangles are similar, then their sides are proportional, in order

You should remember...

- Notation, theorems and axioms from Chapter 6 Geometry I

- How to prove theorems from the Junior Certificate course

Key words

- Axiom
- Theorem
- Corollary
- Converse
- Proof
- Direct proof
- Proof by contradiction
- Congruent
- SSS, SAS, ASA, RHS
- If and only if
- Is equivalent to
- Proposition

10.1 Proofs: An Introduction

In this chapter we will study how to prove certain **propositions**.

> A proposition is a mathematical statement or theorem. It may be true or false.
> A proof is a series of logical steps that we use to prove a statement.

To help us in writing a **proof**, we need to know the meaning of certain terms.

Basic Geometric Terms

> A theorem is a statement that has been proved by following a certain number
> of logical steps or by using a previous theorem or axiom that you already know.

For example: A diagonal of a parallelogram bisects the area.

> An axiom is a rule or statement that we accept without any proof.

For example: There is exactly one line through any two given points.

> A corollary is a statement that follows readily from a previous theorem.

For example: Each angle in a semicircle is a right angle.

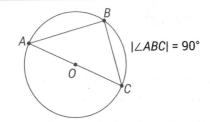

$|\angle ABC| = 90°$

Most geometry theorems begin with a statement (hypothesis), which leads to a conclusion.

> The converse of a theorem is formed by swapping the order of the hypothesis and conclusion.
> The conditional statement 'if A, then B' has an hypothesis (A) and a conclusion (B). In general,
> the converse of 'if A, then B' is 'if B, then A'. Converses may or may not be true.

For example:

Statement: If a transversal makes equal alternate angles on two lines, then the lines are parallel.

Converse: If two lines are parallel, then any transversal will make equal alternate angles with them.

This converse is true.

Another example of a statement with a true converse would be:

Statement: In an isosceles triangle the angles opposite the equal sides are equal in measure.

Converse: If two angles in a triangle are equal in measure, then the triangle is isosceles.

A converse of a statement may not be true. For example:

Statement: If a quadrilateral is a square, then opposite sides are equal in length (True).

Converse: If opposite sides in a quadrilateral are equal in length, then the quadrilateral is a square (False).

> Implies is a term we use in a proof when we can write down a fact we have
> proved from our previous statements. The symbol for implies is ⇒.

For example, consider the triangle *ABC* shown.

The angles in triangle *ABC* are all equal.

$\Rightarrow$ Triangle *ABC* is equilateral.

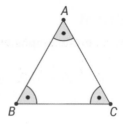

Types of Proof

There are many different types of proof.

Direct proof

One of the most common forms of proof in geometry is that of direct proof.

In a direct proof we prove a statement by a series of logical steps using known facts, theorems or axioms.

Proof by induction

Mathematical induction is a method of mathematical proof used to establish that if a given statement is true for one step in the process, it is also true for the next step.

You learned about proof by induction in Chapter 11 of Book 1.

Proof by contradiction

Proof by contradiction is a method of indirect proof. In a proof by contradiction, the truth of a proposition is established by showing that the proposition being false would lead to a contradiction.

We are required on our course to prove that $\sqrt{2}$ is irrational using proof by contradiction.

You learned how to prove that $\sqrt{2}$ is irrational in Chapter 5 of Book 1.

Exercise 10.1

1. Write down, in your own words, an explanation for the following terms. Use diagrams where necessary and give an example in each case.

   (i) Theorem   (iv) Proof

   (ii) Axiom   (v) Converse

   (iii) Corollary

2. Complete the table below. One has been done for you.

Statement	True/False	Converse	True/False
The diagonals of a parallelogram bisect one another.	True	If the diagonals of a quadrilateral bisect one another, then the quadrilateral is a parallelogram.	True
If a triangle has a 90° angle, it is a right-angled triangle.			
If $n > 3$, then $n^2 > 9$.			
If this month is January, then next month is February.			
If a polygon is a square, then it has four sides.			
If it is a bicycle, then it will have two wheels.			
If a woman is in Galway, then she is in Connaught.			

3. Explain the difference between direct proof and indirect proof. Give examples in each case.

10.2 Congruent Triangles

If two triangles are identical to each other, they can also be described as being **congruent**.

> **Congruent** triangles are triangles where all the corresponding sides and interior angles are equal in measure.

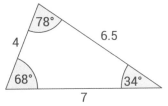 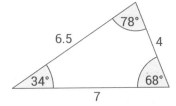

There are four different methods or cases to show that two triangles are congruent. These methods are listed in Axiom 4:

> **Axiom 4**
> Congruent triangles (SSS, SAS, ASA and RHS).

Congruent Triangles: Side, Side, Side (SSS)

> **SSS** means **Side, Side, Side**.

$\triangle ABC$ is congruent to $\triangle DEF$ **or** $\triangle ABC \equiv \triangle DEF$.

The side lengths in $\triangle ABC$ are the same as the side lengths in $\triangle DEF$.

> The symbol $\equiv$ is a shorthand way of describing two triangles as congruent, e.g. $\triangle ABC \equiv \triangle DEF$.

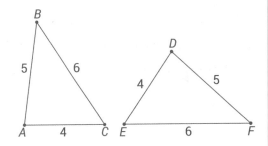

Congruent Triangles: Side, Angle, Side (SAS)

> **SAS** means **Side, Angle, Side**.

$\triangle DEF$ is congruent to $\triangle XYZ$ **or** $\triangle DEF \equiv \triangle XYZ$.

Two sides and the angle in between them are equal.

> The in-between angle can also be called the **included** angle.

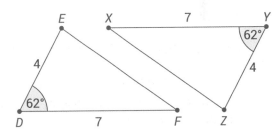

Congruent Triangles: Angle, Side, Angle (ASA)

> **ASA** means **Angle, Side, Angle**.

$\triangle PQR$ is congruent to $\triangle MNO$ or $\triangle PQR \equiv \triangle MNO$.

Two angles and the side in between them are equal.

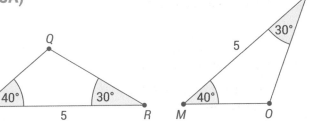

GEOMETRY II

Congruent Triangles: Right Angle, Hypotenuse, one other Side (RHS)

The hypotenuse is the side opposite the right angle; it is also the longest side in the right-angled triangle.

$\triangle RST$ is congruent to $\triangle UVW$ or $\triangle RST \equiv \triangle UVW$.

Both of these triangles are right-angled, their hypotenuses are of equal length, and they have one other side that is equal.

The areas of congruent triangles are equal as well.

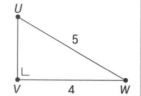

Congruent triangles are a good introduction to the method of writing a geometrical proof.

Worked Example 10.1

Prove that the two triangles ABC and DEF are congruent.

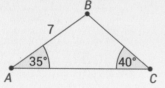 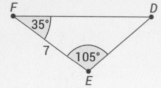

Proof:

Statement	Reason
$\lvert\angle B\rvert = \lvert\angle E\rvert$	As shown
$\lvert\angle A\rvert = \lvert\angle F\rvert$	Given
$\lvert AB\rvert = \lvert EF\rvert$	Given
$\Rightarrow \triangle ABC \equiv \triangle DEF$	ASA
Q.E.D.	

Solution

We must first find $\lvert\angle B\rvert$.

$\lvert\angle B\rvert = 180° - 35° - 40°$ (angles in a triangle)

$\lvert\angle B\rvert = 105°$

Remember to give a reason for your answer.

When writing down statements in the proof section, we must always try to give a reason for the statement, whether we have been given this information or whether we have used a theorem.

We always finish by writing **Q.E.D.**

We will cover proofs more formally later in the chapter.

Statement	Reason
$\lvert\angle A\rvert = \lvert\angle B\rvert$	Isosceles triangle

Q.E.D. stands for the Latin phrase *Quod erat demonstrandum*, which means 'what was to be proved'. It signals the end of the proof.

Worked Example 10.2

Prove that $\triangle XYZ \equiv \triangle XWZ$.

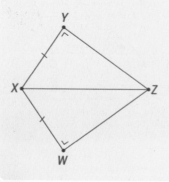

Solution

Solution is not unique.

Proof:

Statement	Reason
$\lvert\angle XYZ\rvert = \lvert\angle XWZ\rvert$	Given
$\lvert XZ\rvert = \lvert XZ\rvert$	Common side
$\lvert XY\rvert = \lvert XW\rvert$	Given
$\triangle XYZ \equiv \triangle XWZ$	RHS
Q.E.D.	

Exercise 10.2

1. Prove that the following pairs of triangles are congruent. Explain your answer fully.

(i)

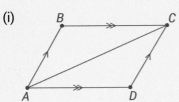

Prove that $\triangle ABC \equiv \triangle ACD$.

(ii)

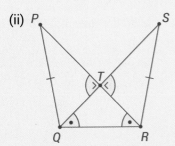

Prove that $\triangle PQT \equiv \triangle RST$.

(iii)

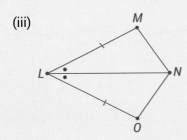

Prove that $\triangle LMN \equiv \triangle LNO$.

(iv)

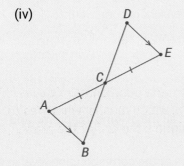

Prove that $\triangle ABC \equiv \triangle CDE$.

(v)

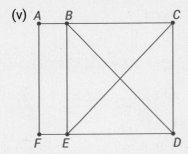

ACDF and ABEF are rectangles.

Prove that $\triangle AFD \equiv \triangle CDF$.

(vi)

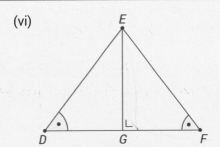

Prove that $\triangle DEG \equiv \triangle EFG$.

2. Two tangents PT and PS are drawn to a circle with centre O from the point P.

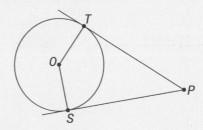

Prove that $|PT| = |PS|$.

3. A circle with a centre O and a chord [PQ] is shown.

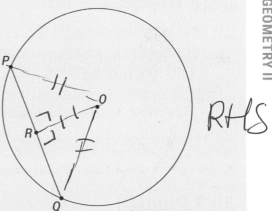

R is a point on the chord such that $|\angle PRO| = 90°$.

Prove that R is the midpoint of the chord [PQ].

4. 'Construction 1: Bisector of an angle' is shown. Prove that $\angle ABC$ is bisected by [BD.

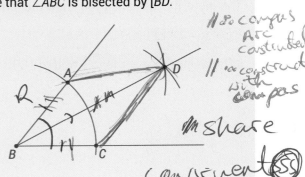

GEOMETRY II

5. In the following diagram, *DEFG* is a parallelogram.

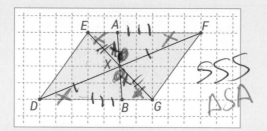

    (i) Prove that △*EXF* ≡ △*DXG*.

    (ii) Hence, show that |*AX*| = |*BX*|.

6. *ABCD* is a rectangle. The midpoints, *P, Q, R* and *S*, of each side of the rectangle are shown.

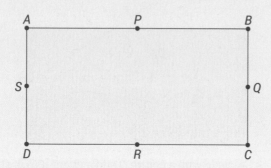

    (i) Prove that △*APS* ≡ △*CQR*.

    (ii) Prove that △*APS* ≡ △*BPQ*.

    (iii) What type of quadrilateral is *PQRS*? Give a reason for your answer.

    (iv) If the area of the rectangle *ABCD* is 32 cm², calculate the area of the quadrilateral *PQRS*.

7. *ABCD* is a parallelogram. *AD* is produced to the point *E* such that *BD* ∥ *CE*.

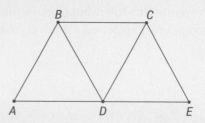

Use congruency to prove that *D* is the midpoint of [*AE*].

8. In △*ABC*, |∠*BAC*| = |∠*BCA*|. Prove that |*AB*| = |*BC*|.

9. In the following diagram, *ABCD* is a parallelogram.

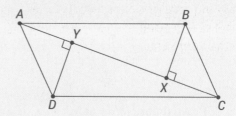

    (i) Show that △*ABX* is congruent to △*CYD*.

    (ii) Show that |*AY*| = |*XC*|.

10.3 Proofs I

We must be able to prove certain theorems and to answer proofs based on all the axioms, theorems and corollaries from our course.

As stated in the syllabus, 'Knowledge of the content and learning outcomes at the corresponding level in the Junior Certificate Mathematics syllabus is assumed.' (Leaving Certificate syllabus, page 8)

Therefore, it is assumed you know the formal proofs of Theorems 4, 6, 9, 14 and 19.

> **Theorem 4**
> The angles in any triangle add to 180°.

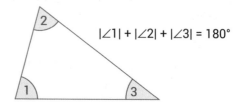

$$|\angle 1| + |\angle 2| + |\angle 3| = 180°$$

Theorem 6
Each exterior angle of a triangle is equal to the sum of the interior opposite angles.

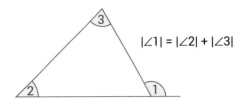

$|\angle 1| = |\angle 2| + |\angle 3|$

Theorem 9
In a parallelogram, opposite sides are equal and opposite angles are equal.

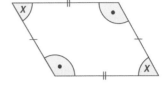

Theorem 14: The Theorem of Pythagoras
In a right-angled triangle, the square of the hypotenuse is the sum of the squares of the other two sides.

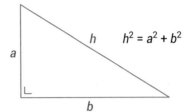

$h^2 = a^2 + b^2$

Theorem 19
The angle at the centre of a circle standing on a given arc is twice the angle at any point of the circle standing on the same arc.

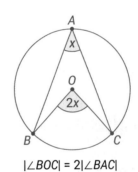

$|\angle BOC| = 2|\angle BAC|$

How to Write a Proof

There follows an example of a proof, with a description of each step involved.

Prove that the diagonals of a parallelogram bisect each other.

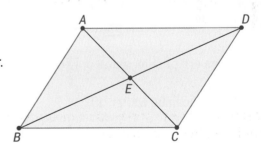

Theorem: The diagonals of a parallelogram bisect each other.

Given: Parallelogram *ABCD*, in which the diagonals intersect at the point *E*

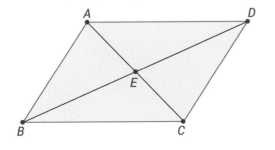

Theorem: Usually use only when you are asked to formally prove a certain theorem.

Given: Write down the information that has been given in the question. Also draw any diagrams that have been used in the question.

GEOMETRY II

To prove:

$|AE| = |EC|$ and $|BE| = |ED|$

Construction:

Not necessary in this proof.

Proof:

$\|\angle EAD\| = \|\angle ECB\|$	Equal, alternate
$\|\angle EDA\| = \|\angle EBC\|$	Equal, alternate
$\|AD\| = \|BC\|$	Opposite sides of a parallelogram
$\therefore \triangle ADE \equiv \triangle CBE$	ASA
$\|AE\| = \|EC\|$	Corresponding side
$\|BE\| = \|ED\|$	Corresponding side

Q.E.D.

To prove: Write down what you need to prove. It helps to know the properties of what you are trying to prove. If we needed to prove that something was a square, we would need to know the properties of a square.

Construction: You may need extra lines or angles to help you to prove the theorem. Construct these lines or angles and label them clearly.

Proof: A proof is made up of a series of statements that follow a logical progression, which leads to the answer. When writing down statements, we must always try to give a reason for each statement, whether we have been given this information or whether we have used a previous theorem. In some proofs, the reason for a statement can be 'by construction'.

Useful Terms

Occasionally, we may encounter the following terms in a proof:

Is equivalent to: This means that something has the same value or measure as something else. For example, €1 is equivalent to 100 cents. If A $\Rightarrow$ B and B $\Rightarrow$ A, then A and B are equivalent.

If and only if: Ben will go to the cinema if and only if his favourite film is on. This means that if his favourite film is on, Ben will go to the cinema **and** if he is going to the cinema then his favourite film is on.

In geometry, we meet the phrase 'if and only if' in statements such as the following:

> Two lines are parallel if and only if for any transversal, corresponding angles are equal.

'if and only if' can be written 'iff'.

'A iff B' means 'If A then B **and** if B then A'.

Worked Example 10.3

XYZ is a triangle. Prove that $|\angle 1| + |\angle 2| + |\angle 3| = 360°$.

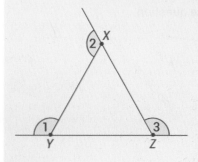

Solution

Given: △XYZ as shown.

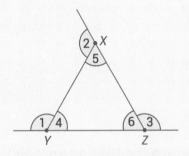

To prove: $|\angle 1| + |\angle 2| + |\angle 3| = 360°$.

Construction: Label angles 4, 5 and 6 as shown.

Proof:

$|\angle 1| = |\angle 5| + |\angle 6|$	Exterior angle
$|\angle 2| = |\angle 4| + |\angle 6|$	Exterior angle
$|\angle 3| = |\angle 4| + |\angle 5|$	Exterior angle
$\Rightarrow |\angle 1| + |\angle 2| + |\angle 3|$ $= 2(|\angle 4| + |\angle 5| + |\angle 6|)$	Adding the 3 lines above
But $|\angle 4| + |\angle 5| + |\angle 6| = 180°$.	Angles in a triangle
$\Rightarrow |\angle 1| + |\angle 2| + |\angle 3|$ $= 2(180°) = 360°$	
Q.E.D.	

Worked Example 10.4

ABCD is a square. BDEF is another square.

Prove that the area of BDEF is twice the area of ABCD.

Solution

Given: Squares ABCD and BDEF

To prove: Area $BDEF = 2 \times$ (Area ABCD)

Construction: Mark the sides of ABCD as x and the sides of BDEF as y.

Proof: Using Pythagoras' theorem:

$$x^2 + x^2 = y^2$$
$$\Rightarrow 2x^2 = y^2$$
$$\Rightarrow 2(\text{Area } ABCD) = \text{Area } BDEF$$

Q.E.D.

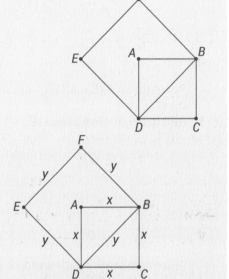

Remember that other mathematical skills may be needed to solve questions. For example, you may need to use trigonometry to help you solve a geometry question.

Exercise 10.3

1. △ABC is an isosceles triangle such that $|AB| = |BC|$. M is the midpoint of [AC].

   Show that [MB] bisects the angle ABC.

   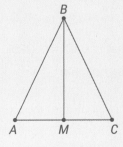

2. Consider the following diagram.

   $|AE| = |AD|$ and $|AB| = |AC|$.

   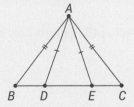

   (i) Prove that $\triangle ABD \equiv \triangle AEC$.

   (ii) Prove that $\triangle ABE \equiv \triangle ACD$.

3. *ABCD* is a quadrilateral.

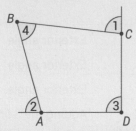

Show that $|\angle 1| + |\angle 2| = |\angle 3| + |\angle 4|$.

4. $\triangle ABC$ is an isosceles triangle as shown, where $|AB| = |AC|$.

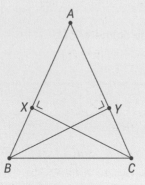

Prove that $\triangle AXC \equiv \triangle AYB$.

5. *ABC* is a triangle as shown.

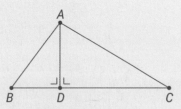

Prove that $|AB|^2 + |DC|^2 = |BD|^2 + |AC|^2$.

6. *O* is the centre of a circle with the chord [*AB*] as shown.

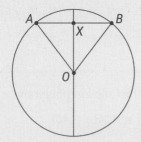

If [*OX*] bisects [*AB*], explain fully why $AB \perp OX$.

7. *l* and *k* are parallel lines.

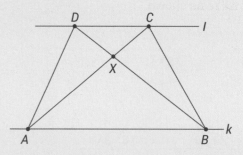

(i) Show that area of $\triangle ABD$ = area of $\triangle ABC$.

(ii) Show that area of $\triangle ADX$ = area of $\triangle BCX$.

8. *AB* and *CD* are parallel line segments. $|CA| = |CD|$.

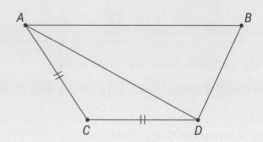

Show that *AD* bisects $\angle BAC$.

9. *DEFG* is a parallelogram.

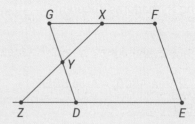

If *Y* is the midpoint of [*GD*], show that the area of *DEFG* = the area of *ZEFX*.

10. [*AB*] and [*QP*] are two diameters of a circle.

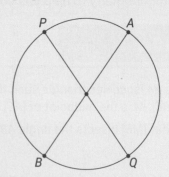

(i) Prove that $|\angle QAB| = |\angle QPB|$.

(ii) Prove that $AQ \parallel PB$.

11. Consider the following diagram. *P*, *R* and *S* are collinear.

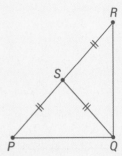

Prove that |∠*PQR*| = 90°.

12. *ABC* is a triangle as shown. *E* is the midpoint of [*AB*] and *D* is the midpoint of [*AC*].

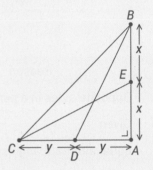

   (i) Write |*BD*|² and |*CE*|² in terms of *x* and *y*.

   (ii) Prove that 4|*BD*|² + 4|*CE*|² = 5|*BC*|².

13. A part for a metal support of a bridge is being manufactured.

For the design to be stable, |∠*A*| = |∠*B*|. Show that this is the case.

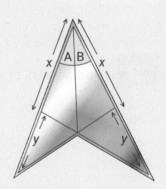

14. *O* is the centre of a circle that has *TB* as a tangent.

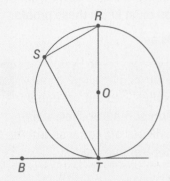

Show that |∠*SRT*| = |∠*STB*|.

15. [*AB*] is the diameter of a circle with centre *O* and tangent *BT*.
|∠*ADC*| = 120°.

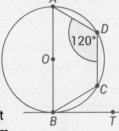

   (i) Show that Δ*BOC* is equilateral.

   (ii) If |*AD*| = |*DC*|, prove that *ADCO* is a parallelogram.

16. In the diagram, [*AC*] is the bisector of ∠*TAB*.

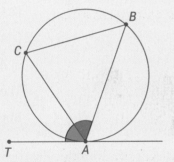

Prove that |*AC*| = |*CB*|.

17. *ABCD* is a parallelogram. [*AX*] and [*BX*] are bisectors of the angles at *A* and *B* respectively.

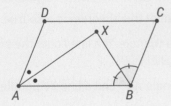

Prove that |∠*AXB*| = 90°.

10.4 Proofs II

On our course we will also cover a set of very important theorems concerning parallel lines and similar triangles. You must know these proofs.

These proofs are:

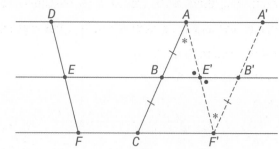

> **Theorem 11**
> If three parallel lines cut off equal segments on some transversal line, then they will cut off equal segments on any other transversal.

The converse of this theorem is also true.

If three lines cut off equal segments on two or more transversals, then the three lines are parallel to each other.

Given: AD || BE || CF, as in the diagram with |AB| = |BC|

To prove: |DE| = |EF|.

Construction: Draw AE' || DE, cutting EB at E' and CF at F'.

Draw F'B' || AB, cutting EB at B', as in the diagram.

Proof:

Statement	Reason
|B'F'| = |BC|	Opposite sides in a parallelogram
= |AB|	Given
|∠BAE'| = |∠E'F'B'|	Equal alternate angles
|∠AE'B| = |∠F'E'B'|	Vertically opposite angles
|∠ABE'| = |∠E'B'F'|	Angles in a triangle
∴ ΔABE' is congruent to ΔF'B'E'.	ASA
Therefore, |AE'| = |F'E'|.	
But |AE'| = |DE| and |F'E'| = |FE|.	Opposite sides in a parallelogram
∴ |DE| = |EF|	
Q.E.D.	

> **Theorem 12**
> Let ABC be a triangle. If a line *l* is parallel to BC and cuts [AB] in the ratio s : t, then it also cuts [AC] in the same ratio.

The converse of this theorem is also true.

Let ABC be a triangle. If a line *l* cuts the sides AB and AC in the same ratio, then *l* is parallel to BC.

Given: A triangle ABC and a line XY parallel to BC which cuts [AB] in the ratio s : t

To prove: |AY| : |YC| = s : t

Construction: Divide [AX] into s equal parts and [XB] into t equal parts. Through each point of division, draw a line parallel to BC.

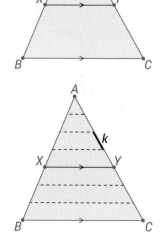

$$\frac{|AX|}{|XB|} = \frac{|AY|}{|YC|} \quad \text{or} \quad \frac{|AB|}{|XB|} = \frac{|AC|}{|YC|} \quad \text{or} \quad \frac{|AB|}{|AX|} = \frac{|AC|}{|AY|}$$

Proof: According to Theorem 11, the parallel lines cut off segments of equal length along [AC].

Let *k* be the length of each of these equal segments.

$\Rightarrow |AY| = sk$ and $|YC| = tk$

$\Rightarrow |AY| : |YC| = sk : tk = s : t$

Q.E.D.

Theorem 13

If two triangles *ABC* and *DEF* are similar, then their sides are proportional, in order:

$$\frac{|AB|}{|DE|} = \frac{|BC|}{|EF|} = \frac{|AC|}{|DF|}$$

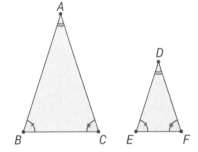

The converse of this theorem is also true.

If, in any two triangles, the sides (in order) are proportional

i.e. if $\dfrac{|AB|}{|DE|} = \dfrac{|AC|}{|DF|} = \dfrac{|BC|}{|EF|}$, then the two triangles are similar to each other.

Given: Similar triangles *ABC* and *DEF*

To prove: $\dfrac{|AB|}{|DE|} = \dfrac{|BC|}{|EF|} = \dfrac{|AC|}{|DF|}$

Construction: Assume triangle *DEF* is smaller than triangle *ABC*.

Mark a point *X* on [AB] such that |AX| = |DE|, and mark a point *Y* on [AC] such that |AY| = |DF| as shown.

Draw [XY].

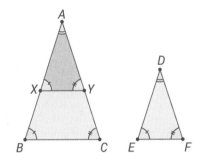

Proof:

Statement	Reason
△AXY is congruent to △DEF.	SAS
$\Rightarrow |\angle AXY| = |\angle ABC|$	
$\Rightarrow XY \parallel BC$	Corresponding angles equal
$\Rightarrow \dfrac{|AB|}{|AX|} = \dfrac{|AC|}{|AY|}$	Theorem 12: If a line *l* is parallel to BC and cuts [AB] in the ratio $s:t$, then it also cuts [AC] in the same ratio.
But |AX| = |DE| and |AY| = |DF|.	Construction
$\Rightarrow \dfrac{|AB|}{|DE|} = \dfrac{|AC|}{|DF|}$	
Similarly, $\dfrac{|BC|}{|EF|} = \dfrac{|AB|}{|DE|}$.	
$\Rightarrow \dfrac{|AB|}{|DE|} = \dfrac{|BC|}{|EF|} = \dfrac{|AC|}{|DF|}$	
Q.E.D.	

GEOMETRY II

Worked Example 10.5

In the diagram, $XY \parallel BC$ and $YZ \parallel CD$.

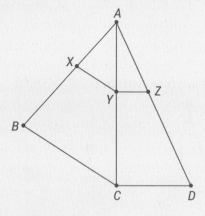

Prove that $XZ \parallel BD$.

Solution

One method of proof is to show that $\frac{|AX|}{|XB|} = \frac{|AZ|}{|ZD|}$.

We must identify which sides and which ratios we will use.

$XY \parallel BC$ $YZ \parallel CD$

$\Rightarrow \frac{|AX|}{|XB|} = \frac{|AY|}{|YC|}$ $\Rightarrow \frac{|AY|}{|YC|} = \frac{|AZ|}{|ZD|}$

We can see that these two equations are linked by the ratio $\frac{|AY|}{|YC|}$.

$\Rightarrow \frac{|AX|}{|XB|} = \frac{|AZ|}{|ZD|}$

$\therefore XZ \parallel BD$

Worked Example 10.6

In the diagram, $BD \parallel CE$ and $DF \parallel EG$.

Prove that $|AC| \cdot |FG| = |AG| \cdot |BC|$.

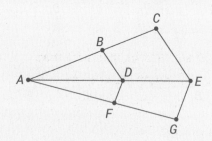

Solution

We note that $|AC| \cdot |FG| = |AG| \cdot |BC|$ could also be written as $\frac{|AC|}{|BC|} = \frac{|AG|}{|FG|}$. This is what we need to prove.

$BD \parallel CE$

$\Rightarrow \frac{|AC|}{|BC|} = \frac{|AE|}{|DE|}$

$DF \parallel EG$

$\Rightarrow \frac{|AE|}{|DE|} = \frac{|AG|}{|FG|}$

$\Rightarrow \frac{|AC|}{|BC|} = \frac{|AG|}{|FG|} \left(\text{As } \frac{|AC|}{|BC|} = \frac{|AE|}{|DE|} = \frac{|AG|}{|FG|} \right)$

$\therefore |AC| \cdot |FG| = |AG| \cdot |BC|$ Q.E.D.

Exercise 10.4

1. Consider the following diagram:

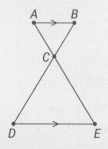

  (i) Prove that $\triangle ABC$ is similar to $\triangle CDE$.

  (ii) Prove that $\frac{|AC|}{|CE|} = \frac{|BC|}{|CD|}$.

2. Consider the following diagram:

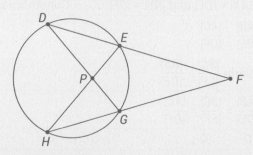

Show that $\triangle DGF$ and $\triangle HEF$ are similar.

3. *PQRS* is a trapezium (where one side of a quadrilateral is parallel to one other side) as shown.

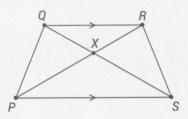

   (i) Prove that △*PXS* is similar to △*QXR*.

   (ii) Show that |*PX*| . |*QX*| = |*XR*| . |*XS*|.

4. △*ABC* is right-angled at *C*. *CD* ⊥ *AB*.

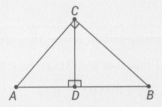

   (i) Establish that △*ABC* and △*BDC* are equiangular (similar).

   (ii) Prove that |*BC*|² = |*AB*| . |*BD*|.

5. *ABC* is a triangle as shown. *EF* ∥ *BC* and *DF* ∥ *EC*.

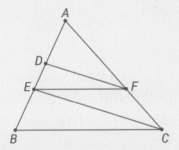

Prove that $\frac{|AD|}{|DE|} = \frac{|AE|}{|EB|}$.

6. In the diagram shown, *SU* ∥ *QR* and *ST* ∥ *QU*.

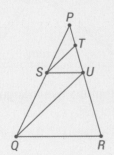

Prove that |*PT*| : |*TU*| = |*PU*| : |*UR*|.

7. Two triangles *ABC* and *DBC* are shown. *EF* ∥ *AB* and *EG* ∥ *BD*.

Prove that *FG* ∥ *AD*.

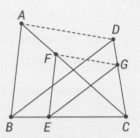

8. *ABCD* is a trapezium as shown. *AB* ∥ *EF* ∥ *DC*.

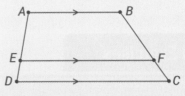

Prove that $\frac{|AE|}{|ED|} = \frac{|BF|}{|FC|}$.

9. *ABC* is a triangle inscribed in a circle of centre *O*. Prove that |*AC*|² = |*AD*| . |*AB*|.

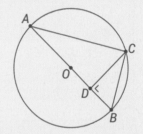

10. *XD* and *BY* are straight lines such that:

   ● In △*ABC*, |*AX*| : |*XB*| = |*AP*| : |*PC*|.

   ● In △*ACD*, |*AP*| : |*PC*| = |*AY*| : |*YD*|.

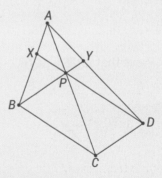

   (i) Prove that *BPDC* is a parallelogram.

   (ii) Prove that *XY* ∥ *BD*.

11. In the triangle *XYZ*, |*XR*| = |*ZS*| and |*YR*| = |*YS*|.

   (i) Prove that *RS* ∥ *XZ*.

   (ii) Prove that △*RTX* and △*STZ* are similar.

   (iii) Prove that △*XTZ* is an isosceles triangle.

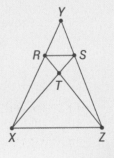

12. A triangle *ABC* with altitudes [*AD*], [*BE*] and [*CF*] is shown.

   (i) Prove that △*ABD* and △*BCF* are equiangular.

   (ii) Prove that △*AEB* and △*AFC* are equiangular.

   (iii) Prove that: |*AB*| . |*CF*| = |*BC*| . |*AD*| = |*AC*| . |*BE*|

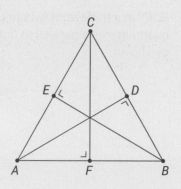

Revision Exercises

Some questions will require the use of trigonometry.

1. (a) Prove that the following pairs of triangles are congruent. Explain your answers fully.

   (i)

   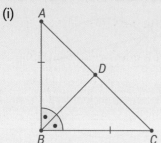

   Prove that △*ABD* ≡ △*BDC*.

   (ii)

   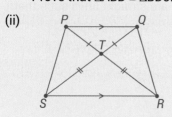

   Prove that △*PTS* ≡ △*QTR*.

   (iii)

   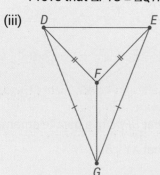

   Prove that △*DFG* ≡ △*EFG*.

   (b) In the triangle *PQR*, |*AP*| = |*BR*| and |*AD*| = |*BD*|.

   (i) Prove that △*PQR* is an isosceles triangle.

   (ii) Show that |*PC*| = |*CR*|.

   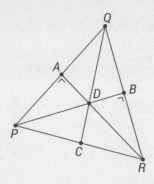

2. (a) Two triangular metal frames are joined to form a door part as shown.

   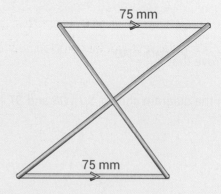

   Show that the two triangular metal frames are identical.

(b) Consider the parallelogram *ABCD*.

(i) Prove that △ *AXD* ≡ △ *BXC*.

(ii) Show that *X* is the midpoint of [*DB*].

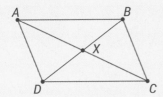

(c) A carpenter marks off the two midpoints of two sides of a square wooden panel. He then cuts along the two lines as shown.

Show that the two cuts are of equal length.

3. (a) Consider the circle with centre *O* and tangents *RP* and *RT*.

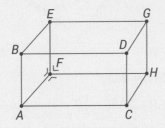

Prove that *RPT* is an isosceles triangle.

(b) A regular rectangular solid is shown.

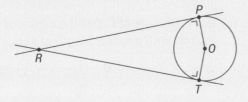

Prove that $|EC|^2 = |AF|^2 + |AC|^2 + |AB|^2$.

(c) A rectangular sheet of metal *ABCD* is shown. A triangular piece of metal *AEF* is to be cut from this sheet. The line *AF* bisects the angle *BAE*.

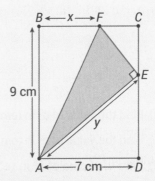

(i) Show that $|CE|^2 = 7(2x - 7)$.

(ii) Find the value of *y*.

(iii) Find the area of the triangle *AFE* in terms of *x*.

(iv) Find, to one decimal place, the value of *x*.

4. (a) Consider the following diagram:

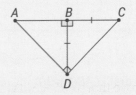

(i) Show that $|AD|^2 = |AB|^2 + |BC|^2$.

(ii) Show that $|DC|^2 = |AC| . |AB|$.

(b) △*ABC* is right-angled at *C*. *CD* ⊥ *AB*.

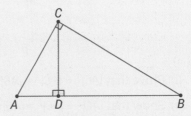

(i) Establish that △*ABC* and △*ADC* are similar (equiangular).

(ii) Prove that $|AC|^2 = |AB| . |AD|$.

GEOMETRY II

(c) The right-angled triangle *ABC* with side lengths of *a*, *b* and *c* is shown. The altitude *d* and the length *y* are also shown.

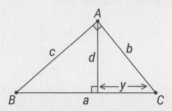

   (i) Find the value of d^2 in terms of *a* and *y*.

  (ii) Find the value of c^2 in terms of *a* and *y*.

 (iii) Find the value of b^2 in terms of *a* and *y*.

 (iv) Hence, show that $b^2 d^2 = c^2 y^2$.

5. (a) Two circles intersect at the points *X* and *Y* as shown. *O* is the centre of the smaller circle.

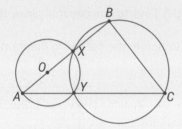

Show that $|\angle ABC| = 90°$.

(b) A right-angled triangle *ABC* is shown.

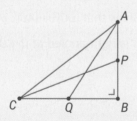

   (i) Prove that $|AC|^2 - |PC|^2 = |AB|^2 - |PB|^2$.

  (ii) Show that $|AC|^2 - |PC|^2 = |AQ|^2 - |PQ|^2$.

(c) The isosceles triangle *PQR* is inscribed in a circle with centre *O*.

RS is a tangent to the circle.

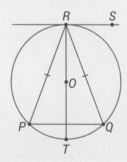

Prove that $PQ \parallel RS$.

6. (a) *PQRS* is a quadrilateral with diagonals [*PR*] and [*QS*] such that $|PR| = |QS|$. Also, $|PS| = |QR|$.

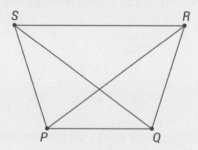

   (i) Identify two congruent triangles. Give reasons for your answer.

  (ii) Show that *PQ* must be parallel to *RS*.

(b) *k* is a circle of radius *r* and centre *O*. *M* is the midpoint of [*OP*].

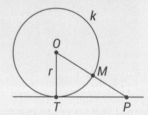

A tangent is drawn to the circle from *P*. It touches the circle at *T*.

Find $|PT|$ in terms of *r*.

(c) In the triangle *ABC*, *O* is the centre of the incircle with a radius length of *r* cm.

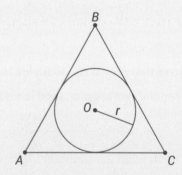

   (i) Show that:

     Area $\triangle ABC = \frac{1}{2}$(Perimeter $\triangle ABC$) $\times r$

  (ii) Find the perimeter of a triangle with an incircle radius length of 8 cm and an area of 500 cm².

7. (a) Let *ABC* be a triangle. Prove that if a line *l* is parallel to *BC* and cuts [*AB*] in the ratio *m* : *n*, then it also cuts [*AC*] in the same ratio.

(b) Consider the triangle *PQR*. *ST* ∥ QR and $|\angle PTS| = |\angle STQ|$.

    (i) Prove that *TQR* is an isosceles triangle.

    (ii) Show that $|PS| \cdot |TQ| = |PT| \cdot |SQ|$.

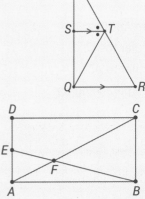

(c) In a rectangle *ABCD*, $|AB| = 2|BC|$.

    The point *E* is the midpoint of [*AD*].

    (i) Show that $\triangle AEF$ and $\triangle BFC$ are similar.

    (ii) If $|BC| = x$ units, find $|AC|$ in terms of *x*.

    (iii) If the point *E* is moved such that $|AE| = \frac{1}{5}|AD|$, find $|EB|$ in terms of *x*.

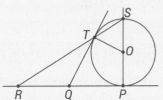

(d) *O* is the centre of a circle with tangents *RP* and *QT*.

    Show that the triangle *QRT* is an isosceles triangle.

Exam Questions

1. (a) Prove that if three parallel lines cut off equal segments on some transversal line, then they will cut off equal segments on any other transversal line.

(b) In the diagram, P_1Q_1, P_2Q_2, and P_3Q_3 are parallel and so also are Q_1P_2 and Q_2P_3.

Prove that $|P_1Q_1| \times |P_3Q_3| = |P_2Q_2|^2$.

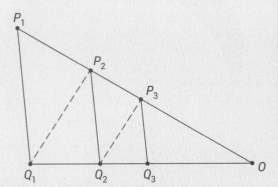

SEC Leaving Certificate Higher Level, Paper 2, 2011

2. (a) In the diagram, l_1, l_2, l_3 and l_4 are parallel lines that make intercepts of equal length on the transversal *k*. *FG* is parallel to *k*, and *HG* is parallel to *ED*.

Prove that the triangles $\triangle CDE$ and $\triangle FGH$ are congruent.

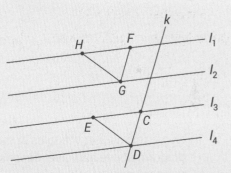

(b) The incircle of the triangle *ABC* has centre *O* and touches the sides at *P*, *Q* and *R*, as shown. Prove that $|\angle PQR| = \frac{1}{2}(|\angle CAB| + |\angle CBA|)$.

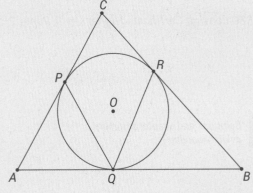

SEC Leaving Certificate Higher Level, Paper 2, 2012

3. (a) A quadrilateral (four-sided figure) has two sides which are parallel and equal in length. Prove that the quadrilateral is a parallelogram.

(b) In the parallelogram *ABCD*

- *DE* is perpendicular to *AC*.
- *BF* is perpendicular to *AC*.

Prove that *EBFD* is a parallelogram.

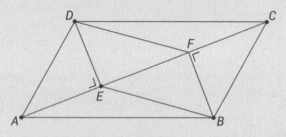

SEC Leaving Certificate Higher Level, Paper 2, 2013

4. (a) Prove that, if two triangles $\triangle ABC$ and $\triangle A'B'C'$ are similar, then their sides are proportional, in order:

$$\frac{|AB|}{|A'B'|} = \frac{|BC|}{|B'C'|} = \frac{|CA|}{|C'A'|}$$

(b) [AB] and [CD] are chords of a circle that intersect externally at *E*, as shown.

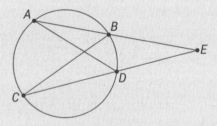

(i) Name two similar triangles in the diagram above and give reasons for your answer.

(ii) Prove that $|EA| \cdot |EB| = |EC| \cdot |ED|$.

(iii) Given that $|EB| = 6.25$, $|ED| = 5.94$ and $|CB| = 10$, find $|AD|$.

SEC Leaving Certificate Higher Level, Paper 2, 2014

5. The triangle *ABC* is right-angled at *C*.

The circle *s* has diameter [AC] and the circle *t* has diameter [CB].

(i) Draw the circle *u* which has diameter [AB].

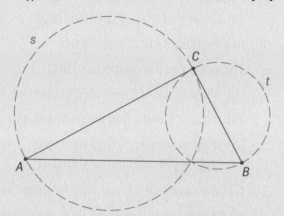

(ii) Prove that in any right-angled triangle *ABC*, the area of the circle *u* equals the sum of the areas of the circles *s* and *t*.

(iii) The diagram shows the right-angled triangle *ABC* and arcs of the circles *s*, *t* and *u*.

Each of the shaded areas in the diagram is called a lune, a crescent-shaped area bounded by arcs of the circles.

Prove that the sum of the areas of the two shaded lunes is equal to the area of the triangle *ABC*.

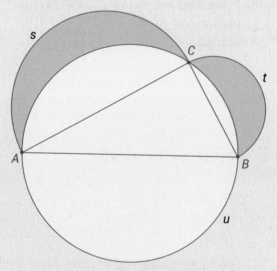

SEC Leaving Certificate Higher Level, Paper 2, 2014

 Solutions and chapter summary available online

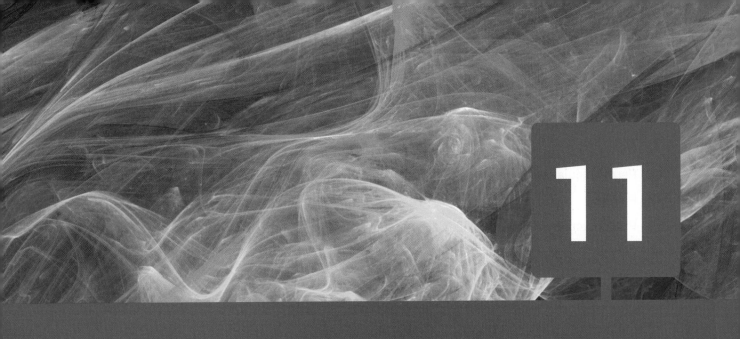

11

Constructions

In this chapter you will learn to:

- ⊙ Construct the circumcentre and circumcircle of a given triangle, using only a straight edge and a compass
- ⊙ Construct the incentre and incircle of a given triangle, using only a straight edge and a compass
- ⊙ Construct an angle of 60°, without using a protractor or a set square

- ⊙ Construct a tangent to a given circle at a given point on it
- ⊙ Construct a parallelogram, given the length of the sides and the measure of the angles
- ⊙ Construct the centroid of a triangle
- ⊙ Construct the orthocentre of a triangle
- ⊙ Work with constructions in real-life contexts

You should remember...

- ⊙ How to draw a line
- ⊙ How to draw a line segment
- ⊙ How to draw a ray
- ⊙ How to measure an angle

- ⊙ Notation used in geometry
- ⊙ Methods of construction
- ⊙ The theorem of Pythagoras

CONSTRUCTIONS

Key words

- ⊙ Bisect
- ⊙ Perpendicular bisector
- ⊙ Parallel
- ⊙ Perpendicular
- ⊙ Tangent
- ⊙ SSS

- ⊙ SAS
- ⊙ ASA
- ⊙ RHS
- ⊙ Hypotenuse
- ⊙ Right-angled triangle
- ⊙ Circumcentre

- ⊙ Circumcircle
- ⊙ Incentre
- ⊙ Incircle
- ⊙ Centroid
- ⊙ Orthocentre

11.1 Introduction

From the design of a new bridge to that of the next video game console, all new ideas, buildings or constructions start off on the drawing board.

Any engineer, architect or designer will first draw out a new design, and from these drawings a new invention is born.

One only has to remember that the Eiffel Tower and the Statue of Liberty (to name a few) were all designed without the aid of computers.

But how do you draw a circle or a triangle accurately? This is where the knowledge and skills of construction play a role.

11.2 Construction Equipment

When doing any construction, accuracy is very important. A mistake of even a few millimetres or half a degree can cause problems. Just ask any engineer!

We use the following equipment when asked to do a construction.

Compass

A compass is used to draw arcs and circles.

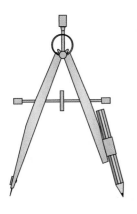 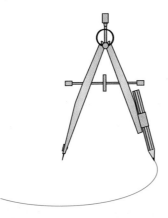 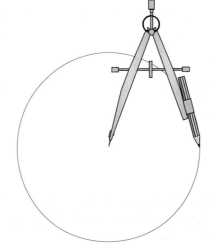

Compass Width

By adjusting the compass width, we can change the size of the arcs or circles that we draw.

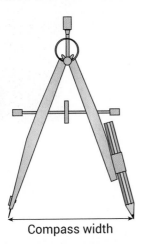

Compass width

Protractor

The protractor is used to construct and measure angles.

Straight Edge

A straight edge is a tool that is used to draw a straight line. It has no markings, so it cannot be used for measuring lines. In practice, we just use the ruler found in the construction set.

Ruler

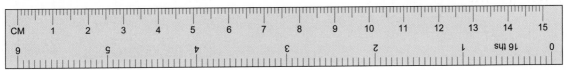

A ruler is used to construct line segments of certain lengths.

Set Square

We can use set squares to draw lines and certain angles. Two set squares are used:

- The 45° set square, which has the angles 45°, 45° and 90°
- The 30° or 60° set square, which has the angles 30°, 60° and 90°

Pencil

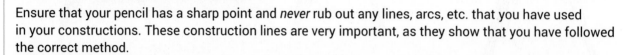

Ensure that your pencil has a sharp point and *never* rub out any lines, arcs, etc. that you have used in your constructions. These construction lines are very important, as they show that you have followed the correct method.

> Constructions 1–15, specified for Junior Certificate Higher Level, should also be known at Leaving Certificate Higher Level.

11.3 Leaving Certificate Higher Level Constructions

> The following constructions were not studied at Junior Certificate Higher Level but must be known at Leaving Certificate Higher Level.

Construction 16

The Circumcentre and Circumcircle of a Given Triangle, using only a Straight Edge and a Compass

Worked Example 11.1

Construct the circumcentre and circumcircle of the triangle *ABC*.

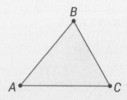

Solution

1 Construct the perpendicular bisector of [*AC*].	**2** Construct the perpendicular bisector of any other side of the triangle – in this case the side [*BC*].
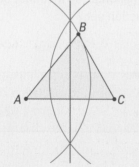	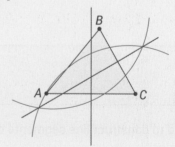

3 Mark the point of intersection of the perpendicular bisectors and label as point *O*.

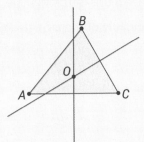

4 Point *O* is the **circumcentre** of the triangle *ABC*.

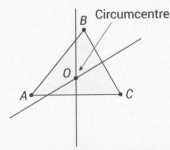

The circumcentre is the point where a triangle's three perpendicular bisectors meet.

5 Place the compass point on *O* and draw a circle of radius length |*OA*|.

This circle is the **circumcircle** of the triangle *ABC*.

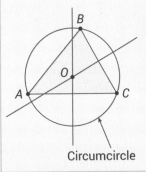

> The circumcircle of a triangle is a circle that passes through all three vertices of the triangle.

6 |*AO*| = |*BO*| = |*CO*|

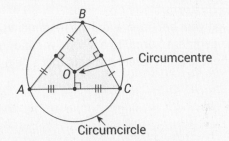

Always clearly label the circumcircle and the circumcentre.

Construction 17

Incentre and Incircle of a Given Triangle, using only a Straight Edge and a Compass

Worked Example 11.2

Construct the incentre and incircle of the triangle *PQR*.

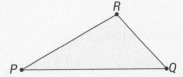

Solution

1 Construct the bisector of the angle *PQR*.

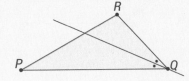

2 Construct the bisector of any other angle in the triangle, e.g. ∠*RPQ*.

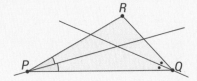

<table><tr><td>

3 Mark the point of intersection of the angle bisectors, and label as point *O*.

Point *O* is the **incentre** of the triangle *PQR*.

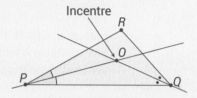

> The incentre is the point where a triangle's three angle bisectors meet.

</td><td>

5 Place the compass point on *O* and the pencil on *S*, and draw a circle. This circle should touch all three sides of the triangle.

This is the **incircle** of the triangle *PQR*.

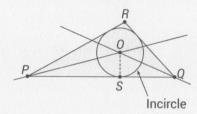

> The incircle of a triangle is the largest circle that will fit inside the triangle. Each of the triangle's three sides is a tangent to the circle.

</td></tr><tr><td>

4 Using your set square, draw a perpendicular line segment from *O* to a side of the triangle. Label the point where it meets this side as *S*.

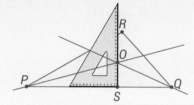

</td><td>

6 $|OS| = |OT| = |OU|$

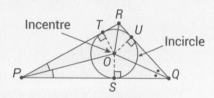

> Always clearly label the incircle and the incentre.

</td></tr></table>

Construction 18

An Angle of 60° without using a Protractor or a Set Square

Worked Example 11.3

Construct an angle of 60° without using a protractor or a set square.

Solution

<table><tr><td>

1 Draw a line segment [*AB*].

</td><td>

2 Place the compass point at *A* and draw an arc of radius length |*AB*|.

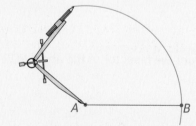

</td></tr></table>

3 Place the compass point at *B* and draw an arc of radius length |*AB*|.

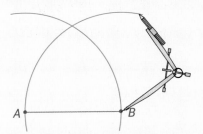

5 Join *C* to *A*. Label |∠*CAB*| as 60°.

(Note: |∠*CAB*| = 60°, as △*ABC* is equilateral and all angles are therefore 60°.)

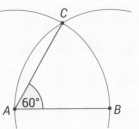

4 Mark the point of intersection of the arcs and label as point *C*.

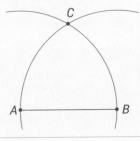

Construction 19

A Tangent to a Given Circle at a Given Point on it

CONSTRUCTIONS

Worked Example 11.4

Construct a **tangent** to the given circle at the point *A*.

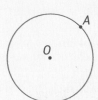

A **tangent** is a line that touches the circle at a single point.

2 Construct a line perpendicular to the ray [*OA* through the point *A*.

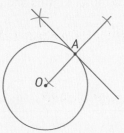

Solution

1 Draw a ray from the centre *O* of the circle through the given point *A*.

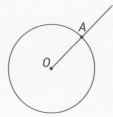

3 This is the tangent to the circle.

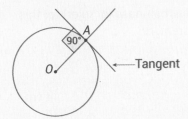

Construction 20

A Parallelogram, Given the Length of the Sides and the Measure of the Angles

Worked Example 11.5

Construct a parallelogram *ABCD* where |*AB*| = 7 cm, |*BC*| = 4 cm and |∠*ABC*| = 60°.

Solution

1 Draw a rough sketch of the parallelogram.

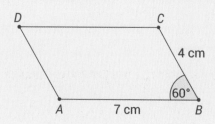

2 Construct the line segment [*AB*] where |*AB*| = 7 cm.

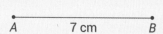

3 At point *B*, construct an angle of 60°, using the line segment [*AB*] as one arm of the angle.

Use your protractor for this angle.

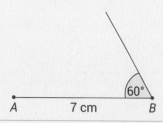

4 Mark the point *C* on this angle such that |*BC*| = 4 cm.

Use your compass (or ruler) for this measurement.

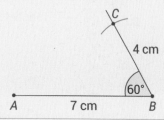

5 At point *A*, construct a ray parallel to *BC*.

Use your protractor to measure the correct angle.

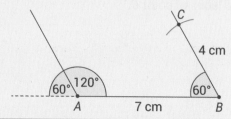

6 Mark the point *D* on this ray such that |*AD*| = 4 cm.

Use your compass (or ruler) for this measurement.

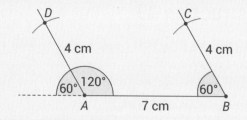

7 Using a ruler, join *C* to *D*.

Label all given measurements.

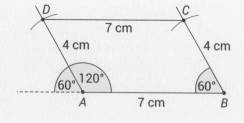

CONSTRUCTIONS

Construction 21

The Centroid of a Triangle

Construct the centroid of the triangle *PQR*.

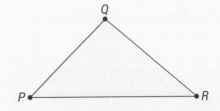

Solution

1 Construct the perpendicular bisector of the side [*PQ*].

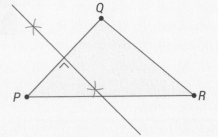

2 Label the midpoint of [*PQ*] as the point *X*.

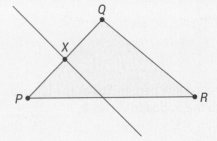

3 Using a straight edge, draw a line segment from *X* to *R*, the opposite vertex of the triangle.

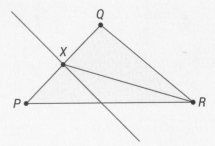

4 This line segment is a **median** of the triangle *PQR*.

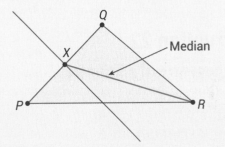

> A **median** of a triangle is a segment that goes from one of the triangle's vertices to the midpoint of the opposite side.

5 Construct the perpendicular bisector of [*PR*] and label the midpoint *Y*.

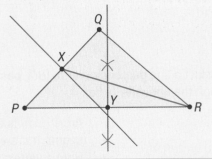

6 Using a straight edge, join *Y* to the opposite vertex, *Q*.

This is a second median.

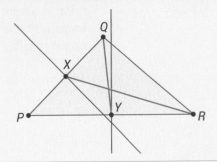

CONSTRUCTIONS

7 Where the medians intersect is the **centroid** of the triangle *PQR*.

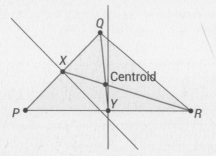

The **centroid** is the triangle's balance point or centre of gravity, i.e. the point where the three medians of the triangle meet.

8 The centroid of a triangle divides each median in the ratio 2:1.

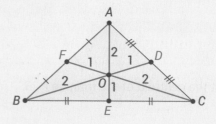

Construction 22

The Orthocentre of a Triangle

Construct the orthocentre of the triangle *ABC*.

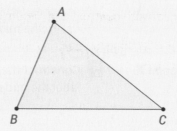

Solution

1 Construct a line perpendicular to [*BC*], passing through the opposite vertex *A*.

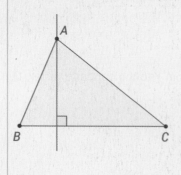

An **altitude** is a segment drawn from a vertex of a triangle to its opposite side such that it forms a right angle with the opposite side.

2 Construct a line perpendicular to [*AC*], passing through the opposite vertex *B*.

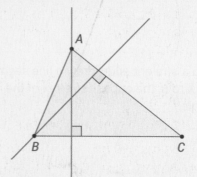

3 Mark the point where these two perpendiculars meet as the point *O*.

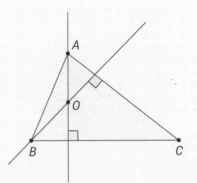

4 O is the **orthocentre** of the triangle *ABC*.

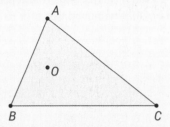

The orthocentre is the point where the altitudes of a triangle intersect.

Summary of the Centres of Triangles

Centre	Intersection of	Properties	Possible Location		
			Inside	Outside	On
Circumcentre	Perpendicular bisectors	Equidistant from the vertices of the triangles	✓	✓	✓
Incentre	Angle bisectors	Equidistant from the sides of the triangles	✓	✗	✗
Centroid	Medians	Divides each median in the ratio 2:1 (distance from vertex to centre is twice the distance from the centroid to opposite side). Centre of gravity	✓	✗	✗
Orthocentre	Altitudes	Collinear with centroid and circumcentre	✓	✓	✓

Note that the type of triangle (acute, obtuse or right-angled) determines whether the circumcentre and/or orthocentre is inside, outside or on the triangle.

Revision Exercises

1. Construct the circumcentre and circumcircle of the triangle *ABC* where |*AB*| = 4 cm, |*BC*| = 5.5 cm and |*AC*| = 7.5 cm.

2. Construct the circumcentre and circumcircle of the triangle *GHI* where |∠*HIG*| = 35°, |∠*GHI*| = 100° and |*IH*|= 9 cm.

3. (i) Construct a right-angled triangle, an acute triangle and an obtuse triangle.

   (ii) Construct the circumcentre of each triangle.

   (iii) Compare the position of the circumcentre for each type of triangle. What do you notice?

4. Construct the incentre and incircle of the triangle *GHI* where |*GH*| = 80 mm, |*HI*| = 70 mm and |*GI*| = 55 mm.

5. (i) Construct a right-angled triangle, an acute triangle and an obtuse triangle.

   (ii) Construct the incentre of each triangle.

   (iii) Compare the position of the incentre for each type of triangle. What do you notice?

6. Construct the incentre and incircle of the triangle *MNO* where |*MO*| = 5.7 cm, |*ON*| = 10.2 cm and |∠*MON*| = 95°.

7. Construct the incentre and incircle of the triangle *PQR* where |*PQ*| = 9 cm, |*PR*| = 7 cm and |∠*QPR*| = 90°.

8. Copy the following line segments into your copybook. Construct an angle of 60° on each line segment without using a protractor or set square.

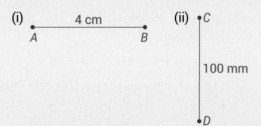

(i) A —— 4 cm —— B

(ii) •C

100 mm

•D

9. (i) Construct an equilateral triangle of side length 8 cm using only a ruler and a compass.

   (ii) Hence, **using only a compass and a straight edge**, construct an equilateral triangle of side length 4 cm.

10. Using only a compass and a straight edge, construct an angle of 30°.
    Explain how you constructed this angle.

11. Construct a circle of radius 60 mm, and construct a tangent to this circle at any point on the circle.

12. Construct the parallelogram *EFGH* where |*EF*| = 5 cm, |*FG*| = 8 cm and |∠*EFG*| = 150°.

13. Construct the rhombus *MNOP* where |*MN*| = 8.4 cm and |∠*OMN*| = 40°.

14. Construct the centroid of the triangle *ABC* where |*AB*| = 8 cm, |*BC*|= 5.2 cm and |*AC*| = 9.4 cm.

15. Construct the centroid of the triangle *TUV* where |*TV*|= 10.2 cm, |∠*UTV*| = 36° and |∠*VUT*| = 90°.

16. Construct the centroid of an equilateral triangle *PQR* where |*PQ*| = 70 mm.

17. Construct the orthocentre of an equilateral triangle *ABC* where |*AB*| = 10 cm.

18. Construct the orthocentre of the triangle *TUV* where |*TV*| = 10 cm, |*UT*| = 7 cm and |∠*TUV*| = 90°.

19. (i) Construct a right-angled triangle, an acute triangle and an obtuse triangle.

    (ii) Construct the orthocentre of each triangle.

    (iii) Compare the position of the orthocentre for each type of triangle.
    What do you notice?

20. The intersection of two paths, Forest Path and Beach Lane, is shown.

(i) Construct the shown diagram, using an appropriate scale.

(ii) A new straight path is to be constructed from Beach Lane to Forest Path, 600 m back from the intersection. This path runs perpendicular to Beach Lane. Construct the possible location of this new path.

(iii) Using a ruler, find the length of this new path to two significant figures.

(iv) Using trigonometry, find the length of this new path to the nearest metre.

21. Two offices are 10 km away from each other as shown.

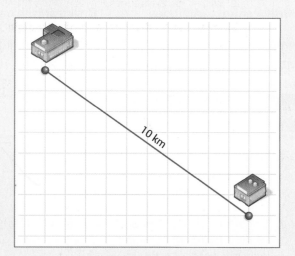

A road is to be built that is equidistant from each office. Show this road on a diagram.
(Use a scale of 1 cm = 1 km.)

22. (i) Construct the line segment [*XY*] such that |*XY*| = 12 cm.

    (ii) Divide the line [*XY*] into five equal parts without measuring it.

    (iii) Draw a ray [*PQ*.

    (iv) Construct on the ray [*PQ* a line segment [*PR*] such that |*PR*| = $\frac{2}{3}$|*XY*|.

23. Copy the following diagram onto graph paper:

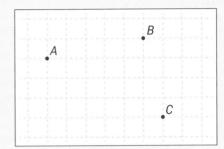

Using only a compass and a straight edge, construct a circle that passes through the points A, B and C.

24. (i) Construct the triangle ABC where |AB| = 7 cm, |AC| = 10 cm and |∠BAC| = 50°.

(ii) Hence, construct the triangle DEF where |DE| = |AC|, |FE| = |BC| and |∠BCA| = |∠FED|.

(iii) Prove that △ABC ≡ △DEF.

25. (i) Construct a non-right-angled triangle ABC.

(ii) Using the constructed triangle ABC, construct a parallelogram ABCD (ABCD is not a rectangle).

26. (i) Construct a triangle PQR where |PR| = 85 mm, |∠PQR| = 90° and |∠RPQ| = 40°.

(ii) Construct the orthocentre of the triangle PQR.

(iii) Find the area of the triangle PQR.

27.

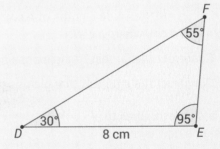

(i) Construct the triangle DEF as shown.

(ii) Draw a line segment [PR] where |PR| = 12 cm.

(iii) Construct a triangle PQR that is similar to the triangle DEF.

(iv) Find |PQ| and |RQ|.

28. (i) Construct the triangle shown in the diagram.

(ii) Using a protractor, find the measure of angles P and Q.

(iii) Construct the circle that circumscribes the triangle.

(iv) Measure the radius of this circle.

(v) Explain why the centre of this circle is the midpoint of the hypotenuse.

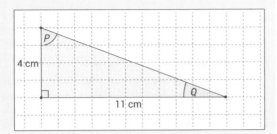

29. (i) Construct a circle of radius 70 mm.

(ii) Construct two tangents to this circle that are parallel to each other, using only a compass and a straight edge.

30. The diagram shows four circles inscribed in a rectangle.

The radius of each circle is 35 mm.

(i) Construct the rectangle FGHI.

(ii) Using only a compass and a straight edge, construct the four circles inscribed in the rectangle. Explain how you constructed these four circles.

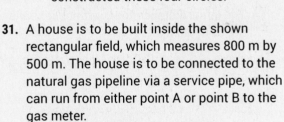

31. A house is to be built inside the shown rectangular field, which measures 800 m by 500 m. The house is to be connected to the natural gas pipeline via a service pipe, which can run from either point A or point B to the gas meter.

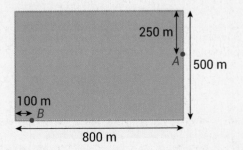

The gas meter is located in the exact centre of the field.

(i) Construct the shown diagram, using an appropriate scale.

(ii) Mark on your construction the position of the gas meter G.

(iii) Draw on your construction the location of the two possible service pipes.

(iv) Using a ruler and your construction, find the length of the two service pipes to two significant figures.

32. A blue snooker ball is hit from the point *A* and travels in the direction as shown on the diagram. A red snooker ball is hit from the point *C* and moves parallel to the side of the snooker table *AD*. The balls intersect at the point *B*.

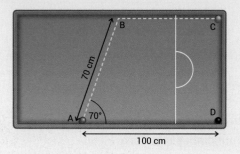

(i) Construct the shown diagram, using an appropriate scale.

Using a ruler and your construction find, to the nearest cm:

(ii) The distance travel by the red snooker ball

(iii) The shortest distance the red snooker ball is from the side of the snooker table *AD*

(iv) The initial distance the two snooker balls are from each other

33. An advertising company wants to design a logo of a circle inscribed by an equilateral triangle as shown.

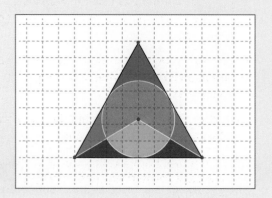

(i) If the equilateral triangle has sides of length 10 cm, construct this logo.

(ii) It is decided to add two further circles, each of which has half the radius of the original circle, as shown.

Add these circles to your construction.

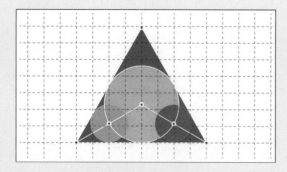

34. Using only a ruler and a compass, construct the shape shown below. Use a clearly indicated suitable scale.

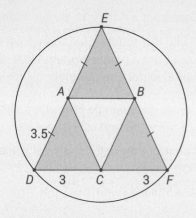

35. A triangle *ABC* has side lengths of 8 cm, 5 cm and *n* cm, where $n \in N$.

(i) Construct the largest triangle possible.

(ii) Construct the smallest triangle possible.

36. An architect wishes to design a new window and produces a blueprint. The radius length for the arcs *EC* and *DE* is equal to |*AB*|. The centre for the arc *EC* is *D* and the centre for the arc *DE* is *C*.

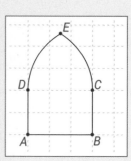

|*AD*| = 2 m and |*AB*| = 3 m.

The architect uses a scale of 1 cm = 40 cm or 1 : 40.

(i) Construct the scaled drawing of this window.

(ii) Find the area of this window.

It is then decided to insert a design of a triangle in the window as shown.

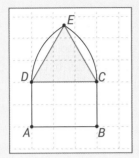

(iii) Prove that the triangle *DEC* is an equilateral triangle.

37. A scaled diagram of a sail is shown.

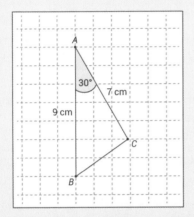

(i) Construct the sail shown. If the scale used to build the sail is 1:25, use your construction to find the length of the side of the sail [*BC*].

(ii) Calculate |*BC*| using the Cosine Rule and, hence, calculate the percentage error for you answer to part (i).

(iii) The sail is to be divided up into coloured strips. |*AD*| = |*DE*| = |*EB*| and |*AF*| = |*FG*| = |*GC*|. Use your construction to find |*DF*| and |*EG*| (scale 1:25).

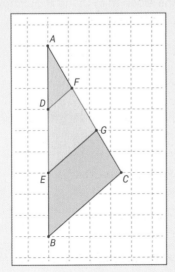

38. A landscaper is given a design for a lawn. The lawn should be in the shape of a triangle and have dimensions of 7 m, 8 m and 5.5 m.

(i) Construct a scaled drawing of this lawn.

(ii) The landscaper decides that a large circular flower-bed should surround the lawn, with each corner of the lawn touching the circular flower-bed. Construct this flower-bed.

(iii) Find the area of this flower-bed using the measurements from your construction.

39. A local council plan to build a heritage centre in the middle of a National Park. The park is bounded by three roads as shown on the diagram.

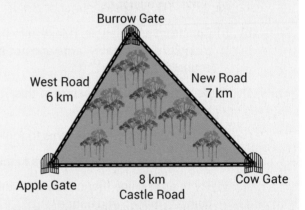

People can access the park through the three gates marked. The council must decide on the best location of the heritage centre, taking into account that at least one road will have to be built from the existing roads to the centre.

(i) Construct the shown diagram, using an appropriate scale.

(ii) Use your construction to estimate the approximate size of the National Park.

Councillor P suggests building the heritage centre at an equal distance from all three gates.

(iii) Construct on your diagram the location the councillor is suggesting.

(iv) Using your diagram, find the approximate distance the heritage centre will be from each gate.

Councillor Q suggests building the heritage centre at a location so that it is of equal distance from each road.

(v) Construct on your diagram the location this councillor is suggesting.

(vi) Using your diagram, find the approximate distance the heritage centre will be from each road.

Due to environmental concerns, it is proposed that the heritage centre be located such that the access road is of shortest distance.

(vii) Which councillor's suggestion (P or Q) is to be used?

40. (a) (i) Construct an equilateral triangle of sides 10 cm.

(ii) Construct the circumcentre of this triangle.

(iii) Construct the centroid of this triangle.

(iv) Construct the orthocentre of this triangle.

(v) What do you notice?

(b) (i) Construct any triangle. (Make sure the triangle is reasonably large and not an equilateral triangle.)

(ii) Construct the circumcentre of this triangle.

(iii) Construct the centroid of this triangle.

(iv) Construct the orthocentre of this triangle.

(v) Try to draw a line that contains all three points. What do you notice?

This line is called the Euler line and is named after Leonhard Euler (1707–1783), a famous Swiss mathematician and physicist.

● For any non-equilateral triangle, the Euler line is determined and will pass through the circumcentre, the centroid and orthocentre of the triangle.

● However, the incentre lies on the Euler line only for isosceles triangles.

41. (i) Construct the triangle and its incircle as shown in the diagram.

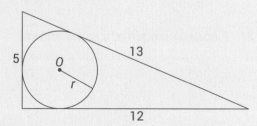

(ii) Prove that the incircle of a right-angled triangle with side lengths of 5 cm, 12 cm and 13 cm has a radius length of 2 cm.

(Note: Measurement from your construction is not a proof.)

Exam Questions

1. (a) (i) Given the points B and C below, construct, without using a protractor or set square, a point A such that $|\angle ABC| = 60°$.

(ii) Hence construct, on the same diagram above, and using a compass and straight edge only, an angle of 15°.

(b) The incircle of the triangle ABC has centre O and touches the sides at P, Q and R, as shown.

Prove that $|\angle PQR| = \frac{1}{2}(|\angle CAB| + |\angle CBA|)$.

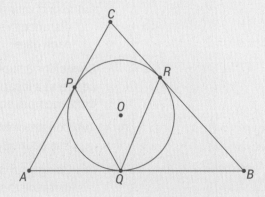

SEC Leaving Certificate Higher Level, Paper 2, 2012

2. (a) Complete each of the following statements.

    (i) The circumcentre of a triangle is the point of intersection of _____

    (ii) The incentre of a triangle is the point of intersection of _____

    (iii) The centroid of a triangle is the point of intersection of _____

(b) In an equilateral triangle, the circumcentre, the incentre and the centroid are all in the same place. Explain why this is the case.

SEC Leaving Certificate Higher Level, Paper 2, 2012

3. (a) Construct the orthocentre of the triangle *ABC* below. Show all construction lines clearly.

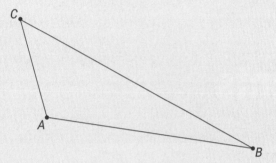

SEC Leaving Certificate Higher Level, Paper 2, 2013

(b) Given the line segment [*BC*], construct, without using a protractor or set square, a point *A* such that |∠*ABC*| = 60°. Show your construction lines.

SEC Leaving Certificate Higher Level, Paper 2, 2014

(c) Construct the centroid of the triangle *ABC* below. Show all construction lines. (Where measurement is used, show all relevant measurements and calculations clearly.)

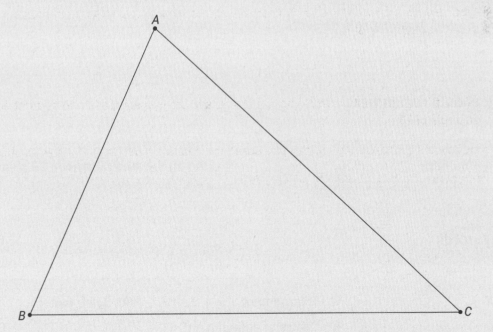

SEC Leaving Certificate Higher Level, Paper 2, 2015

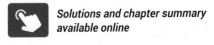

Solutions and chapter summary available online

CONSTRUCTIONS

12

Enlargements

In this chapter you will learn to:

- Investigate enlargements, paying attention to:
  - Centre of enlargement
  - Scale factor k, where $0 < k < 1$, $k > 1$, $k \in Q$
  - Area
- Solve problems involving enlargements

You should remember...

- Transformations
- Finding the area of various 2D shapes

Key words

- Object
- Image
- Enlargement
- Centre of enlargement
- Scale factor

12.1 Transformations

In geometry, a **transformation** occurs when a shape's size or position is changed or transformed. The point or shape we start with is called the **object**. The transformed shape is called the **image**.

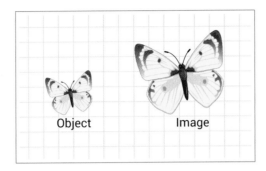

Object   Image

There are many different types of transformations.

Translation

We can move the triangle *ABC* under the **translation** $\vec{PQ}$.

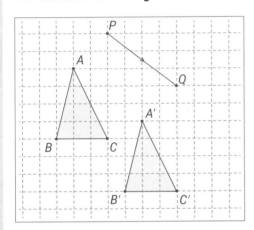

A′ (pronounced 'A prime') is the image of the point *A* under the given transformation.

A translation occurs when a point or shape is moved in a straight line. A translation moves every point the same distance and in the same direction without changing orientation of the shape or rotating it.

In a translation, the image and the object are identical and face the same way. The image shape has the same area as the object shape.

Each point in the object shape has been moved the same distance as |PQ|, parallel to *PQ* and in the direction of *P* to *Q*.

If △*ABC* is the object, then the image can be labelled as △*A′B′C′*.

Central Symmetry (in a Point)

In a **central symmetry**, each point is mapped through a specific point and reflected out the other side, the same distance in the same direction.

For example, in the diagram shown, object *DEF* is transformed under a central symmetry in the point *O* to image *D′E′F′*.

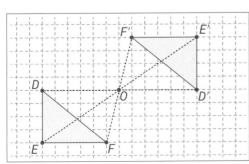

$|DO| = |OD'|$ and $\vec{DO} = \vec{OD'}$

$|EO| = |OE'|$ and $\vec{EO} = \vec{OE'}$

$|FO| = |OF'|$ and $\vec{FO} = \vec{OF'}$

A central symmetry is a reflection through a point.

The object undergoes a central symmetry in the point C.

> In a central symmetry, the image will be upside down and back to front.

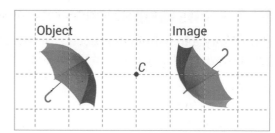

Object   Image

Axial Symmetry (in a Line)

In an **axial symmetry**, each point is mapped through a line (axis) at right angles and reflected at right angles the same distance out the other side.

In the diagram, the object undergoes an axial symmetry in the y-axis. Note how each point in the image is the same distance (3, 6 and 4 units) away from the y-axis as the object. The image is the same size as the object.

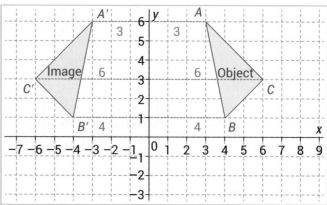

> An axial symmetry is a reflection in a line or axis. The line acts as a mirror. In an axial symmetry, the image and object are the same distance from the axis used, and one is a mirror image of the other.

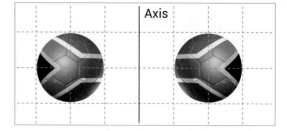

Axis

Summary of Symmetries

Consider the parallelogram A drawn on the co-ordinate plane and its images B, C and D under various transformations.

An axial symmetry in the x-axis maps the parallelogram A onto image C.

An axial symmetry in the y-axis maps the parallelogram A onto image B.

A central symmetry in the origin (0,0) maps the parallelogram A onto image D.

> An axial symmetry in the x-axis followed by an axial symmetry in the y-axis (or vice versa) is equivalent to a central symmetry in the origin.

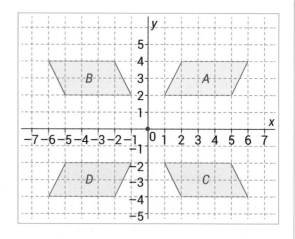

Rotations

Another type of transformation is a **rotation**.

The amount the shape rotates is called the angle of rotation.

This is given either as an angle or as a fraction of a complete turn, for example, 270° or $\frac{3}{4}$ turn.

> A rotation transforms a shape to a new position by turning it about a fixed point called the centre of rotation.

The direction of rotation is given as clockwise (negative) or anti-clockwise (positive).

The fixed point about which the object is rotated is called the **point (centre) of rotation**.

Therefore, when describing the rotation of an object, we should include, if possible:

(i) The centre of rotation

(ii) The angle of rotation

(iii) The direction of rotation (positive or negative)

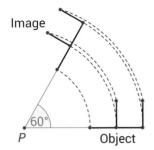

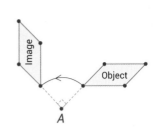

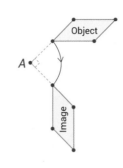

| Every point on this object has been rotated anti-clockwise through an angle of 60° about the point *P*. | Positive (anti-clockwise) rotation of 90° about the point *A*. This is denoted as $R_{90°}$. | Negative (clockwise) rotation of 90° about the point *A*. This is denoted as $R_{-90°}$. |

Enlargement

A transformation that we will encounter on our course is that of an **enlargement**.

> An **enlargement** is a transformation in which both the size and the position of a shape changes.

To enlarge a shape, we need to know two things:

● The **centre of enlargement**

● The **scale factor**, *k*

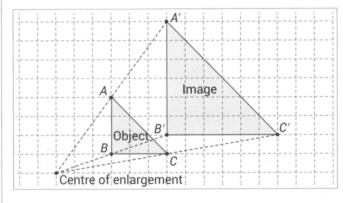

> The **centre of enlargement** is the point from which the enlargement is constructed.

> The **scale factor**, *k*, is the number by which the object is enlarged.

If a shape is enlarged by a scale factor of *k*, then each side of the image will be *k* times the length of the corresponding side of the object.

A scale factor of 3 means that the length of each image side will be three times the length of each corresponding object side.

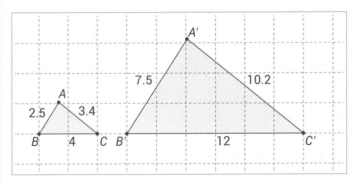

> Any scale factor *k* that is greater than 1 will result in the image being bigger than the object.

ENLARGEMENTS

A scale factor of $\frac{1}{3}$ would mean that the length of each image side will be $\frac{1}{3}$ the length of each corresponding object side.

Any scale factor that is greater than 0 and less than 1 will result in the image being smaller than the object. This can still be described as an enlargement but is more commonly called a reduction.

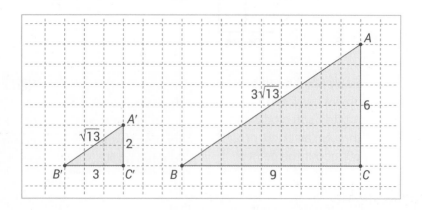

Worked Example 12.1

Enlarge the triangle ABC by a scale factor of 2.5, with a centre of enlargement O.

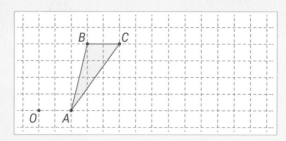

Solution

1 Draw rays from O, the centre of enlargement, though each of the vertices of the object shape.

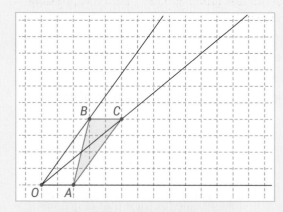

2 Using a ruler, measure the distance |OA|.

|OA| = 3 cm

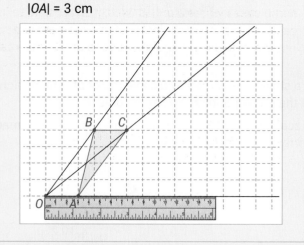

3 Using your ruler, mark off a new point A' such that $|OA'|$ is 2.5 times the distance $|OA|$.

$|OA'| = 2.5 \, |OA|$

$\quad\quad = 2.5 \times 3$ (Show your workings.)

$|OA'| = 7.5$ cm

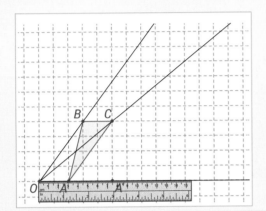

4 Measure $|OB|$.

Using a ruler, mark off a new point B' such that $|OB'|$ is 2.5 times the distance $|OB|$.

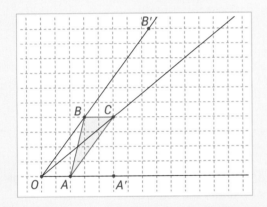

5 Measure $|OC|$.

Using a ruler, mark off a new point C' such that $|OC'|$ is 2.5 times the distance $|OC|$.

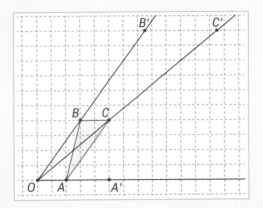

6 Draw the triangle $A'B'C'$.

The triangle $A'B'C'$ is the image of the triangle ABC under the required enlargement.

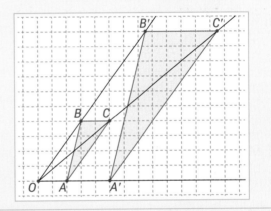

In some cases where a grid is used, it is possible to locate the image points by using only the given grid. In cases where the scale factor of enlargement is a natural number (such as 2, 3, 4, etc.) it is possible to use a compass and straight edge to locate the image points.

Worked Example 12.2

Enlarge the triangle ABC by a scale factor of 3 with a centre of enlargement O.

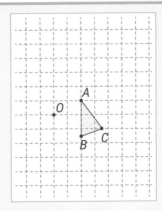

Solution

1 Draw rays from *O* though each of the vertices of the shape.

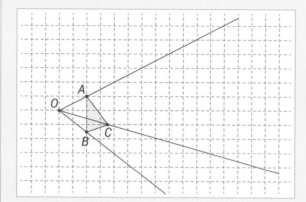

2 Using a compass, measure the distance |*OA*|.

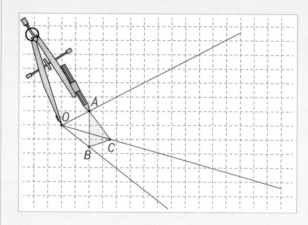

3 Mark off a new point *A'* such that |*OA'*| = 3|*OA*|.

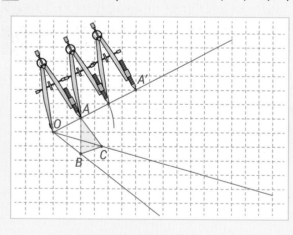

4 Using a compass, find |*OB*|. Mark off a new point *B'* such that |*OB'*| = 3|*OB*|.

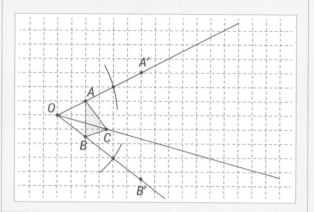

5 Repeat for *C*.

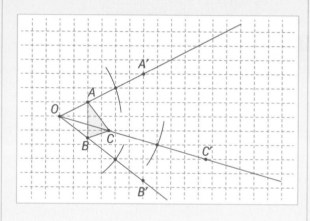

6 Draw the triangle *A'B'C'*.

The triangle *A'B'C'* is the image of the triangle *ABC* under the required enlargement.

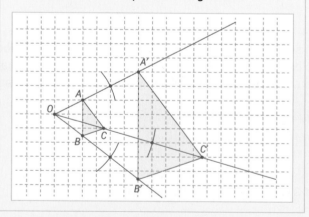

We sometimes encounter enlargements where the centre of enlargement is a point either on or inside the object.

Worked Example 12.3

Enlarge the triangle *ABC* by a scale factor of 1.8 with a centre of enlargement *A*.

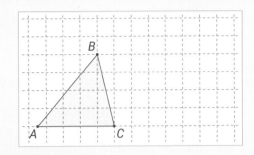

Solution

1 Draw rays from *A* through each of the remaining vertices.

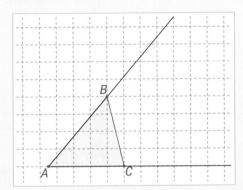

2 Using a compass or ruler, find |*AB*|.

Mark off a new point *B'* such that |*AB'*| = 1.8 × |*AB*|.

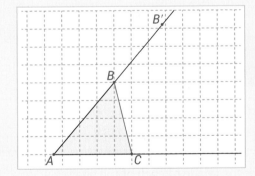

3 Find |*AC*|.

Mark off a new point *C'* such that |*AC'*| = 1.8 × |*AC*|.

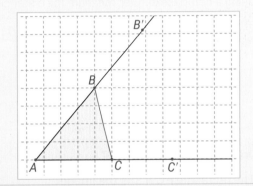

4 Draw the triangle *AB'C'*.

The triangle *AB'C'* is the image of the triangle *ABC* under the required enlargement.

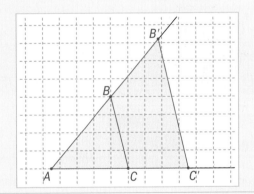

A scale factor of less than 1, for example $\frac{1}{2}$, would mean that the length of each image side will be $\frac{1}{2}$ the length of the corresponding object side.

Worked Example 12.4

Enlarge the rectangle *PQRS* by a scale factor of $\frac{1}{2}$ with a centre of enlargement *O*.

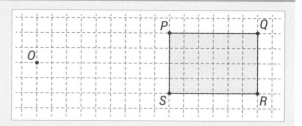

Solution

1 Draw rays from *O* though each of the vertices of the shape.

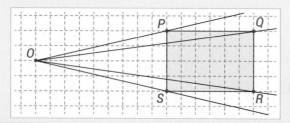

2 Using a compass or ruler, measure the distance |*OP*|.

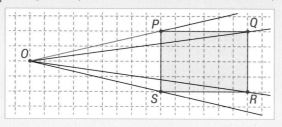

3 Mark off a new point *P'* such that $|OP'| = \frac{1}{2}|OP|$.

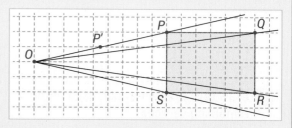

4 Repeat for the other vertices *Q*, *R* and *S*.

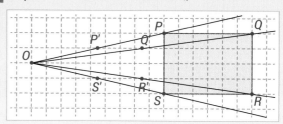

5 Draw the rectangle *P'Q'R'S'*.

The rectangle *P'Q'R'S'* is the image of the rectangle *PQRS* under the required enlargement.

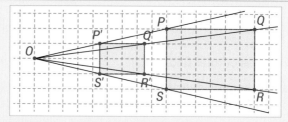

If the scale factor is *k*, then:

(i) If $k > 1$, the figure is enlarged.   (ii) If $0 < k < 1$, the figure is reduced.

Exercise 12.1

1. Copy the following diagrams onto graph paper and show the image of each of the shapes under an enlargement with a scale factor of 1.5 and centre *O*:

(i)

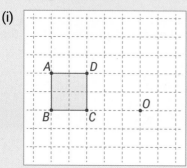

(ii)

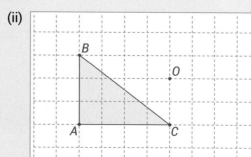

(iii)

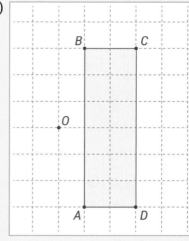

(iv)

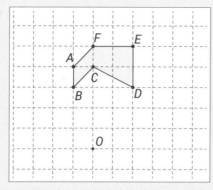

2. Copy the following diagrams onto graph paper and show the image of each of the shapes under an enlargement with a scale factor of 1.6 and centre *A*:

(i)

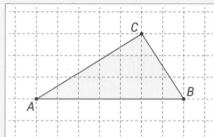

(iii)

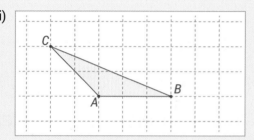

(ii)

(iv)

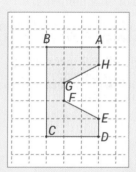

3. Copy the following diagrams onto graph paper and show the image of each of the shapes under an enlargement with a scale factor of $\frac{1}{2}$ and centre *O*:

(i)

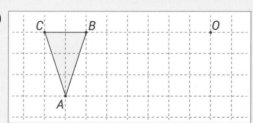

(ii)

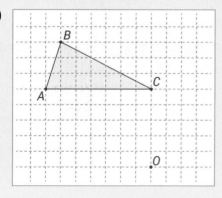

ENLARGEMENTS

(iii)

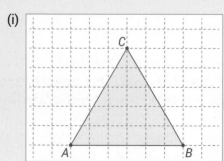

(iv)

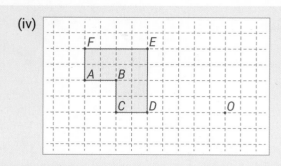

4. Copy the following diagrams onto graph paper and show the image of each of the shapes under an enlargement with a scale factor of $\frac{2}{3}$ and centre A:

(i)

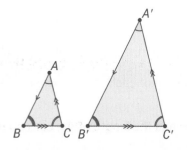

(ii)

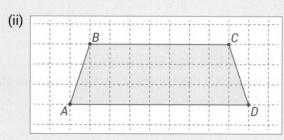

12.2 Properties of Enlargements

Now that we have explored how enlargements are constructed, we can investigate the various properties of enlargements.

From our investigations, we can determine the following characteristics of enlargements.

Similarity

Under an enlargement, **the object and image are similar to each other**.

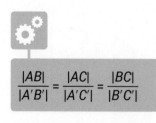

$|\angle ABC| = |\angle A'B'C'|$

$|\angle ACB| = |\angle A'C'B'|$

$|\angle BAC| = |\angle B'A'C'|$

$AB \parallel A'B'$

$AC \parallel A'C'$

$BC \parallel B'C'$

The corresponding sides of the object and image are in the same ratio:

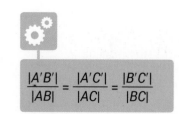

$$\frac{|AB|}{|A'B'|} = \frac{|AC|}{|A'C'|} = \frac{|BC|}{|B'C'|}$$

or

$$\frac{|A'B'|}{|AB|} = \frac{|A'C'|}{|AC|} = \frac{|B'C'|}{|BC|}$$

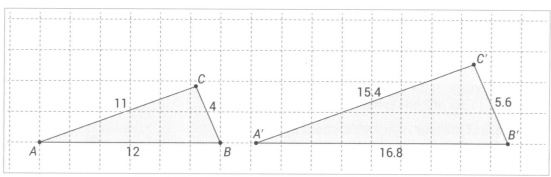

In this case:

$$\frac{|AB|}{|A'B'|} = \frac{12}{16.8} = \frac{5}{7} \qquad \frac{|AC|}{|A'C'|} = \frac{11}{15.4} = \frac{5}{7} \qquad \frac{|BC|}{|B'C'|} = \frac{4}{5.6} = \frac{5}{7}$$

Find the Centre of Enlargement

To find the centre of enlargement, often labelled as the point O, we draw lines through the corresponding vertices of the object and image. The point where these lines intersect is called the **centre of enlargement**.

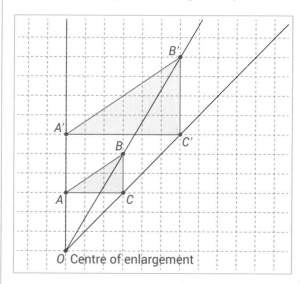

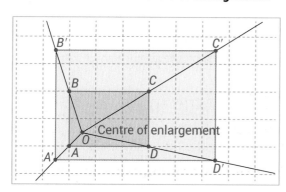

We only need to connect two pairs of corresponding vertices to find the centre of enlargement.

Find the Scale Factor

To find the scale factor, we measure the length of a side of the image and the length of the corresponding side of the object.

Scale factor $(k) = \dfrac{\text{Image length}}{\text{Object length}}$

It is important to remember that it is **Image length ÷ Object length** that will give us the scale factor.

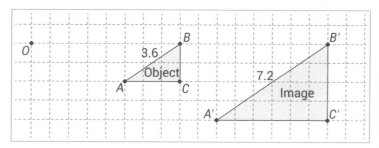

In this example:

Scale factor $k = \dfrac{7.2}{3.6}$

$$\therefore k = 2$$

Worked Example 12.5

Consider the rectangle *ABCD*.

(i) Construct the image of the rectangle *ABCD* under a scale factor of 3 and centre *O*.

(ii) Find the areas of both the object *ABCD* and image *A'B'C'D'*.

(iii) Show that the area of the image = k^2(area of object).

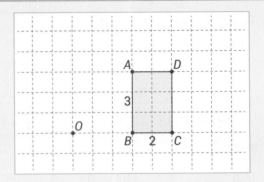

Solution

(i)

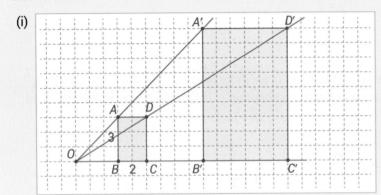

(ii) Area of object = $|AB| \times |AD|$ = 3×2 = 6 units^2

Area of image = $|A'B'| \times |A'D'|$

$|A'B'| = k \times |AB| = 3 \times 3 = 9$

$|A'D'| = k \times |AD| = 3 \times 2 = 6$

∴ Area of image = 9×6 = 54 units^2

(iii) Area of image = $|A'B'| \times |A'D'|$

But $|A'B'| = k \times |AB|$ (from enlargement)

Also $|A'D'| = k \times |AD|$ (from enlargement)

∴ Area of image = $k(|AB|) \times k(|AD|)$

$= k^2(|AB| \times |AD|)$

$= k^2$(area of object)

Scale Factor and Area

If an object is enlarged by a scale factor of k, then the area of the image will be increased by a factor of k^2.

> Image area = k^2 × Object area **or** $\dfrac{\text{Image area}}{\text{Object area}} = k^2$

For the example shown:

$k = 2$

Image area = $(2)^2$ × Object area

$= 4 \times 24$

$= 96$ units^2

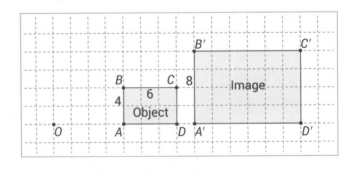

ENLARGEMENTS

Worked Example 12.6

$\triangle A'B'C'$ is the image of $\triangle ABC$ under an enlargement of scale factor k and centre O.

(i) Find the value of k.

(ii) Find $|B'C'|$.

(iii) Find $|AC|$.

(iv) The area of $\triangle ABC$ is 0.65 square units; find the area of $\triangle A'B'C'$.

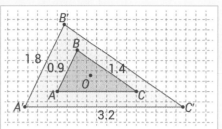

Solution

(i) $k = \dfrac{\text{Image length}}{\text{Object length}} = \dfrac{1.8}{0.9} = 2$

(ii) $\quad k = 2$

$\therefore |B'C'| = 2 \times |BC|$

$|B'C'| = 2 \times 1.4$

$|B'C'| = 2.8$ units

We could also have used the properties of similar triangles to find $|B'C'|$:

$\dfrac{|B'C'|}{|BC|} = \dfrac{|A'B'|}{|AB|}$

$\dfrac{|B'C'|}{1.4} = \dfrac{1.8}{0.9} \Rightarrow \dfrac{|B'C'|}{1.4} = \dfrac{2}{1}$

$|B'C'| = 2 \times 1.4$

$|B'C'| = 2.8$ units

(iii) $\quad k = 2$

$\therefore |A'C'| = 2 \times |AC|$

$\Rightarrow |AC| = \dfrac{|A'C'|}{2}$

$|AC| = \dfrac{3.2}{2}$

$|AC| = 1.6$ units

Again, we could have used the properties of similar triangles to find $|AC|$.

$\dfrac{|AC|}{3.2} = \dfrac{0.9}{1.8}$

$\dfrac{|AC|}{3.2} = \dfrac{1}{2}$

$2|AC| = 3.2$

$|AC| = 1.6$ units

(iv) We remember that $\dfrac{\text{Image area}}{\text{Object area}} = k^2$, and let the area of $\triangle A'B'C' = x$.

$\Rightarrow \dfrac{x}{0.65} = 2^2$

$\dfrac{x}{0.65} = 4$

$x = 4 \times 0.65$

$x = 2.6$ square units

Exercise 12.2

1. Copy the following diagram onto graph paper. $\triangle A'B'C'$ is an enlargement of $\triangle ABC$.

(i) Find the centre of enlargement.

(ii) Find the scale factor.

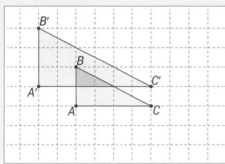

2. Copy this diagram of two rectangles onto graph paper. *AB'C'D'* is the image of the rectangle *ABCD* under an enlargement.

   (i) Find the centre of enlargement.

   (ii) Find the scale factor, *k*.

   (iii) Find the ratio
      Area of *AB'C'D'* : Area of *ABCD*.

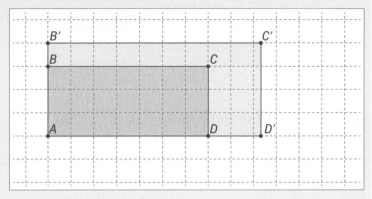

3. The square *P'Q'R'S'* is the image of *PQRS* under an enlargement.

   (i) Find the scale factor.

   (ii) Find the ratio
      Area of *P'Q'R'S'* : Area of *PQRS*.

   (iii) Find the ratio
      Perimeter of *P'Q'R'S'* : Perimeter of *PQRS*.

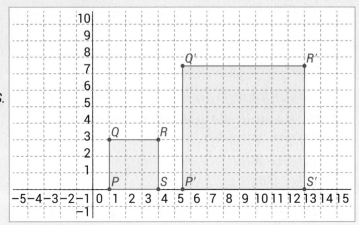

4. △*ABC* is the image of △*XYZ* under an enlargement of scale factor *k*.

   (i) Find the value of *k*.

   (ii) Find |*AB*|.

   (iii) Find |*YZ*|.

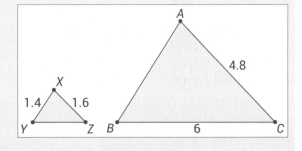

5. Square *ABCD* is the image of square *NMSD* under an enlargement. |*DS*| = |*SC*|

   (i) What point is the centre of this enlargement?

   (ii) What is the scale factor of the enlargement?

   (iii) What is the ratio Area of *ABCD* : Area of *NMSD*?

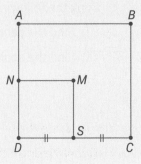

6. $\triangle AB'C'$ is the image of $\triangle ABC$ under an enlargement with centre A, of scale factor 2.

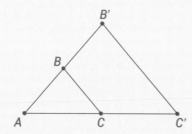

State whether the following are true or false:

(i) $\dfrac{|AB'|}{|AB|} = 2$

(ii) $\dfrac{|BC|}{|B'C'|} = \dfrac{1}{2}$

(iii) $|AC'| = \dfrac{1}{2}|AC|$

(iv) $\dfrac{\text{Area } \triangle AB'C'}{\text{Area } \triangle ABC} = 2$

(v) $\dfrac{\text{Area } \triangle AB'C'}{\text{Area } \triangle ABC} = 4$

(vi) $|\angle AB'C'| = 2|\angle ABC|$

(vii) $B'C' \parallel BC$

7. Plot the points $A(2,6)$, $B(8,4)$ and $C(8,1)$ on the xy-co-ordinate plane.

(i) Draw $\triangle ABC$.

(ii) Find the area of $\triangle ABC$.

(iii) Draw $\triangle A'B'C'$, the image of $\triangle ABC$ under an enlargement of scale factor $\dfrac{1}{2}$ and centre $O(0,0)$.

(iv) Find the area of $\triangle A'B'C'$.

(v) Find the ratio $\dfrac{\text{Area } \triangle A'B'C'}{\text{Area } \triangle ABC}$.

8. $\triangle PQR$ is an enlargement of $\triangle XYR$. Both triangles are right-angled, as shown.

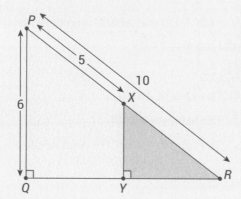

(i) Name the centre of enlargement.

(ii) Write down the value of k, the scale factor.

(iii) Find $|QR|$.

(iv) Find $|XR|$ and $|YR|$.

(v) Calculate the ratio Area $\triangle PQR$: Area $\triangle XYR$.

9. (i) Construct an equilateral triangle DEF of side 8 cm.

(ii) Construct the image of the triangle DEF under an enlargement with scale factor 0.45 and centre D.

(iii) Using the formula Area $\Delta = \dfrac{1}{2}ab \sin C$, show that the area of the triangle DEF is $16\sqrt{3}$ cm².

(iv) Calculate the area of the image (of the triangle) to one decimal place.

10. The triangle ADE is the image of the triangle ABC under an enlargement of scale factor k and centre A.

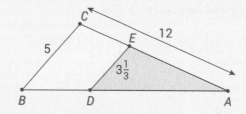

$|AC| = 12$ cm, $|BC| = 5$ cm and $|DE| = 3\dfrac{1}{3}$ cm.

(i) Find the scale factor, k.

(ii) Find $|AE|$.

(iii) The area of the triangle ADE is 9.85 cm². Find the area of the triangle ABC.

(iv) Write down the area of the region $BCED$.

11. The triangle OPQ is the reduction of triangle ORS, with scale factor k and centre O. $|OP| = 2$ and $|PR| = 7$.

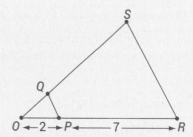

Find:

(i) The value of k

(ii) The ratio $|OQ| : |OS|$

(iii) Area $\triangle OPQ$: Area $\triangle ORS$

(iv) The area of the quadrilateral $PRSQ$, given that the area of triangle ORS is $20\dfrac{1}{4}$ square units.

12. $A(0,2)$, $B(4,0)$, $C(2,-2)$ and $D(-2,0)$ are four points.

(i) Illustrate these points on the xy-co-ordinate plane.

(ii) Show that $ABCD$ is a parallelogram.

(iii) Construct the image of $ABCD$ under an enlargement with scale factor 1.5 and centre of the origin.

(iv) Investigate if the image is also a parallelogram.

13. Draw any triangle PQR. Show $\triangle PQ'R'$, the image under enlargement of $\triangle PQR$, centre P, scale factor 3.

Explain why QR is parallel to $Q'R'$.

14. Triangle ABC has sides x, $x-1$ and $x+1$ as shown.

(a) If $|\angle ABC| = 90°$, find the value of x.

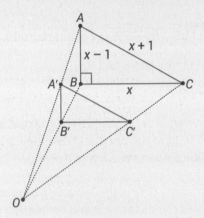

(b) Triangle $A'B'C'$ is the image of triangle ABC under a reduction, centre O, scale factor $\frac{4}{5}$.

Find the lengths of the sides of triangle $A'B'C'$ and verify that it is also right-angled.

15. (i) Construct a right-angled triangle ABC such that:

$|\angle BAC| = 90°$, $|AC| = 6$ cm, $|AB| = 2.5$ cm and $|BC| = 6.5$ cm

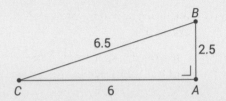

(ii) Verify Pythagoras' theorem in this case:

$|BC|^2 = |AB|^2 + |AC|^2$

(iii) Construct $\triangle AB'C'$, the image under enlargement of $\triangle ABC$, centre A, of scale factor 2.

(iv) Investigate if:

$|B'C'|^2 = |AB'|^2 + |AC'|^2$

(v) What does this prove about $\triangle AB'C'$?

16. $ABCD$ is a square of side 10 cm. P is the midpoint of $[AB]$.

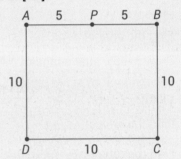

$A'B'C'D'$ is the image of $ABCD$ under the enlargement, centre P, of scale factor 0.4 (i.e. a reduction).

Illustrate $ABCD$ and $A'B'C'D'$ on a diagram.

Write down:

(i) $|A'B'|$

(ii) The area of $A'B'C'D'$

(iii) The ratio $|A'B'| : |AB|$

(iv) The ratio Area $A'B'C'D'$: Area $ABCD$.

17. The diagram below shows the right-angled triangle *ABC*, which is used in the logo for a company called *Deane Construction Limited* (DCL). The triangle *PQR* is the image of *ABC* under an enlargement.

(a) (i) Construct the centre of enlargement and label it *O*.

(ii) Measure, in centimetres, |*OB*| and |*OQ*|.

(iii) Use your measurements to find the scale factor of the enlargement, correct to one decimal place.

(b) The area of the triangle *ABC* is 7.5 cm². Use the scale factor to find the area of the image triangle *PQR* under the enlargement.

(c) (i) Given that |*AB*| = 5 cm, use the scale factor to find |*PQ*|.

(ii) Given that |*QR*| = 8.7 cm, use the scale factor to find |*BC*|.

(iii) Hence, show that |∠*ABC*| = |∠*PQR*|.

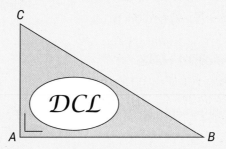

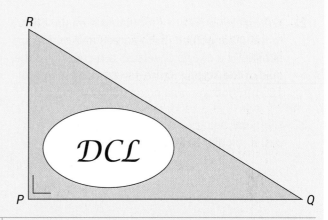

18. The planned supports for the roof of a building form scalene triangles of different sizes.

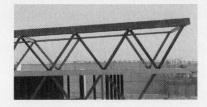

The triangle *EFG* is the image of the triangle *CDE* under an enlargement and the triangle *CDE* is the image of the triangle *ABC* under the same enlargement.

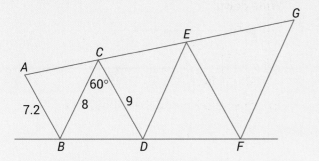

The proposed dimensions for the structure are |*AB*| = 7.2 m, |*BC*| = 8 m, |*CD*| = 9 m and |∠*DCB*| = 60°.

(i) Find the length of [*FG*].

(ii) Find the length of [*BD*], correct to three decimal places.

(iii) The centre of the enlargement is *O*. Find the distance from *O* to the point *B*.

(iv) A condition of the planning is that the height of the point *G* above the horizontal line *BF* cannot exceed 11.6 m.

Does the plan meet this condition? Justify your answer by calculation.

19. Δ*A′B′C′* is the image of Δ*ABC* under an enlargement of scale factor *k* and centre *O*.

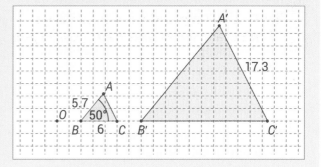

(i) Find, to one decimal place, the value of *k*.

Hence, find:

(ii) |*A′B′*|

(iii) |*B′C′*|

(iv) Using your answers from (ii) and (iii), find to one decimal place, the area of Δ*A′B′C′*.

20. A parallelogram *ABCD* is enlarged using a scale factor *k* and through a centre of enlargement *O*.

$A = (3,0)$, $B = (2,-2)$, $C = (5,-2)$ and $D = (6,0)$.

If $B' = (5,-8)$ and $D' = (15,-3)$, find, without plotting on an *xy*-co-ordinate plane:

  (i) The value of *k*

  (ii) The centre of enlargement, *O*

  (iii) The co-ordinates of *A'*

  (iv) The co-ordinates of *C'*

21. A projector projects a rectangular image onto a rectangular screen. Both screen and image are similar. The image covers an area one third the size of the screen. If the screen has an area of 189 m², find the area covered by the image.

22. A regular hexagon of side 12 cm has a perpendicular height of *x* cm as shown.

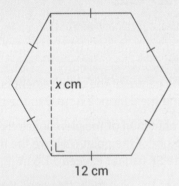

12 cm

  (i) Calculate the value of *x*.

  (ii) Calculate the area of the hexagon.

  (iii) When the hexagon is enlarged by a scale factor *k*, its area is $1{,}944\sqrt{3}$ cm².

    Calculate the perpendicular height of the enlarged hexagon.

23. Four different types of paper are used in an office: A1, A2, A3 and A4. All types are similar to each other.

A1 paper is double the area of A2, which is double the area of A3, which is double the area of A4.

If A2 paper has a length of 594 mm and A4 has a width of 210 mm, calculate the dimensions (to the nearest mm) and area (to the nearest cm²) of each type of paper.

Exam Questions

1. Two triangles are drawn on a square grid as shown. The points *P*, *Q*, *R*, *X*, and *Z* are on vertices of the grid, and the point *Y* lies on [*PR*]. The triangle *PQR* is an enlargement of the triangle *XYZ*.

  (a) Calculate the scale factor of the enlargement, showing your work.

  (b) By construction or otherwise, locate the centre of enlargement on the diagram.

  (c) Calculate |*YR*| in grid units.

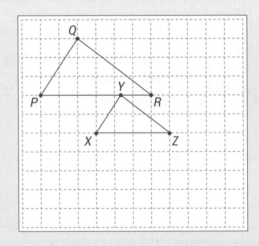

SEC Leaving Certificate Higher Level, Paper 2, 2011

 Solutions and chapter summary available online

ENLARGEMENTS

Answers

Chapter 1

Exercise 1.1

9. (i) Heights of plants, colour of leaves
(ii) Heights (numerical), colour (categorical)
(iii) Continuous   (iv) Centimetres   (v) Nominal
12. (i) Discrete   (ii) Continuous   (iii) Discrete   (iv) Discrete
13. Discrete numerical, continuous numerical, discrete numerical, discrete numerical, ordinal categorical
16. (i) and   (iii) are incorrect   17. Alan did not collect the data himself

Exercise 1.2

1. Simple random sample   2. (i) A − 20, B − 35, C − 5, D − 10
(ii) Stratified random sampling   3. (i) Cluster sampling
(ii) Quota sampling   4. (i) Simple random sampling
(ii) Census   9. No   10. (i) Yes   (ii) Use a stratified random sample

Exercise 1.3

1. (i)

Scores	1	2	3	4	5	6
Frequency	10	10	7	5	8	10

(ii) 10   (iii) 10   (iv) 10%

2. (i)

Mode	Walks	Bus	Car	Rail
Frequency	9	5	4	2

(ii) Walk   (iii) Rail

3. (i)

Number of goals	0	1	2	3	4
Frequency	7	9	11	3	5

(ii) 35   (iii) 7   (iv) 23   (v) 7

4. (i)

Result	3Hs	2Hs	1H	0H
Frequency	3	11	9	2

(ii) 36%

5. (i) 47

(ii)

Age	Frequency
20−29	8
30−39	9
40−49	15
50−59	10
60−69	5

6. (a) Students, retired, stay-at-home persons, disabled

(b) (i)

		At work	Unemployed	Not in the labour force
Persons aged 15 years and over	2006	57.9%	3.5%	38.6%
	2011	50.4%	10.1%	39.5%

(ii)

		At work	Unemployed	Not in the labour force
Total population	2006	46.1%	2.8%	51.1%
	2011	39.6%	8.0%	52.4%

7. It is a leading question   8. You may tick more than one box
9. (i) There are no clear boundaries between the three categories offered

Exercise 1.4

1. (iii) 76   (iv) 29   (v) Skewed right   (vi) Most were in their 30s and 40s   2. (ii) Height of students (in cm)
(iii) Numerical   (iv) 28%   3. (ii) 17   (iii) 2   (iv) 55%
4. (ii) 35   (iii) 15   5. (ii) Skewed right   6. (a) Skewed right
(b) Reasonably symmetric   (c) Skewed left

7.

Time (minutes)	Frequency (%)
0−1	2
1−2	3
2−3	5
3−4	2
4−5	1

(i) 10   (ii) 15.38%   (iii) Almost symmetric

8. (i)

Weight (kg)	Frequency
0.5–1.5	6
1.5–2.5	2
2.5–3.5	14
3.5–4.5	18
4.5–5.5	9
5.5–6.5	15
6.5–7.5	8
7.5–8.5	6

(iii) There are two clusters: one between 2.5 and 4.5 and the other between 4.5 and 7.5

9. (i)

Weight (kg)	Frequency
2–2.5	5
2.5–3	8
3–3.5	13
3.5–4	4

(iii) 43.3%, 13.3%

(iv)

Weight (kg)	Relative Frequency (%)
2–2.5	16.7
2.5–3	26.7
3–3.5	43.3
3.5–4	13.3

(v) You can more easily compare the size (frequency) of one class interval with that of another

10. (ii)

Price	Frequency
0.8–0.9	1
0.9–1	4
1–1.1	3
1.1–1.2	4
1.2–1.3	3
1.3–1.4	0
1.4–1.5	5
1.5–1.6	4
1.6–1.7	1
1.7–1.8	1

11. (ii) 75 mm   **12.** (i) 18   (ii) 1   (iii) Running increases your pulse.   **13.** (ii) Yes   **14.** (ii) Yes   (iii) He could have used a larger sample size

Exercise 1.5

1. (ii) 0.94   (iii) Strong positive correlation   **2.** (ii) 0.82
(iii) Strong positive correlation   **4.** (i) Weak positive
(ii) 0.6   (iii) Systolic = 112, diastolic = 44 (mmHg)
5. (i) Moderately strong positive correlation   (ii) Very strong negative correlation   (iii) Weak positive correlation
(iv) Close to perfect negative correlation   (v) No correlation
6. (i) Strong positive correlation   (ii) 0.8   (iii) 3.6, 3.7, 3.9 and 3.9   (iv) 14.1   **7.** (ii) 0.18   (iii) No, as the correlation co-efficient indicates an extremely weak positive correlation.
8. (i) 7.9 litres / 100 km   (ii) 1,000 cc   (iii) 0.98
A near-perfect positive correlation   (iv) False   **9.** (ii) 0.90
(iii) Strong positive correlation   **10.** (i) Strong positive correlation   (iii) 0.96

Exercise 1.6

1. (ii) 0.93   **2.** (ii) −0.82   (iv) Strong negative correlation
3. (ii) 0.95   (iv) Strong positive correlation   (vi) $y = 1.3x − 7$
4. (ii) 0.96   (iii) Strong positive correlation   (vi) $y = 4x + 6$
(vii) €18,000   **5.** (ii) 0.9987   (iv) Perfect positive correlation
(v) $y = \frac{11}{7}x − \frac{51}{7}$ **6.** (ii) 0.99   (iii) Near-perfect positive correlation   (v) $y = 2.5x + 14$ (vi) 39%

Revision Exercises

1. (i) Discrete numerical   (ii) Continuous numerical
(iii) Categorical (nominal)   (iv) Discrete numerical
(v) Discrete numerical   **2.** (i) Adults living in Ireland
(ii) 1,000 adults, randomly selected   (iii) Inferential
(iv) Frequency of use of Internet for shopping
(v) Categorical   **3.** (i) Quota sampling   (ii) No   (iii) Busy people, shy people, people without strong opinions

4.

	Explanatory	Response
(i)	Weight	Cost
(ii)	Mock mark	Final mark
(iii)	Distance	Time
(iv)	Volume of water	Amount of electricity

6. (i) Test score   (ii) Discrete numerical data (of only whole number scores were possible)   (iv) Slightly skewed right
7. (ii) Discrete data   (iii) Group 1: skewed right; Group 2: slightly skewed right   (iv) Stratified random sample
(v) 225   (vi) Yes (Group 1)   **8.** (ii) 0.86   (iii) Strong positive correlation   (v) $y = 0.7x − 1$ (vi) 43.1 days   **9.** (i) 0.10
(ii) Almost no correlation   (iii) (a) 0.1   (b) 0.9
10. (ii) Skewed right   (iii) 60%

Exam Questions

1. (a) −0.75   (b) Age: 47 years; max. heart rate: 137 bpm
(c) 176 bpm   (d) −0.7   (e) $MHR = 207 − 0.7 \times (age)$
(g) He should exercise a bit more intensely.   **2.** (b) (i) 0
(ii) The pattern suggests a quadratic relationship
3. (i) Disagree   (ii) Liam's   (iii) 51.2%   **4.** (b) (ii) 0.88

Chapter 2

Exercise 2.1

1. (i) 6   (ii) 26   (iii) 4,320   (iv) 8   (v) 504   (vi) 10   (vii) 11
(viii) 14   (ix) 20   (x) 420   **2.** 42   **3.** 30   **4.** 260
5. (a) (i) No   (ii) No   (iii) Yes   (b) (i) 6   (ii) 120   (iii) 40,320
6. (i) 120   (ii) 360   (iii) 720   **7.** 24   (i) 6   (ii) 18   (iii) 12
8. (i) 5,040   (ii) 2,520   (iii) 42   **9.** (i) 720   (ii) 120   (iii) 24
(iv) 240   (v) 480   **10.** (i) 5,040   (ii) 1,440   (iii) 3,600
(iv) 1,440   (v) 3,600   **11.** (i) 40,320   (ii) 720   (iii) 4,320
(iv) 10,080   (v) 30,240   **12.** (i) 362,880   (ii) 30,240
(iii) 17,280   (iv) 40,320   (v) 151,200   **13.** (a) (i) 10   (ii) 330
(iii) 23   (iv) 156   (b) (i) n (ii) $n + 1$ (iii) $n − 1$
(c) (i) 18   (ii) 192   **14.** 245   **15.** 15   **16.** 48
17. (i) 468,000   (ii) 1,800   **18.** 80   **19.** 78,000   **20.** 59,280
21. 32   **22.** 200   **23.** (i) 120   (ii) 12   **24.** 144
25. (i) 362,880   (ii) 80,640   (iii) 282,240   (iv) 2,880
26. (i) 720   (ii) 240   (iii) 168   **27.** (i) 72   (ii) 42

Exercise 2.2

1. 45; 165; 35; 14; 190; 84; 84; 78; 3,060; 3,060   **4.** $k = 5$
7. 1,365   **8.** (i) 35   (ii) 15   (iii) 20   **9.** (i) 715   (ii) 315
(iii) 15   **10.** (i) 66   (ii) 220   **11.** (i) 105   (ii) 91   **12.** (i) 56

(ii) 35   (iii) 21   (iv) 20   **13.** 91   **14.** 78   **15.** (a) 380   (b) 96
16. (i) 126   (ii) 81   (iii) 5   **17.** (i) 8,145,060
(ii) 1,086,008   (iii) 7,059,052   (iv) 397,800   **18.** (i) 252
(ii) 126   (iii) 35   (iv) 462   **19.** 300   **20.** (i) 210   (ii) 252
(iii) 378   **21.** 660   **22.** (i) 2,598,960   (ii) 249,900
(iii) 2,349,060   (iv) 48   (v) 4,512   **23.** $n = 21$ **24.** $n = 11$
25. $x = 6$

Exercise 2.3

1. Fifty–fifty C; Certain E; Very unlikely B; Impossible A; Very
likely D   **2.** (i) 0.8   (ii) 48   **3.** Getting tails on single flip of a
fair coin – R; getting a 4 on a single roll of a fair six-sided die – Q;
getting a 7 on a single roll of a fair six-sided die – P;
a person being born on a day that ends with the letter 'y' – T;
a person not being born on a Sunday – S   **4.** (i) 13%
(ii) Conor's punctuality has not improved. He is late ≈15% of
the time vs. 13% last year.   **5.** (i) After 40: 0.4; after 60: 0.4833;
after 80: 0.5125; after 100: 0.49   (iii) Yes   **6.** (i) 76%   (ii) 35
(iii) Pundit A is most accurate; Pundit B is least accurate
7. (i) 57.5%   (ii) No   **8.** (i) After 20 rolls 0.15, after 30 rolls
0.2, after 40 rolls 0.175, after 50 rolls 0.16
(iii) No, as the relative frequency tends towards 0.1666... or $\frac{1}{6}$,
which is what we would expect for a fair die   **9.** (i) 52.5%
(ii) 30 successes   (iv) No   **10.** (i) Cathal's data   (ii) 20 times
11. (i) Relative frequency: 1: 0.296; 2: 0.170; 3: 0.110;
4: 0.094; 5: 0.078; 6: 0.072; 7: 0.065; 8: 0.057; 9: 0.058   (ii) Yes
(iv) True

Exercise 2.4

1. $\frac{1}{2}$ **2.** (i) $\frac{1}{2}$ (ii) $\frac{2}{3}$ (iii) $\frac{1}{2}$ **3.** (i) $\frac{3}{8}$ (ii) $\frac{3}{8}$ (iii) $\frac{5}{8}$ **4.** (i) $\frac{8}{15}$
(ii) $\frac{7}{15}$ (iii) $\frac{1}{6}$ (iv) $\frac{1}{10}$ A girl who wears glasses would be
chosen on 12 days.   **5.** (i) $\frac{1}{4}$ (ii) $\frac{1}{2}$ (iii) $\frac{1}{13}$ (iv) $\frac{3}{4}$ (v) $\frac{4}{13}$
(vi) $\frac{7}{13}$ **6.** (i) $\frac{7}{10}$ (ii) $\frac{3}{4}$ (iii) $\frac{27}{10}$ **7.** (i) Yes   (ii) No   (iii) Yes
(iv) No   (v) Yes   (vi) No   (vii) No   (viii) Yes   (ix) No   (x) Yes
8. P(E) = 0.4   P(F) = 0.6   P(E∩F) = 0.1   P(E∪F) = 0.9
9. (a) (i) $\frac{1}{2}$ (ii) $\frac{1}{4}$ (iii) $\frac{3}{20}$ (iv) $\frac{3}{5}$ (v) $\frac{7}{20}$ (vi) $\frac{9}{20}$ (vii) $\frac{1}{2}$
(viii) $\frac{2}{5}$ (b) (i) $\frac{7}{20} = \frac{10}{20} - \frac{3}{20}$ (ii) $\frac{3}{5} = \frac{10}{20} + \frac{5}{20} - \frac{3}{20}, \frac{3}{5} = \frac{12}{20}$
10. (i) $\frac{3}{4}$ (ii) $\frac{11}{24}$ (iii) $\frac{1}{3}$ (iv) $\frac{7}{8}$ (v) $\frac{1}{4}$ (vi) F   (vii) T   (viii) F
(ix) T   (x) T   **11.** (i) 5,040   (ii) 720   (iii) $\frac{1}{7}$ **12.** (a) (i) 0.4
(ii) 0.9   **13.** (i) $\frac{1}{12}$ (ii) $\frac{1}{6}$ (iii) $\frac{1}{6}$ (iv) $\frac{1}{2}$ (v) $\frac{1}{2}$ (vi) $\frac{17}{36}$
(vii) $\frac{11}{12}$ **14.** S = {(H,H,H), (H,H,T), (H,T,T), (H,T,H), (T,H,H),
(T,H,T), (T,T,H), (T,T,T)}   (i) 8   (ii) $\frac{1}{8}$ (iii) $\frac{7}{8}$ (iv) $\frac{1}{2}$ **15.** (i) $\frac{1}{12}$
(ii) $\frac{1}{4}$ (iii) $\frac{1}{2}$ **16.** (a) (i) $\frac{1}{5}$ (ii) $\frac{7}{10}$ (iii) $\frac{3}{4}$ (iv) $\frac{3}{5}$ (v) $\frac{1}{4}$
(b) Yes   **17.** $n = 8$ **18.** (i) $\frac{33}{50}$ (ii) $\frac{2}{5}$ (iii) $\frac{1}{10}$ (iv) $\frac{27}{50}$
19. (i) 216   (ii) $\frac{1}{216}$ (iii) $\frac{5}{216}$ (iv) $\frac{1}{24}$ **20.** (i) 0.085   (ii) 0.077
(iii) 0.16   **21.** (i) 0.1   (ii) No   (iii) P(E) = 0.4; P(F) = 0.3;
P(E∩F) = 0.1; P(E∪F) = 0.6   (iv) 0.6 = 0.4 + 0.3 – 0.1
22. (i) 0.65   (ii) 0.35   (iii) 0.8 = 0.35 + 0.65 – 0.2   **23.** (i) 10%
(ii) 25%   (iii) 20%   **24.** (i) 0.13   (ii) 0.6   (iii) 0.36   (iv) 0.3
25. (a) (i) $k = 0.08$ (ii) 0.65   (iii) 0.15   (iv) 0.3   (v) 0.65
(b) (i) 0.75 = 0.53 + 0.35 – 0.13   (ii) 0.47 = 1 – 0.53
26. (b) (i) P(E) = $\frac{3}{25}$, P(F) = $\frac{14}{25}$ (ii) Yes   (iii) P(E∪F) = $\frac{17}{25}$
(iv) No   **27.** (iii) No   (iv) {7,8,9,10}, {4,5,6,7}

Exercise 2.5

1. (i) 0.25   (ii) 0.1667   **2.** (a) A = {(6,3), (6,4), (6,5), (6,6), (5,4),
(5,5), (5,6), (4,5), (4,6), (3,6)}   B = {(6,1), (6,2), (6,3), (6,4), (6,5),

(6,6), (1,6), (2,6), (3,6), (4,6), (5,6)}   A ∩ B = {(6,3), (6,4),
(6,5), (6,6), (3,6), (4,6), (5,6)}   (b) (i) P(B|A) = $\frac{7}{10}$
(ii) P(A|B) = $\frac{7}{11}$ **3.** (i) 6   (ii) $\frac{3}{5}$ **4.** 0.25   **5.** (i) 0.75   (ii) 0.5
(iii) 0.25   (iv) 0.375   (v) 0.5833   (vi) 0.8571   **6.** (i) 0.7059
(ii) 0.8   **7.** 0.8537   **9.** (i) $\frac{1}{18}$ (ii) $\frac{5}{36}$ (iii) $\frac{38}{45}$ **10.** (i) $\frac{2}{3}$ (ii) $\frac{1}{3}$
11. P(E) = $\frac{1}{6}$ P(F) = $\frac{11}{36}$ P(E ∩ F) = $\frac{2}{36}$ P(F|E) = $\frac{1}{3}$
P(E|F) = $\frac{2}{11}$ **12.** P(A) = $\frac{5}{11}$ P(B) = $\frac{5}{11}$ P(A ∩ B) = $\frac{2}{11}$
P(A|B) = $\frac{2}{5}$ P(B|A) = $\frac{2}{5}$ **13.** (i) 0.6   (ii) $\frac{1}{3}$ (iii) 0.33   (iv) 0.67
14. P(A|B) = 0.4   P(B|A) = 0.6667   **15.** P(B) = 0.4
16. (i) $x = 0.2, y = 0.3$ (ii) 0.4   **17.** (i) $x = 0.1, y = 0.2$
(ii) P(B|C) = $\frac{13}{30}$ P(C|B) = $\frac{26}{37}$ (iii) $\frac{33}{76}$ (iv) 0.175   (v) 0.26
18. (i) 0.66   (ii) 0.16   (iii) $\frac{8}{15}$ (iv) $\frac{8}{33}$ (v) $\frac{26}{55}$ (vi) 0.4375
19. 33%   **20.** (ii) 0.3   (iii) $\frac{5}{6}$ **21.** (i) 0.75   (ii) 0.25

Revision Exercises

1. (a) (i) 5,040   (ii) 240   (b) (i) $\frac{1}{36}$ (ii) $\frac{11}{36}$ (iii) $\frac{5}{36}$ (iv) $\frac{1}{9}$
2. (i) 336   (ii) 56   (iii) $\frac{1}{56}$ (iv) $\frac{55}{56}$ **3.** (i) 0.2   (ii) $\frac{2}{3}$ (iii) $\frac{2}{5}$
4. (i) You are more likely to get a sum of 3   (ii) P(sum of 2) = $\frac{1}{12}$;
P(sum of 3) = $\frac{1}{4}$; P(sum of 4) = $\frac{1}{3}$; P(sum of 5) = $\frac{1}{3}$ **5.** (a) 72
(b) (i) 5,040   (ii) 360   (iii) 720   (iv) $\frac{1}{7}$ **6.** (i) 120   (ii) 112
(iii) $\frac{1}{15}$ **7.** (i) $\frac{2}{3}$ (ii) $\frac{1}{5}$ (iii) $\frac{7}{9}$ **8.** (i) 0.7   (ii) 0.2   (iii) 0.1
9. (i) 35   (ii) 20   (iii) 15   (iv) $\frac{4}{7}$ **10.** (i) Things have
improved slightly by 0.4%   (ii) 10 muggings
11. (a) (i) 0.625   (ii) 0.375   (b) $n = 14$ **12.** (i) {HH1, HH2,
HH3, HH4, HT1, HT2, HT3, HT4, TH1, TH2, TH3, TH4, TT1,
TT2, TT3, TT4}   (ii) $\frac{1}{16}$ (iii) $\frac{1}{8}$ (iv) $\frac{1}{4}$ **13.** (i) 84   (ii) 40
(iii) $\frac{1}{84}$ (iv) False   **14.** (i) Fred Harry Murphy   (ii) 2,600
15. (i) 0.1   (ii) No   (iii) $\frac{1}{6}$ (iv) 0.9   **16.** (a) (i) 792   (ii) $\frac{25}{132}$
(b) (i) 0.9   (ii) 0.7   **17.** (b) (i) 0.9   (ii) 0.1   (iii) 0.14

Exam Questions

1. (i) 0.31   (ii) 0.08   (iii) 0.48   **2.** 3

Chapter 3
Exercise 3.1

1. (i) $\frac{1}{4}$ (ii) $\frac{3}{4}$ **2.** (i) $\frac{1}{216}$ (ii) $\frac{1}{24}$ **3.** (i) $\frac{1}{16}$ (ii) $\frac{15}{16}$ **4.** (i) $\frac{1}{32}$
(ii) $\frac{31}{32}$ **5.** (i) $\frac{8}{29}$ (ii) $\frac{91}{435}$ (iii) $\frac{344}{435}$ **6.** (i) $\frac{4}{663}$ (ii) $\frac{1}{221}$
(iii) $\frac{188}{221}$ (iv) $\frac{33}{221}$ **7.** (a) (i) $\frac{1}{5,525}$ (ii) $\frac{5,524}{5,525}$ (b) (i) $\frac{1}{2,197}$
(ii) $\frac{2,196}{2,197}$ **8.** (a) 0.6   (b) (i) 0.36   (ii) 0.16   (iii) 0.84   (iv) 0.48
9. (a) 0.875   (b) (i) 0.766   (ii) 0.670   (iii) 0.513   **10.** (i) $\frac{1}{24}$
(ii) $\frac{1}{4}$ (iii) $\frac{3}{4}$ **12.** (i) $\frac{3}{8}$ (ii) $\frac{7}{8}$ **13.** Not independent   **14.** 0.6
15. (i) $\frac{55}{72}$ (ii) $\frac{17}{72}$ **16.** (i) 0.0005   (ii) 0.002   **17.** (i) $\frac{2,041}{2,401}$
(ii) $\frac{89}{144}$ **18.** $\frac{10}{21}$ **19.** $\frac{13}{102}$ **20.** $\frac{5}{18}$ **21.** $\frac{3}{8}$ **22.** 0.0625   **23.** 0.42
24. (i) $\frac{5}{42}$ (ii) $\frac{5}{14}$ **25.** (i) $\frac{5}{33}$ (ii) $\frac{5}{66}$ (iii) $\frac{13}{66}$ (iv) $\frac{19}{66}$ (v) $\frac{47}{66}$
27. Independent   **28.** (i) 2   (ii) 0.2   (iii) Independent
29. (i) Independent   (ii) Not independent   **30.** $\frac{1}{3}$ **31.** 20
32. (i) 400   (ii) $\frac{21}{400}$ (iii) Not independent

Exercise 3.2

1. (a) (i) $\frac{67}{560}$ (ii) $\frac{117}{280}$ (iii) $\frac{3}{14}$ (iv) $\frac{11}{14}$ (b) (i) $\frac{83}{512}$ (ii) $\frac{1,521}{4,096}$
(iii) $\frac{45}{256}$ (iv) $\frac{211}{256}$ **2.** (i) $\frac{1}{6}$ (ii) $\frac{4}{9}$ (iii) $\frac{5}{9}$ **3.** (i) $\frac{1}{4}$ (ii) $\frac{9}{400}$
(iii) $\frac{169}{400}$ (iv) $\frac{1}{80}$ **4.** (i) 0.10 (ii) 0.09 **5.** (i) $\frac{1}{4}$ (ii) $\frac{120}{343}$
6. (i) 0.0061 (ii) 0.11 (iii) 0.94 **7.** (i) $\frac{1}{6,561}$ (ii) $\frac{1}{81}$ (iii) $\frac{112}{243}$
8. (i) $\frac{1}{100}$ (ii) $\frac{18}{25}$ (iii) $\frac{7}{25}$ **9.** (i) $\frac{1}{4}$ (ii) $\frac{13}{32}$ (iii) $\frac{1}{16}$ **10.** (i) $\frac{25}{196}$
(ii) $\frac{15}{196}$ (iii) $\frac{15}{28}$ (iv) $\frac{1}{28}$ **11.** 5 **12.** 26, 7 **13.** (i) $\frac{1}{3}$ (ii) $\frac{2}{9}$ (iii) $\frac{6}{27}$
14. (i) 0.0164 **15.** (a) (i) $\frac{1}{3}$ (ii) $\frac{1}{2}$ (iii) $\frac{1}{2}$ (iv) $\frac{2}{3}$ (v) $\frac{1}{2}$ (vi) $\frac{1}{3}$
(vii) 0 (viii) $\frac{1}{6}$ (b) (i) N (ii) Y (iii) Y (iv) N (c) $\frac{2}{3}$
16. (i) 0.16 (iii) 0.6 **17.** (a) (i) 6 (ii) 2 (iii) 24
18. (i) 0.275 (ii) 0.2375 (iii) 0.072 **19.** $\frac{5}{108}$ **20.** (i) 0.108
(ii) 0.892 (iii) 0.162 (iv) 0.027 (v) 0.345 **21.** (i) 0.395
(ii) 0.089 (iii) 0.107 **22.** (i) $\frac{4}{5}$ (ii) $\frac{1}{3}$ (iii) $\frac{41}{60}$ **23.** 0.5139
24. (i) 0.294 (ii) 0.1 (iii) 0.126 (iv) 0.356 (v) 0.25
25. (i) 0.0192 (ii) 0.295 (iii) 0.0788 (iv) 0.357

Exercise 3.3

1. 3.5 **2.** 6 **3.** Good bet **4.** (i) $\frac{3}{5}, \frac{2}{5}$ (ii) 8 (iii) No **5.** No
6. (ii) 7 (iii) Yes **7.** (ii) 7.75 (iii) 60 **8.** 7.875 **9.** Yes
10. (i) 7.5 **11.** Bad bet **12.** (i) Choice 2: €769.23, choice 3:
€2,777.78 (ii) Pick choice 3 **13.** (i) 8,145,060 (ii) 1.23×10^{-7}
(iii) No **14.** (a) 0.101 (b) 0.086 (c) €616.91 (d) €520.39
(e) €1,071.09, €503.61 (f) €448 **15.** (ii) 1.1 (iii) $\frac{1}{18}$
16. (i) $a = b = 0.3$ (ii) $\frac{1}{3}$

Exercise 3.4

1. Yes for 1, 4, 5(i), 6, 7, 8 **2.** 0.3125 **3.** 0.3858
4. (i) 0.2734 (ii) 0.03125 (iii) 0.0352 **5.** (i) 0.2373
(ii) 0.3955 (iii) 0.3672 **6.** 125 **7.** 0.287 **8.** 0.25
9. 0.8208 **11.** 0.27 **12.** 0.103 **13.** (i) 0.0512
(ii) 0.05792 **14.** (i) 0% (ii) 25% (iii) 94% **15.** (i) 0.29
(ii) 0.16 (iii) 0.0037 **16.** (i) 0.60 (ii) 0.0849 **17.** (i) 0.01
(ii) 0.29 (iii) 0.7969 **19.** (i) 36% (ii) 64% (iii) True

Exercise 3.5

1. 0.15625 **2.** 0.058 **3.** (i) 0.25 (ii) 0.125 **4.** 0.0604
5. 0.0779 **6.** 0.0481 **7.** 0.09261 **8.** 0.0352 **9.** 0.036
10. 9 **11.** 13 **12.** 7

Exercise 3.6

1. (i) 0.9452 (ii) 0.0548 (iii) 0.0548 (iv) 0.0792 (v) 0.1359
(vi) 0.1218 (vii) 0.1151 (viii) 0.8973 (ix) 0.871 (x) 0.3094
(xi) 0.3094 (xii) 0.9876 (xiii) 0.0215 (xiv) 0.0206
(xv) 0.8664 (xvi) 0.9616 (xvii) 0.0094 (xviii) 0.7372
(xix) 0.95 (xx) 0.9 **2.** (i) 68% (ii) 95% (iii) 100%
3. (i) 1.84 (ii) 0.92 (iii) −0.63 (iv) 0.69 (v) 0.44 **4.** 1.96
5. 0.43 **6.** 2.3 **7.** 0.32 **8.** $x = 0.6755$; $x = 0$; $x = -0.6755$
9. $k \approx -0.84$; $t \approx 0.52$ **10.** $k \approx 2.58$

Exercise 3.7

1. 2.28% **2.** (a) (i) 0.8849 (ii) 0.0139 (iii) 0.673
(b) 4.46% **3.** 0.0228 **4.** (i) 0.242 (ii) 0.383 (iii) 0.0301
5. True **6.** (i) 0.0668 (ii) 105 **7.** (i) 0.2266 (ii) No **8.** 4%
9. (i) 0.0475 (ii) 0.0475 (iii) 0.905 **10.** 22% **11.** (i) 0.0271
(ii) 10 (iii) Yes **12.** 40 **13.** 20 **14.** 176.92 **15.** Seán

Revision Exercises

1. (a) (i) 0.335 (ii) 0.402 (iii) 0.263 (b) 0.134 (c) (i) $\frac{1}{8}$
(ii) $\frac{7}{10}$ **2.** (a) 0.7698 (b) 0.215 **3.** (b) (ii) Yes
4. (b) (i) 0.311 (ii) 0.092 **5.** (a) (i) 0.9452 (ii) 0.8904
6. (a) 124 (b) 94.35% **7.** (ii) 0.04285 (iii) 0.0693 (iv) No
8. (a) (i) $x = 0.25$, $y = 0.1$ (ii) Not independent (b) 0.0668
9. (i) $\frac{21}{32}$ (ii) $\frac{1}{64}$ (iii) $\frac{21}{64}$ (iv) −€0.28 (v) No (vi) €43
(vii) No (viii) 13.5% **10.** (i) $\frac{385}{1,728}$ (ii) $\frac{1,343}{1,728}$ (iii) Karen
(iv) 13 **11.** (a) $\frac{5}{8}$ (c) (i) $\frac{3}{64}$ (ii) $\frac{5}{32}$ **12.** (iii) 0.3280
(iv) 0.1225 (v) No

Exam Questions

1. (a) 12 ways (b) Game B (c) 0.2 **2.** (b) (i) $\frac{5}{18}$
(ii) 0.3767 (iii) 0.0791 **3.** (b) 0.2 (c) 0.2 (d) A and B are
independent **4.** (a) 0.448 (b) 0.072 (c) 0.748 (e) (ii) 7
(f) (i) 0.75

Chapter 4

Exercise 4.1

1. (i) Mean = 78.95; median = 78.4 (ii) Mean = 40.38;
median = 40.6 (iii) Mean = 6.3; median = 6.1
(iv) Mean = 29.32; median = 27.9 (v) Mean = 97.57;
median = 98 **2.** (i) 35 (ii) 44.49 g (iii) 45 g
(iv) The mean and median are similar in value
(v) The distribution is almost symmetric (vi) No
3. (i) ≈ 10.91 °C (ii) ≈ 10.38 °C. The mean temperature in
2009 is higher than for 1961−1990 (iii) Not really
4. (i) 10.88 °C (ii) 0.18% (iii) 9.45 °C (iv) There has been
an increase in the annual mean soil temperature during this
period. This may be as a result of global warming.
5. (i) 2000 (ii) 2009 (iii) 155,048.8 (iv) 155,696.5
(v) The economic crash of 2008 would have led to fewer new
cars being purchased **6.** (i) 43.65 mins (ii) 16 **7.** (i) 96
(ii) 33.91 years (iii) 25% **8.** (i) Continuous

(ii)

Hours	Tally	No. of days
0–1	IIII I	6
1–2	IIII IIII	10
2–3	IIII	4
3–4	III	3
4–5	III	3
5–6	IIII	4

(iv) Skewed right (v) Median = 1.85 hrs (vi) 2.46 hours
(vii) 2.376 hrs (viii) 3.82% **9.** (i) 159.03 cm (iii) Quite
symmetric **10.** (i) Continuous

(ii)

Temp	Tally	No. of days
29–31	II	2
31–33	IIII III	8
33–35	IIII III	8
35–37	IIII III	8
37–39	II	2
39–41	II	2

(iv) Slightly skewed right (v) 34.25 °C
(vi) 34.4 °C (vii) ≈ 34.53 °C (viii) ≈ 0.37%

Exercise 4.2

1. (i) Mean or median   (ii) Mode   (iii) Mean or median
(iv) Mode   (v) Median   **2.** (i) Mean   (ii) Mode   (iii) Median
3. Mean = 32.8, median = 18. I would use the median, as the
mean is raised in value by the outlier value of 188
4. (i) Categorical (nominal)   (ii) Mode   **5.** (i) Median
(ii) Not really   (iii) Mean   **6.** (i) Skewed right
(ii) €35,216 = median; €41,819 = mean   (iii) A data set
containing the ages at retirement of the workers in the Irish
civil service   **7.** Brian: 178 cm, Sonia: 173 cm, Henry: 188 cm,
Rory: 174 cm, Cillian: 175 cm, Colin: 178 cm, Liam: 193 cm,
Derval: 168 cm

Exercise 4.3

1. (i) $Q_1 = 2$; $Q_3 = 7$; IQR = 5   (ii) $Q_1 = 4$; $Q_3 = 7$; IQR = 3
(iii) $Q_1 = 2.5$; $Q_3 = 6.5$; IQR = 4   (iv) $Q_1 = 4$; $Q_3 = 7$; IQR = 3
(v) $Q_1 = -2$; $Q_3 = 2$; IQR = 4   (vi) $Q_1 = -3$; $Q_3 = 7$; IQR = 10

2. (i)

Stem	Leaf
12	1, 1, 6
13	0, 1, 1, 1, 6, 9
14	1, 1, 3, 5
15	0 Key: 14|1 = 141

(ii) $Q_1 = 130$; $Q_3 = 141$ (iii) 57.14%   (iv) 11   **3.** (i) 59
(ii) 72   (iii) 13   (iv) Skewed left

4. (i)

Stem	Leaf
0	7, 7, 7, 8, 9, 9, 9, 9
1	0, 1, 1, 1, 1, 1, 2, 3, 3, 3, 4
1	6 Key: 1|1 = 11 kWh

(ii) Skewed right   (iii) 9   (iv) 11   (v) 3.5

5. (i)

Stem	Leaf
8	3, 6, 8
9	
10	5, 7, 8
11	0, 1, 2, 3, 4, 4, 7
12	0, 9, 9
13	3, 7, 8
14	0, 2, 5
15	
16	0, 3
17	3, 5, 9
18	0, 0
19	
20	6 Key: 17|3 = 17.3 inches

(ii) Skewed right   (iii) 12.3   (iv) 12.9   (v) 4.9
6. (a) (i) 29.165   (ii) 29.025   (iii) 20.77   (iv) 34.82
(v) 14.05   (vi) 6.2   (b) (i) 0.14   (ii) The distribution does not
contain outliers

7.

	Area 1	Area 2	Area 3
Mean	37.31	40.10	38.89
Minimum	36.71	39.38	38.24
Q_1	37.01	39.73	38.53
Median	37.18	39.98	38.80
Q_3	37.50	40.62	39.05
Maximum	38.85	40.80	40.08
IQR	0.49	0.89	0.52
Range	2.14	1.42	1.84

Exercise 4.4

1. (i) Neither. $\sigma_A = 2.83$, $\sigma_B = 2.83$ (ii) Neither. $\sigma_A = 3.22$,
$\sigma_B = 3.22$ (iii) A. $\sigma_A = 111.80$, $\sigma_B = 11.18$ (iv) Neither.
$\sigma_A = 2.74$, $\sigma_B = 2.74$ (v) Neither. $\sigma_A = 3.22$, $\sigma_B = 3.22$
(vi) Neither. $\sigma_X = 1.12$, $\sigma_Y = 1.12$ (vii) Neither. $\sigma_X = 2.74$,
$\sigma_Y = 2.74$ **2.** 10.71%   **3.** (a) (i) 15   (ii) €1.30   (iii) €2.90
(iv) €2.05   (v) €0.53   **4.** (i) Mean: €150,015,750,000;
standard deviation: €8,388,808,478   (iii) 2014   (iv) 2011
5. (iv) Symmetric   (v) Mean: 135.43 mmHg, standard deviation:
10.08 mmHg   (vi) Less   **6.** (i) 70 mins   (ii) ≈ 27 mins
7. (i) 32 years   (ii) ≈ 18 years   **8.** (i) €32   (ii) ≈ €17
9. (i) 71.96 cm   (ii) 5.30 cm

10. (i)

Regular Coke			
Weight (g)	360–365	365–370	370–375
Frequency	2	5	3

Diet Coke			
Weight (g)	345–350	350–355	355–360
Frequency	1	8	1

(iii) Regular Coke   (iv) $\sigma_{\text{Regular Coke}} = 3.5$, $\sigma_{\text{Diet Coke}} = 2.24$

Exercise 4.5

1. (i)

Stem	Leaf
5	1, 2, 3, 3, 3, 4, 4, 4, 5, 6, 6, 9
6	0, 1, 2, 8
7	2, 3, 3, 4, 5, 7, 8
8	0, 0, 0, 1, 1, 3, 5 Key: 7|3 = 73

(ii) 81   (iii) 53   (iv) 54   (v) 78   (vi) 85   (vii) 59.5
(viii) The 70th percentile

2. (i)

Stem	Leaf
1	8
2	
3	
4	2, 3, 7, 8
5	6, 6, 8
6	1, 5, 7
7	1, 4, 6, 7
8	3, 6, 7, 7, 8, 9, 9
9	0, 4, 5, 5, 7, 8, 9
10	0 Key: 7|4 = 74

(ii) 72.5   (iii) 89   (v) 27th percentile

3. (i)

Stem	Leaf
5	3
5	5, 5, 7, 8, 8, 9, 9
6	2, 2, 3, 3, 3, 3, 3, 3, 4
6	5, 5, 7, 8, 8, 8, 9, 9, 9
7	0, 0, 1, 3
7	5
8	0, 0, 3, 4 Key: 6|5 = 65 bpm

(ii) Skewed right   (iii) 73 bpm   (iv) 58 bpm   (vi) 23 bpm
4. (i) Skewed right   (ii) €29   (iii) €21   (iv) €31
5. (i)

Distance (m)	Frequency
14.25–15.00	1
15.00–15.75	0
15.75–16.50	2
16.50–17.25	4
17.25–18.00	9
18.00–18.75	7
18.75–19.50	4
19.50–20.25	1

(iii) Slightly skewed left   (iv) 19.12 m   (v) ≈ 40th percentile
6. The units are standard deviations from the mean
8. (i) 23 cm   (ii) 3.29   (iii) −3.29   (iv) Yes
9. (i) 60 IQ points   (ii) 3.75   (iii) 3.75   (iv) Yes   **10.** (i) −1
(ii) 1   (iii) −2.5   (iv) 6   **11.** The English score is better

Exercise 4.6

1. (i) 68%   (ii) 95%   (iii) 99.7%   **2.** (i) 18.6   (ii) 4.22
(iii) [14.38, 22.82]   **3.** (i) [175, 225]   (ii) [80, 120]   (iii) [18, 22]
(iv) [22.5, 27.5]   **4.** (i) [210, 350]   (ii) [60, 180]   (iii) [21, 29]
(iv) [24, 46]   **5.** (i) [75, 225]   (ii) [255, 345]   (iii) [14, 26]
(iv) [85, 115]   **7.** 186.5 cm   **9.** 68%

Revision Exercises

1. (i) Mean: 70.95, median: 71.95   (ii) Mean: 52.94,
median: 52.8   (iii) Mean: 16.3, median: 16.1   **2.** Mean: 191.8,
median: 155   **3.** Mean: 50, median: 50   **4.** (i) Q_1: 5, Q_3: 10,
IQR: 5   (ii) Q_1: 40, Q_3: 70, IQR: 30   (iii) Q_1: 1, Q_3: 3.5, IQR: 2.5
(iv) Q_1: −30, Q_3: 70, IQR: 100

5. (i)

Survival time (days)	Frequency
0–250	6
250–500	10
500–750	7
750–1,000	5
1,000–1,250	2
1,250–1,500	3
1,500–1,750	2
1,750–2,000	3
2,000–2,250	2
2,250–2,500	2
2,500–2,750	1

Note: 0–250 includes 0 but not 250.
(ii) 925.12 days   (iii) Skewed right   (iv) Most patients don't
survive   (v) No   (vi) Both   (vii) Yes   **6.** (i) 2.83   (ii) 1.41
(iii) 7.07 (iv) 141.42

7. (i)

Price (€)	Frequency
0–3	2
3–6	9
6–9	10
9–12	5
12–15	1
15–18	3

Note: 0–3 includes €0 but not €3   (iii) Almost symmetric
(iv) Mean = 7.82   (v) σ = 3.65 (standard deviation)
(vi) Minimum: increases by €2; maximum: increases by €2;
mean: increases by €2; standard deviation: unchanged;
median: increases by €2; IQR: unchanged
8. (ii) P_{90} = 71, P_{10} = 43   (iii) Q_1: 44, Q_3: 68
9. (i)

Level of cholesterol (mg/dl)	Frequency
0–200	11
200–400	11
400–600	5
600–800	6
800–1,000	2
1,000–1,200	1

Note: 0–200 includes 0 but not 200
(ii) Skewed right   (iii) 702   (iv) 127   (vi) 684   **10.** (i) 74 cm
(ii) 11.84   (iii) 11.84   (iv) Highly unusual

11.

	68%	95%	99.7%
	$[\bar{x} \pm \sigma]$	$[\bar{x} \pm 2\sigma]$	$[\bar{x} \pm 3\sigma]$
(i)	[175, 225]	[150, 250]	[125, 275]
(ii)	[80, 120]	[60, 140]	[40, 160]
(iii)	[18, 22]	[16, 24]	[14, 26]
(iv)	[22.5, 27.5]	[20, 30]	[17.5, 32.5]

Exam Questions

3. (a)

	A	B	C	D
Data skewed left	✗	✗	✓	✗
Data skewed right	✓	✗	✗	✗
Mean = Median	✗	✓	✗	✓
Mean > Median	✓	✗	✗	✗
There is a single mode	✓	✓	✓	✗

(b) D

Chapter 5

Exercise 5.1

1. (i) Approximately normal distribution
(ii) Mean = μ; SD = $\frac{\sigma}{20}$ **2.** 0.0011   **3.** (i) 0.6613   (ii) 0.9812
(iii) The underlying population is normally distributed
4. (i) 0.52   (ii) ≈ 1   **5.** (i) 0.5636   (ii) 0.7088   (iii) No
6. (i) 42.91%   (ii) 0.0371   **7.** n = 12   **8.** (i) Approximately
normal distribution   (ii) Mean = μ; SD = $\frac{\sigma}{\sqrt{n}}$ **10.** (i) 0.34%
(ii) Assumption: Population from which sample was chosen
has mean of 6 ppb and SD of 10 ppb   **11.** (i) ≈ 0.0158 hours
(iii) 2.87%   (iv) 43   (v) Expected distribution would be very
similar to actual sample distribution of sample means found
in part (i)

Exercise 5.2

1. $62.31 \leqslant \mu \leqslant 63.69$ **2.** $108.82 \leqslant \mu \leqslant 111.18$
3. $170.69 \leqslant \mu \leqslant 173.31$ **4.** $67.25 \leqslant \mu \leqslant 70.35$
5. $149.38 \leqslant \mu \leqslant 196.62$ **6.** (a) $4.23 \leqslant \mu \leqslant 4.77$
(b) $\bar{x} = 0.57$ **7.** (i) Mean = 147.22   (ii) (140.7584677,
153.6815323)   (iii) (€98,530.98, €107,577.07)

8. €395.10 ⩽ μ ⩽ €404.90   **9.** (a) 0.6293   (b) 0.0311
(c) 46.363 ⩽ μ ⩽ 47.637   **10.** (i) 105.53, 108.47
(ii) 90% CI: (105.76625, 108.23375), 99% CI: (105.06875,
108.93125)   **11.** (i) ±1.321

Exercise 5.3

1. (a) 0.444 ± 0.111   (b) 0.8 ± 0.1   (c) 0.427 ± 0.194
(d) 0.66 ± 0.053   **2.** (a) 0.040   (b) 0.0248   (c) 0.400
(d) 0.0054   **3.** (a) 0.66 < p < 0.72   (b) No
4. (a) 0.134 < p < 0.194   **5.** (a) 0.226 < p < 0.298
6. (a) ±0.06610461406   (b) 0.5838953859 < p <
0.7161046141   **8.** 2,401 households   **9.** (a) 18% < p < 31%
(b) 720 deer   (c) Yes   **10.** (b) (i) Population: All people
watching the television programme. Sample: The 610 people
who voted.   (ii) $\hat{p} = \frac{480}{610} = \frac{48}{61}$ ← The proportion of the sample
who favoured a uniform   **11.** (i) (0.41198005, 0.476908838)
(ii) (0.401793518, 0.48709537)   (iii) Reducing the sample
size would increase the width of a confidence interval
12. (i) 1,600   (ii) (0.343834587, 0.406165412)
13. (i) Method 1: (0.0706, 0.1294), Method 2: (0.05, 0.15)
(ii) Method 1: (0.451, 0.549), Method 2: (0.45, 0.55)
14. (a) −0.083 < p < 0.307   (b) That between 0% and 3%
will buy something   (c) It won't be cost-effective as 5% lies
outside our confidence interval

Exercise 5.4

2. Yes   **3.** False   **4.** Yes   **5.** Yes   **6.** (i) 0.478   (ii) 0.142
(iii) 0.00988   (iv) 0.0036   (v) 0.0024   (vi) 0.2502
(vi) 0.095   (viii) 0.0688   **7.** Yes, 0.0124 p value   **8.** No
9. We conclude the mean body temperature ≠ 98.6°F;
0.002 p value

Revision Exercises

3. 0.0038   **4.** 0.0228   **5.** [81.616, 83.184]   **6.** (i) [93.53, 96.47]
(ii) [93.766, 96.234]   (iii) [93.069, 96.931]   **7.** [50.07%,
56.59%]   **8.** No   **9.** No   **10.** (b) 0.613326 < p < 0.720006
12. (a) $97,300   (b) $4,242.64   (c) Approximately normal
distribution   (e) −1.838   (f) 3.29%

Exam Questions

1. (i) ≈ 29.66%   (ii) Approximately normal distribution
(iii) ≈ 103 or ≈ 104

2. (a)

Boys							
No. of sports	0	1	2	3	4	5	6
Frequency	1	10	12	20	4	3	0

Girls							
No. of sports	0	1	2	3	4	5	6
Frequency	0	9	6	22	9	3	1

(b) Similarity: 3 is the modal and median number of sports
for both groups. Difference: boys' mean = 2.5; girls'
mean = 2.88. (c) Yes (d) Improvements (i) Use stratified
random sampling   (ii) Survey teenagers, not just those
enrolled in GAA club

Chapter 6
Exercise 6.1

5. (ii) Corresponding   (iii) Corresponding   (iv) Vertically
opposite   (v) Corresponding   **6.** (i) Any two of the
following: ∠6 and ∠4, ∠5 and ∠3, ∠8 and ∠1 or ∠2 and ∠7

(ii) ∠5 and ∠1 and ∠2 and ∠4   (iii) Any two of the following:
∠6 and ∠2, ∠5 and ∠8, ∠1 and ∠3 or ∠4 and ∠7
7. (2) 117°   (3) 117°   (4) 117°   (5) 63°   (6) 63°   (7) 63°
(8) 117°   (9) 63°   **8.** (i) 9   (ii) 7   (iii) 15   **9.** (i) A = 55°,
B = 125°   (ii) A = 40°, B = 40°, C = 110°, D = 70°   (iii) A = 110°,
B = 110°, C = 70°   (iv) A = 45°, B = 55°, C = 135°   (v) A = 105°,
B = 50°, C = 50°   (vi) A = 67°, B = 67°, C = 53°   (vii) A = 100°
10. (i) x = 30°, y = 10°   (ii) x = 7, y = 8

Exercise 6.2

1. (i) A = 51°, B = 66°   (ii) A = 75°, B = 60°, C = 60°   (iii) A = 30°,
B = 120°, C = 150°   (iv) A = B = 64.25°, C = 51.5°   (v) A = 54°,
B = 63°, C = 54°   (vi) A = 48°, B = 14°   (vii) A = 93°, B = 96°,
C = 120°   **2.** (i) x = 66, y = 47   (ii) x = 59, y = 11
3. (i) Smallest C, largest B   (ii) Smallest DE, largest DF
(iii) Smallest angle HIG, largest angle GHI   (iv) Smallest JL,
largest JK   **4.** (i) No   (ii) Yes   (iii) Yes   (iv) No   (v) Yes
(vi) Yes   **5.** (i) 9   (ii) 14   (iii) 9 ⩽ a ⩽ 14   **6.** (i) 9   (ii) 16
(iii) 9 ⩽ b ⩽ 16   **7.** (i) 72°   (ii) 20°   **8.** (i) 52°   (ii) 52°
(iii) 38°   **9.** P   **10.** (i) 54°   (ii) 72°   (iii) 36°   (iv) 90°
11. (i) 549 km   (ii) 151 km   **12.** (i) 104°   (ii) 76°   (iii) 71°
(iv) 109°   **13.** (i) G, B, H, C, I, E   (ii) G, H, I, D   (iii) A, B
(iv) A, B, C   **14.** (i) 70°   (ii) 22°   (iii) 66°   **15.** (ii) Group B
16. 1 ⩽ c ⩽ 22   **17.** x = 10 or 11   **18.** Smallest (min. value) =
3 [x >2], largest (max. value) = 17 [x <18]

Exercise 6.3

1. (i) A = 41°, B = 49°, C = 90°   (ii) A = 37.5°, B = 52.5°,
C = 90°   (iii) A = 40°, B = 80°, C = 60°   (iv) A = 71°, B = 103°,
C = 61°, D = 71°, E = 67°   (v) A = 60°, B = 70°, C = 60°, D = 30°
2. (i) x = 2, y = 3   (ii) x = 7, y = 3   **3.** (i) 7.665 units²
(ii) 17.63 units²   (iii) 8.05 units²   (iv) 65 units²
(v) 14.7 units²   (vi) 432 units²   **4.** (i) 6.75   (ii) 4.28
(iii) 5.17   **5.** (i) 5 cm   (ii) 15 cm²   **6.** 8 : 1   **7.** (i) 25°
(ii) 83°   (iii) 34°   (iv) 63°   **8.** (a) (ii) 4x − 20 = 120°; 3x =
105°; 2x − 25 = 45°   (b) 108°   (c) 120°   (d) 135°   (e) No
(f) (i) 156°   (ii) 15

Exercise 6.4

1. (i) x = 3, y = 8   (ii) x = 1, y = $\frac{7}{2}$ (iii) x = 2, y = 1   **2.** (i) $\frac{2}{5}$
(ii) $\frac{1}{4}$ (iii) $\frac{4}{1}$ (iv) $\frac{3}{7}$ **3.** (i) 3 : 5   (ii) 3 : 2   (iii) 5 : 2   **4.** (i) $\frac{28}{3}$
(ii) 8   **5.** AB ∥ DE   **6.** (i) 1   (ii) 8   **7.** (i) x = 7, y = 20
(ii) x = $\frac{40}{3}$, y = $\frac{50}{3}$ (iii) x = $\frac{26}{3}$, y = $\frac{64}{3}$ (iv) x = √220,
y = √120   (v) x = 7.25, y = 2.75   (vi) x = 3√5, y = √20
(vii) x = 12.25, y = 8.75   **8.** (i) No   (ii) Yes   **9.** (i) x = √65,
y = √145   (ii) x = $\frac{13\sqrt{29}}{2}$, y = 7√26   (iii) x = 8√3, y = 4√3
(iv) x = 13.44, y = 3.92   **10.** (ii) 20   (iii) 16   (iv) 8   **11.** (ii) $\frac{128}{3}$
12. (i) 18.75   (ii) 22.5   (iii) 59.93 units²   (iv) 210.67 units²
(v) 71.25   **13.** (i) 2√74   (ii) 2√113   (iii) 2√138   **14.** (i) 20√2
(ii) 5√17   (iii) 5√21   **15.** (i) 9.1   (ii) 7   (iii) 2   **16.** (i) 8.75 m
(ii) 420 m   (iii) 1.79 m   **17.** 15 m   **18.** (ii) 6 m   **19.** 2.56 km²
20. (ii) Building A 28 m, Building B 42 m   **21.** (i) 1.05 m
(ii) 2.97 m   **22.** Red squirrel's pole: 5.6 m; grey squirrel's
pole: 6.4 m   **23.** (i) 31.62 m   (ii) 40 m   **24.** 2.4

Exercise 6.5

2. (i) 58°   (ii) 32°   (iii) 16°   **3.** (i) 150°   (ii) 105°   **4.** (i) 150°
(ii) 75°   (iii) 38°   (iv) 53°   **5.** (i) 112°   (ii) 80°   (iii) 100°
(iv) 80°   **6.** (i) 90°   (ii) 40°   (iii) 70°   (iv) 40°   (v) 30°
(vi) 30°   **7.** (i) ∠RCS   (ii) ∠QRP   (iii) ∠QPS   **8.** (i) 52°
(ii) 26°   (iii) 15°   **9.** 4.5   **10.** (i) 54°   (ii) 44°   (iii) 68°
(iv) 49°   (v) 22°   **11.** (i) 36°   (ii) 74°   (iii) 108°   (iv) 36°
(v) 106°   **12.** (i) 10   (ii) ≈ 10.5463   **13.** (i) 7   (ii) 1cm

(iii) 49 (iv) $35\sqrt{2}$ **14.** (i) 30 cm (ii) 14 cm **15.** (i) 12 cm
(ii) $3\sqrt{17}$ cm (iii) $12\sqrt{2}$ cm **16.** 48 cm **17.** (i) ≈ 49.29°
(ii) 27.5281 (iii) ≈ 69.74

Revision Exercises

1. (i) 112° (ii) 68° (iii) 34° (iv) 34° (v) 56° (vi) 90°
(vii) 90° (viii) 112° **2.** (a) (i) 70° (ii) 110° (iii) 70°
(iv) 110° (b) 115° **3.** (a) (i) $x = 4.5, y = 7.5$
(ii) $\angle 1 = 120°, \angle 2 = 60°, \angle 3 = 60°, \angle 4 = 120°, \angle 5 = 60°,$
$\angle 6 = 120°$ **4.** (a) (i) 72° (ii) 114° (iii) 39° (iv) 27°
(b) (i) $x = 1, y = 2$ (ii) $|AB| = 10, |DC| = 10, |AD| = 11$ **5.** 800 m
6. (a) (i) $\frac{3}{7}$ (ii) $\frac{3}{7}$ (iii) $\frac{7}{4}$ (b) No (c) (i) 22.5

(ii) 11.85 (iii) 5 (iv) $\frac{3}{2}$ **7.** (a) (i) 4.36 m (ii) 6.39 m²
(b) 5 cm (c) (i) 16.31 (ii) 8 (iii) 39.65 **8.** (a) 233 cm
(b) (i) 8 (ii) 18 m (c) (i) 8.57 m (ii) A: 57.14 m, B: 42.86 m
9. (a) $\frac{7y}{(5-y)}$ (b) 1,225 : 144 **10.** (a) 13.86 km (b) 7.79 cm

11. (a) (ii) $r^2 - \frac{y^2}{4}$ (b) (i) $\frac{\sqrt{3}x}{2}$ (ii) $\frac{x}{\sqrt{3}}$ (iii) $\frac{x}{2\sqrt{3}}$ (iv) 1 : 4

Chapter 7

Exercise 7.1

1. (i) 29 (ii) 85 (iii) 3 (iv) 24 (v) 24 (vi) 40
2. (i) $x = \sqrt{10}$ (ii) $x = \sqrt{2}$ (iii) $x = \sqrt{34}$ (iv) $x = 2\sqrt{6}$ **3.** 2.5 m
4. (i) $x = 5, y = 12$ (ii) $x = 85, y = 77$ (iii) $x = 96, y = 4$
(iv) $x = 10, y = 24$ **5.** (i) 60 cm (ii) 100 cm (iii) 4,800 cm²

6. (a)

a	b	c
12	16	20
15	20	25
18	24	30
21	28	35

(b)

a^2	b^2	c^2
36	64	100
81	144	225
144	256	400
225	400	625
324	576	900
441	784	1,225

7. (i) $\sin A = \frac{5}{13}$, $\cos A = \frac{12}{13}$, $\tan A = \frac{5}{12}$ (ii) $\sin A = \frac{21}{29}$,
$\cos A = \frac{20}{29}$, $\tan A = \frac{21}{20}$ **8.** (i) $\sin A = \frac{20}{29}$, $\sin B = \frac{21}{29}$,
$\cos A = \frac{21}{29}$, $\cos B = \frac{20}{29}$, $\tan A = \frac{20}{21}$, $\tan B = \frac{21}{20}$
(ii) $\sin A = \frac{3}{\sqrt{13}}$, $\sin B = \frac{2}{\sqrt{13}}$, $\cos A = \frac{2}{\sqrt{13}}$, $\cos B = \frac{3}{\sqrt{13}}$, $\tan A = \frac{3}{2}$,
$\tan B = \frac{2}{3}$ (iii) $\sin A = \frac{1}{\sqrt{5}}$, $\sin B = \frac{2}{\sqrt{5}}$, $\cos A = \frac{2}{\sqrt{5}}$, $\cos B = \frac{1}{\sqrt{5}}$,
$\tan A = \frac{1}{2}$, $\tan B = 2$ **9.** (i) 0.2588 (ii) 0.8660 (iii) 3.7321
(iv) 0.2419 (v) 0.9004 (vi) 0.0872 (vii) 0.2126
(viii) 0.5000 (ix) 5.6713 (x) 0.4791 (xi) 0.7218
(xii) 0.9823 (xiii) 0.5210 (xiv) 0.2830 (xv) 0.8581
(xvi) 0.5490 (xvii) 0.8934 (xviii) 7.4947 (xix) 0.0307
(xx) 0.8923 **10.** (i) 38.26° (ii) 29.61° (iii) 19.76°
(iv) 25.94° (v) 20.62° (vi) 82.84° (vii) 58.54°
(viii) 46.23° (ix) 64.93° (x) 63.11° (xi) 8.26° (xii) 41.23°
11. (i) 2°30′ (ii) 2°15′ (iii) 2°45′ (iv) 25°24′ (v) 1°12′
(vi) 0°20′ **12.** (i) 2.52° (ii) 10.67° (iii) 25.83° (iv) 70.37°
(v) 11.62° (vi) 33.55° **13.** (i) 75°57′ (ii) 48°14′ (iii) 43°55′
(iv) 41°34′ (v) 17°42′ (vi) 26°49′ (vii) 73°54′ (viii) 13°57′
(ix) 22°12′ (x) 58°01′ (xi) 25°36′ (xii) 23°4′ **14.** 13°
15. 28°04′ **16.** (i) 8.66 (ii) 10.32 (iii) 8 (iv) 28.28

(v) 4.37 (vi) 24.24 (vii) 6.93 (viii) 19.92
17. $x = 64.28, y = 11.33$ **18.** $x ≈ 3.6, y ≈ 4.7, z = 12$
19. (i) 7.2 km (ii) 34° (iii) E 4°N **20.** (i) 118 km
(ii) 23 kmh⁻¹ (iii) 59 kmh⁻¹ **21.** $h = 449.17$ m
22. $d = 346.41$ m **23.** 11.44 m

Exercise 7.2

1.

Degrees	90°	180°	270°	360°	30°	45°	60°
Radians	$\frac{\pi}{2}$	π	$\frac{3\pi}{2}$	2π	$\frac{\pi}{6}$	$\frac{\pi}{4}$	$\frac{\pi}{3}$

2. (i) 90° (ii) 270° (iii) 450° (iv) 240° (v) 225° (vi) 50°
(vii) 720° (viii) 1,080° (ix) 135° (x) 330° (xi) 80°
(xiii) 144° **3.** (i) $\frac{\pi}{2}$ (ii) $\frac{3\pi}{2}$ (iii) $\frac{\pi}{4}$ (iv) $\frac{\pi}{12}$ (v) 3π (vi) $\frac{\pi}{6}$
(vii) $\frac{12\pi}{5}$ (viii) $\frac{5\pi}{12}$ (ix) $\frac{5\pi}{24}$ (x) $\frac{5\pi}{6}$ (xi) $\frac{7\pi}{6}$ (xii) $\frac{49\pi}{9}$ **4.** (i) 2nd
(ii) 1st (iii) 1st (iv) 3rd (v) 3rd (vi) Between 3rd and 4th
(vii) 4th (viii) 1st (ix) 2nd (x) 2nd (xi) 4th (xii) 3rd

Exercise 7.3

1. (i) 0 (ii) −1 (iii) 0 (iv) 1 (v) 0 (vi) −1 (vii) 0
(viii) 1 (ix) 0 (x) 0 (xi) 1 (xii) 0 (xiii) 0
2. (a)

Angle	Quadrant	Reference Angle
210°	3rd	30°
340°	4th	20°
225°	3rd	45°
280°	4th	80°

(b)

Angle	Quadrant	Reference Angle
315°	4th	45°
135°	2nd	45°
210°	3rd	30°
240°	3rd	60°

3. (a) (i) $-\frac{1}{\sqrt{2}}$ (ii) $\frac{1}{2}$ (iii) $-\frac{1}{2}$ (iv) $-\frac{1}{2}$ (v) $\frac{1}{\sqrt{3}}$ (vi) $\frac{1}{\sqrt{2}}$ (vii) $\frac{\sqrt{3}}{2}$
(viii) $\frac{-\sqrt{3}}{2}$ (ix) $-\sqrt{3}$ (x) $\sqrt{3}$ (b) (i) −0.82 (ii) 0.34 (iii) −0.64
(iv) −0.09 (v) 0.84 (vi) 0.82 (vii) 0.64 (viii) −0.64
(ix) −0.18 (x) −0.36 **4.** (i) $\frac{1}{\sqrt{2}}$ (ii) $\frac{1}{2}$ (iii) $\sqrt{3}$ (iv) $\frac{\sqrt{3}}{2}$
(v) $-\frac{\sqrt{3}}{2}$ (vi) 0 (vii) $-\sqrt{3}$

Exercise 7.4

1. (a) (ii) Range [−1, 1] (iii) Period 2π (b) (ii) Range [−1, 1]
(iii) Period π (c) (ii) Range [−2, 2] (iii) Period π
(iv) Range = [−a, a], period = $\frac{2\pi}{b}$ **2.** (a) (ii) Range [−1, 1]
(iii) Period 2π (b) (ii) Range [−1, 1] (iii) Period π
(c) (ii) Range [−2, 2] (iii) Period π (iv) Range = [−a, a],
period = $\frac{2\pi}{b}$ **3.** (a) (ii) Range (−∞, ∞) (iii) Period π
(b) (ii) Range (−∞, ∞) (iii) Period $\frac{\pi}{2}$ (iv) Range (−∞, ∞),
period $\frac{\pi}{6}$ (v) Period $\frac{\pi}{3}$, range (−∞, ∞)

4.

	Period	Range
(i)	$\frac{\pi}{2}$ or 90°	[−1, 1]
(ii)	2π or 360°	[−2, 2]
(iii)	2π or 360°	[−3, 3]
(iv)	π or 180°	[−1, 1]
(v)	π or 180°	[−3, 3]
(vi)	$\frac{\pi}{2}$ or 90°	[−2, 2]
(vii)	$\frac{\pi}{2}$ or 90°	[−∞, ∞]

5.

	Period	Range
(i)	2π	$[-1, 1]$
(ii)	$\frac{\pi}{2}$	$[-1, 1]$
(iii)	$\frac{\pi}{2}$	$[-\infty, \infty]$
(iv)	$\frac{\pi}{3}$	$[-\infty, \infty]$
(v)	$\frac{2\pi}{3}$	$[-2, 2]$
(vi)	$\frac{\pi}{2}$	$[-4, 4]$
(vii)	$\frac{2\pi}{3}$	$[-a, a]$
(viii)	$\frac{2\pi}{k}$	$[-3, 3]$

6. (i) $-\frac{13\pi}{7}, -\frac{6\pi}{7}, \frac{\pi}{7}, \frac{8\pi}{7}$ (ii) $\theta = 60°, 120°, 420°, 480°$
(iii) $\theta = \frac{4\pi}{3}, \frac{5\pi}{3}, \frac{10\pi}{3}, \frac{11\pi}{3}$ **7.** (i) $g(x) = 3\sin 2x$ (ii) $g(x) = 3\sin 2x$
(iv) Yes, at $(-\pi, 0)$, $(0,0)$ and $(\pi, 0)$ **8.** (i) $\left(-\frac{\pi}{2}, -1\right), \left(\frac{\pi}{6}, \frac{1}{2}\right), \left(\frac{5\pi}{6}, \frac{1}{2}\right)$
9. (i) (a) $(0,0), (\pm\pi, 0), (\pm 2\pi, 0), (\pm 3\pi, 0), (\pm 4\pi, 0)$
(b) Max = 1, min = -1 (ii) $h(x) = \sin\left(\frac{x}{2}\right)$ (iii) $g(x) = 3\sin\left(\frac{x}{2}\right)$
(iv) Period = 4π, range = $[-3, 3]$ (v) $h(x) = \sin\left(\frac{1}{2}x\right)$

Exercise 7.5

1. B $y = 3$, 1, $[2, 4]$; C $y = -1$, 1, $[-2, 0]$; D $y = -2$, 1, $[-3, -1]$;
E $y = 2$, 1, $[1, 3]$; F $y = -3$, 1, $[-4, -2]$; G $y = 1$, 1, $[0, 2]$
2. (b) Shifted up 3, reflected across x-axis and stretched
vertically by a factor of 4, 4, $[1, 7]$, π (c) Shifted down 4,
reflected across x-axis and stretched vertically by 2, 2,
$[-6, -2]$, $\frac{2\pi}{3}$ (d) Shifted down 1, stretched vertically by 5, 5,
$[-6, 4]$, π (e) Shifted up 5, reflected across x-axis, 1,
$[4, 6]$, 4π (f) None, stretched vertically by 3, 3, $[-3, 3]$, $\frac{2\pi}{3}$
(g) Shifted up 1, none, 1, $[0, 2]$, $\frac{\pi}{2}$ (h) Shifted up 0.5,
stretched by a factor of 5, 5, $[-4.5, 5.5]$, 2π (i) Shifted up 3,
reflected across x-axis and stretched by 3, 3, $[0, 6]$, $\frac{2\pi}{3}$
(j) Shifted up 0.25, reflected across x-axis and stretched by a
factor of 0.5, 0.5, $[-0.25, 0.75]$, 6π **3.** (a) Black = $\sin 4x$,
red = $4 + 2\sin 4x$ (b) Black = $4 - 2\sin x$, red = $4 + 2\sin x$
5. (c) 0.65 m   (d) Above   **6.** (ii) $A = 12$, $B = 6$ (iii) 6 hrs 8 mins
(iv) 28 February and 8 October   (v) $36\pi\,m^2$ (vi) Between 55°
N and 60° N   (vii) 3,113 km

Exercise 7.6

1. (i) $|\angle BAC| = 30°$ (ii) $|AB| = \sqrt{3}$ (iii) $|AC| = 2$ **2.** (i) 45°
(ii) 7   **3.** (i) $x = y = 4$ (ii) 45°   **4.** (i) $\frac{-1}{\sqrt{2}}$ (ii) $-\frac{1}{2}$ (iii) $-\sqrt{3}$
(iv) $\frac{-\sqrt{3}}{2}$ (v) $\frac{1}{\sqrt{2}}$ (vi) $\frac{-1}{\sqrt{2}}$ (vii) $\frac{-1}{\sqrt{2}}$ (viii) $\frac{1}{\sqrt{2}}$ (ix) $\frac{1}{\sqrt{3}}$
(x) $\frac{1}{\sqrt{2}}$ (xi) $-\frac{\sqrt{3}}{2}$ (xii) -1 (xiii) $\sqrt{3}$ (xiv) $-\frac{2}{\sqrt{3}}$ (xv) -2
5. 1   **6.** 4   **7.** $\frac{4}{3}$ **9.** (i) 1   (ii) $\sqrt{3} - 1$ (iii) $-\frac{2}{\sqrt{3}}$

Exercise 7.7

1. (i) 60° or 300°   (ii) 45° or 225°   (iii) 240° or 300°
(iv) 135° or 225°   (v) 60° or 120°   (vi) 135° or 225°
(vii) 45°, 135°, 225°, 315°   (viii) 135° or 315°   (ix) 60°, 120°,
240°, 300°   **2.** (i) $\frac{\pi}{6}$ or $\frac{5\pi}{6}$ (ii) $\frac{\pi}{6}$ or $\frac{7\pi}{6}$ (iii) $\frac{\pi}{4}$ or $\frac{7\pi}{4}$
(iv) $\frac{5\pi}{4}$ or $\frac{7\pi}{4}$ (v) $0, \pi, 2\pi$ (vi) $x = \pi$ **3.** (i) $A = 23.6°$ or 156.4°
(ii) $A = 115.4°$ or 244.6°   (iii) $A = 105.9°$ or 285.9°
(iv) 53.1° or 306.9°   (v) $A = 10.5°$ or 169.5°
(vi) $A = 142.3°$ or 322.3°   **4.** (i) $\sin\theta = \frac{3}{5}$, $\tan\theta = \frac{3}{4}$
(ii) $\cos\theta = -\frac{12}{13}$, $\tan\theta = -\frac{5}{12}$ **5.** (i) $\theta = 15°, 75°, 195°, 255°$
(ii) $\theta = 30°, 150°, 210°, 330°$ (iii) $\theta = 58.1°, 118.1°, 178.1°, 238.1°$,

298.1°, 358.1°   (iv) $\theta = 90°$ or 210° or 330°   (v) $\theta = 300°$
6. (i) $\frac{\pi}{2} + 2n\pi$, $n \in Z$ (ii) $\frac{3\pi}{4} + 2n\pi$, $\frac{5\pi}{4} + 2n\pi$, $n \in Z$
(iii) $\frac{\pi}{2} + 2n\pi$, $\frac{3\pi}{2} + 2n\pi$, $n \in Z$ (iv) $\frac{\pi}{4} + 2n\pi$, $\frac{3\pi}{4} + 2n\pi$, $n \in Z$
(v) $\frac{\pi}{2} + \frac{2n\pi}{3}$, $n \in Z$ **7.** First design is in line with regulations,
second is not   **8.** $\theta > 40°$, not economical

Exercise 7.8

1. (i) $|\angle YZX| = 21.2°$, $|\angle YXZ| = 98.8°$, $|YZ| = 13.7$
(ii) $|\angle RQS| = 70°$, $|QR| = 8.8$, $|RS| = 10.9$
(iii) $|\angle RQP| = 34.8°$ or 145.2°, $|\angle QRP| = 125.2°$ or 14.8°,
$|QP| = 14.3$, $|QP| = 4.5$ **2.** (i) 30°, $x = 1$,   (ii) 60°, 60°, 2
3. (i) $a = 4.58$ (ii) $a = 3.87$ **4.** (i) $A \approx 82°$ (ii) $A = 120°$
5. $|AD| = 79$, $|AC| = 130$ **6.** $\theta = 108°$ **8.** (i) $|\angle WYX| \approx 42.5$
(ii) $|XY| = 14.8$ (iii) $|WZ| = 24.1$ **9.** $|DC| = 4.9$ **10.** $|PQ| = 73.73$ m,
$|PR| = 65.22$ m   **11.** (i) 100°   (ii) 101.54 m   (iii) 77.8 m
13. (i) $\cos\alpha = \frac{p^2 + d^2 - c^2}{2pd}$, $\cos\beta = \frac{q^2 + d^2 - b^2}{2qd}$

Exercise 7.9

1. 73.72 units²   **2.** 123.61 units²   **3.** 70.91 units²
4. (i) 45.51 units²   (ii) 23.66 units²   (iii) 24.63 units²
5. (i) $x = 6$ cm   (ii) $x = 4$ cm   (iii) $x = 38°$ **6.** (i) 35 cm²; 7 cm
(ii) 2.704 cm²; 1.04 cm   (iii) 308.39 m²; 51.40 cm   **7.** 45.71 cm,
area of slice = 117.81 cm²   **8.** $\frac{3}{2}$ radians   **9.** (i) 9 cm²
(ii) 4.09 cm²   (iii) 4.91 cm²   **10.** (i) $|AB| = \sqrt{3}r$ cm   (ii) $\pi\sqrt{3}r$ cm
11. 87.59 cm²

Exercise 7.10

1. (a) 11.1 m   (b) 16.2°   **2.** (a) 25.5 cm   (b) 11.3°
3. 35.26°   **4.** 13.1 cm   **5.** 14.59°   **6.** (i) 14 m   (ii) $2\sqrt{41}$ m
(iii) 66°   **7.** (i) 5 cm   (ii) 13 cm   (iii) 13.34°   (iv) 22.61°
8. (i) ≈ 8.13 cm   (ii) ≈ 9.96 cm   (iii) 55°   **9.** 32.07°
10. (i) 33.1 m   (ii) 40.83°   **11.** (i) 20 m   (ii) 30.6 m

Exercise 7.11

1. (i) $\frac{\sqrt{3}-1}{2\sqrt{2}}$ (ii) $\frac{\sqrt{3}+1}{2\sqrt{2}}$ (iii) $\frac{\sqrt{3}-1}{2\sqrt{2}}$ (iv) $2 + \sqrt{3}$ (v) $\frac{\sqrt{3}-1}{2\sqrt{2}}$
(vi) $-\frac{1}{2}$ (vii) $\frac{\sqrt{3}+1}{2\sqrt{2}}$ (viii) -2 (ix) $\frac{1}{\sqrt{2}}$ (x) $\frac{1}{2}$ **2.** $\frac{16}{13}$ **3.** $\frac{5}{12}$
4. (i) $\frac{4}{5}$ (ii) $\frac{4}{3}$ (iii) $\frac{5}{13}$ (iv) $\frac{5}{12}$ (v) $\frac{16}{65}$ (vi) $\frac{63}{16}$
5. $\tan A = \frac{1}{2}$ or $\tan A = -2$ **6.** $\tan A = \pm\frac{1}{5}$ **7.** $\tan B = \frac{3}{5}$
8. (i) $\sin 8\theta + \sin 4\theta$ (ii) $\frac{1}{2}(\cos 4\theta + \cos 2\theta)$
(iii) $\frac{1}{2}(\sin 4A - \sin 2A)$ (iv) $\frac{1}{2}(\cos 2x - \cos 8x)$
(v) $\cos 5\theta + \cos 3\theta$ (vi) $\frac{1}{2}(\sin 8x + \sin 4x)$
(vii) $\cos 5\theta - \cos 3\theta$ (viii) $\sin\theta$ (ix) $\frac{1}{2}[\sin 6x + \sin 4x]$
(x) $\cos 2x + \cos \pi$ **9.** (i) $\frac{1}{4}$ (ii) $\frac{\sqrt{3}+2}{2}$ **10.** (i) $2\sin 3x \cos x$
(ii) $2\cos 2x \sin x$ (iii) $2\cos 6x \cos 3x$ (iv) $2\sin 2x \cos x$
(v) $2\cos\frac{3x}{2}\sin\frac{x}{2}$ (vi) $2\sin 6x \cos 4x$ (vii) $-2\sin 5\theta \sin 3\theta$
(viii) $2\sin 3x \sin 2x$ (ix) $-2\sin 30° \sin x$ (x) $2\sin x \cos 60°$
11. (i) $\frac{1}{\sqrt{2}}$ (ii) $-\frac{1}{\sqrt{2}}$ **13.** (i) $\frac{4}{7}$ (ii) $\frac{3}{11}$ (iii) 1

Revision Exercises

1. $x = 5$ cm, $\sin\alpha = \frac{12}{13}$, $\cos\alpha = \frac{5}{13}$, $\tan\alpha = \frac{12}{5}$,
$\sin\beta = \frac{5}{13}$, $\cos\beta = \frac{12}{13}$, $\tan\beta = \frac{5}{12}$

2.

Degrees	Radians
90°	$\frac{\pi}{2}$
180°	π
270°	$\frac{3\pi}{2}$
360°	2π
120°	$\frac{2\pi}{3}$
45°	$\frac{\pi}{4}$
60°	$\frac{\pi}{3}$

3. (i) 216° (ii) 36° (iii) 300° **4.** (i) $\frac{5\pi}{6}$ (ii) $\frac{8\pi}{5}$ (iii) $\frac{3\pi}{5}$

(b)

	Curve	Vertical Translation	Vertical Shape	Amplitude	Range	Period
(i)	$g(x) = 1 + 3\cos x$	Up 1	Stretch by 3	3	[−2, 4]	2π
(ii)	$g(x) = 4 + 3\cos\frac{1}{2}x$	Up 4	Stretch by 3	3	[1, 7]	4π
(iii)	$g(x) = 5\sin x + 1$	Up 1	Stretch by 5	5	[−4, 6]	2π

17. (i) $2\cos 4x \sin x$ (ii) $2\cos 4x \cos 3x$ **18.** $\frac{1}{2\sqrt{2}} - \frac{1}{4}$

19.

A	30°	45°	60°
sin A	$\frac{1}{2}$	$\frac{1}{\sqrt{2}}$	$\frac{\sqrt{3}}{2}$
cos A	$\frac{\sqrt{3}}{2}$	$\frac{1}{\sqrt{2}}$	$\frac{1}{2}$
tan A	$\frac{1}{\sqrt{3}}$	1	$\sqrt{3}$

(i) $A = 30° \pm n(360°)$ or $150° \pm n(360°), n \in N$
(ii) $B = 45° \pm n(180°), n \in N$ (iii) $C = 45° \pm n(180°), n \in N$
(iv) $D = 60° + n(360°)$ or $120° + n(360°), n \in N$
20. (a) (i) $A = 23.6°$ or $156.4°$ (ii) $A = 115.4°$ or $244.6°$
(iii) $A = 105.9°$ or $285.9°$ (iv) $A = 120°$ or $240°$
(v) $A = 60°$ or $120°$ (b) (i) $\theta = 20°$ or $100°...$ (ii) $\theta = 30°$ or $60°...$
21. (i) $\approx 24°$ (ii) Carol **22.** (i) 1,190.628 cm² (ii) 476.00 cm²
23. (i) 14.04° (ii) 6.19 m (iii) $d = 0.77$ m
24. (i) $d = 110.28$ km (ii) 4 hours 31 minutes (iii) 1 hour
29 minutes **25.** (i) 4 cm (ii) 8.378 cm² (iii) 84.87 cm²
(iv) 68.11 cm² **26.** $\theta = 30°$ **27.** (i) 19.06 m
(ii) 5.4° **28.** (i) 7.36 m (ii) 242 cm (iii) 14°
29. (i) 1.31 m (ii) 1.9 m **30.** $|\angle PRQ| = 120°$ **31.** (i) 1 m
(ii) 2.97 m (iii) 56° **32.** 23.13 m **33.** (b) $h \approx 194.1750$ m
(c) 2nd estimate: $h \approx 194.0727$ m; 3rd estimate:
$h \approx 194.1149$ m (d) $h \approx 19,412$ cm (g) Range = 3.8 m

Exam Questions

1. (b) 1.885 m (c) 10.37 m **2.** (i) $|AB| = 3.66$ m (ii) 20.30 m
4. (i) 3.42 m (ii) 31.71 m² (iii) 26.72 m² ⩽ area of roof ⩽
37.07 m² **5.** (a) $3\theta = \frac{\pi}{3} + 2n\pi$, or $3\theta = \frac{5\pi}{3} + 2n\pi$, where $n \in \mathbb{Z}$
$\therefore \theta = \frac{\pi}{9} + \frac{2n\pi}{3}$, or $\theta = \frac{5\pi}{9} + \frac{2n\pi}{3}$, where $n \in \mathbb{Z}$ (b) $f: x \to 3\cos 2x$,
$g: x \to 2\cos 3x, h: x \to \cos 3x$

Chapter 8

Exercise 8.1

1. (i) (a) 13 (b) $3\sqrt{10}$ (c) 3 (d) $\sqrt{74}$ (ii) (a) $\left(\frac{11}{2}, 8\right)$
(b) $\left(-\frac{3}{2}, -\frac{5}{2}\right)$ (c) $\left(6, \frac{21}{2}\right)$ (d) $\left(-\frac{1}{2}, -\frac{9}{2}\right)$ **2.** (i) 2 (ii) (a) (6,0)
(b) (0,−12) **3.** (11,12) **4.** (i) $|PQ| = 4\sqrt{5}$; $|PR| = 2\sqrt{10}$;

5. (i) 17 m (ii) 30° **7.** (a) $\sin\alpha = Q$, $\cos\alpha = P$, $\tan\alpha = \frac{Q}{P}$
(b) (i) 10.64 (ii) $y = 10.02$ **8.** (i) $\frac{1}{\sqrt{2}}$ (ii) $\frac{\sqrt{3}}{2}$ (iii) −14.301
(iv) 0.978 (v) −0.901

9. (b)

		Horizontal Midway Line	Amplitude	Range
a	$h(x) = 3 + \sin x$	3	1	[2, 4]
b	$h(x) = -1 + \sin x$	−1	1	[−2, 0]
c	$h(x) = -2 + \cos x$	−2	1	[−3, −1]

10. (a) (i) Red = $\cos\theta$, green = $\sin\theta$ (ii) Red = $\sin 2x$,
green = $2\cos x$ (iii) $\tan\theta$ (iv) $\tan 2\theta$

$|QR| = 2\sqrt{10}$; isosceles as $|PR| = |QR| \neq |PQ|$ (ii) (−1,−1)
5. $a = 2$; $b = -3$ **8.** $a = 6$ **9.** (i) $2\sqrt{10}$ (ii) (3,1) (iv) (3.8,3.4)
(v) Slope $l = -\frac{1}{3}$; slope $AB = 3$; $AB \perp l$ **10.** Radius = $\sqrt{40}$, $t = 8$
or −4, $q = -2$ or 10 **11.** (−3,1) or (5,5) **12.** −3
13. (i) €50 (ii) €90 (iii) 1 (iv) $\frac{1}{min}$ (v) $y = x + 50$ (vi) €170
14. (i) (−12,11) (ii) 30 m

Exercise 8.2

1. (−2,4) **2.** (4,15) **3.** (3,2) **4.** (−2,3) **5.** (ii) 2 : 1
6. $A(0,5)$; $E\left(\frac{5}{2}, 0\right)$ **7.** 1 : 1 **8.** 4 : 1

Exercise 8.3

1. (i) $3x + y - 26 = 0$ (ii) $2x - 3y + 2 = 0$ (iii) $4x + 10y - 11 = 0$
(iv) $2x - y - 3 = 0$ **2.** (i) $x - y - 1 = 0$ (ii) $x - 3y + 10 = 0$
(iii) $2x - y + 9 = 0$ **3.** (i) $x + 3y - 4 = 0$ (ii) $x - y + 6 = 0$
(iii) $14x + 9y - 39 = 0$ **4.** $x + y = 0$ **5.** $j: y = 1$; $l: 4x - y - 2 = 0$;
$k: x + y + 1 = 0$ **6.** $x + 3y + 2 = 0$ **7.** $2x + 3y - 6 = 0$
8. $3x - 2y - 12 = 0$ **9.** $6x + y + 16 = 0$ **10.** $2x - y + 4 = 0$
11. $x + y - 4 = 0$ **12.** $3x - 4y - 6 = 0$ **13.** $2x + y - 2 = 0$
14. $x - 8y = 0$ **15.** (i) $DE: x + y - 4.5 = 0$; $AB: x - y = 0$
(ii) $D(1.5,3)$; $E(3,1.5)$ (iii) ≈ 3.35 units
16. $3x - 4y + 24 = 0$ **17.** (iii) $x - y - 3 = 0$
(iv) $x + y + 1 = 0$ (v) (1,−2) (vi) $\sqrt{10}$

Exercise 8.4

1. (i) 9.5 units² (ii) 22 units² (iii) 4 units²
(iv) 13 units² (v) 24 units² (vi) 12 units²
(vii) $\frac{5}{2}$ units² (viii) 12 units² **2.** 12.5 units²
3. $\frac{3}{2}$ units² **4.** 8 units² **5.** $C(3,0)$ or (−29,0) **6.** 29 units²
7. ±3 **8.** $k = 0$ or $k = 4$

Exercise 8.5

1. (i) 2.1 units (ii) 5 units (iii) 1 unit (iv) $\sqrt{5}$ units
(v) $\sqrt{2}$ units **2.** (i) $\sqrt{5}$ units (ii) $4\sqrt{2}$ units (iii) $2\sqrt{5}$ units
(iv) $4\sqrt{13}$ units **3.** $\frac{32\sqrt{13}}{13}$ units **4.** $\frac{51\sqrt{61}}{61}$ units
6. Point is equidistant **7.** $k = \pm 8$ **9.** (i) $3x - 4y - 29 = 0$

(ii) $\frac{38}{5}$ units   **10.** $\frac{15\sqrt{34}}{34}$ **11.** (i) 3 units   (ii) $k = -32$

12. 1 unit   **13.** $x - 3y - 9 = 0$ or $3x - y + 5 = 0$

14. $15x - 8y + 78 = 0$ or $15x - 8y - 92 = 0$

15. $x + 2y + 30 = 0$ or $x + 2y - 40 = 0$ **16.** $\frac{3}{4}$

Exercise 8.6

1. (a) (i) $\approx 10.30°$ (ii) 45°   (iii) $\approx 71.57°$ (iv) 45°   (v) 45°
(b) (i) 162.9°   (ii) 110.22°   (iii) 116.57°   (iv) 167.47°
(v) 126.87°   **2.** (i) 60° or 120°   (ii) 30° or 150°   (iii) 90°
(iv) 45° or 135°   (v) 18° or 162°   **3.** $\approx 26.57°$ **4.** 135°
5. $\approx 80.54°$ **6.** $7x + 5y = 0$ or $5x - 7y = 0$
7. $3x - y - 3 = 0$ or $x + 3y - 11 = 0$ **8.** $\approx 48°$ **9.** 10.15°
10. $m = \frac{1}{4}$ or 2; $\approx 49°$ **11.** There is a risk of water damage
12. 110.96°

Revision Exercises

1. (a) (i) $2\sqrt{5}$ (ii) $2\sqrt{13}$ (iii) $2\sqrt{10}$ (iv) $\sqrt{6}$ (v) $\frac{\sqrt{65}}{6}$
(b) (i) (3,3)   (ii) (0,0)   (iii) $\left(-\frac{1}{2}, -2\right)$ (iv) $\left(-1, \frac{1}{\sqrt{2}}\right)$ (v) $\left(\frac{3}{4}, \frac{1}{3}\right)$
(c) (i) $2x - y - 3 = 0$ (ii) $2x + 3y = 0$ (iii) $6x - 2y - 1 = 0$
(iv) $x - \sqrt{2}y + 2 = 0$ (v) $24x - 3y - 17 = 0$ **2.** $[AB] \frac{2}{3}, [CD] = -\frac{3}{2},$
$[EF] = 4, [GH] = -\frac{1}{6}, [IJ] = 5, [KL] =$ no slope, $[N] = 0$
4. (ii) (1,−2)   (iv) −1   (v) $x + y + 1 = 0$ (vi) (−1, 0)   **5.** ±3
6. 9 or −7   **7.** (i) 45°   (ii) $\sqrt{34}$ (iii) $\frac{15}{2}$ units^2 (iv) $x - 3y + 7 = 0$
(v) $\frac{\sqrt{10}}{10}$ **8.** 204.20 units^2 **9.** $a = -\frac{5}{6}b$ **11.** $3x - 7y - 36 = 0$
12. $x - 5y - 4 = 0$ **13.** (i) $P\left(\frac{-k}{3}, 0\right), Q\left(0, \frac{k}{5}\right)$ (ii) $\pm 10\sqrt{3}$
14. $x - 3y - 3 = 0$ or $3x + y - 19 = 0$ **15.** 53 units^2
16. $Q(8,0), R(0,-12)$ **17.** (a) $PQ = \sqrt{40}, PR = \sqrt{290}, QR = \sqrt{250}$
(c) 50 units^2 **18.** (a) $2x - 5y + 18 = 0$ (b) $x + y = 12$ (c) (3,9)
(e) 31.5 units^2 **19.** (a) $k = 7$ or $k = 3$ (b) (ii) $x + y - 4 = 0$
20. (i) $AB = 48$ (ii) $A = 8 B = 6$ **21.** (i) $2x + y - 3 = 0$
(ii) $3x - y - 2 = 0$ (iii) 45° and 135°   **22.** $b = 2$
23. (i) $x - 2y = k, k \in R$ (ii) $x - 2y - 11 = 0$ **24.** (i) $-3x + y = k, k \in R$
(ii) $3x - y - 27 = 0$ **25.** (ii) $\frac{3}{8}$ cups   (iii) $\frac{1}{16}$ (iv) $y = \frac{1}{16}x$
(v) 3.125 cups   **26.** (i) 40 kmh^{-1} (ii) 18 secs   (iii) $y = x + 30$
(iv) $y = 30$; initial speed (on passing traffic light)   (v) 20 kmh^{-1}
(vi) 55 kmh^{-1} **27.** (i) €150,000   (ii) €20,000/unit
(iii) $y = 20x + 150$ **28.** (ii) 231.2 mins   (iii) 6.3̇6̇ kg   **29.** (i) Red:
2,400 cm^2, green: 1,800 cm^2, blue: 4,200 cm^2 (ii) Yes
30. (i) 20   (b) Selling price per unit   (ii) $y = 20x$
(iii) $y = 10x + 40$ (iv) Break-even point is 40,000 units

Exam Questions

1. (a) $y = 3x + 2$ (d) No   **2.** (a) $2x + y - 6 = 0$ (b) $D(0,6)$
(c) $\frac{13\sqrt{5}}{5}$ (d) 13 units^2 **3.** (b) Slope $AB = -\frac{15}{8}$, $\tan(\angle ABC) = \frac{171}{140}$
4. (a) $x + 2y = -4$: Line l, $2x - y = -4$: Line m, $x + 2y = 8$:
Line j, $2x - y = 2$: Line n (c) $x + 2y = 4$ **5.** (b) It is a
parallelogram

6. (a)

Description	Line(s)
A line with a slope of 2.	l
A line that intersects the y-axis at $\left(0, -2\frac{1}{2}\right)$.	l
A line that makes equal intercepts on the axes.	h
A line that makes an angle of 150° with the positive sense of the x-axis.	m
Two lines that are perpendicular to each other.	l and K

(b) 30°   **7.** (b) $4x + 3y - 25k + 5 = 0$ (c) 2   (d) (6,7)
8. (a) $\left(-\frac{25}{3}, 0\right)$ (c) $m = \frac{8}{15}, c = \frac{20}{3}$ **9.** (a) −5   (b) $\frac{|18 - 4k|}{5}$
(c) (i) $k = \frac{3}{4}$ or −48   (ii) 3

Chapter 9

Exercise 9.1

1. (i) $x^2 + y^2 = 25$ (ii) $x^2 + y^2 = 64$ (iii) $x^2 + y^2 = 1$
(iv) $x^2 + y^2 = 169$ (v) $x^2 + y^2 = 289$ (vi) $x^2 + y^2 = 2$
(vii) $x^2 + y^2 = 3$ (viii) $16x^2 + 16y^2 = 9$ (ix) $4x^2 + 4y^2 = 1$
(x) $x^2 + y^2 = 3.24$ (xi) $x^2 + y^2 = 75$ (xii) $x^2 + y^2 = 63$ **2.** (i) 8
(ii) 9   (iii) 2   (iv) 7   (v) $\sqrt{3}$ (vi) $\frac{3}{2}$ (vii) $\frac{10}{3}$ (viii) $\frac{7}{5}$
(ix) $\frac{5}{2}$ (x) $\sqrt{\frac{7}{3}}$ **3.** $x^2 + y^2 = 100$ **4.** (i) $r = 25$ (ii) $x^2 + y^2 = 625$
5. (i) (0,0)   (ii) 5   (iii) $x^2 + y^2 = 25$ **6.** (i) (0,0)   (ii) $2\sqrt{10}$
(iii) $x^2 + y^2 = 40$ (v) $4\sqrt{10}\pi$ (vi) 125.66 units^2
(vii) 160 units^2 **7.** Area: (i) $\frac{9\pi}{4}$ (ii) $\frac{\pi}{a^2}$ (iii) $\frac{m^4}{n^4} \cdot \pi$
(iv) $(a + 1)^2 \pi$; circumference: (i) 3π (ii) $\frac{2\pi}{a}$ (iii) $\frac{2m^2}{n^2} \cdot \pi$
(iv) $2|a + 1|\pi$ **8.** $x^2 + y^2 = 25$ **9.** $10x^2 + 10y^2 = 81$
10. $17x^2 + 17y^2 = 1$ **11.** (i) $x^2 + y^2 = 125$ (ii) $t = 11$
12. (i) $y = 4$ (ii) $104\frac{1}{6}$

Exercise 9.2

1. (i) Centre: (5,2), radius length: 9
(ii) Centre: (−2,−5), radius length: 7
(iii) Centre: (1,−3), radius length: 10
(iv) Centre: (0,8), radius length: 7
(v) Centre: (0,0), radius length: 10
(vi) Centre: (0,−3), radius length: $\sqrt{5}$ **2.** (i) $(x - 3)^2 + (y + 5)^2 = 4$
(ii) $(x + 8)^2 + (y - 1)^2 = 16$ (iii) $x^2 + (y - 7)^2 = 16$ (iv) $x^2 + y^2 = 5$
(v) $(x + 3)^2 + (y + 8)^2 = \frac{1}{4}$ (vi) $\left(x - \frac{1}{2}\right)^2 + \left(y + \frac{1}{4}\right)^2 = 144$
(vii) $(x + 1)^2 + (y - 6)^2 = \frac{49}{4}$ (viii) $(x + 2)^2 + \left(y + \frac{3}{4}\right)^2 = 18$
3. (i) $\sqrt{41}$ (ii) $(x - 1)^2 + (y - 1)^2 = 41$ **4.** (i) $\sqrt{20}$
(ii) $(x + 2)^2 + (y + 1)^2 = 20$ **5.** (i) (1,1)   (ii) $\sqrt{13}$
(iii) $(x - 1)^2 + (y - 1)^2 = 13$ **6.** (i) (7,0) or (−3,0)   (ii) (3,0)
or (−9,0)   (iii) (5,0) or (−15,0)   (iv) (6,0) or (−8,0)
7. (i) (0,13) or (0,−5)   (ii) (0,15) or (0,−5)   (iii) (0,5) or (0,−7)
(iv) (0,2) or (0,−4)   **8.** $(x + 3)^2 + (y - 2)^2 = \frac{1}{2}$ **9.** $(x - 1)^2 + (y - 3)^2 = 4$
10. $(x - 5)^2 + (y + 2)^2 = \frac{441}{10}$ **11.** (ii) $\left(x + \frac{30}{13}\right)^2 + \left(y + \frac{19}{13}\right)^2 = \frac{225}{13}$
12. $(x + 5\sqrt{2})^2 + (y - 5\sqrt{2})^2 = 50$ **13.** (i) $(x - 10)^2 + (y + 10)^2 = 25$
(ii) $100 - 25\pi$ units^2

Exercise 9.3

1. (i) Centre: (2,−3), radius length: 4
(ii) Centre: (1,1), radius length: 1
(iii) Centre: (−1,−4), radius length: 3
(iv) Centre: (−5,4), radius length: 7
(v) Centre: $\left(\frac{2}{3}, -1\right)$, radius length: 1
(vi) Centre: (3,0), radius length: 4
(vii) Centre: (−5,3), radius length: $\sqrt{13}$
(viii) Centre: (0,0), radius length: 1
(ix) Centre: (0,−5), radius length: 5
(x) Centre: $\left(-\frac{3}{2}, \frac{7}{2}\right)$, radius length: 4
(xi) Centre: $\left(\frac{4}{3}, \frac{2}{3}\right)$, radius length: 1
(xii) Centre: $\left(\frac{1}{3}, -1\right)$, radius length: 1
2. (i) $x^2 + y^2 - 4x - 6y - 3 = 0$ (ii) $x^2 + y^2 + 2x - 14y + 25 = 0$
(iii) $x^2 + y^2 - 6y + 5 = 0$ (iv) $4x^2 + 4y^2 + 32x - 4y - 259 = 0$
(v) $x^2 + y^2 - 12x + 25 = 0$ (vi) $4x^2 + 4y^2 + 12x + 16y - 171 = 0$

(vii) $x^2 + y^2 + 4x + 2y + 2 = 0$ **3.** c_2: $U(0,5)$ on circle; c_3: $V(4,4)$ outside circle; c_4: $W(5,1)$ on circle; c_5: $X(0,0)$ inside circle; c_6: $Y(-2,-3)$ on circle; c_7: $Z(3,-6)$ outside circle
4. (i) $(3,0)$ or $(1,0)$ (ii) $(-15,0)$ or $(5,0)$ (iii) $(3,0)$ or $(-1,0)$
(iv) $(7,0)$ or $(-5,0)$ **5.** (i) $(0,7)$ or $(0,-3)$ (ii) $(0,5)$ or $(0,1)$
(iii) $(0,0)$ or $(0,8)$ (iv) $(0,-4)$ or $(0,2)$ **6.** $a = 6$ **7.** $a = 1$
8. $b = -5$ **9.** $m = 6$; $n = -5$ **10.** (i) $C(4,4)$
(ii) $x^2 + y^2 + 2(-4)x + 2(-4)y + 16 = 0$
11. $-3 - 2\sqrt{3} < a < -3 + 2\sqrt{3}$ **13.** $b = \pm12$ **14.** 4 **15.** 4
16. $-7 < t < 3$ **17.** $\{k < -9\}$ or $\{k > 3\}$

Exercise 9.4

1. $(3,1)$ and $(1,3)$ **2.** $(3,2)$ and $(-2,-3)$ **3.** $\left(\frac{17}{5}, -\frac{19}{5}\right)$ and $(-1,5)$
4. $\left(\frac{79}{25}, \frac{3}{25}\right)$ and $(-3,1)$ **5.** (i) $(2,1)$ and $(1,2)$
(ii) $(-1,0)$ and $(0,1)$ (iii) $(1,7)$ (iv) $(5,-1)$ and $(4,4)$ (v) $(3,4)$
(vi) $(2,1)$ (vii) $(-1,-2)$ and $\left(-\frac{331}{41}, -\frac{1,898}{205}\right)$ (viii) $(1,1)$
and $\left(\frac{84}{29}, \frac{7}{29}\right)$ **9.** (iii) Centre: $(1,-7)$, radius: $2\sqrt{5}$
10. (iii) Centre: $\left(\frac{3}{8}, -\frac{23}{4}\right)$, radius: $\frac{9\sqrt{5}}{8}$
11. (ii) Centre: $(-4,3)$, radius: 20 **12.** (iv) Centre: $\left(-\frac{7}{4}, 3\right)$,
radius: $\frac{9}{4}$ **13.** $k = 20$ or $k = -14$

Exercise 9.5

1. (i) $3x + y = 10$ (ii) $2x - y + 10 = 0$ (iii) $3x + 4y = 0$
(iv) $2x - y - 5 = 0$ (v) $2x + 3y - 9 = 0$ (vi) $3x - 2y - 26 = 0$
(vii) $4x + y - 11 = 0$ **2.** (i) $\left(2 + \frac{2\sqrt{3}}{3}\right)x - y - 2 - 2\sqrt{3} = 0$
or $\left(2 - \frac{2\sqrt{3}}{3}\right)x - y - 2 + 2\sqrt{3} = 0$ (ii) $y = -1$ or $21x - 20y - 146 = 0$
(iii) $5x - 12y + 7 = 0$ and $5x + 12y - 17 = 0$
(iv) $y = 0$ and $12x + 5y = 0$ **3.** $21x - 20y + 14 = 0$; $x = 6$
4. Circles don't touch internally **7.** Circles touch internally
8. (ii) $2x + y - 5 = 0$ (iii) $2x + y + 5 = 0$
9. $3x - 2y - 3 = 0$ or $3x - 2y - 29 = 0$ **10.** $k = 105$
11. Externally: $\left(x - \frac{9}{2}\right)^2 + y^2 = \frac{9}{4}$, internally: $\left(x - \frac{9}{2}\right)^2 + y^2 = \frac{225}{4}$

Exercise 9.6

1. (i) $3x^2 + 3y^2 + 17x - 5y - 22 = 0$ (ii) $x^2 + y^2 - 7x + 3y + 12 = 0$
(iii) $2x^2 + 2y^2 - 7x + 2y - 34 = 0$ (iv) $x^2 + y^2 - 4x - 2y = 0$
(v) $5x^2 + 5y^2 + 48x - 12y + 47 = 0$ (vi) $x^2 + y^2 - 13x - 2y + 22 = 0$
2. $x^2 + y^2 - 4x - 2y = 0$ **3.** $x^2 + y^2 - 2x - 2y - 3 = 0$
4. $x^2 + y^2 - 10x - 4y + 4 = 0$ **5.** (ii) $x^2 + y^2 - 10x + 2y + 1 = 0$
6. $x^2 + y^2 - 4x - 6y + 9 = 0$ and $9x^2 + 9y^2 - 100x - 150y + 625 = 0$
7. (i) $(2,2)$ (ii) $r = 2$ **8.** $x^2 + y^2 + 2x - 4 = 0$ or $x^2 + y^2 + 2x - 4y = 0$
9. $x^2 + y^2 - 10x - 10y + 25 = 0$ or $x^2 + y^2 + 4x + 4y - 17 = 0$
10. $x^2 + y^2 + 2x + 6y + 5 = 0$ **11.** $x^2 + y^2 - 4x + 2y - 20 = 0$

Revision Exercises

1. (b) $x^2 + y^2 = 50$ (c) $p = \pm5$ (d) $n = 6$
2. (a) $(x - 1)^2 + (y - 1)^2 = 25$ (b) $k = 4$ or -6
(c) $x^2 + y^2 - 12x - 4y + 20 = 0$
3. (a) Centre: $\left(\frac{1}{2}, -\frac{3}{2}\right)$, radius: $\sqrt{3}$ (b) $x^2 + y^2 - 10x + 4y + 4 = 0$
(c) $x^2 + y^2 - 6x - 14y + 38 = 0$ **4.** (a) $k = -2$
(b) $(x + 2)^2 + (y - 6)^2 = 50$ (c) $x - y - 2 = 0$; $x - 7y - 6 = 0$
(d) $36.87°$ **5.** (a) $A(0,1)$, $B(8,17)$; $[AB]$ is a diameter
(b) $x^2 + y^2 - 7x - 5y + 6 = 0$ **6.** (b) $\sqrt{21}$ **7.** (a) $3x + 4y + 25 = 0$
(b) $x^2 + y^2 - 6y - 1 = 0$; $x^2 + y^2 + 4x + 2y - 5 = 0$
8. (i) $x^2 + y^2 = 169$ (ii) $y = 12$ (iii) $5x + 12y = 169$
9. (a) $(x + 2)^2 + (y - 3)^2 = 58$ (b) (ii) $\left(\frac{7}{5}, \frac{4}{5}\right)$ (c) (ii) $\sqrt{7}$

10. (a) (i) $(x - 2)^2 + (y - 3)^2 = 2$ (iv) $x + y - 7 = 0$
(b) $x^2 + y^2 + 30x - 30y + 225 = 0$ or $x^2 + y^2 + 6x - 6y + 9 = 0$
(c) (iv) $x^2 + y^2 + 2x + 6y - 40 = 0$
11. (a) $(x + 3)^2 + (y - 2)^2 = 16$ (b) $-\frac{41}{19}$ or 1
12. (a) $(x - 4)^2 + (y - 9)^2 = 20$ (b) $2x + y - 27 = 0$ (c) $R\left(\frac{27}{2}, 0\right)$
13. (i) $x + 3y + 12 = 0$ (iii) $a = -4.5$ (iv) $\left(x + \frac{9}{2}\right)^2 + \left(y + \frac{5}{2}\right)^2 = \frac{5}{2}$
(v) $3x - y + 16 = 0$

Exam Questions

1. (a) $x^2 + y^2 - 14x - 6y + 49 = 0$
2. $\left(x - \frac{7}{2}\right)^2 + \left(y - \frac{11}{2}\right)^2 = \frac{45}{2}$ **3.** (a) c_1: centre $(3,5)$, radius $\sqrt{5}$,
c_2: centre $(1,1)$, radius $3\sqrt{5}$ (d) $x + 2y - 18 = 0$ **4.** $3 + 2\sqrt{2}$
5. (a) $x^2 + y^2 + 6x + 4y + 9 = 0$, $(1,1)$, 3 (b) (i) $\left(-\frac{7}{5}, -\frac{4}{5}\right)$
(ii) $4x + 3y + 8 = 0$ **6.** (a) $(1,-6)$, $6\sqrt{10}$ (b) (i) $(5,6)$
(ii) $(x - 5)^2 + (y - 6)^2 = 40$ (c) $x + 3y - 43 = 0$ **7.** (i) $4\sqrt{2}$,
$(-2,-3)$ (ii) $\sqrt{2}$ (iv) $2x^2 + 2y^2 - 2x - 18y + 37 = 0$ (v) 13

Chapter 10

Exercise 10.3

12. (i) $|BD|^2 = y^2 + 4x^2$ $|CE|^2 = x^2 + 4y^2$

Revision Exercises

3. (c) (ii) $y = 9$ (iii) $4.5x$ units^2 **4.** (c) (i) $ay - y^2$ (ii) $a^2 - ay$
(iii) ay **6.** (a) (i) triangles PQS and PQR (b) $r\sqrt{3}$ (c) (ii) 125 cm
7. (c) (ii) $x\sqrt{5}$ (iii) $\sqrt{\frac{x^2}{25} + 4x^2}$

Exam Questions

4. (b) (iii) 9.504

Chapter 11

Revision Exercises

20. (iii) 860 m (iv) 857 m **26.** (iii) 18 cm^2 **28.** (ii) $|\angle P| \approx 70°$,
$|\angle Q| \approx 20°$ (iv) 5.9 cm **31.** (iv) $|AG| = 400$ m and $|BG| = 390$ m
32. (ii) 76 mm (iii) 66 mm (iv) 120 mm **36.** (ii) 11.53 m^2
37. (ii) 5.22 m **39.** (ii) 20.4 km^2 (iv) 4.1 km (vi) 1.9 km
(vii) Councillor Q

Exam Questions

2. (a) (i) The perpendicular bisectors of the sides of the triangle (ii) The bisectors of the angles of the triangle
(iii) The medians of the triangle

Chapter 12

Exercise 12.2

1. (ii) 1.5 **2.** (ii) $\frac{4}{3}$ (iii) 16 : 9 **3.** (i) 2.5 (ii) 25 : 4
(iii) 5 : 2 **4.** (i) 3 (ii) 4.2 (iii) 2 **5.** (i) D (ii) 2 (iii) 4 : 1
6. (i) True (ii) True (iii) False (iv) False (v) True
(vi) False (vii) True **7.** (ii) 9 units^2 (iv) 2.25 units^2
(v) 1 : 4 **8.** (i) R (ii) 2 (iii) 8 (iv) $|XR| = 5$, $|YR| = 4$
(v) 4 : 1 **9.** (iv) 5.6 units^2 **10.** (i) $\frac{2}{3}$ (ii) 8 cm (iii) 22.16 cm^2
(iv) 12.31 cm^2 **11.** (i) $\frac{2}{9}$ (ii) 2 : 9 (iii) 4 : 81 (iv) 19.25 units^2
14. (a) $x = 4$ (b) $|A'B'| = 2.4$; $|B'C'| = 3.2$; $|A'C'| = 4$ **16.** (i) 4 (ii) 16

(iii) 2 : 5   (iv) 4 : 25   **18.** (i) 12.5 m   (ii) 8.544 m
(iii) 34.176 m   (iv) Yes   **19.** (i) 3.5   (ii) 19.95   (iii) 21
(iv) 160.5 units^2 **20.** (i) 2.5   (ii) (0,2)   (iii) (7.5,−3)
(iv) (12.5,−8)   **21.** 21 m^2 **22.** (i) 12$\sqrt{3}$ cm   (ii) 216$\sqrt{3}$ cm^2

(iii) 36$\sqrt{3}$ cm   **23.** Dimensions: A4 = 297 × 210 mm;
A3 = 420 × 297 mm; A2 = 594 × 420 mm; A1 = 840 × 594 mm;
area: A4 = 624 cm^2, A3 = 1,247 cm^2, A2 = 2,495 cm^2,
A1 = 4,990 cm^2